U. S. Dept. Agriculture Handbook No. 18

Soil Survey Manual

By
SOIL SURVEY STAFF
U. S. Bureau of Plant Industry, Soils, and
Agricultural Engineering

This is a Revision and Enlargement of U. S. Department
of Agriculture Miscellaneous Publication 274, the
Soil Survey Manual, Issued September 1937,
and Supersedes it.

Effective 1952, the Soil Survey was transferred from the former
Bureau of Plant Industry, Soils, and Agricultural Engineering to the
SOIL CONSERVATION SERVICE
Reissued in October 1962 with no change in text.

Agricultural Research Administration

UNITED STATES DEPARTMENT OF AGRICULTURE

For sale by the Superintendent of Documents, U.S. Government Printing Office
Washington, D.C. 20402

CONTENTS

INTRODUCTION

The *Soil Survey Manual* is intended for use by soil scientists engaged in soil classification and mapping. Attention is directed primarily to problems and methods of making and interpreting detailed basic soil surveys in the United States and territories.

The earlier edition,[1] published in the autumn of 1937, reflected the developments growing out of the ideas, work, and publications of hundreds of scientists since the beginning of the United States Soil Survey in 1899. Substantial progress has been made since 1937 in the soil survey itself and in related fields of soil research. Further, soil surveys are now used by more people, in more ways, and, above all, with more precision than formerly.

The increased use of soil maps and interpretations has led to increased testing of the results, both scientifically and practically. Inadequacies appeared that required correction. Continually, new knowledge about soils needs to be incorporated into the classification and into the interpretations. New research methods and new cartographic methods need to be evaluated, adapted, and used as they are appropriate to improve soil surveys and to reduce their costs.

Nearly the whole of the earlier edition of the *Manual* has had to be revised. Although some appear to be drastic, few of the revisions are out-and-out changes; most of them are modifications and elaborations to achieve the specificity and completeness required to make the final results more nearly quantitative and more useful. For example, essentially all soil mapping is now done on aerial photographs, and the discussion of the older cartographic methods has been condensed in appendices.

Some new terms have been added and a great many redefined, especially to permit increased accuracy. This process of redefining will need to go on as long as soil research continues. The discovery of new relationships and the formulation of new concepts require an expansion of language.

Many of the technical terms used in soil science are common words, taken out of the body of language and given precise and sometimes unusual meanings. A large part of them originated as folk terms among rural people. Such words as "loam," "texture," "structure," "heavy," "light," "profile," "horizon," and even "soil" may have a deceptive familiarity to the layman using the language of soil science. Similar technical words have arisen in the same way in the other languages, often with slightly different shades of meaning, not revealed in the ordinary lexicon. The meaning of coined words, like "Lithosol" and "illuviation," or of those taken bodily from other languages, like "gley" or "Chernozem," once

---

[1] SOIL SURVEY MANUAL. U.S. Dept. Agr. Misc. Pub. 274, 136 pp., illus. 1937.

learned, are not so likely to be confused with other meanings as are redefined common words.

Even though newly coined words are more easily defined than the older ones are redefined, their use on soil maps and in soil survey reports intended for the general reader is limited. For some new concepts a writer has no alternative to technical terms. These he needs to define for the general reader. Commonly, however, the older more general words must be used in soil survey reports, insofar as possible, in order to capitalize on the readers' present understanding. But in the scientific work itself specific terms should be used in the sense of accurate definitions. Thus there is no escape from a certain amount of "double language."

Need of accurate definition.—Special effort has been made in this revised text of the *Manual* to define terms and to use them as specifically as possible. Since the early edition, much progress has been made toward uniformity of terminology among soil scientists. Better definitions are still needed within our own language, and especially better transliterations among the various languages. Some nearly arbitrary selection among alternatives has been necessary in the *Manual*.

A separate glossary is not included because much duplication would result and because many definitions are clearer when set within an explanatory context. Where definitions might lead to long and highly technical statements, explanations are given instead. Page numbers of the Index in bold type refer to definitions and explanations of the terms.

The relationships of the soil survey to other researches have deepened and broadened as its uses and interpretations have expanded. It has seemed that this *Manual* should be broad enough in scope to lead into the most important of these relationships, but it cannot develop them in detail. Even the field of soil classification, above the lower categories, lies mostly outside of its scope. A few references to fuller discussions are given in the text, and a suggested reference shelf is included near the end.

Since the earlier edition was prepared (during 1935–36) all phases of the work have been under study by the Soil Survey staff. Following intensive study and revision, mimeographed copies of new statements about many individual subjects treated in the *Manual* were circulated both for guidance in making soil surveys and for criticisms and suggestions. Since all the basic soil survey work in the United States is carried on cooperatively with the State land-grant colleges and universities, several scientists in those institutions have helped a great deal in criticizing statements on special subjects and the draft of this edition of the *Manual*. Besides, informal cooperation is carried on with the research organizations of several foreign countries. Scientists from these countries have given us the benefit of their valuable experiences and judgments. Several read all or parts of the draft manuscript and made valuable suggestions for its improvement.

Other modifications can be expected, especially in classification and nomenclature, as our knowledge and experience advance.

Some prospective changes are under study and are mentioned here and there in the text.

The authors have had great help from the criticisms and comments given by readers of the *Manual* published in 1937. It is hoped that readers of this revised edition will note errors and omissions and call them to the attention of the Soil Survey staff so that any subsequent edition may be improved.

Arrangement of topics.—It is assumed that most readers of the *Manual* will have had training equivalent to that of a graduate holding the Bachelor of Science degree from a curriculum in soil science like that officially recommended by the Soil Science Society of America.[2] It is expected that many readers will need to carry on collateral reading in soil classification, general soil science, geology, interpretation of aerial photography, geography, economics, and general agriculture.

The authors have further assumed that soil survey party chiefs and those wishing to prepare for such responsibilities will want to study all parts of the *Manual*. Therefore, the topics are arranged roughly in the order that problems arise in starting, carrying out, and completing a soil survey, although, of course, a party chief must have a view of all aspects to begin with, since the several phases of the work are closely interrelated. It is assumed that others who are not concerned in the whole job may find the *Manual* a helpful reference for particular items that can be located from the table of Contents or the Index.

---

[2] Soil Sci. Soc. Amer. Proc. 6: 507. 1941.

SOIL AND LANDSCAPE

First let us briefly review the working concepts of soil and of the principles of scientific method upon which this *Manual* is based. These have been formulated only after many years of trial and error.

When the Soil Survey began in the United States, more than 50 years ago, there was no organized body of knowledge that we have come to know as soil science. This is not to say that nothing was known about soils. Indeed farmers had learned a great deal through experience over the centuries, and much of their knowledge had been brought together in several compilations, some as early as Roman times. With the rise of agricultural chemistry during the nineteenth century, more was learned about soils that was useful. Yet it was not until some time near the end of the century that the knowledge about soils gained from farming, from agricultural chemistry, from biology, and from geology was coordinated. Nor could it be coordinated without some unifying concept of the soil itself.

The early concepts.—With few exceptions, like Hilgard's ideas,[1] the notions of soils held by soil workers at the time the Soil Survey began were based upon assumptions stemming mainly from the ideas of the great German chemist, Liebig, as modified and perfected by agricultural chemists and plant physiologists working on samples of soil in laboratories and greenhouses and on small plots of soils in the field. The soils were rarely examined below the layer turned in regular tillage. The assumption of soil character, or working theory, which was more or less unconsciously conceived, may be briefly summarized as the balance-sheet theory of plant nutrition or the-soil-is-like-a-bank idea. Soils were considered to be more or less static storage bins for plant nutrients that could be used by plants but had to be replenished as used. Of course, the amounts of nutrients removed from soil by harvested crops and those returned in manure, lime, and fertilizers are important to an understanding of soil productivity;

---

[1] The soil scientists of today cannot help being amazed at the general neglect of E. W. Hilgard's important and pioneer work, first in Mississippi (GEOLOGY AND AGRICULTURE OF THE STATE OF MISSISSIPPI. 391 pp., Jackson, Miss. 1860.); then in the Cotton Belt as a whole (A REPORT ON COTTON PRODUCTION IN THE UNITED STATES; ALSO EMBRACING AGRICULTURAL AND PHYSIO-GEOGRAPHICAL DESCRIPTIONS OF THE SEVERAL COTTON STATES AND CALIFORNIA *in* volumes 5 and 6 of the 10th Census of the United States. Washington. 1884); and finally in California (SOILS; THEIR FORMATION, PROPERTIES, COMPOSITION, AND RELATIONS TO CLIMATE AND PLANT GROWTH IN THE HUMID AND ARID REGIONS. 593 pp., illus. New York and London. 1906.).

but a great deal more is needed for our understanding of soils and their management requirements. In fact, this simple balance-sheet theory, by itself, has but little prediction value.[2]

The early geologists generally accepted this notion of soil fertility. They filled the conceptual storage bin with ground rock of various sorts—granite, sandstone, calcareous till, and the like. They went further, however, and showed how the weathering processes modified this material and how the geological processes of landscape formation used it in the construction of land forms, such as glacial moraines, alluvial plains, loessial blankets, and marine terraces. Shaler's monograph on the origin and nature of soils[3] went about as far as it was possible to go with this geological concept of soils; although many details were added in Merrill's treatise.[4]

Professor Milton Whitney and his coworkers in the new soil research unit of the United States Department of Agriculture, established near the end of the nineteenth century, were impressed by the great variations among natural soils—persistent variations in no way due to the effects of agricultural use. Special emphasis was given to soil texture and to the ability of the soil to furnish plants with moisture as well as nutrients. Professor F. H. King of the University of Wisconsin was also emphasizing the physical characteristics of soils.[5]

The Soil Survey began in response to the recognized need for helping farmers locate themselves on soils responsive to management and, once located, for helping them to decide what crops and what management practices were best for the particular kinds of soil on their farms.

In early surveys, soils were conceived to be the weathering products of recognized geological formations, defined by land form and lithological composition. Many of the earlier field workers were trained in geology, because only geologists were skilled in field methods and in the scientific method of correlation appropriate to the field study of soils.

Shortly after field work began, it became obvious that many important soil characteristics were not definitely related to either broad land form or rock type. It was noted that naturally poorly drained soils have different characteristics than naturally well drained soils, and that sloping soils are unlike level ones. On broadly similar glacial till from Maine to Montana, and down to the Ohio River, markedly contrasting soils are developed in

---

[2] See KELLOGG, CHARLES E. CONFLICTING DOCTRINES ABOUT SOILS. Sci. Monthly 66: 475–487. 1948.

[3] SHALER, N. S. THE ORIGIN AND NATURE OF SOILS. U. S. Geol. Survey Ann. Rpt. 12: 213–345, illus. 1891.

[4] MERRILL, G. P. A TREATISE OF ROCKS, ROCK-WEATHERING AND SOILS. New ed., 411 pp., illus. New York and London. 1906.

[5] See for example, KING, F. H. A TEXTBOOK OF THE PHYSICS OF AGRICULTURE. Ed. 3, 604 pp., illus. Madison, Wis. 1910.

the various climatic and biotic zones. Yet for several years the geological view dominated in the field, and the balance-sheet theory of plant nutrition in the laboratory. Although they were taught in many classrooms until the late 1920's, neither theory actually worked well in the field as a basis for reliable predictions to farmers. As a consequence, all sorts of special little concepts were formed that broke down in contradiction when applied to a great continental area like the United States.

Broader and more useful concepts of soil were developing among some American soil scientists, especially Hilgard. The necessary data for formulating these broader concepts came in rapidly from the field work of the Soil Survey during the first decade of its operations. After Hilgard, the longest reach toward a more satisfactory concept was made by Coffey.[6]

Soil profiles and the concept of individual soils.—Meanwhile, beginning in 1870, a new concept of soil was developing in the Russian school of soil science.[7] The results of this work became generally available to Americans through the publication of Glinka's great textbook in German and especially through its translation into English by C. F. Marbut.[8] Boiled down to its essentials, soils in the Russian concept were conceived to be independent natural bodies, each with a unique morphology and resulting from a unique combination of climate, living matter, parent rock materials, relief, and time. The morphology of each soil, as expressed in its profile, reflected the combined effects of the particular set of genetic factors responsible for its development.

This was a revolutionary concept, as important to soil science as anatomy to medicine. The soil scientist did not need to depend wholly upon inferences from the geological nature of the rocks, or from climate, or from other environmental factors, considered singly or collectively; rather, he could go directly to the soil itself and see the integrated expression of all these in its morphology. This concept made it not only possible but necessary to consider all soil characteristics collectively, in terms of a complete, integrated natural body, rather than individually. In short it made a soil science possible.

---

[6] COFFEY, G. N. A STUDY OF THE SOILS OF THE UNITED STATES. U. S. Dept. Agr. Bur. Soils Bul. 85, 114 pp., illus. 1912.
[7] See the following references:
GEDROIZ, K. K. SOIL-ABSORBING COMPLEX AND THE ABSORBED SOIL CATIONS AS A BASIS OF GENETIC SOIL CLASSIFICATION. (Trans. by S. A. Waksman) Nossov Agr. Expt. Sta. Paper 38, 29 pp. Lenigrad. [In papers on soil reaction 1912-25.]
KELLOGG, CHARLES E. RUSSIAN CONTRIBUTIONS TO SOIL SCIENCE. Land Policy Rev. 9: 9-14. 1946.
NEUSTRUEV, S. S. GENESIS OF SOIL. Russ. Pedol. Invest. 3, Acad. Sci., 98 pp. Leningrad. 1927.
[8] GLINKA, K. D. THE GREAT SOIL GROUPS OF THE WORLD AND THEIR DEVELOPMENT. (Trans. from the German by C. F. Marbut.) 235 pp. Ann Arbor, Mich. 1917.

With the early enthusiasm for the new concept and for the rising new discipline it made possible—soil science[9]—some went so far as to suggest that the other sciences were unnecessary to soil study. Perhaps some extreme statements in this tone were made to declare a certain sense of autonomy and freedom from the older concepts of geology and agricultural chemistry rather than from thoughtful conviction. Certainly the reverse of independence from other sciences was true, for besides laying the foundation for a new science with its own principles, the new concept made the other sciences even more useful. In soil morphology, the soil scientist found a firm basis on which to classify the results of observation, of experiments, and of practical experience, and to develop principles of prediction value.

Under the intellectual leadership of C. F. Marbut[10] the new concept was further broadened and adapted. As first explained, this concept emphasized individual soil profiles—soils at points on the earth's surface—even to the subordination of external soil features and surface geology. This weakness become more clearly evident in the United States, perhaps, because of the great emphasis upon detailed soil maps for their practical prediction value. Progress was rapid because of the large body of important field data already accumulated. By 1925 a large amount of morphological and chemical work was being done on soil profiles throughout the country. The data available around 1930 were summarized and interpreted in accordance with this concept, as

[9] Terminology is still confused. A large amount of applied soil science, and even some fundamental soil science, is still included under agronomy in several colleges and universities in the United States. Partly to differentiate it from applied agricultural science, another large field of application is termed "soils engineering." Terms like "soils geology" and "forest soils" are also used for parts of the field of soil science. "Soil technology" has been used in the narrow sense of soil manipulation—drainage, irrigation, erosion control, tillage, and the like—and also in the broader sense of all applied soil science. Similarly, "soil conservation" is commonly used not only in the narrow sense of erosion control but also in various broader senses up to "soil management for sustained production."

In Europe generally, the word "scientist" has a somewhat more exalted connotation than in the United States. Thus individuals hesitate to call themselves "soil scientists." They prefer a single word like "pedologist." Unfortunately, in the United States, pedology has come to mean only those phases of the more general field of soil science that relate directly to soil morphology, genesis, and classification. In this sense pedology is even too narrow for the work of the Soil Survey. Further, the term "soil science" has at least some self-evident connotation to the layman. The authors see no better alternative in the United States than "soil science" for the general field—for the science that treats of soils, including their nature, properties, formation, functioning, behavior, and response to use and management. In many countries this also defines "pedology" as the term is now used in them.

[10] See the following:
MARBUT, C. F. THE CONTRIBUTION OF SOIL SURVEYS TO SOIL SCIENCE. Soc. Prom. Agr. Sci. Proc. (1920) 41: 116–142, illus. 1921.
——— A SCHEME FOR SOIL CLASSIFICATION. 1st Internatl. Cong. Soil Sci. Comm. 5, Proc. and Papers 4: 1–31, illus. 1928.
SOIL SCIENCE SOCIETY OF AMERICA. LIFE AND WORK OF C. F. MARBUT. 271 pp., illus. Columbia, Mo. 1942.

viewed by Marbut, in his great work on the soils of the United States.[11]

Marbut always emphasized strongly that soil classification should be based on soil morphology, since theories of soil genesis were both ephemeral and dynamic. He was led to emphasize this point so much—perhaps even to overemphasize it—because of the previous errors made by acceptance of the balance-sheet theory and the geological concept under which soils had been assumed to have certain characteristics without the scientists taking the trouble to examine the soils to see whether they were like they had been assumed to be. Marbut was trying to make the point abundantly clear that examinations of the actual soils were essential for developing a system of soil classification and for making soil maps of prediction value. (This still needs emphasis today. Even yet schemes of soil classification and mapping are occasionally put forward that are designed to avoid the work of profile examination!)

Extreme interpretations of Marbut's emphasis upon morphology as the basis for classification led to the suggestion that the soil classifier could neglect genetic principles and relationships. Such extremes should be avoided. A soil is not really understood until its genesis and the reasons why it varies from other soils are known. Not until the morphology and genesis of a soil are known can research to discover new and improved management systems be planned most effectively. Without such organized knowledge, purely empirical mass plot work alone must be resorted to with the hope that something will work. This is the situation now with many tropical soils. The Ground-Water Laterite soils are an example. Until their genesis is worked out, finding practical systems of soil management by empirical plot trials alone seems nearly hopeless. Fundamental soil research should be emphasized more as a basis for classification, applied research, and the invention of new techniques.

One may conceive, perhaps, of the development of an accurate system of soil classification on the basis of morphology alone; but in practice it is doubtful that completely satisfactory results can be had. Besides accurate morphology, genesis is needed to guide the work and to test the results. Neither one nor the other can be neglected. Yet in the meantime, classification of soils of obscure genesis shall need to be handled as well as possible, largely on the basis of morphology alone.

Soils as dynamic three-dimensional landscapes.—The concept of soil was gradually further broadened and extended around 1930 and the years immediately following.[12] This revision in concept was not so dramatic as the earlier one; it was more a matter of consolidation and balance. Previously the major emphasis had been on the soil profile. Soil profiles come very near to occupying

---

[11] MARBUT, C. F. SOILS OF THE UNITED STATES. *In* U. S. Dept. Agr. Atlas of American Agriculture, pt. 3, Advance Sheets No. 8, 98 pp., illus. 1935.

[12] See KELLOGG, CHARLES E. MODERN SOIL SCIENCE. Amer. Scientist 36: 517–536, illus. 1948.

single points on the earth's surface; whereas soils have shape and area, breadth and width, as well as depth. Morphological studies began to be extended from single pits to long trenches or to a series of pits over a soil area. The morphology of a soil is expressed by a range of profiles from a modal profile, not by a single profile or even by a typical one. Further, early emphasis upon genetic soil profiles had been so great as to suggest that in the absence of such genetic profiles, as in a young Alluvial soil, there was no "true" soil! A sharp distinction had been drawn between rock weathering and soil formation. Although distinction between these sets of processes is necessary, it is equally necessary to recognize that rock weathering and soil formation are sets of processes going on at one time in the same landscape. Soils are dynamic not only as soil profiles but also as landscapes.

Clarification and broadening of the concept of soil also grew out of the continuing emphasis upon detailed soil mapping and especially with the emphasis upon predictions of estimated yields for adapted crops under physically defined sets of management practices for each kind of soil shown on the maps. Many of the older descriptions of soils had not been sufficiently quantitative, and the classificational units had been too heterogeneous for making the yield predictions and management predictions needed for individual farm planning. The use of air photos, begun during the late 1920's, had greatly increased the accuracy of plotting soil boundaries. To meet the needs for farm planning, greater precision of interpretation was also required. This development of schemes for summarizing predicted yields and soil behavior under defined sets of management practices not only made the soil survey far more useful but also forced a reconsideration of the very concept of the soil itself.

Soil defined.—First of all, soil is the natural medium for the growth of land plants, whether or not it has "developed" soil horizons. Soil in this sense covers land as a continuum, except on rocky slopes, in regions of continuous cold, in very salty playas, and elsewhere that the cover of soil disappears. Soil has many forms. Its characteristics in any one place result from the combined influence of climate and living matter, acting upon the parent rock material, as conditioned by relief, over periods of time, including the effects of the cultural environment and man's use of the soil.

In studying the characteristics of soil and in predicting its potentialities for use, we cannot work with the whole continuum at once. Individual kinds of soil must be recognized. To make use of experience and of the results of research, classification becomes a necessity. It is through classification, as a tool, that we organize our knowledge and remember it, see relationships among soils and between them and their environment, and formulate principles of prediction value.

In the sense of an individual in the continuum, a soil is a dynamic three-dimensional piece of landscape that supports plants. It has a unique combination of both internal and external characteristics that have definable ranges of expression. Each individual kind of soil has a modal set of characteristics within the limits set by *our* logic. Its upper surface is the surface of the land; its lower surface is defined by the lower limits of soil-forming processes; and its sides are boundaries with other kinds of soil, where changes occur in one or more differentiating characteristics, related, in turn, to one or more of the genetic factors. Through research, the behavior of soils under defined conditions can be predicted.

Many thousands of unique kinds of soil exist in the world—as many as there are significant combinations of the genetic factors. The characteristics of each can be learned through observation and research in the field and in the laboratory. The history of a soil and its potentialities are contained in these characteristics, considered collectively. *The influence on soil behavior of any one characteristic, or of a variation in any one, depends upon the others in the combination.* (Probably more faulty predictions about soils result from failures to recognize this principle than from any other error.) A general system of soil classification comprehends all observable relevant characteristics.

Soils, then, are landscapes as well as profiles. The soil mapper has always recognized this in drawing soil boundaries. Commonly they come at the foot of an escarpment, at the margin of the swamp forest, or at some other obvious boundary among natural landscapes. The hardest soil boundaries of all to plot are those that can be located only through repeated examination of soil profiles because the controlling genetic variable is obscure. In detailed soil mapping, examinations of soil profiles are always essential to test the location of boundaries and to identify the bounded landscapes.

In the concept of soil as landscape, slope is an important soil characteristic. Soils, like other natural bodies, have shape. Formerly one wrote "soils on sloping land;" now we say simply, and more correctly, "sloping soils." Temperature is an important soil characteristic, even though it cannot be preserved in samples. The same may be said of stoniness and microrelief. A soil is a natural thing out-of-doors. Like a river or a glacier or a volcano, it cannot be brought into the laboratory. Thus, no matter how much and how valuable are the data we obtain on soil samples in the laboratory, the final synthesis into predictions can be made accurately only on the basis of all the characteristics of a soil as a landscape out-of-doors.

Since one cannot distinguish accurately under all conditions between "soil" and "not-soil," a precise general definition is impossible. The same is true of other well-understood basic words like "house," "plant," or "stone." Many thousands of individual kinds of soil have been defined. In most of these, but not all, one can decide clearly between the soil and the not-soil beneath it. Ordinarily we think of soil as including the upper part of the earth's crust that has properties different from the rock material because of the influence of the soil-forming factors. Yet the definitions of many individual soils must go further and include layers beneath that influence their behavior. Then, some soil-landscapes that support plants gradually thin to moss-covered rock and finally to bare rock with no clear separation between soil and not-soil that applies generally. Plants may be grown under glass in pots filled with samples of soil, with peat, with sand, or even with water. Under proper conditions all these media are productive of plants but some are not-soil. Plants even grow on trees; but trees are regarded as not-soil. Yet perhaps the most important quality of soil is its productivity for plants.

The following general definition of soil may serve those who need one: *Soil is the collection of natural bodies occupying portions of the earth's surface that support plants and that have properties due to the integrated effect of climate and living matter, acting upon parent material, as conditioned by relief, over periods of time.*

Scientific methods.—To understand the significance of any particular soil characteristic, or of any one genetic factor, sets of soil characteristics must be defined and compared. These sets are the units in soil classification.[13] To find the place of an unknown soil in the system of classification, or to understand the relationship of one soil to others in the system, the sets of characteristics are compared. This method of scientific correlation is the principal tool in soil classification.

Because of its universe and methods, soil science does not fit neatly with the physical sciences, the biological sciences, or the earth sciences. It is all three, but is not any one exclusively. Principles and methods from all three are used, in addition to those that are peculiar to soil science itself.

A large and growing body of fundamental scientific knowledge is the concern of soil science and of no other discipline. These facts emphasize the importance of seeing the science as a whole. No matter how much a soil scientist specializes, he must maintain a broad view of the whole field. In some sciences, like chemistry and plant physiology, for example, dependence is placed chiefly on one general scientific method—the experimental method. Unconsciously, some have assumed that the experimental method is the only method in science. Certainly it is a very useful one in soil science. With this method, the specific effects of variations in individual soil characteristics, and groups of soil characteristics, can be observed under defined conditions. The scientist then sets up experiments on plots representing an individual soil in which he can control the other variables, or at least account for their effects, besides the one under study. A large part of what has been learned about the behavior of specific kinds of soil has resulted from controlled field experiments, natural experiments, and the analyses of the records of operating units—farms, gardens, and forests.

[13] See section on Units of Soil Classification and Mapping.

Yet a great many matters must come under scientific study that cannot be subjected to experiment. For example, we can get at the relative influences of different climatic regimes on the genesis of unlike soils from granite, say, through the use of both the experimental method and the method of correlation. The experimental method deals with soils at small places, almost points. Through the method of correlation the sets of data from different places are compared and principles developed from them that fit the facts.

Useful results can only come out of those experimental plots that are fair samples of a defined kind of soil. To interpret the results, either for an understanding of soils or for predictions about their behavior, they must be synthesized in terms of defined soil units. This is the function of soil classification. Its stuff comes from observation and the experimental method; its working tool is the method of logical scientific correlation.

Soil classification depends upon the results from all branches of fundamental and applied soil science. On the other hand, the results from the other branches of soil science can only be synthesized for accurate application through soil classification, whether soil maps are made or not. Soil classification has been so intimately associated with soil mapping, for which it is an immediate necessity, that some individuals in other branches of soil science have not always seen that, in the long run, soil classification is just as important to their work, especially to the orderly application of their results.

In applying soil science to forestry, farming, grazing, and engineering, some means must be had for recognizing the individual units of the classification system in the field. Few people among those needing to use the principles and predictions of soil science can identify these units. Thus it is essential to have soil maps. Assuming an adequate system of soil classification, with the units consistently named and with reliable predictions, an accurate soil map makes possible the orderly application of our knowledge to specific areas—fields, farms, forests, gardens, roadways, and the like.

Soil mapping itself is an applied science or art. The quality and usefulness of the result, however, depend upon a vast background of both fundamental and applied science. They depend upon what is known generally and upon what is known specifically by the particular group of scientists doing the work. Every soil survey area presents a new challenge. It is by no means simply a matter of mapping a few dozen standard soil types and phases. Soils are not so easily standardized. The relationships between each soil and its neighbors, and between each soil and the factors of its environment, must be sought out and clarified. All likely potentialities for use must be explored and definite judgments arrived at, insofar as possible, in quantitative terms.

This places a high premium on the resourcefulness of the field scientist in making full use of all existing data and principles and in capturing the essentials in the soil-use experience laid out before him. Nor can the field scientist depend exclusively upon local sources of information. Important potentialities are suggested from experiences on similar soils elsewhere, even in other countries. Then the final results must be presented in terms of adapted crops, management practices, and land use systems, with awareness of the factors that influence such systems. In short, a modern soil survey is a difficult research undertaking requiring intense thoroughness and broad scope.

The rewards of work well done can be very satisfying, both intellectually and emotionally.[14] Certainly the complexities involved in understanding a soil and predicting its behavior are enough to tantalize the imagination of any man. Then with accurate soil maps, land users everywhere can make full use of science and technology to bring forth the great potentialities in the soil, under efficient management systems, for the sustained abundance the world so desperately needs.

---

[14] For the personal story of a soil surveyor's life in the field, see Macy H. Lapham's CRISSCROSS TRAILS: NARRATIVE OF A SOIL SURVEYOR. 246 pp., illus. Berkeley (Calif.) 1949.

CHARACTER OF SOIL MAPS AND REPORTS

A *soil map* is a map designed to show the distribution of soil types or other soil mapping units in relation to other prominent physical and cultural features of the earth's surface. The units may be shown separately or as soil associations named and defined in terms of taxonomic units. This definition is intended to exclude maps showing single soil characteristics like texture, slope, depth, color, or arbitrary combinations or two or more of these; maps showing soil qualities like fertility or erodibility; or maps showing individual soil genetic factors or combinations of them.

Maps of one or more soil features may be made directly from field observations or by selection and generalization from a soil map. On a soil map, however, combinations of all observable features relevant to the nature and behavior of the soil are comprehended as named taxonomic units—natural bodies with distinct sets of soil characteristics.

Selected interpretations of soil conditions may be shown on maps. From a soil map one may derive a series of simple interpretive maps of the same area showing, for example, the relative adaptability to alfalfa, corn, or other plants, erosion hazards under defined classes of management, drainage requirements for optimum production, irrigation potentialities, and many others. In the making of such generalizations, some soil boundaries are omitted; for example, those boundaries between soils equal in erosion hazard on the map of erosion hazard. But these particular boundaries may be important on another interpretive map, say one showing productivity classes. Thus different boundaries are omitted on different interpretive maps made from the same soil map.

Most such interpretations are ephemeral. They need to change with changes in the agricultural arts and in the cultural environment. If a basic soil map is made accurately, such interpretive maps can be revised easily from time to time as needed. But if only "judgment" maps are made on the spot, without a soil map, with any significant change in the agricultural arts or the cultural environment all the field work needs to be done over again. In planning soil surveys, this point can scarcely be overemphasized. Occasionally "short-cut" rural land surveys are made for some narrow objective, perhaps at a slightly lower cost than for a basic soil survey, only to become obsolete in a short time. Such maps cannot be repaired because vital data were ignored, facts were mixed with interpretations, boundaries between mapping units were drawn inaccurately, or because of some combination of these. Some rural areas have been mapped more than once by such short-cut surveys at a total cost approximating or even exceeding that of a basic soil survey and still there is no usable map for making predictions or recommendations to farmers about adapted crops, estimated yields, and soil management practices.

A soil map by itself, without a text guide to its interpretation, cannot be useful to anyone except those soil scientists intimately acquainted with the units as named in the map legend. To all others an accompanying text, as well as the map legend, is essential. The soil survey includes both map and text. In the text, commonly called the *soil survey report,* are described the natural and cultural features of the area surveyed; the characteristics, use capabilities, management requirements, predicted average crop yields, and predicted long-time effects of management systems for each of the soil types, phases, and other mapping units; and the principal factors responsible for soil formation.

The character and form of soil surveys vary with the soil conditions, the agricultural potentialities, and the problems to be dealt with. Also, they have changed over the years with advancements in soil science and in cartographic techniques. Even more important has been the increased demand for precision in order to make effective use of the great developments in agricultural technology.

UNITS SHOWN ON THE MAPS

Identification of units.—The first step in making a soil survey is the establishment of the units of classification to be shown on the maps. Their nomenclature within the general system of classification *follows* their accurate definition, based upon observations made in the field as supplemented by data from the laboratory. The basic unit is the natural soil type—the lowest[1] unit in the natural (or genetic) system of soil classification. By "natural system" is meant the system in which all relevant features of soils are considered as unique interrelated sets of characteristics, including those important to the practical purposes that soil maps serve, but without exclusive emphasis upon any one of them.

Each soil type is unique. It is defined as a unique combination of surface features, like slope and stoniness, and of internal characteristics—the texture, structure, color, chemical composition, thickness, and other properties of the horizons that make up the soil profile to whatever depth is significant. These units are characterized by field and laboratory observations of the chemical, physical, biological, and mineralogical features of the horizons, the geological nature of the parent rock material, and the geomorphological characteristics of the landscape.

Any one soil type includes the soils that are alike in characteristics that are significant to the nature and functioning of the soil in the natural landscape. Differences in features that are not significant in the natural landscape, but which are significant to

---

[1] The soil phase as a subdivision of a soil type may be regarded, from some points of view at least, as a lower unit. But since phases are separated within soil types, series, families, and great soil groups on the basis of differences significant (as differentiating soil characteristics) only under culture and not in the natural landscape, they are not usually regarded strictly as essential parts of the natural system. (See also p. 289 *et seq.*)

the use of the soil in farming, forestry, or grazing are recognized in subdivisions within the soil type (or soil series). Commonly, differences in slope, stoniness, or degree of erosion within the soil type that are not significant in the natural landscape but which are significant to its use are shown as *soil phases*. Whereas soil types are defined within a narrow range of a whole set of characteristics, including all those of genetic or applied significance, phase distinctions within soil types are based wholly on applied considerations. Thus soil types everywhere should be defined in the same way; but phases are more narrowly defined where the agriculture is intensive and less narrowly defined where it is extensive. The guides to phase distinctions are wholly pragmatic.

In defining the classificational units, including phase distinctions, emphasis is given to the relatively permanent features that influence response to management and not to ephemeral or transitory features, like the differences in plant nutrients caused by recent fertilization, liming, or similar soil management practices. It must be recognized that the immediate productivity of areas of the same soil type, or phase, may vary because of recent management history. This is especially true of soil types that respond greatly to fertilizers. Nevertheless, there should not be significant differences in productivity for climatically adapted crops among areas of the same kind of soil, if properly mapped, *when given the same management*. In very old agricultural areas, however, practices have changed the soils fundamentally, and their classification.

Observable features and inferred qualities.—In carrying out the soil survey and in reporting the results, the observable features need to be clearly distinguished from those soil qualities that are learned only by inference.

In the completed soil survey, the features of each kind of soil are listed. Among those observed directly are slope (degree, shape, and pattern), stoniness, depth, and the color, structure, texture, and other significant features of each horizon of the soil profile. Other observations include soil temperatures, kinds of plants and their rooting habits, features caused by erosion, and so on. Many characteristics are determined partly through the use of scientific instruments. Among these are the contents of clay, organic matter, plant nutrients, exchangeable cations, and the various clay minerals in the soil horizons. The pH of each soil horizon is also determined. As needed, the degree of aggregation, permeability, kind and amount of soluble salts, and the effects of additions of water are determined. It may be emphasized again that the soil units may be grouped and interpretive maps made according to one of these observable characteristics, but such maps are not basic soil maps.

Through interpretation from observed features, the qualities of kinds of soil may be learned by inference. Soil fertility, for example, may be estimated from observable characteristics, from the results of experimental plots, and from the experiences of farmers having records on fields consisting largely of one kind of soil. Soil fertility, however, is not directly observable. It is the quality that enables the soil to provide the proper compounds, in the proper amounts and in the proper balance, for the growth of specified plants, when other factors, such as light, temperature, moisture, and the physical condition of the soil, are favorable. Thus soils may be grouped into fertility classes only by inference. The same is true of tilth—the physical condition of the soil in respect to its fitness for the growth of a specified plant. Combining both of these qualities, fertility and tilth, one arrives at the concept of productivity, defined as the capability of the soil for producing a specified plant or sequence of plants under a specified set of management practices.

Groupings of soils by inferred qualities are essential to the interpretation of a soil survey. Besides fertility, tilth, and productivity, several other qualities may be inferred from the basic soil survey if the research is carried on competently. These qualities include erodibility, irrigability, response to drainage, workability or physical condition in respect to tillage, and crop adaptability. Groupings of soils according to use capability, either in the general sense or in the special sense employed by the Soil Conservation Service in its program of assistance to farmers, are easily made from the detailed soil map and report, or can be read directly from the soil map.

Identification of boundaries.—Having established the units of classification and identified these units on the ground, boundaries are drawn among them on accurate base maps or aerial photographs. The scales to be used depend upon the uses to be made of the map and the relative intricacy of the soil pattern.

After the soil units have been defined and their relationships to the environment worked out, most soil boundaries can be located on the land surface by recognizing where changes in one or more of the genetic factors occur. That is, excavations or borings are needed chiefly to identify the profile of a soil landscape. The actual boundary can usually be drawn most accurately by careful observations of the landscape. Nonetheless, there are important exceptions where the relationships between the differentiating soil features and genetic factors are obscure. For example, the depth and thickness of an iron crust or of a horizon of carbonate accumulation, or the depth to a water table, may be variable although there is no corresponding variation in surface features. In such instances, examinations of the soil are necessary for locating boundaries as well as for identification.

Soil boundaries must be drawn accurately. Despite the large proportion of attention given to soil classification in contrast to methods of soil mapping, a large part of the poor soil maps in the world are poor mainly because of inaccurate boundaries—boundaries guessed at rather than determined. In soil survey work great emphasis must be given to honesty in research. It is more difficult to check the results of a soil mapper than to check those of a laboratory worker, and the damage from incorrect soil boundaries may be very serious to the map user.

KINDS OF SOIL MAPS

Depending upon the detail with which boundaries between the mapping units are plotted in the field, three general kinds of original soil maps are recognized: (1) Detailed, (2) reconnaissance, and (3) detailed-reconnaissance. Of these the detailed soil survey is the most useful and most important. The third, detailed-reconnaissance, is not really a separate kind but is a soil map having parts of each of the first two kinds.

Besides original soil maps made from field surveys, there are relatively small scale soil maps showing associations of the taxonomic units. *Generalized* soil maps are developed through orderly abstraction from original field surveys, either detailed or reconnaissance. *Schematic* soil maps are compiled from spot field observations of the soils and their genetic factors, and from maps of geology, climate, land form, vegetation, and relief. Generalized soil maps of representative areas guide the compilation of schematic maps and are usually included in some parts of them.

Detailed soil maps.—On a modern detailed soil map, the soil types and phases are mapped in the detail required to show all boundaries between mapping units, including areas of one unit within another, that are significant to potential use (generally to plan field management systems). The classificational units are defined narrowly enough to be homogeneous genetically and to permit making such significant differential predictions as available knowledge permits; and the boundaries between mapping units are plotted on base maps or aerial photographs from observations made throughout their course, along with such natural features as streams and lakes and such significant cultural features as ditches, roads, railways, and houses.

Specific guides on the many items are presented elsewhere in this *Manual*. The base map needs to be complete and accurate because land lines (section lines, township boundaries, and the like), roads, houses, streams, and other obvious features are needed as local reference points by map users. Great detail in soil mapping, without a detailed base, is largely wasted, since the user is usually unable to locate himself properly and read the map accurately. Accuracy of a soil map is therefore not determined primarily by general geodetic accuracy but by what might be called local accuracy—the relation of the soil boundaries to the other features that the map user can identify. For example, even though a soil boundary may be plotted within the general limits of accuracy, should it be on the wrong side of a house or road, the usefulness of the map and the user's confidence in it are greatly reduced.

The detail of boundaries required depends partly upon the prospective use of the map. If small bodies of one kind of soil occur within areas of another kind of soil and thereby significantly affect management, the small bodies of soil should be separated or indicated on the map by defined symbols, even if they are an acre or less in extent. Judgment in mapping such areas is also influenced by the relative contrast between the two kinds of soil.

Even with large map scales some taxonomic units are often so intricately interlaced with one or more others that the association of them needs to be recognized as the mapping unit. In mapping areas of complex patterns where all the soils contained in paddocks or fields are treated alike, it may be more useful to show well-defined soil complexes than to map individual taxonomic units in minute and intricate detail.

The scale of mapping depends upon the purpose to be served, the intensity of soil use, the pattern of soils, and the scale of other cartographic materials available. Commonly a scale of 4 inches equal 1 mile (1:15,840) is now used for field mapping and one of about 2 inches equal 1 mile (1:31,680) for publication. Few detailed soil surveys that meet modern standards can be made in field scales less than 1:20,000 except in comparatively uniform terrain. For planning irrigation developments and in areas of very intensive farming the field mapping scales may need to be larger, say 1:7,920 or even 1:5,000. For engineering work, like planning for highway or airport construction, the detail needed may require a field mapping scale of around 1:2,500 or even 1:1,000,

In former years many soil maps were made in the field at a scale of 1 inch equals 1 mile (1:63,360 or 1:62,500) and published at the same scale. Later, the field mapping scale was doubled to 1:31,680. After the use of aerial photographs became general, the field scale was increased again to around 1:20,000 or 1:15,840. Publication scale continued for some time at 1:63,360 or 1:62,500. Some of the detailed maps plotted in the field on aerial photographs and reduced to these scales in publication are extremely difficult to read. So the publication scale was later increased to 1:48,000 and then again to 1:31,680 or 1:24,000. These larger scales have become necessary for easy legibility, although broad geographic relations among the soils are less clearly seen with the reduced total area of land on a single map sheet. The advantage of having the detailed soil survey of a county on one single map, however, has had to be sacrificed for clear reading of detail in reference to individual fields and farms.

No general rule can be laid down for guiding the number of soil examinations required per unit area nor for the intervals between traverses, except that these can rarely be more than one-fourth mile wide and usually need to be narrower.

Reconnaissance soil maps.—On a reconnaissance soil map the boundaries between the mapping units are plotted from observations made at intervals and not necessarily throughout their whole course as on the detailed soil maps. Reconnaissance maps vary widely, from "semidetailed" soil maps that approach the specifications of a detailed soil survey to maps of soil associations made from traverses at intervals of several miles. Reconnaissance maps are usually planned for exploratory purposes—to discover and outline areas of soil suitable for more intensive development (see page 435 *et seq.*). They are particularly useful in new and relatively undeveloped regions for identifying areas of promise for settlement or more intensive use.

In some reconnaissance surveys, the classification units are less precisely defined than in detailed soil surveys. Usually the mapping scale is smaller and fewer mapping units can correspond to the taxonomic units. In older reconnaissance work, it was customary to show named soil types on the map for areas that were really undefined mixtures of that soil type with others. This was done especially where research was insufficient to develop a complete classification. It is now possible to make far better and more useful maps by using defined soil associations.

In modern reconnaissance mapping, the taxonomic units are sought out, defined, and named as in a detailed soil survey. These are then mapped in groups as geographic associations. Such an association may contain several sharply contrasting soil types and phases. Each association is defined in terms of the named taxonomic units, their relative proportion, and their pattern. The associations are named in terms of the more prominent taxonomic units.

During the progress of the work, representative sample areas of each soil association are mapped in the detail required to meet the specifications of a detailed soil survey. These areas are carefully located, and small maps showing the detail are reproduced separately in the accompanying text. The usual supplemental laboratory data and other data are assembled by taxonomic units. Predictions about adapted crops, estimated yields, management requirements, and so on are also made for these units as they are in the detailed soil survey.

Agricultural scientists and advisers can examine the sample areas and learn how to identify the individual taxonomic units within the particular soil associations that concern them.

This scheme of reconnaissance soil mapping has a wide application in new and relatively undeveloped areas. It makes possible better appraisals of regional potentialities than the older reconnaissance soil maps with poorly defined mapped units. It permits the rapid surveying of large areas where development cannot await the completion of a detailed soil survey. At the same time it gives advisory agriculturists an opportunity to make those specific recommendations that can only be made on the basis of local, narrowly defined soil types and phases.

Good reconnaissance maps can be made only if there is enough detailed mapping of representative sample areas to establish the modal definitions of the taxonomic units and their permissible ranges of variability. Specifications for individual maps will vary widely. In mountainous regions or other areas not likely to be used intensively, traverses are made at less frequent intervals than on land suitable for farming.

Many of the soil maps made in the earlier years of research in the United States, which were looked upon as detailed soil maps in terms of the techniques of that time, are regarded as reconnaissance soil maps under modern specifications. The increased detail did not come in any single year and there were wide variations in the skill and vision of individual supervisors and soil survey party chiefs.

Detailed-reconnaissance soil maps.—On a detailed-reconnaissance map some portions satisfy the specifications for detailed soil maps, whereas other portions are reconnaissance soil maps. Such maps are made of counties or other geographic units containing areas of soil used or potentially useful for agriculture and other large areas that are unsuited. The part covered by reconnaissance may be rough mountainous land, raw acid peat soils, stony desert soils, dry sandy plains or hills, or other landscapes unsuited to farming.

The boundaries between the detailed and reconnaissance types of survey on the one map may be made in one of two ways: (1) The boundaries may follow section lines or other land lines and be shown in a smaller sketch map on the margin of the soil map; (2) the legend on the map may be divided into two parts. The mapping units listed under the reconnaissance legend, and boundaries among them, are defined and mapped according to the specifications for the reconnaissance map; whereas those units listed under the detailed legend and boundaries among them and between them and the units listed under the reconnaissance legend, are mapped according to the specifications of the detailed soil map.

Where the area covered by reconnaissance is considerably larger than the area covered in detail, it may be convenient to publish the reconnaissance portion separately from the detailed mapping. The detailed maps can then be published on extra sheets at a larger scale.

Generalized soil maps.—In order to see the broad geographic relations among soils, small-scale maps are necessary to bring out the contrasts among regions. The best of these are generalized from detailed soil surveys. Such maps vary in scale and detail from soil association maps of counties at a scale of 1 inch equals 1 mile (1:63,360) to single maps of large regions showing associations dominated by one or more great soil groups.

The descriptive legends of soil association maps indicate the relative proportions and patterns of the several classificational units that compose them. If the map is included as a part of a detailed soil survey, the text that explains the individual taxonomic units on the detailed soil map can serve for both. If the soil association map is published separately, descriptions and predictions for all taxonomic units within the associations should be attached, perhaps in tabular form.

The publication of detailed soil maps at scales as large as 1:31,680 and 1:24,000 has increased the need for generalized soil association maps so that broad areas can be viewed as a whole. Since the county is a convenient unit for many kinds of agricultural work in the United States, a soil map is needed to exhibit the whole county in such a way that the various parts of it stand out according to the principal soil features and patterns that are basic to types of farming and community problems.

Since the uses of generalized soil maps are so varied, it is more difficult to write specifications for them than for detailed soil maps. For the lowest level of generalization, the one most useful in agricultural advisory programs, we may proceed on the following basis: Farms are usually made up of several soil types. It is the combination of soil types that gives the soil association its distinctive character and sets the potentialities and limitations within the farm unit. Experience on individual fields is synthesized, classified, and extended on the basis of soil types and phases as defined in the detailed soil survey. Experience with whole farm units, made up of combinations of soil types, is synthesized, classified, and extended on the basis of soil associations. Consequently, the legend and detail of a useful soil association map are planned to show the use suitabilities of these broad geographic groups of soils. Of course, boundaries between soil associations cross some farms, just as the soil type boundaries cross some fields. If large areas of a single soil type do dominate many whole farms, the soil type may be shown separately. But rarely is this possible. In recognizing very small strips of highly productive Alluvial soils, for example, it must be recalled that the Alluvial soil usually is only part of the farm and is used in association with the adjacent uplands. In such instances, it may be misleading to separate small strips of Alluvial soils as a distinct association and the upland soils as one or more others. In other words, excessive detail in the soil association map can lower its usefulness.

The development of a proper legend for such a generalized soil association map requires judgment based upon a study of both soils and farming systems in whole farm units. The form of the legend for a soil association map is influenced by cultural environment, or expected cultural environment in a new area, more than is that for a detailed soil map. It must be so influenced if the soil association map is to be most useful for indicating whole-farm and community problems and potentialities. Well-made soil association maps interpreted in the light of data from experimental plots, fields, and farms, are exceedingly valuable for classifying farms according to their basic potentialities and for guiding agricultural advisers in the geographic emphasis they should give within a county or district to various educational and demonstration programs. Soil association maps serve as an excellent basis, in fact the only satisfactory one, for suggesting the approximate locations of experimental farms, pilot-research farms, and demonstration farms[2], and for suggesting where the experience from these farms is most applicable. For the exact location and plans of such farms a detailed survey is required. Soil association maps indicate the areas where the agricultural adviser should emphasize liming, erosion control, drainage, forest planting, use of phosphatic fertilizers, expansion of pastures, and like practices or combinations of them.

Still smaller scale soil association maps of States or regions are useful in assisting the advisers in community development.[3] On these, the smallest land area to claim attention is larger than a farm, generally about the minimum size for a homogeneous agricultural community.

Schematic soil maps.—In form and appearance these resemble generalized maps of soil associations. Scales are usually small, say 1:1,000,000 or smaller, although useful ones are made at larger scales. For many areas, especially in new and undeveloped regions, it is useful to have an approximate or estimated soil map even in advance of an organized field soil survey, either reconnaissance or detailed. Such maps may be made by estimating the soil pattern. If carefully done by highly competent scientists, this is a great deal more than guessing.

First, all available data, both at spots and in map form, on the soils and the climate, vegetation, geology, and land form, are gathered and studied. In wild areas, these data may consist mainly of notes taken by scientific travelers and rough maps made from aerial photographs without proper ground control. A soil is the unique result of five interrelated factors: (1) Climate and (2) living matter, as conditioned by (3) relief, acting on (4) parent rock materials for periods of (5) time. Therefore, if reasonably good estimates can be had of all but one of these factors, the missing one may be interpreted by geographic correlation. This is the principle. If good topographic maps are available, often surprisingly good soil maps can be forecast by experienced soil scientists thoroughly familiar with the combinations of environmental factors that produce different kinds of soil.

Since the amount and reliability of available data vary greatly from place to place, schematic soil maps always need to be accompanied by a sketch map showing relative reliability.

---

[2] An *experimental farm* is one on which experiments are conducted on single enterprises without regard to the farm unit as a whole, say plot studies of fertilizers, crop varieties, and rotations, or pasture experiments with grazing animals. On a *pilot-research farm* the aim is to find the optimum combination (or combinations) of practices suited to the farm as a unit. Both the experimental and pilot-research farms are managed for research results, and decisions are made by the scientists in charge. On the *demonstration farms*, proved practices are applied mainly by concentrating advisory services to help the *operator* make the best decisions possible toward optimum farm and home development. *Predevelopment* farms, part way between pilot-research and demonstration farms, are sometimes established a few years in advance of settlement as guides to the new settlers.

[3] For an example of this use see MONTGOMERY COUNTY [Alabama] FARM PROGRAM. Agricultural Extension Office, Montgomery, Ala., 61 pp. (c. 1947.)

The interpretation and use of schematic soil maps for agricultural and engineering purposes follow the same course as for generalized maps. The soil associations need to be defined according to the taxonomic units that compose them, their proportions, and their patterns. Then the characteristics and predictions may be given for the individual taxonomic units insofar as they can be estimated; and soil potentialities and problems for community development may be given for whole soil associations. Commonly it is not possible to go further down the scale in the taxonomic classification than great soil groups, with subdivisions according to parent rock, slope, depth, and stoniness.

The compilation of a schematic soil map is often the first logical step in planning more detailed study and survey of a large undeveloped area. After compilation of the schematic soil-association map, representative sample areas may be mapped in detail. Keys and tables of predictions for the local soil types and phases *within* each soil association can be worked out. After the sample areas have been mapped in detail, the approximate schematic map first drafted can be revised. The schematic map can then be published, along with the detailed sample maps and their explanations, as a useful guide for appraising the potentialities of the various parts of the region. The published survey should include specific guides that will enable agricultural advisers to recognize local soil types and phases, for these will aid them in making specific recommendations to soil users.

Exploratory soil maps.—These maps resemble schematic soil maps except that the mapping units are identified mainly by original observations of soils within the area, even though the boundaries are largely compiled from other sources.[4]

REQUIREMENTS FOR THE SOIL SURVEY REPORT

The report, or text accompanying the soil map, is an essential part of the soil survey. Since its form and content depend upon the purposes to be served, these must be thoroughly understood in advance. The report is not an extra chore to be done after the map is made; it needs to be developed along with the mapping in the field. For a basic general-purpose soil survey, a complete statement of all essential soil characteristics and their variabilities needs to be included, regardless of the immediate practical needs to be served. The soil scientists in the field need to know as much as possible about the probable uses; but they must also not be prejudiced by these to the point of omitting significant soil characteristics because they seem relatively unimportant at the moment. Time and time again, soil surveys have been found to be very useful indeed for purposes never dreamed of by the soil survey party doing the original field work. If the essential facts were recorded, the maps could be interpreted readily for the new purpose; otherwise, the field work had to be done over again.

---

[4] As one example see KELLOGG, CHARLES E., and NYGARD, IVER J. EXPLORATORY STUDY OF THE PRINCIPAL SOIL GROUPS OF ALASKA. U. S. Dept. Agr. Agr. Monog. No. 7, 138 pp., illus (map). 1951: Washington, D. C.

The uses of the soil survey are expanding so much that more than one report is sometimes necessary. For the lay reader, explanation of interpretations as they relate to his immediate problems may be all that is required. This may be included in the basic report or published separately. Such statements may need to be revised from time to time with changes in the agricultural arts and in economic conditions, and issued as supplements. Then too, special reports on engineering features or other interpretations may be necessary. Ordinarily, the publication of such special reports in the United States is a responsibility of the cooperating local research institute, like the State agricultural experiment station, rather than the Federal Soil Survey.

Normally, as the work progresses, the soil survey report grows out of the descriptive soil legend. The soil descriptions are already complete when the mapping is finished. The available geological, climatic, and agricultural data are obtained in advance of the field mapping, for they are useful in developing the descriptive legend and guiding the taking of field notes.

PURPOSE OF SOIL MAPS AND REPORTS

The Soil Survey includes those researches necessary (1) to determine the important characteristics of soils, (2) to classify soils into defined types and other classificational units, (3) to establish and to plot on maps the boundaries among kinds of soil, and (4) to correlate and to predict the adaptability of soils to various crops, grasses, and trees, their behavior and productivity under different management systems, and the yields of adapted crops under defined sets of management practices.

The fundamental purpose of a soil survey, like that of any other research, is to make predictions. Although the results of soil research are being applied increasingly to engineering problems, such as the design and maintenance of highways, airports, and pipelines, applications are chiefly in the agricultural field, including forestry and grazing. It is purposeful research.

The many thousands of different kinds of soil have unlike management requirements for economic, sustained production. For centuries farm families learned as best they could through trial and error what methods worked best on their various fields. This knowledge passed on from father to son, but it could not be transferred readily to other areas, nor could the experience on other farms be applied safely.

With the development of modern science, agriculture is being made continually more efficient. Progress has been phenomenal during the 50 years since soil surveying began in the United States. Even the rate at which agricultural efficiency is being increased is itself accelerating as this *Manual* is being written. Experiments with soils, plants, and animals are being continued in many parts of the world. New farming systems are being tested in both research and practice. Fundamentally, soil classification serves as the basis for classifying, synthesizing, and reporting these results of research and experience. The more agricultural science progresses, the more important this work becomes. The investments in machinery and materials per acre of cultivated land are increasing. The planning of farm systems for optimum sustained production needs to be done far in advance of the operations for the best results made possible by modern science, with revisions from season to season. The importance of precise recommendations—differential recommendations from field to field and from farm to farm—increases. Soil maps serve as the basis for such differential recommendations.

Crop plants and soil management practices are so sensitive to the differences in soil that a soil survey adequate for this basic need is certain to serve a great many other purposes as well. In fact, no other maps of large areas of land are made in such detail and involve so many significant factors as do soil maps.

SYNTHESIS OF AGRICULTURAL DATA FOR APPLICATION
TO SPECIFIC AREAS

The soil survey is an integral part of an effective agricultural research and advisory program. It is clearly impossible to carry out exhaustive and expensive researches on every field and farm. Representative samples of land must be chosen. The soil type or phase, accurately defined and named in a standard system of classification, is the only reliable basis yet found for selecting such samples. Every experimental plot is a sample of a landscape. It should be an accurate and representative sample of a kind of soil worth sampling. Thus the soil survey has an important rôle in the planning of research, especially in the selection and location of experimental fields and farms.

New discoveries from experimental work and on farms need to be extended to other areas of similar soils. For optimum use, new methods must be tested widely in farming systems. As the new discoveries are tested, the results can be classified by kinds of soil. When we know that a certain soil area is Miami silt loam, let us say, a great body of research and farm experience is available to allow us to predict its management requirements, the crops that may be grown and their yields, and the long-time effect of various management systems on its productivity.

Without the results of a large amount of correlative research and of careful farm analyses to help them, the scientists in soil survey will be unable to give good predictions. Contrariwise, it is through the soil survey that the results of a host of other researches can be precisely applied.

Through study and comparison of soil types and phases which are defined as sets of soil characteristics, of the sets of genetic factors that go with them, and of the synthesized results of farm analyses and correlative research, general principles of soil behavior are developed for various levels of soil groupings. In going to the higher categorical levels of classification, from soil type to series, to families, to great soil groups, and finally to suborders, the number and precision of the generalizations are reduced.

For detailed predictions and recommendations, the soil type, or a phase of a soil type, is the safest base because of the narrow range of characteristics. If all possible interpretations are to be given, it is the only possible base. But for some one interpretation, as response to liming or the erosion hazard, several soil types and phases can be grouped together.

It should be emphasized that soil scientists, acting strictly as soil scientists, give predictions rather than recommendations. The prediction statements and tables in a soil survey report are designed to predict the results from using the soil types or phases in various defined ways. But the alternative to be recommended for a specific operating farm depends upon the economic environment of the farm and the skill, facilities, and desires of the operator. Then too, for most soils several combinations of practices are possible.

Given an accurate soil map of a farm, alternative cropping and soil management systems for that farm may be developed from the predictions given. With competent soil survey work, with predictions about the other production factors—livestock feeding, performance of machinery, disease protection, and the like—and with adequate consideration of the economic factors, optimum farming systems can be developed.[1] Clear statements of the alternatives are necessary so that agricultural advisers and farm operators can make proper selections from among them.

Since the decisions about farming practices are made within millions and millions of individual managerial units, classification must be detailed enough to include all the significant soil characteristics—all basic land features that significantly affect soil use and management. The maps must be detailed enough to indicate areas of soils significant to a farm management system. They must show these areas accurately in relation to local reference points shown on the map that the user may recognize on the ground.

FARM PLANNING

Increasingly, the results of the soil survey and of the correlative research are applied by the farmer, often with some advice, through the development of a farm plan. Such a plan to be useful does not need to be elaborate. In addition to the use of each field, it shows field boundaries, alternative boundaries, and more or less permanent structures, such as buildings, fences, drainage and irrigation canals, terraces, waterways, and the like. The soil boundaries may be obtained from the soil map. A few of these may coincide with certain field boundaries. In fact, a major contribution of soil mapping to farm planning is the help it gives in relocating field boundaries in order to make fields more nearly uniform. A field containing one kind of soil can be handled more effectively than one containing two or more contrasting soils. The use of the several fields should be indicated tentatively as far in advance as practicable, with alternative cropping systems, so that shifts can be made with unusual weather or with significant changes in economic conditions.

A good farm plan is carried beyond the field layout and cropping system to a farm budget. Such a budget is very important as a test against the physical layout. Farm plans that have called for drastic changes have often failed unless first tested against an estimated budget. To make a budget, at least rough inventories are required of carry-over feeds, machinery, and livestock.[2] For most farms, several alternative plans, with budgets, may be calculated, any one of which will maintain and improve the soils.

[1] For a discussion of the development of optimum farming systems, see BLACK, JOHN D., et al. FARM MANAGEMENT. 1,073 pp., illus. New York. 1947.

[2] See JOHNSON, NEIL W., and BARNES, C. P. PLANNING FARM RETURNS. U. S. Dept. Agr. Yearbook 1943–47. (Science in Farming): 905–910, Washington, 1947; and also Black, J. D., et al. in the General Bibliography.

The one chosen depends upon the skill, resources, and likes of the farm family.

It is unnecessary here to go into a detailed explanation of farm planning except to point out its requirements so that those making detailed soil surveys can make sure their work will be satisfactory for the purpose. In planning, the farmer and his adviser should consider the enterprise combinations that are adapted to the farm as a whole, their economic feasibility, and the skills, resources, and desires of the farm family. No matter how listed, all phases of soil use and farming practices are interrelated. With that in mind, the following is a check list of the principal elements in the farm plan for sustained production that depend wholly or partly upon a proper interpretation of the soil conditions that are taken into account in soil classification and mapping and in the soil survey report.

1. *Major land uses.*—The plan needs to be balanced among the major land uses—crops requiring tillage, forestry, and pasture—according to the pattern of soil types on the farm and the requirements for balance among the several enterprises. Where livestock is produced, the farm needs a proper balance between pasture and feed crops. The several farm operations have to be balanced in relation to the labor supply. Provision needs to be made for the home orchard and garden where practicable.

2. *Cropping system.*—A well-planned cropping system is needed that fits the kinds of soil on the farm. Usually crops should be grown in rotations or mixed cultures. Good seed of those varieties having the greatest disease resistance, drought tolerance, yield, and quality should be used. Most soils produce best with crop rotations that include meadows having deeply rooted legumes or grass-legume mixtures.

3. *Tillage methods.*—The methods employed in tillage should be aimed to prepare seedbeds properly and on time, to make the soil receptive to water, to incorporate organic material, lime, and fertilizer deeply where necessary, and to control weeds. Where soil blowing is a hazard, the surface must be left cloddy and trashy. Many good machines are available from which selections can be made. On some soil types, the moldboard plow, or turning plow, is best; on others, it should not be used.

4. *Protection.*—Both crops and livestock should be given the necessary protection against winds, insects, and other hazards. It is often important to know whether or not the soil can be used for growing shelter belts.

5. *Water control, use, and disposal on the land.*—Every farm needs an orderly system of water use and disposal. Many farms have naturally well-drained soils and dependable rainfall. A large number do not. Excess runoff of rain water must be reduced to the minimum with protective close-growing plants, strip cropping, terracing, or in other ways, so that the water will soak into the soil for plant growth and not be lost or cause erosion. On

erodible soils where rains are intense, unless the management plan provides for runoff and erosion control, all other practices may come to nothing. Although the amount of erosion that has already taken place is significant, the important thing is to assess the hazard of erosion, whether or not much has taken place. Some soils need drainage. Low lands need protection from floodwaters. Many soils will respond to irrigation. Some of these practices require community effort, but a lot can be done by the farm family itself.

6. *Use and conservation of organic matter.*—Large and unnecessary losses of animal manure and crop residues often take place through fire, leaching, and neglect. Yet many soils respond enormously to the addition of organic matter. Part of the need for soil organic matter can be met in a cropping system itself by using a grass-legume mixture, deeply rooted legumes, green-manure crops, and cover crops.

7. *Reaction control.*—On acid soils liming is a first essential to create soil conditions favorable for the availability of the other plant nutrients and for the deeply rooted legumes. In the regions of low rainfall, provisions are required for eliminating excess salt or alkali and for preventing their accumulation under irrigation.

8. *Fertilization.*—A system of fertilization may need to be developed in the farm plan to make possible the best combination of high-yielding crops. We must always recall that fertilization may offer an excellent opportunity to expand the choice of crops that may be grown. One cannot recommend the precise amounts of fertilizer to use from the soil map alone; other aspects of the farming system already mentioned and previous use must be considered. For both lime and fertilizer recommendations, it is helpful to have the results of appropriate chemical tests in areas where reliable ones have been developed. The reader should be able to interpret from the soil map and report, however, the general fertilizer requirements and the production that may be expected from systems involving their use; but the need for phosphorus, say, on any one field will depend also on the amounts that have been used in former years and on other phases of the farm plan.

These aspects of farm planning are so clearly interrelated that decisions about one influence the others. The crop rotations, for example, depend on liming and fertilizing and the erosion hazard; the nitrogen fertilizer required depends partly on the legumes grown and the manure applied; and so on.

Farm classification can be a great aid to advisory work and to farm planning, especially where the soils, and the optimum sets of practices to go with them, are contrasting. With a detailed soil map and the pattern of farm boundaries, farms may be grouped according to amounts and kinds of soil resources into classes of farms having similar potentialities and problems. The need for this kind of farm classification is greatest in areas where the local variations among soils are greatest. In Iowa, for example, the need is less striking than in a State like Tennessee, where the local soil variations are many and great.

RURAL LAND CLASSIFICATION

The results of the soil survey are often applied through an intermediate grouping of the soil types and phases, often called "land classification." The soil units shown on the map may be grouped into classes on any one of several bases, such as (1) degree of some characteristic like texture, stoniness, slope, or acidity; (2) adaptability to some crop or group of crops; (3) productivity under certain sets of management practices; (4) erosion hazard and general management requirements for erosion control; (5) potential irrigability; and (6) response to lime, phosphate, potash, or other fertilizers. It is clearer to call groupings like these "soil groups" than to label them "land classes," in order to avoid the broad connotation of the word "land."

The data of the soil survey are often used to classify, for various purposes, specific geographically defined bodies of land, like sections, "forties," or farms, as shown in a cadastral survey. A clear distinction is needed between the classification of specific land tracts—sections, lots, or other cadastral subdivisions— perhaps more aptly referred to as land classification, and the classification of land into kinds, types, or classes irrespective of cadastral or property boundaries. In the former, distance from market, size of tract, and other relevant factors of the institutional environment can be evaluated with some accuracy; whereas distance from market or size of area are not relevant in grouping the soils, let us say, according to productivity for adapted crops, except as the general social and economic environment fix the perimeter within which the groupings need to be made. No one recommends, for example, that research be undertaken now to find the productivity of soils in Maryland for paddy rice, nor of those producing sugarcane in Hawaii for buckwheat or rye.

Multiformity of land classes.—In a sense the soil survey may be called a kind of land classification. Although it does not include all the characteristics of place, it certainly recognizes a larger proportion of the ones relevant to local land use, and more accurately, than any other survey systematically carried over large areas. But as the term "land classification" has been most commonly used, it usually refers to something far less complete and detailed than a modern soil survey.

The term "land classification" can easily become very confusing. The attributes of any area are exceedingly numerous, and their relevance varies enormously in different parts of the world; yet any one or any combination of the attributes *may* be chosen as criteria for a "land classification." The matter is even worse than that. Many "land classifications" are more or less personal interpretations of undefined combinations of attributes, economic appraisals, or use experiences, often in relationship to a shifting undefined standard. Lands have been classified using tax delinquency, condition of farm buildings, growing vegetation, intensity of use, patterns of use, and so on as criteria of use capability or other land qualities, in both meticulous detail and broad sweeps. Many of these classifications have been useful but some have been misleading indeed, partly because ephemeral standards were used in the work and especially because factors relevant and vital to the purpose of the classification were not taken into account.

The misuse of land classifications often comes about by shifting a fixed method from one soil or cultural region to another. For example, in some areas a general relationship has been found between soil quality for farming and tax delinquency, partly because of the common overassessment of unresponsive soils. In such an area, land classification based primarily on tax delinquency and whether or not land is cleared may give a workable basis for rural zoning. A similar classification fails badly, however, in an area where there is plenty of labor for clearing land, or where unresponsive soil is not overassessed. In some soil regions an exceedingly close relationship exists between native vegetation and soil groups based on the productivity of the kinds of soil for cultivated crops. Yet possibly only 100 miles away, with a slight difference in climate, the "good indicator" species push well over onto soils unsuited to farming. Since plants grow as a result of a combination of growing conditions, they cannot be taken as a certain evidence of either climate or soil. Examples of similar errors could be multiplied many times.

Land classifications based mainly on present land use are perhaps the most likely to mislead. Yet they can be very useful, too. Many institutional, economic, and historical factors, besides soil productivity, have combined to determine present use. Intensive use does not necessarily indicate highly responsive soils, adapted crops, nor optimum farming systems. Large areas of responsive soils in the world remain largely unused because of lack of transport or industry, or from the accidents of colonization; but land-use maps, especially where intensity of use can be interpreted from the maps, can be useful as a supplement to the soil map. By comparing the two maps, one may ascertain what users have found to be possible and what areas are used with less than the possible intensity. Such comparisons give a beginning point for searching out the obstacles to optimum soil use, many of which may turn out to be economic or institutional.

Another source of confusion in land classification to many has been the search for a simple, all-purpose classification of land according to its characteristics and capabilities. This the authors now regard as an impossibility, despite hopes expressed in the first edition of this *Manual* and elsewhere. If the classification is simple, relevant factors must be omitted. The number of significantly different soil series runs into the thousands for the continental United States alone. There are even more in the tropics. Then, when we add to these the necessary phase distinctions for variations within soil types, the number of kinds of soil becomes much larger. Besides soil, as defined in this *Manual*, there are climatic variations that are significant to growing plants within the environment even of some soil types. All sorts of variations in vegetation may be expected. Thus the classification cannot be simple except for an easily defined, narrow, single purpose. As already explained, it is generally far cheaper to make a basic soil survey from which a great many simple groupings, or "land classifications," may be derived by interpretation, than to concentrate on one narrow immediate objective at a time in separate surveys.

Nor can there be an all-purpose classification or grouping. A grouping made primarily to indicate erosion hazard and for planning erosion control will not serve adequately as a grouping for tax assessment, for example. It will fail one purpose or the other. Even with an accurate, highly detailed soil survey in hand, an up-to-date timber cruise may be needed for some kinds of land classification, or perhaps a detailed map of field patterns and land use. For still other purposes, additional research to establish costs for drainage, irrigation, or land clearing is required. To go ahead and get all these data, along with the detailed soil survey, on the chance that they may be needed some day, would increase the cost beyond reason.

Groupings by use capabilities can be made from a good soil survey with adequate correlative research; but such groupings are bound to be transitory and will need to be changed with changes in the agricultural arts, especially in new or undeveloped areas.

Some confusion between soil maps and land classification has resulted from assumptions of 25 years and more ago that soils were defined in terms of soil profile alone. (Regrettably, some in the Soil Survey staff once made this error, too.) Actually, as already explained, landscapes are classified and mapped in soil surveys, not simply soil profiles. Some who accepted the early definition of a soil type as a profile, and who realized that any mapped area had actually a range of profiles, attempted to get around the difficulty by conceiving "land types" or "natural land types" as mapping units defined in terms of soil profile, slope, stoniness, depth (including truncation by erosion), and the like. Such a definition of "land type" is not necessarily different than the present concept of "soil type." But some went further too, and included, under the same name, other mapping units now recognized as soil phases or soil complexes. This led to great confusion, especially in the absence of nomenclature and definitions to differentiate kinds or groupings of "land types." As nearly as one can make out, these "natural land types" can be placed in soil classification as (1) soil types, as now defined in terms of all soil characteristics, including slope, stoniness, and depth, as well as soil profile; (2) phases of soil types; and (3) associations (or complexes) of soil series, soil types, or phases. By using defined units in soil classification, one may go ahead, with orderly abstraction, to the higher taxonomic groups and to soil associations for generalized maps.

Clearly it is best to use soil classification and nomenclature throughout.[3] Then the results of research and experience can be utilized at all levels of generalization. It is difficult to see the need for the "natural land type." Assuming that "land types" could be somehow standardized and research results related to them, they still remain an inadequate basis for genetic classification. For this, we must fall back on soil classification. Future progress in taxonomic land classification seems to lie primarily along the line of improving our soil classification and of including better definitions of the categories, the individual units within the categories, and the geographic associations of taxonomic units. There appears to be no other reliable basis for a scientific classification. Conceivably, one might develop a nongenetic system, based wholly upon morphology, but the prospects are dim.

Classification of social units of land.—The very term "land" itself connotes use. The broad use classes include: (1) Cropping, (2) grazing, (3) forestry, (4) recreation, (5) mining, (6) urban, (7) public services (highways, railroads, airports, electric power lines, cemeteries, and so on), (8) wildlife preservation, and (9) protection (land managed to protect water supplies or other lands). Some of these are often combined, as for example, forestry, protection, recreation, and wildlife preservation. Besides, some land is essentially not capable of producing materials or services of value and may be called *wasteland*. One might add still another class as *idle land*—land capable of producing but not now being used.

The soil survey is concerned primarily with the first three use classes—cropping, grazing, and forestry—but also has a great deal to contribute to management plans for the others. Some kinds of soil can be used only in certain of these general use classes. That is, some are not useful for cropping but may be used for forestry or grazing. Other kinds of soil can be used in any of the ways listed, except perhaps for mining. Thus, often the same kind of soil has a different set of capabilities within these several broad use classes. Generally, of course, people tend to use the soils for the most intensive use for which they are economically capable. But there are many exceptions. Usually soils unsuitable for farming are used for forestry, recreational parks, and the like; but in a densely populated community on highly productive soils, some of those productive for crops may need to be used for wood lots, parks, and public services.

In the classification of specific tracts of land—farms, ranches, forests, pastures, or gardens—according to potential productivity, say for tax assessment, or of prospective tracts according to irrigability, assumptions of the use class must be made. The determination of the use class of a particular tract is partly a matter of the potential productivity of the kind of soil, and partly a matter of its geographic position and size in relationship to other kinds of soil, to existing or proposed roads, canals, wells, and markets, and to other land tracts.

[3] Except for miscellaneous land types as defined later.

For example, one cannot assign a soil area to use for crops unless the area is large enough for an economic unit. Thus, in regions of soil dominantly suited only to grazing or forestry, small areas of soils well suited to crops must be assigned to the other dominant use, except as they may be located strategically at a ranch or forest headquarters. Soils suitable for grazing cannot be so used, at least with full intensity, in the absence of a water supply. On the other hand, a small area of soil suited only to grazing or forestry, but surrounded by a large area of soil well suited for crops, may be little more than wasteland if no economical management plan can be developed for it.

Although distance from market does not directly affect the classification of taxonomic soil groups or land classes, it may greatly affect the classification of social land units or tracts. As a simple example, we might imagine a large area of Chestnut soils, well suited to the usual range of crops, extending out from a railway station. For the first 5 or 6 miles potatoes may be grown in the rotation. At greater distances from the market, wheat may dominate, first primarily for direct sale and, at greater distances, with increasing amounts used for stock feed. Finally, a place is reached where essentially all the crops, both forage and grain, are marketed through livestock. From an analysis of production and marketing costs a schedule may be prepared showing the percentage reduction in the basic rating of the units because of this distance factor. Then too, the distance must be corrected according to transport facilities: Poor roads must count more than good roads. The relationship between the effective distance and the rating factor is a second order differential equation, not a linear one, since the differences in costs of marketing per acre of cropland between, say, 5 and 6 miles are much greater than those between, say, 35 and 36 miles because of the difference in use.[4] Somewhat similar schedules are needed for land units with intermittent water supply.

The contrast between simple taxonomic land classification and the classification of specific land tracts may be illustrated in a system designed for classifying land according to irrigability. As a first step, a detailed soil classification and map is made for the area. For purposes of planning the layout of the project, the soils are grouped according to their arability under irrigation, without regard to location within the area. Such a soil grouping, or "land classification," and map predict what would be the result of irrigation for every part of the area. Then questions need to be raised about the accessibility of specific tracts of arable soils to roads and canals and about the combination of various soil areas into economic farm units. Some areas of soils cannot be irrigated economically, of course, because of their unresponsiveness or likelihood of deterioration, regardless of location; some other soil areas are highly suitable except where isolated in small

---

[4] Such an equation and its development is explained in A METHOD OF RURAL LAND CLASSIFICATION by Charles E. Kellogg and J. K. Ableiter. U. S. Dept. Agr. Tech. Bul. 469, 30 pp., illus. 1935.

tracts that cannot be reached economically or fitted into a farm unit; and areas of other kinds of soil are called irrigable if water can be supplied conveniently, but nonirrigable if water charges are high.

Thus, two quite different maps of the same area, both accurate, might be called "land classification according to irrigability." The first one represents the distribution of taxonomic groups and might better be called, perhaps, "a grouping of soils according to arability under irrigation." The second map, made on the basis of the first one with consideration of the additional factors of location, is a classification of geographically defined areas and should be called, perhaps, "a classification of land according to irrigability." This second map follows an accurate development of the first one from a detailed soil survey. Besides serving this immediate purpose of developing the land classification according to irrigability, the detailed soil survey is used for developing individual cropping and soil-management systems optimum for the specific kinds of soil that were grouped into the more general classes.

The classification of specific geographically located areas of land ordinarily must take account of those characteristics of place that influence decisions among the land-use classes and the decisions about relative intensity of use within the classes. In classifying land for tax assessment, for example, the soil units— types and phases—are first rated according to their productivity under alternative systems of management, within each use class, on a taxonomic basis. Secondly, the use classes of the geographic land tracts—sections, forties, or farms—are determined. Many tracts have mixtures of the use classes, say both cropping and grazing. Thirdly, ratings of the taxonomic groups within the use classes for each geographic land tract are adjusted according to distance from market, water supply, and so on, as these influence potential production.

This brief discussion has dealt only with a few principles and examples, but it is hoped that readers may test old schemes of "land classification" and new ones certain to be proposed. Further discussion would scarcely be appropriate in this *Manual*. No general guides for "land classification" exist, partly because of the wide variety of activities included by at least someone under this term.

LAND APPRAISAL

Rural land appraisals for determining the value of land as mortgage collateral or for tax assessment might be regarded as special kinds of land classification. Social land units, mainly farms, are evaluated in terms of potential production within the institutional and legal environment.

Tax assessment.—Some of the essentials of a method of land classification for tax assessment have been outlined as an example under the heading Multiformity of Land Classes (p. 28). For accurate work, a basic detailed soil survey is required, partly because of the need for indicating the relevant factors in relation to farm boundaries, and partly because adjustments will need to be made from time to time as conditions change.

If the basic soil factors are recorded, as in a basic soil survey, reinterpretations and regroupings in the light of changed conditions can be made easily and in an orderly fashion. But if they are not and only judgments of soil productivity, or of soil groups based on such judgments, are recorded, each revision will require a complete resurvey. For example, let us think of a modern detailed soil survey that indicates 150 or so separate kinds of soil for some area, like a county. These units may be grouped into 5 or 10 productivity classes, or into any other number of classes, according to the accuracy required and the availability of precise data for evaluating differences in responses to management. If, however, *only* these classes are mapped, the survey is soon out of date. If the soil types and phases are accurately mapped, the groupings can be readjusted and revisions made in the appraisal of specific tracts without additional mapping.

Besides the basic soil resource, the appraisal may need to take account of farm improvements—buildings, fences, and the like— according to the State laws governing appraisal. In some States improvements are not taxed; in most they are. If these improvements are appraised in terms of replacement value, absurd results may be had, say where previous owners have constructed buildings far larger and more elaborate than the farm unit requires. Often the laws require that land must be appraised according to its productivity in the most intensive possible use, say for crops, even though it is actually used for extensive grazing or forestry. In the various States special statutes may permit present use to carry some weight. Laws vary widely in the degree to which potential use of farm land for urban or suburban residences must be weighted in assessment. Presumably the ideal in assessment is to make appraisals, according to potential productivity, that differentiate fairly among all the properties. Everyone realizes that excessively high taxes are unfair. A great deal of land that has reverted to the State because of nonpayment of taxes would have remained in private hands had the assessments been reasonably based upon the productivity in such uses as forestry and grazing, instead of on a presumed productivity for farming. But very low taxes are also unfair. Speculators may be allowed to hold undeveloped or only partially developed land needed for settlement at little or no cost—land which they hope to sell or use later at great profit.

Before a proper job of soil groupings and alternative ratings for the various use groups can be developed, and especially before attempts are made to appraise social units, a study needs to be made of both common laws and statute laws that influence assessment. Then appropriate schedules can be developed and adjusted ratings of the taxonomic groups made, in terms of the combinations of present characteristics that need to be dealt with, for each property within the area. Nearly every area presents special problems.

Appraisal for loans.—An accurate detailed soil map with ratings of the individual soil types and phases according to crop potentialities, estimated yields, and long-time effects of the alternative management systems furnishes the best basis for estimating the productivity of a farm and its basic long-time value. It is, of course, helpful to have also records of the individual farm business.

The appraisal of a farm cannot be based, however, upon the soil alone. The distance from market and other characteristics of place must be considered as they affect the kinds of uses for the farm and the productivity of the farm unit. Buildings, fences, and other improvements need to be evaluated in relation to the potential use of the farm unit, as well as water supply, noxious weeds, and the like.

Besides the basic value of the land and its improvements in relation to potential use, the loan appraiser can scarcely escape taking account of the prospective manager of the farm and his skill in relationship to its potentialities.

SETTLEMENT OF NEW LANDS

For centuries land settlement was on a trial-and-error basis. Those fortunate enough to find responsive soil in an area large enough for effective community development, and able to adapt their practices to kinds of soil new to them, were successful. Many thousands of settlers were not so fortunate; their work and efforts came to little or nothing, and their most productive years were wasted.

Through the use of soil surveys these wastes can be largely avoided, at least those due to improper soil and lack of advanced knowledge of what soil management practices to follow. Some exceptions must be allowed for little known kinds of soils never before used by civilized man equipped with the tools and services of modern industry. But the number of these is really small outside the tropics.

It must be emphasized, however, that the soil survey of a new or undeveloped area needs to be correlated with soil conditions in known areas. The necessary predictions of crop adaptability, yields, and management requirements will need to be based, in new areas, upon research results and farm experience gained from similar soils elsewhere, although perhaps not identical ones.

In planning a community, the soil map is useful in locating roads, schools, and other public services in order to keep costs at a minimum and provide orderly settlement as compactly as possible. Helter-skelter settlement with individual settlers far from one another, even though on responsive soils, raises serious social problems and results in high costs for medical facilities, transport, and schools.

In a new area, usually the best procedure is to make a reconnaissance or schematic soil association map (as defined earlier) from existing data and scattered observations in order to identify the most promising places for settlement. This map serves for broad planning of highways and other public services. Then detailed soil surveys should follow in the various parts of the area according to priority of development, considering soil character and other relevant factors. Beyond these considerations, the use of the soil survey for settlement is not unlike its use in settled areas.

GUIDANCE OF PROSPECTIVE FARM BUYERS

The modern soil map and report furnish the prospective farm purchaser with more relevant information upon which to make a decision than does any other single publication. This point is important, and those writing soil survey reports need to bear it in mind. A part of the use of the soil survey for this purpose parallels its use for land appraisal for loans, already briefly outlined. In addition, it gives a picture of the surrounding land and the potentialities of community development. The soil map and report help a prospective buyer select the area in which he wants to buy before he gets down to considering a particular farm. The report explains the farming systems followed by other farmers, the crops grown, the market facilities, and so on. In short, the soil survey report and map should give the prospective buyer a clear picture of the principal potentialities and problems.

After reading from the soil map the kinds of soil on a farm he may be considering, the prospective buyer can consult the tables of yield predictions and management requirements and develop a tentative farm plan with budget estimates of expenses and income. For accuracy, these need to be adjusted to other soil differences due to past management. Where practicable, he should compare these estimates with other budgets from similar farms as another check.

No matter how accurate the soil map or complete the supporting data, purchasers should be advised to visit a farm before making a final decision. Factors that are important to an individual family defy accurate description in writing and figures.

LAND-USE PLANNING

Most land users have some sort of plan to guide their operations. Some farmers have only a simple plan of the crop pattern for the following year; others have carefully prepared plans in writing, with a map, for several years in advance—plans that are revised with the seasons. As science and technology are used more and more for optimum sustained production, individual farm planning becomes increasingly important. This kind of planning is usually called "farm planning," since it deals mainly with decisions made within farm boundaries.

The term "rural land use planning" on the other hand, is commonly used for policies and programs that influence the use of lands in a whole community or area containing many individual farms or other units of operation. Examples include the planning of irrigation or drainage districts, rural transport systems, electric power distribution lines, flood-control structures, large dams, public land acquisition, rural zoning, and the like.

Many county plans or goals have been made by farm leaders and agricultural advisers jointly. These vary widely in detail and scope.[5] For the best development of these plans or programs, a detailed soil survey and carefully generalized soil association map are most helpful. Because the soil survey for individual farm planning needs to be detailed, it is difficult to obtain a view of the soil resources in the whole community and in the contrasting parts of counties except with a soil-association map generalized from it.

For many planning purposes, it is helpful to the users to have the boundaries of soil associations as an overlay on the detailed soil map and also separately on a smaller scale map showing the roads, say on a scale of about 1 or ½ inch equals 1 mile. As has already been pointed out, the experience gained from pilot-research farms, demonstration farms, and from the analysis of other farms can be synthesized by soil associations in order to guide advisory programs and other public programs designed to eliminate handicaps for economic sustained production.

The planning of irrigation.—An especially detailed soil map is required in planning irrigation. This map is often a difficult one to make because soil characteristics need to be considered in relation to a very different environment than the natural one. Deep layers that contain soluble salts or that are impervious to water, which may have little or no influence on the soil under desert or semiarid conditions, may be very important to its behavior under irrigation. Soils that are well drained naturally may become swamped with extra water. The soil survey must predict such conditions and whether or not they may be overcome and, if so, by what methods.

Here, too, generalized maps, based upon the detailed ones, are needed for planning the transport and water facilities in the area as a whole and for arriving at a final map of irrigability as explained previously in the discussion of land classification.

The planning of drainage.—In principle, planning of drainage is similar to the planning of irrigation. Here also, soil characteristics of little influence in the natural state become very important when the soil is drained. Many expensive drainage projects have failed because the soils were unproductive after drainage. In some instances, the soils were very sandy, and after a brief period

---

[5] A large number of these have been developed. This is not the place to review this work in detail. A recent example, among a great many, is the one already cited—MONTGOMERY COUNTY [Alabama] FARM PROGRAM (c. 1947). A pioneer rural plan was published by Lee Roy A. Schoenmann as LAND INVENTORY FOR RURAL PLANNING IN ALGER COUNTY, MICHIGAN (Mich. Acad. Sci., Arts, and Letters 16: 329–361, illus. 1932) based upon the SOIL SURVEY OF ALGER COUNTY (U. S. Dept. Agr., 1934). Other examples include: LAND USE CLASSIFICATION IN MIDLAND COUNTY, MICHIGAN, LAND-USE PLANNING REPORT (Bur. Agr. Econ., U. S. Dept. Agr. and Mich. State Col. 1940); and AGRICULTURAL PLANNING, VALLEY COUNTY, MONTANA. (Bur. Agr. Econ., U. S. Dept. Agr., and Mont. State Col. 1941. [Processed.]).

of cultivation the organic matter disappeared and the soils became too loose and too dry in summer for crop growth. Others had organic soils so acid that enormous quantities of lime were required for raising the pH to that level necessary for crop plants. Such additions of lime, besides being costly, often worsen the problem of other nutrient deficiencies through unbalance.

Drainage of peat lands raises problems requiring the special attention of soil survey parties. After drainage, organic soils often shrink and settle unevenly. For this reason tile drainage frequently fails. The tiles may get out of position. In detailed soil surveys where drainage of such lands is proposed, through soundings and study of the deep materials, it is possible to predict such settling and recommend measures by which difficulties may be avoided. Often it is necessary to arrange for keeping the water table nearly constant through combined drainage and subirrigation, even using the same canals.

Public land acquisition.—Land purchase, as for blocking out National or State forests or grazing districts or for the development of public parks, needs to be planned in relation to the use capabilities of the whole area affected by the purchase units. The detailed soil survey is an essential basis for appraising individual parcels, and, if supplemented with a generalized map of soil associations, for planning the project boundaries. Such purchases can have pronounced influences on community development and, with proper planning, can reduce scattered settlement and otherwise assist the objectives of rural zoning.

The planning of large dams for water storage.—The effects of alternative locations and heights of the structures upon land use needs to be taken into account. By carefully plotting alternative pool lines on the detailed soil map, accurate comparisons can be made. Thus it may be found that one alternative may cover with water much more soil productive for crops than another. Then, after the pool line has been established, plans can be developed with a detailed soil map for the economic use of all partially flooded farm units, through reorganization, in order to keep the "taking line" (the line below which land is purchased) as near the pool line as possible and thus hold the area of unused land or public land around the pool to a minimum. In the margins of some pools, areas of highly productive soil are flooded only occasionally. Such areas may be used for crops to good advantage a large part of the time if attached to an economic farm unit. With a detailed soil survey, such planning can be done in an orderly way.

Planning measures for flood reduction.—Often planning for flood reduction involves the study of the soil conditions of a whole watershed in order to estimate infiltration rates, runoff, and the effects of land management and structures on runoff and erosion. Costs and benefits of alternative plans should be calculated. A detailed soil survey, supplemented by a generalized soil-association map, furnishes a very large part of the basic data for such planning. A full set of predictions and yield estimates under alternative systems of management for each mapping unit is essential for accurate results.

Rural zoning.—Ordinances are often developed by county governments to promote orderly use of the land.[6] Roads, schools, and other social services for scattered farms in areas generally unsuited to farming are very costly for other taxpayers. Such isolated settlers often increase the fire hazard in forests. By blocking out areas suited mainly to forestry, grazing, or recreational use, in which settlement for farming is not permitted, roads and schools may be provided for the community more efficiently. Accurate soil maps, along with interpretations made according to use capability, furnish a sound basis for developing such ordinances.

These few brief examples are only intended to give the reader an idea of the kinds of use to which soil surveys are often put in rural land-use planning. All such uses cannot be specifically anticipated in advance; but when a soil survey is undertaken in any area, supervisors should be fully aware of any such possible uses. Even though a rural zoning ordinance does not yet exist, for example, if it is clearly needed to solve serious problems of local government management, the soil survey work should be done in anticipation of its use for that purpose.

ASSESSING POTENTIALITIES FOR SPECIAL CROPS

The economical production, use, and marketing of many special crops depends upon having more than the minimum volume of production needed to support canneries, freezing units, or other special processing and marketing facilities. When a new enterprise of this sort is undertaken in a community, a large area, often split among many different farms, must be developed at once, along with the factory and marketing facilities. Special interpretations of the soil mapping units may be made for the crop, and interpretive maps prepared from the soil map showing classes of soils according to their use capabilities for the particular crop. Such maps serve as a sound basis for assessing the potentialities for the enterprise in a community and for indicating the particular farmers that may cooperate.

FOREST MANAGEMENT

Foresters are becoming increasingly aware of the importance of an understanding of soils and their relation to growth, stand composition, and other factors affecting optimum forest management. Even the incidence of certain forest diseases, like little-leaf of shortleaf pine for example, is related to groups of soils. The soil survey makes possible the synthesis of results from research and from experience and the orderly application of the available

---

[6] See the following: ELY, R. T., and WEHRWEIN, G. S. LAND ECONOMICS. 512 pp., illus. New York. 1940; and WEHRWEIN, G. S. THE ADMINISTRATION OF RURAL ZONING. Jour. Land and Pub. Util. Econ. 19: 264-291. 1943.

knowledge, in forest management in much the same way as in farm management.

ENGINEERING USES

Soil surveys are being used increasingly in engineering work, especially in highway and airport planning and construction and for predicting trafficability of heavy vehicles. The basic facts about soils needed to predict their behavior in fields include most of those needed to predict their behavior as subgrades or foundation materials. The several soil properties have different relevancies for the two interpretations—agricultural and engineering —but the same basic classification serves both.

Detailed soil maps are helpful first of all in planning locations for structures and for predicting the problems of construction and maintenance to be dealt with. Especially in the absence of detailed geological surveys, they are useful in locating such materials as sand, gravel, clay, and suitable "topsoil" for dressing banks and other areas to be planted.

For detailed highway and airport planning, a highly detailed original survey is usually needed on a scale of about 1:1,200, using the same basic soil classification as that described in this *Manual*, with such refinements as may be required, especially for indicating the physical properties of deep strata. After engineering tests on soil horizons have been made and classified by soil type, each type can be characterized and its behavior subsequently predicted without extensive testing. Classification by tests alone, unrelated to genetic soil types, gives little that can be used as a basis for prediction at a new or proposed site without additional time-consuming and costly testing.

Since the interpretation of soil classification and soil maps for engineering purposes is a highly specialized field in itself, the reader is referred to a special manual on the subject,[7] and to a summary of soil surveys in the United States as they pertain to engineering uses.[8]

OTHER USES

Soil surveys, besides their many widely recognized uses, also serve a host of others to which some attention must be given. For many areas they are the most complete base map and are so used in the absence of up-to-date topographic or planimetric maps. This fact, and the fact that detailed soil maps, detailed topographic maps, and detailed geological maps are often used to supplement one another, emphasizes the need for geodetic accuracy, standard scales in publication, standard symbols, and correct naming of features.

Soil maps have been used to locate and design pipelines. They are helpful in locating radio stations. With interpretation, they

[7] MICHIGAN STATE HIGHWAY DEPARTMENT. FIELD MANUAL OF SOIL ENGINEERING. Rev. ed., 304 pp., illus. Lansing. 1946.
[8] OLMSTEAD, F. R., HICKS, L. D., and BODMAN, G. B. ENGINEERING USE OF AGRICULTURAL SOIL MAPS. Highway Res. Bd. Bul. No. 22, 128 pp., illus. 1949.

can be used as maps of surface geology. They are useful in studying land form and geomorphological processes. With study of sample areas, they can be used to construct maps of the original vegetation and to predict successions of plant cover.

The hazards of nutritional deficiencies among plants and even among animals may be anticipated from soil maps where the relationships of deficiencies to soil types have been identified through correlative research at sample sites. In recent years, important relationships have been worked out between many soil types (and soil groups) and deficiences of such trace elements as copper, boron, manganese, molybdenum, iron, cobalt, and zinc, as well as of phosphorus, potassium, calcium, nitrogen, magnesium and sulfur. By no means all important soil types have been characterized, especially for the trace elements, and much more research is needed. As already explained, recommendations for an individual field depend partly on previous and current management as well as on soil type; yet the area where these deficiencies are likely, and the general practices to be followed, can be interpreted from a proper soil map.[9]

With generalized and schematic soil association maps, broadly defined agricultural potentialities and problems that relate to the soil or soil use can be seen regionally, nationally, or even on a world-wide basis of comparison.

INTERNATIONAL COORDINATION

Since all places in the world having the same combination of soil genetic factors have the same kind of soil, knowledge gained through research and experience in one place is relevant to all like places. Contrariwise, good practices for sustained production on one kind of soil may be wasteful or even ruinous on a different kind.

The need for close correlation between those engaged in soil surveying and other researches is obvious if proper definitions and predictions are to be developed for soil types and if full and accurate use is to be made of other research results. This is true internationally as well as nationally. To make optimum use of agricultural science in any country, it is essential to have a consistent world-wide scheme of soil definition and nomenclature. That is, the results of competently managed research on a well-defined Latosol, Podzol, or Chernozem are useful in all countries having soils like the ones investigated, regardless of where the work is done.

Much work has been done in this field of soil geography. More is needed. The unrealized opportunities for improving the planning of agricultural research and for increasing its effectiveness to all are very great. Fortunately, as this *Manual* is being prepared, greatly increased emphasis is being given to soil classification and mapping in many countries and to the exchange of soil scientists and of information about soils.

---

[9] See Ignatieff, as cited in the General Bibliography.

PREPARATION FOR FIELD WORK

Before going to the field for survey work, plans are made and the essential materials and equipment assembled.

WORK PLAN

Most soil survey work in the United States is conducted as an integral part of the soil research programs of the United States Department of Agriculture and the State agricultural experiment stations. Besides, other State and Federal research, service, and educational agencies cooperate in projects of special interest to them by furnishing personnel or materials.

Many technical details and the services of several kinds of specialists are involved in a soil survey. Besides the soil scientists in field and laboratory, at least some assistance, often a great deal, must be had from geologists, plant scientists, and others. Skilled photogrammetrists, cartographers, draftsmen, and editors are essential to the work. Several agencies are usually involved as participants or as interested users of the results.

A clear understanding of the work to be done and the rôle of each participant needs to be had at the start. The general specifications, plan, and assignment of professional workers are set forth in a *Soil Survey Work Plan*, drawn up by the supervisory scientist, with the help of those responsible for cartography and laboratory services, and agreeable to the sponsoring agencies. Above all, a qualified scientist needs to be selected for *party chief*. Upon him, more than upon any other individual, depends the thoroughness of the research and the quality of the final soil map and report.

The essential items of the *Soil Survey Work Plan* are:

1. Name, location, size, and boundaries of survey area. (Include sketch map for areas other than whole counties.)
2. A paragraph describing the principal physical features of the area.
3. The names of initiating and cooperating agencies.
4. Reasons for the survey, together with any special uses to be made of it.
5. Type of survey (detailed, detailed-reconnaissance, reconnaissance of soil associations) and features to be mapped, including any special features not included in the standards for a basic soil survey.
6. Field and publication scales for the maps.[1]
7. An annotated list of previous surveys of soil, relief, geology, or vegetation.[1]
8. Equipment and transport needed and agencies responsible for supplying.
9. Names of proposed workers (and agency of each) for soil survey party, including party chief.
10. Kind, scale, quality, source, and availability of base map materials and the primary control in the area.[1]
11. Scale and other features of map to be published and method of construction from field sheets.[1]
12. Plans for preparation and publication of report.

13. Date for initiating field work, location of first field headquarters, and estimated date for completion of field work.
14. Plans for supplementary laboratory work and scientists responsible for it.[2]
15. Estimated costs by contributing agencies:
    (a) Field mapping by man-days, including salaries, travel, and equipment.
    (b) Supplemental research and summaries for soil ratings and soil survey report.
    (c) Supplemental laboratory work.
    (d) Map preparation and editing.[1]
    (e) Publication.[1]

[1] Developed jointly with Cartographic Section.
[2] Developed jointly with laboratories of cooperating agencies.

ASSEMBLY OF CARTOGRAPHIC DATA

The use of good cartographic base material is essential for a successful soil survey. On it depends the accuracy of plotting the soil boundaries and symbols, the rate of progress, the methods and costs of map construction, and the quality of the published map. Since all these items directly affect the cost and accuracy of soil maps, supervisory scientists need to give the assembly of cartographic materials first priority once an area is selected for survey.

Even the order in which areas are taken up for soil survey should be guided by a study and analysis of available cartographic data. That is, no area should be selected for survey in advance of aerial photography or equally good base material unless the most compelling reasons exist for doing so; and areas having good topographic base maps made with the aid of aerial photographs should be given preference.

Preliminary study and analysis.—Before its selection for use in the field, cartographic material needs to be studied in relation to all operations in both the field and the cartographic office, considering accuracy, economy, any special needs of a cooperating agency, and efficiency of use by the field party and by the cartographers. All available cartographic material is considered. Some may be helpful even though it is not used directly as the principal base.

If new aerial photography is under contract, usually a soil survey should be postponed until the photographs are released. The availability of new topographic maps, still in manuscript form and not yet generally available, should influence the selection of a specific area. Although uncontrolled aerial mosaics may appear useful at first glance, in the final analysis they may be more expensive than individual aerial photographs because of poor quality, lack of stereoscopic coverage, and inaccuracies. Topographic maps made with high standards of accuracy may have to be discarded because of insufficient detail and small scale. The efficient use of aerial photographs may be limited in some areas by insufficient control for constructing an accurate base map.

Without such an analysis, an area may be selected for which so little good material is yet available that costs for field work or map preparation, or both, may be very high; or a poor combination of materials may be selected from among those available. Such failures in initial planning lead to inaccurate soil boundaries, excessive costs, and substandard published maps. Plans for the survey are worked out jointly by soil scientists and cartographers, so that all costs—for field work, map compilation, and publication—are taken into account. A minor change in field operations, for example, may have a large influence on later costs.

Locating material.—So many agencies obtain aerial photography, prepare aerial mosaics and planimetric and topographic maps, and establish control that the field scientists cannot be expected to know all that is available or about to become available. Although some agencies release map information periodically, these reports do not cover many activities in planning and operational stages. Since most Federal mapping agencies and many commercial firms maintain offices in the Washington area, the Cartographic Section of the Division of Soil Survey maintains liaison with nearly all map-making groups. It is a regular function of the cartographic office to maintain records of all available materials and of work in progress and to seek materials from all agencies for any new survey area. In this way, it is possible to obtain complete information on the status of aerial photography, mapping, and control activities for any area in the United States.

Selection of scale.—Many factors need to be weighed together to determine the best scale to use for a soil survey.

The purpose of the map needs first consideration. Since most detailed soil maps are designed to carry the data needed in planning efficient farming systems, the map must have large enough scale to indicate areas of significance in farming, either by boundaries or by defined symbols. This does not mean that the scale needs to be large enough so that field boundaries, terraces, ditches, and farm buildings can be plotted directly on the soil map. Most farm plans should be drawn on enlarged aerial photographs or other large sheets so that details important only to the specific farm may be written on them. Soil maps on such large scales would be too unwieldly to file and use. The scale of the soil map needs only to be great enough to permit accurate plotting and recording of the significant data.

If the survey is reconnaissance—with a generalized or schematic map of soil association and only samples of each association in detail—the scale can be much smaller.

Generally, the scale of mapping increases with the intricacy and complexity of the soil pattern and especially with intensity of soil use or potential use. The patterns of soil types and phases are very complex in areas of Ground-Water Podzols and Half Bogs or of Lithosols and Alpine Meadow soils, for example, but the low potentialities for use argue against the practicality of highly detailed mapping except in sample areas to define the mapping complexes or associations. Where small areas of soil must be enclosed with boundaries, the scale needs to be large enough to show them without exaggeration and to permit placing clear symbols in them. If field sheets have a large proportion of the symbols outside of the areas they represent and keyed into them with an arrow, the scale is too small, excessive detail is being mapped, the symbols are too long, or there is some combination of these evidences of poor planning.

The scale should be no larger than necessary to show the details required for the objective of the survey. A large increase in scale increases the number of separate sheets to deal with, the amount of joining of sheets, and costs for compilation and reproduction.

The scale of manuscript maps made in the field or generalized from highly detailed field sheets needs to be reasonably close to the publication scale. Except in special surveys, where the field sheets indicate data not to be published, and photographed copies of them serve the special purpose, the field scale should rarely be more than twice the publication scale. Otherwise the published map is likely to be too complex for easy reading or data on the field sheets must be omitted. The selection of only part of the data from the field sheets increases compilation costs and the chances for error. Some poor soil maps have been made at great cost by publishing at 1 inch to the mile (1:63,360) work done in the field at 4 inches to the mile (1:15,840). If a field scale of around 1:7,920 is clearly needed and the map is to be published at 1:31,680, a manuscript map (besides the field sheets) ordinarily is required at some scale above 1:15,840.

In the United States most detailed basic soil maps are now made with field scales between 1:15,000 and 1:20,000 and published at 1:24,000 and 1:31,680. Yet, very detailed surveys, say in irrigated areas or other intensive areas of complex soils, may be made at field scales as large as 1:5,000. For detailed highway and airport planning, soil maps are often required at scales as low as 1:1,000, but those rarely need to be reproduced in large editions. Scales for soil association maps made in reconnaissance surveys may run from 1:20,000 to 1:500,000, depending on the purpose.

Except for detailed-reconnaissance surveys, uniform scale should be used throughout an area. Mappers using base material of varying scale are likely to map the soils in varying detail also. A lack of uniformity in the kinds and sizes of soil areas shown greatly reduces the usefulness of the soil map, since it presents a distorted picture of the soil pattern. Such distortion can be seen on a few published soil maps for which field sheets of unlike scales had been assembled to a uniform scale.

Much cartographic base material is flexible enough to permit reproduction at a number of scales for field use. Many aerial negatives have a scale of 3.168 inches equal 1 mile (1:20,000). Prints of excellent quality and detail can be had at scales from 2 inches equal 1 mile (1:31,680) to 8 inches equal 1 mile (1:7,920). Of course, aerial film may be at various scales; yet reduction and enlargements are usually satisfactory within one-half to three times the original scale. Aerial mosaics or planimetric and topographic maps can be considerably enlarged or reduced to appropriate scales for field mapping.

The cartographic laboratory of the Division of Soil Survey is equipped to prepare enlargements and reductions of aerial photographs, aerial mosaics, planimetric maps, and topographic maps as may be required in cooperative soil surveys.

Since it is usually possible to obtain the base material at a proper and uniform scale, it is important to decide on a definite scale for the soil survey in the planning stage, and to make the original requests for material at that scale. This is far more economical than attempting changes in scale after the base material is received. Such changes may require recopying and cause avoidable delays.

Factors determining type of material selected.—Frequently two or more kinds of cartographic material suitable as bases for soil mapping may be available. An area may be wholly or partly covered by two or more types of aerial photographs, aerial mosaics, planimetric maps, or topographic maps. The choice of materials depends upon their relative advantages for the whole job, including map compilation and reproduction as well as field use. The base material selected must be adequate for the whole job, not for just one activity alone.

Uncontrolled aerial mosaics, for example, may appear advantageous for field use, yet they may be wholly unsatisfactory for constructing the final map because of inaccuracies. Obsolete or substandard maps present similar problems. Such maps often require so many revisions that their value is offset by time-consuming corrections in both field and office. Work plans calling for the use of such materials, made without analyses of the whole process, have led to high costs in relation to the accuracy of the published map.

Available materials of possible use may include aerial photographs, of single or multiple lens, aerial mosaics of varying accuracy, photo maps, planimetric maps, or topographic maps. If no suitable base maps or aerial photographs are available, and the survey must be made, the field scientist may need to make a map with the plane table or, in wild heavily wooded country, with the compass. (See pp. 455 to 463.) Where two or more types of base material must be used, careful evaluation should be made to obtain uniformity in accuracy, planimetric detail, and scale. Other uses of the survey besides publication influence the selection. If, for example, a detailed classification of land tracts is to be made, as in irrigation planning or in assessment, a different base may be better and cheaper than that employed for the usual basic soil survey. Time is sometimes an important element in selection. Material readily available may be used even though better material will be available at some later date. If differences in quality are great, the survey schedule should be altered if possible.

Generally, the best base materials for detailed soil surveys, in order of preference, are single-lens aerial photographs, controlled aerial mosaics, transformed multiple-lens aerial photographs, standard-accuracy topographic quadrangles, standard-accuracy planimetric maps, and original plane-table maps. It is best of all to have both good aerial photographs and accurate topographic maps.

Relatively large-scale reconnaissance surveys are best made on controlled aerial mosaics or standard-accuracy topographic or planimetric maps. Small-scale reconnaissance surveys are made on many types of general maps having good accuracy and planimetric detail or on aerial photo indexes.

Since a complete soil survey is expensive, proper selection of the base material can have a great influence on efficiency. Frequently mistakes in planning are caused by overemphasizing the cost of the base material. Where aerial photography is available, costs for pictures rarely exceed 1 to 2 percent of the cost of the entire field work. Even original aerial photography would seldom exceed 5 to 10 percent of the total. Yet the base material frequently means the difference between an excellent soil map and a poor one. Costs of base material need to be weighed against its use in all operations—field mapping, map preparation, and publication. The use of low-cost materials may give apparent savings for the field sheets, but result in doubling the costs of map preparation and reproduction. Since conditions vary widely from place to place, no hard-and-fast rule can be given for selecting base material. Each area must be studied as an individual problem.

Procedure for obtaining base material.—After the work plan has been developed and the base material decided upon, it is furnished through Cartographic Section or, by arrangement with them, directly from other sources. Plans should be made as far in advance as possible, since many agencies have small staffs available for supplying photographic prints and other materials and some delays are inevitable.

KINDS OF BASE MATERIALS

The characteristics, advantages, and disadvantages of the principal kinds of base material used in soil mapping are outlined in the following paragraphs.

Aerial photographs.—Nearly all detailed soil mapping is now done on aerial photographs. Improvements in them and in their use and interpretation are being made continually.

Types.—Oblique and vertical pictures may be regarded as two basic types of aerial photography. Multiple-lens photography is a combination of the two. Single-lens vertical photographs are best for soil mapping, although oblique and multiple-lens photographs can be used. Thus emphasis in this *Manual* is given to single-lens vertical photographs flown to the specifications of the United States Department of Agriculture.

Stereoscopic and alternate coverage.—Specifications of the United States Department of Agriculture for aerial photography require the overlap in line of flight to be about 60 percent; whereas the overlap between adjacent flight lines averages around 30 percent. This overlap, with which all ground images appear on two or more photographs, permits stereoscopic vision of any ground object within the area. Such photography is said to have *stereoscopic coverage;* and adjoining photographs are called *stereoscopic pairs.*

If every other photograph in a continuous stereoscopic series is removed, the remaining series is called *alternate coverage,* and adjoining photographs, *alternate pairs.* Alternate pairs of photographs overlap only about 20 percent—too little to permit stereoscopic study of the entire area. Such alternate coverage is inadequate for constructing base maps by photogrammetric methods based upon stereoscopic coverage.

Contacts and enlargement.—Aerial photography is exposed on film or glass negatives at a predetermined scale and fixed negative size. The scale of the photograph depends on the height of the aircraft and the focal length of the camera. The size of the negative varies with the aerial camera.

The scale of aerial photography depends on the purpose of the photographs. Most of the aerial photography for the United States Department of Agriculture is flown with an 8.25-inch focal length aerial camera at altitudes of about 15,000 feet. The resulting scale is approximately 3.168 inches equal 1 mile, or 1:20,000. Such negatives give satisfactory reductions and enlargements within a scale range of about 1:7,500 to 1:32,000. Most needs for soil mapping can be met within this range of scale.

Aerial photographs made directly from the original negatives are called *contact prints.* These have the same scale as the negatives. In contact printing no rectification of errors or scale changes can be made, although poorly exposed negatives can be improved. Contact prints are the most economical to make. When properly processed they are best in quality.

Aerial photographs may be readily enlarged or reduced; this is one of their great advantages as a base for soil mapping. The process requires projection of light through the negative and precise adjustments for scale. It is therefore slower and more expensive than contact printing. Some detail is lost in the preparation of enlargements, but with skillful operators using modern processing equipment and the original negatives the loss is negligible.

Enlarging has certain advantages. With adequate ground control, all prints in an area can be brought to a nearly uniform scale. Prints having excess tilt, causing displacement of objects and scale changes, can be rectified to minimize the errors. Pictures for areas having photography at two or more contact scales can be brought to a common scale. Such operations require more time than simple enlarging; and for scale-ratioing or rectification, adequate ground control is essential. Nonetheless, later savings may more than offset the cost of bringing pictures to a common scale.

Satisfactory enlargements from average film should not be expected at scales requiring more than a 2½-diameter enlargement from the contact negative. The photograph becomes grainy and much detail is lost.

Photographs flown for the United States Department of Agriculture are usually made with aerial cameras having a negative size of either 7 by 9 inches or 9 by 9 inches. Enlargements, of course, increase the size of the photograph as well as the scale. The following shows how the size of sheets, in inches, varies with enlargement:

Contact prints (Scale 1:20,000 3.168 in. = 1 mile) Inches	Enlargements (Scale 1:15,840 4.00 in. = 1 mile) Inches	Enlargements (Scale 1:7,920 8.00 in. = 1 mile) Inches
7 by 9	11 by 14	22 by 27
9 by 9	14 by 14	27 by 28

Photo indexes.—Photographic indexes are available for most of the photography available in the United States Department of Agriculture, and in other government agencies as well. These are prepared by fastening the individual photographs of an area together. The images are matched and the photographs overlapped so that all marginal data are visible. The assembly is then photographed at a smaller scale, often in several sheets for convenient handling. Most indexes available in the United States Department of Agriculture are on sheets about 20 inches by 24 inches and have a scale of around 1 inch to the mile (1:63,360). Four to five index sheets cover an average county.

Photo indexes are useful for determining the number and location of individual photographs within an area. Since the low cost of the indexes is easily made up in the time saved, they should always be obtained when available. They are also useful for schematic mapping.

Advantages and disadvantages.—The greatest single advantage of aerial photography in soil surveying is the wealth of ground detail shown. Physical and cultural features that it would be impractical to show on base maps are represented in infinite detail on the aerial photograph. Field boundaries, isolated trees, small clumps of bushes, rock outcrops, buildings, and plant cover all assist the soil scientist in orientation and in plotting his data. Photographs increase both the speed and accuracy of his work. Streams, lakes, and swamps that are difficult to plot accurately by ground methods become control on the photographs.

Because large areas can be photographed rapidly, field scientists may be supplied with highly detailed base material in a short time. Compared to other methods of obtaining original bases with comparable detail, aerial photography is by far the most rapid and economical method. Isolated areas, difficult to map by ground methods, are no handicap to the photographic aircraft, provided suitable landing fields are within operating distances. Aerial pictures are especially helpful to the soil scientist faced with the problem of making accurate soil surveys in wild areas proposed for agricultural development.

Stereoscopic vision, or the ability to see depth, is another advantage of aerial photographs in soil mapping. With photographs having overlap adequate to permit stereoscopic study, the soil scientist has before him a relief model of the area, complete with all of its intricate cultural and physical detail. Such a model affords an opportunity for study of the area in advance of field work. His traverses can be laid out most effectively. The study of plant cover, relief, drainage patterns, and other details helps greatly in planning the field work. Streams, swamps, and other features may be tentatively drawn in advance.

Adequate base maps having the necessary detail to carry the soil survey data can be constructed economically and within a reasonable time from aerial photographs, provided that the photography is of good quality, that the ground control is adequate, that modern photogrammetric facilities are available, and that qualified photogrammetrists supervise the work.

Despite these advantages, aerial photography has some disadvantages and limitations in soil surveying. Photographs are inferior to good topographic or planimetric maps in the following ways: (1) Elevations are not shown; (2) the photographs lack a precisely uniform scale throughout the area because of variations in ground elevations and altitudes of the photographic aircraft; (3) the soil scientist is forced to handle more sheets than when using large maps, resulting in more matching, joining, and filing; (4) differences of scale between adjoining photographs create some minor difficulties in matching and transferring soil boundaries from one photograph to another; (5) distances and directions cannot be so accurately measured because of distortions due to tilt, displacement, and other inherent errors; and (6) although far more detail is shown than on standard maps, it is not always so legible and more skill is required to interpret it. Many details on aerial photographs, such as field boundaries, fence rows, wooded areas, and crops are ephemeral and change more rapidly than the selected features shown on a standard map. For this reason old photographs may be more difficult to use than good maps made from them about the same date as they were taken. Yet these limitations are small in relation to the advantages.

Procedure for obtaining.—Approximately 90 percent of the United States has been photographed during the past 15 years. The major portion of this photography is suitable for soil mapping. Much of it is old and difficult to use because of changes in vegetation and cultural detail. Areas are being continually reflown, however, as changes justify.

Once the survey area is selected the order for photographs should be placed as soon as possible. Such requests should give the exact boundaries of the proposed survey, the scale of photography needed, whether stereoscopic or alternate coverage is to be used, and the date the survey is to commence. Any special requirements, such as weight of paper or finish, should be added also. Aerial film held by other Federal agencies is normally available on loan to the Cartographic Section for the preparation of reproductions. Because of limited facilities, however, it is necessary to have some photographic prints prepared by the agency having the original film. As prints from much of the aerial film are in great demand, it often takes a long time to get prints or enlargements.

In estimating the time required to obtain original aerial photography, time must be allowed for preparing specifications, awarding contracts, photographing the area, and inspection and acceptance of the work. Perhaps the most uncertain factor is weather. The frequency of suitable days for photographic flying varies in different parts of this country and in different seasons. In places aerial photography taken at some seasons is better than that taken in others. For example, the best photography in the southeastern part of the United States is had during the winter months, when the vegetation least obscures the ground.

Costs.—The cost of original aerial photography varies greatly, depending on the local weather conditions, availability of airfields, and so on. That flown to specifications of the United States Department of Agriculture has varied considerably in different contracts from year to year. During the 10-year period 1939-49, yearly average costs varied from $1.93 per square mile in 1939 to $4.06 in 1945. Costs in 1949 average $2.71 per square mile, or less than one-half cent per acre.

Reproductions from original film are furnished from other agencies at rates based on costs of labor and materials. Within the United States Department of Agriculture unit costs in 1950 for reproduction were as follows:

Quantity:	Contact prints (1:20,000) Each	Enlargement (1:15,840) Each
1 to 5	$0.80	$1.55
6 to 100	.50	1.00
Over 100	.45	.90
County coverage	.40	.80

Where original aerial photography is available the cost of contact prints in stereoscopic coverage for a county is about 26 cents per square mile. For stereoscopic coverage with 1:15,840 enlargements the cost per square mile is 52 cents. These costs are a minor fraction of the total for a basic soil survey.

Aerial mosaics.—Aerial mosiacs are made by assembling and matching individual aerial photographs to form a continuous photographic image of an area. A few photographs may be used to cover a small area, or hundreds of them may be assembled for a large one. Several methods of assembly may be used, and the results vary widely in accuracy and usefulness.

Types.—The two general types of aerial mosaics are the uncontrolled and the controlled. The uncontrolled mosaic is made simply by matching like images on adjoining photographs without the use of ground control. No corrections are made for scale, tilt, or displacement. Since the photographs are matched by picture images only, without geographic control of their position, an uncontrolled mosaic is not suitable for accurate mapping and is difficult to use in map construction. In making a controlled mosaic, the photographs are adjusted to ground control; distances and directions are measurable; and the individual photographs are brought to correct scale and corrected for tilt and displacement. Each photograph is matched and adjusted so that image points on the photograph fall in their true geographic positions on the map grid. Since a controlled mosaic closely approaches the accuracy of a good planimetric map, the soil scientist can use it as a base in soil surveying.

Between the inaccurate, uncontrolled mosaic, on the one hand, and the accurate, controlled one, on the other, are a wide variety of semicontrolled mosaics for which different forms of ground control are used. Thus mosaics vary greatly and must be carefully checked for adequacy before use in detailed soil mapping.

Advantages and disadvantages.—An aerial mosaic has the advantage of covering a large area in one photograph. Thus fewer sheets need be matched. Mosaics can be made to cover a specific area, like a township, a small watershed, or a drainage basin. Where controlled mosaics are available, their accuracy over that of the individual photographs is also an advantage to the soil scientist in plotting soil boundaries and in transferring them to adjoining sheets.

In reproducing sheets for field use from a mosaic, a small margin of overlap can be retained, or the sheets can be reproduced to match without overlap. This is an advantage, since the soil scientist frequently has difficulty in matching adjoining aerial photographs that have wide margins of overlap.

A major disadvantage of aerial mosaics in soil surveying, as compared to overlapping photographs, is that mosaics themselves cannot be used for stereoscopic study of the area. The great value of such advance study of an area has already been emphasized.

As with planimetric and topographic maps, the accuracy of mosaics cannot always be assessed by their appearance. They must be field checked. Extreme difficulty may be had in the field with a mosaic that appears in the office to be of top quality. Even though an uncontrolled or semicontrolled mosaic may be usable in the field, it may be impossible to construct an accurate map for publication except at great additional expense. Thus the whole job should be considered when planning the use of an aerial mosaic.

Preparation.—The Cartographic Section of the Division of Soil Survey is equipped to prepare a limited number of controlled aerial mosaics suitable for soil mapping in areas with adequate ground control already established. The normal procedure is as follows: Obtain all ground control in the area, plot it, lay out the projection, and construct a radial plot; obtain the original aerial film; restitute all prints to fit the controlled grid, using care in the processing to insure a uniform tone and quality; trim the photographs, apply the adhesive, and adjust and assemble the prints on the mosaic board; prepare the necessary sheet borders, titles, and footnotes; make copy negatives of the complete mosaic; and reproduce the number of copies required.

Procedure for obtaining.—Where it is best to use controlled mosaics for a soil survey, the request for such work should be made well in advance. Facilities are not available for preparing mosaics for all soil surveys, nor should mosaics be recommended unless they will expedite field work, use of field sheets by cooperating agencies, and map publication.

Costs.—The cost of aerial mosaics for a soil survey is naturally higher than for the individual pictures used; yet in some areas the use of a good controlled mosaic may reduce the total cost of the survey. Part of the costs may be charged to the normal cost of the map preparation. Obtaining control data, preparing the control plot, and making the necessary sheet layouts are a normal part of the map preparation in many areas. The aerial prints have to be supplied to the field party anyway; therefore only the operations of assembling, adjusting, and reproducing the mosaic are added costs.

The cost of mosaics is generally less than that of preparing a planimetric map for the soil survey and higher than that for individual aerial photographs.

Photomaps.—The photomap is a form of aerial mosaic. Unlike the conventional mosaic, physical and cultural features are shown as they are on a planimetric map, and the sheets are laid out uniformly on a definite projection, as is done with standard topographic or planimetric maps. Photomaps are usually reproduced in large quantities by offset lithography or some similar process. Frequently, the planimetry is shown in color. Color emphasizes and gives greater legibility to planimetric detail, for it contrasts with the black-and-white photographic background.

Types.—No fixed standards have been established for photomaps. Although good accuracy may be generally assumed, because of the expense of constructing and reproducing a photomap, the soil scientist should test the accuracy of a photomap before using it in the field.

Photomaps are usually published in sheets in minutes of latitude and longitude depending on the scale; but in sectionized parts of the United States, the sheets may be laid out to cover one or more townships.

Photomaps vary widely, depending on scale and purpose. Some are published with only grid lines and appropriate titles and footnotes; others show the usual planimetric features—roads, drainage, buildings, railroads, power lines, and the like—sharply defined with appropriate standard symbols, and with place names for the prominent features. On printed copies of some photomaps the planimetric detail is indicated by overprints in color—drainage in blue, cultural features in black, and special features in other appropriate colors. Such photomaps are sometimes called *planisaics*. A few photomaps include topography or terrain form lines, with the contours or form lines printed in brown, as on standard topographic quadrangles. These are called *toposaics*. Photomaps with contours to show exact topography can usually be assumed to be well constructed and accurate. Where approximate form lines of the terrain are shown instead, the photomap is probably made to less precise standards.

Three general types of photomaps can be roughly defined as follows: (1) Those reproduced in small editions by photography rather than lithography, in which the photographic background appears like it would in the aerial photograph, with lines and symbols in black or white lines on this background; (2) those printed in large editions by offset lithography in black and white, with planimetric line work overrun in black on a photographic halftone background made with a fine dot screen; and (3) those reproduced by offset lithography in two or more colors, with the photographic background shown by halftone screens in black or grey and the planimetry, contours, or other special features overrun in appropriate contrasting colors.

Advantages and disadvantages.—Since the photomap is an advanced stage of the aerial mosaic, it has many of the same characteristics, advantages, and disadvantages. The delineation of cultural and drainage features is a major advantage over the conventional controlled mosaic, since it eliminates or reduces the possibility of errors in interpretation of planimetric detail and the resulting errors in soil boundaries that may occur when mosaics are used. The soil surveyor normally spends less time classifying and delineating such detail with a recent photomap than with an aerial mosaic.

Normally, the photomap can be relied upon to be more precise than the conventional mosaic. Photomaps sufficiently precise to meet the standards for published soil maps can be used readily in the map assembly.

The disadvantages of the photomap are similar to those of the controlled mosaic. Photomaps cannot be used for stereoscopic study of an area. This is a handicap, but not so great a one as that encountered with the conventional mosaic, on which physical and cultural details are not delineated.

Because of methods used in producing them in large numbers, photomaps frequently lack the photographic detail found on photographic copies of a mosaic. Unless exceptionally fine screens are used in the offset lithography, the photographic detail reproduced is not of high quality.

Procedure for obtaining.—Photomaps prepared by other organizations, like other base materials, are obtained through the Cartographic Section. Full information on the accuracy of photomaps needs to be had before their use is recommended. It is not practical to prepare photomaps for use in soil surveying alone.

Accurate identification of drainage and cultural features require field editing.

From time to time, however, photomaps may be produced for publishing a soil map. A controlled mosaic can be constructed in advance of field mapping and used by the soil scientist as a base for mapping. The surveyor classifies the cultural and drainage features on the mosaic while making the soil survey. By using the original mosaic as a base, and preparing color separations for drainage, culture, and soils, the Cartographic Section can prepare the soil map as a photomap.

Cost.—A photomap costs more than a conventional controlled mosaic, because costs for field editing, drafting the cultural and drainage features, and making lithographic reproductions must be added. The cost of a soil map as a photomap should be comparable to that for the conventional soil map, provided color tints for soils were omitted from the photomap.

Topographic maps of standard accuracy.—A topographic map presents both horizontal and vertical positions of the physical features of a land area on a flat plane at definite scales. Published maps usually show such cultural features as roads, railroads, and buildings in black; drainage features in blue; and contour lines in brown. Some also show additional features, such as vegetation, in overprints of green or other colors.

Most topographic maps published by the United States Geological Survey and other Federal maps meeting these requirements carry marginal notes indicating compliance with the National standards of map accuracy. The standards for horizontal accuracy of maps published at scales larger than 1:20,000 prescribe that not more than 10 percent of the tested points shall be in error by more than one-thirtieth of an inch. On maps published at scales smaller than 1:20,000, the error shall not be more than one-fiftieth of an inch. These limits of accuracy apply only to positions of well-defined points, like roads, monuments, large structures, and railroads, which are readily visible and which can be plotted at the scale of the map within one-hundredth of an inch. Standards for vertical accuracy require that not more than 10 percent of the tested elevations be in error by more than one-half of the contour interval.

Types.—Because of the prescribed standards of accuracy, topographic maps vary little, even though published by different agencies. Some differences may be noted in format, scales, boundaries of latitude and longitude, and classification and presentation of planimetric detail—differences due primarily to needs for meeting specific requirements.

Standard topographic maps are published in quadrangles bounded by parallels of latitude and meridians of longitude. Generally, topographic quadrangles are 30 minutes, 15 minutes, 7½ minutes, or 3¾ minutes of latitude and longitude. Scales vary with topography and contour interval. The most usual publication scales are 1:24,000, 1:31,680, 1:48,000, 1:62,500, and 1:63,360.

Maps of smaller scale are useful to the soil scientist only for reconnaissance mapping. Few topographic maps are published at scales larger than 1:24,000.

Advantages and disadvantages.—The reliable accuracy of standard topographic maps gives them definite advantages in measuring distances and directions. The topographic pattern is very helpful to an understanding of soils and in the study of drainage, irrigation, and erosion cycles. The planimetric detail on the maps relieves the soil surveyor of a part of this task when mapping soils.

As a base for detailed soil mapping, the topographic quadrangle lacks the ground detail—field boundaries, isolated trees and bushes, fences, and similar features—that are shown on a good aerial photograph or mosaic. The small scale of many topographic quadrangles and the lack of coverage for large areas are further disadvantages. Drainage patterns on the standard topographic quadrangle are not shown in the detail needed for soil maps. Some old topographic maps are not accurate and need a great many revisions. The topographic maps of recent years, made from aerial photographs, are much more accurate.

In planning the use of topographic quadrangles in the preparation of soil maps for publication it must be recalled that a great deal more is involved than simply transferring soil boundaries to the quadrangles. Their use may or may not reduce costs, depending on the project.

Where recent, large-scale topographic quadrangles cover all, or a large part, of a soil survey area they are very useful in publishing the soil map. The use of such accurate quadrangles eliminates the necessity of constructing a base, which is especially helpful in areas with much culture. Then too, in densely wooded areas an accurate topographic map shows more points for location than an air photo. Such quadrangles serve only as a manuscript base, however, even after they are assembled into sheets of the size needed for the soil map. It is still necessary to transfer the soil data to this manuscript and prepare glass negatives or nonphotographic metal-mounted blue-line manuscript maps[1] for the color separations that show culture, soils, and drainage. These color separations are then drafted or engraved, new lettering layouts are prepared, and the printed lettering is applied to the color separations. Plates for the soil separation tints are then made and the various tints blocked out. Composite proofs are prepared and edited. The complete color separations are then copied, lithographic plates made, and the lithographic copies printed.

With old topographic quadrangles, made to less precise standards and requiring much revision, it may cost more to prepare the soil map than to make a new base from aerial photographs. The difficulties of transferring soil boundaries and symbols from the aerial photographs and adjusting them to fit old

---

[1] See Notes on Map Compilation and Reproduction, Appendix III.

quadrangles, and of revising the planimetry, more than offset the saving made by using them.

Only recent large-scale topographic quadrangles covering most of the survey area are recommended for use as a base. It is best of all if both aerial photographs and recent topographic maps made from aerial photographs are available.

Procedure for obtaining.—Standard topographic maps are published mainly by the Topographic Branch of the United States Geological Survey, the United States Coast and Geodetic Survey, and the Army Map Service of the Corps of Engineers.

The Cartographic Section of the Division of Soil Survey receives new lists and new topographic quadrangles as they are published and can supply available topographic maps needed for soil surveys. In addition, the Cartographic Section can supply information about areas in progress, expected dates of completion, and details concerning the topographic mapping program. Frequently preliminary proofs or copies of manuscript material may be obtained in advance of publication, where the need is urgent. When aerial photographs are supplied for a soil survey the Cartographic Section normally forwards all available standard topographic quadrangles as well, since such maps are helpful as reference for place names and for soil study, even though not used as the mapping base.

Costs.—The topographic quadrangle of standard accuracy is expensive to construct and publish. It serves many useful purposes, besides serving as a planimetric base for soil maps.

Planimetric maps of standard accuracy.—A planimetric map presents the horizontal position of the physical features of an area on a flat plane at definite scales. Unlike the topographic maps, no vertical distances are indicated. Otherwise, they are usually published in a form like topographic maps. Although no generally accepted precise standards for planimetric maps have been established, many mapping agencies have established standards that approach or equal those for topographic maps. Only such accurate planimetric maps are used for soil mapping.

Types.—Although standards for planimetric maps vary more than those for topographic maps, they are usually published in quadrangles similar to topographic maps and at approximately the same scales. Some differences result from variations in the map needs of the agencies preparing them. As a base for soil mapping, these differences are minor, compared to accuracy.

Advantages and disadvantages.—Planimetric maps have some of the same advantages of topographic maps as a base for soil surveying. A major exception is the omission of topography so valuable for soil study and interpretation. Then too, accuracy is less certain. Where accuracy is equal to that of good topographic maps, planimetric maps are helpful, even though the soil mapping is done on aerial photographs.

Procedure for obtaining.—As with standard topographic maps, the Cartographic Section receives copies of published planimetric quadrangles and can obtain them when needed. Where available, they are normally supplied with the aerial photographs for reference.

Cost.—Although cheaper than topographic maps, accurate planimetric maps cost more than the conventional controlled mosaics for comparable areas.

Other types of maps.—Many other types of maps are published by public and private agencies. These range from the small-scale road maps distributed by oil companies to the large-scale detailed maps used in city planning. Most of these are designed, constructed, and reproduced to meet a special purpose. Certain details on such maps are usually emphasized to meet special requirements by exaggerating certain items and subordinating others. The small-scale road map is a typical example. On such a map the highways, highway numbers, towns, cities, points of interest, and mileage distances are prominently shown, while drainage, railroads, pipelines, power lines, and public land lines are omitted or subordinated.

Aeronautical charts are special-purpose maps designed and constructed specifically for air navigation. The scale is small so that large areas may be shown on a single sheet. Ground features prominent from the air are emphasized in bold and simple symbols. Other features of equal importance on the ground but less noticeable from the air are subdued or omitted entirely. Elevations are shown in gradient tints, permitting the navigator to determine quickly the necessary flight altitude over a given area. Navigation data are shown in bright overprints.

The plats prepared from public land surveys are another form of special-purpose map, designed to present the data of the survey. The scale is large, and plats usually include a survey unit, such as a township. Courses and distances, subdivisions of sections, acreage figures, and other data from the survey are shown. Cultural and drainage features are reduced to a minimum and are accurate only on the survey lines.

Special-purpose maps of the kinds described in preceding paragraphs have little or no value as bases for detailed soil surveys. Such maps are very useful, however, for reference.

For broad reconnaissance soil surveys special maps may be useful as bases. Aeronautical charts, for example, are useful for rapid small-scale surveys of large areas. They have sufficient detail for orientation, accuracy is good at the small scale, and the generalized relief facilitates soil mapping.

The Cartographic Section can supply field parties with many special maps, including aeronautical charts, geologic maps, forest maps, coast and harbor charts, conservation survey maps, Census Bureau maps, Post Office maps, and highway maps.

EQUIPMENT

Requirements for equipment vary so widely from area to area that only those of general use are discussed here. Other sections of the *Manual* mention items for special needs. Plane tables, and accessories for them, and compasses are dealt with in the Appendices.

SPECIAL EQUIPMENT FOR AERIAL PHOTOGRAPHS

The materials used to delineate culture, soil boundaries, and symbols on aerial photographs and mosaics should be selected for ease of use, including correction, neatness, clarity, and permanence. These materials are now sufficiently standard that they may be readily obtained from commercial suppliers.

Pencils.—Despite a wide range in personal preference for types and hardness of pencils, the basic requirements are the same. The pencil marks need to be sharp, clear, and legible, but made without scratching or cutting the photographic emulsion. Pencils should be soft enough to leave a legible line yet not soft enough to smear with ordinary handling of the pictures. Too soft a pencil leaves a coarse heavy line that smears a dirty residue over the surface of the photograph and conceals other data. A very hard pencil scratches or indents the photographic emulsion, makes inking difficult, and requires such hard erasures for making corrections that the photographic emulsion may be broken.

Variations in the surface of the aerial photograph and in atmospheric conditions partly govern the choice of pencils. On hard and glossy photographs it is necessary to use a soft pencil for the line work to adhere. On the softer matte finishes, a harder pencil is better. A softer pencil is used during damp weather or in humid climates than is used during dry weather or in the desert.

Depending on conditions just mentioned, standard drafting pencils of good quality ranging from H to 4H are used in dry regions, and HB to 3B for moist regions or during periods of damp weather.

Inks.—Inks should be bright-colored, of opaque density, free-flowing, waterproof, rapid-drying, and of the kinds that photograph well.

Where the inking is done directly on the aerial photograph, a standard waterproof drafting ink should be used. If the inking is done on an acetate or plastic overlay, rather than directly on the aerial photography, special inks are used that adhere well to these media and that are easy to handle. These are called acetone inks and they etch the plastic slightly. Such special inks are too difficult to remove for use directly on photographs; in their removal the photographic emulsion is frequently damaged and brown stains are left. Standard waterproof drafting inks may be used on acetate or plastic overlays if sealer coatings are applied over the ink work immediately to prevent rubbing off or chipping. Such plastic sealer coatings can be applied with a soft cloth, brush, or spray. They dry rapidly, are transparent, and can be marked on with pencil or ink. Only a light coat of sealer should be applied. In preparing some kinds of contact prints from the original sheets, the sealer sticks to the rollers if too much has been used.

Only those colored inks are used that permit good photographic copies of the field sheets. Many colors do not photograph well unless copied through filters. Such filters may bring out any one color by subduing another. The use of filters also increases the time required for copying. Generally, black, red, and brown photograph well. The photographic qualities of blue, green, and yellow are normally poor but may be increased by mixing small amounts of the more photographic colors with them.

Mixed colors, as for example, black mixed with blue, should contrast on the field sheets and yet permit satisfactory copying. If a line is to appear in blue on a field sheet yet contain enough black to permit good photo copies, only a little black ink should be mixed in the blue.

Transparent overlays.—A number of transparent materials suitable for overlays on aerial photographs or mosaics are on the market. These fall into two general classes: (1) Plastics and (2) acetates. Both can be obtained in a variety of thicknesses and finishes.

Overlay materials should have dimensional stability. If one without dimensional stability is selected, difficulties are had in maintaining registry between the overlay and the photograph and in matching one overlay with another.

The most useful materials for overlays range from 0.005 to 0.080 inch in thickness. Enough thickness is needed to give stiffness and to avoid curling, yet not so much that sheets are bulky and difficult to handle.

The best overlays are transparent, with a grained surface. These have maximum transparency and their surface is suitable for both pencil and ink work. India ink can be used on ungrained acetate or plastic if soiling with perspiration or other oily substances is avoided. A sealer needs to be applied immediately afterward.

A transparent dimensionally stable material, with matte finish on one side and about 0.008 inch thick, is entirely satisfactory.

Types of photo paper.—In ordering aerial photographs and mosaics it is sometimes helpful for the soil scientist to specify the type and finish of paper on which the photographs are to be printed. Of the many kinds, some are satisfactory and others unsatisfactory for soil mapping.

Most photographic papers are available in three thicknesses or weights, as light, single, and double. Lightweight papers are too thin and flexible for most soil mapping. They tend to curl and lack dimensional stability. Where copies of field photographs thin enough to use over a light table in transferring data from one sheet to another are wanted, the lightweight papers are satisfactory. An extra thin paper is made that is especially good for this purpose.

Single-weight paper is somewhat thicker than the lightweight papers and is commonly used for printing aerial photographs to be used only in offices. Even this weight is too light for satisfactory field use where photographs are handled a great deal and exposed to variable weather conditions.

Double-weight paper is approximately twice the thickness of single-weight. It is stiff and does not curl, has a reasonable degree of dimensional stability, and is best for photographs that are to be used in the field for soil mapping.

Photographic finishes are classed broadly as glossy, semimatte, and matte. The surface of a glossy photograph is too slick and polished to accept pencil or ink well, and cannot be used conveniently. Semimatte and matte finishes take pencil and ink well, and these finishes are used on photographs on which survey data are to be plotted.

Waterproof papers are advantageous on some soil surveys. They can be processed somewhat faster than the conventional photographic paper and, if properly processed, their dimensional stability is somewhat better. For soil surveys in warm humid regions the waterproof paper has the advantage of absorbing less moisture.

Pens.—Pens should have points ranging from medium-fine to fine. Pens with stiff firm points are much preferred to those having soft flexible nibs. Unless used by an expert, pens with highly flexible nibs spread, and lines are either too heavy or too light. Such points soon lose their spring if abused and need to be discarded. The stiffer, coarser pen lasts longer and permits more uniform and consistent line work.

Erasers.—For cleaning soft pencil lines from aerial photographs art gum is usually satisfactory. Hard pencil lines can be removed with a soft pliable eraser. Ink lines not removable with a soft pliable eraser can be taken off by first dampening with alcohol or water and then erasing. Care must be taken not to let the photographic emulsion become wet enough to break or tear with erasing. Coarse or abrasive erasers should not be used on photographs. The emulsion becomes so scratched and broken that reinking is difficult or impossible.

The sketchmaster.—The sketchmaster is a small instrument used to reflect the image of the aerial photograph to a manuscript map. The photograph is mounted parallel to the manuscript map on a tripod-supported frame. The operator looks down through a half-silvered mirror at the front of the instrument and sees the image of the photograph superimposed on the manuscript map (fig. 1). He can adjust the length of the three legs to correct for tilt and difference in scale. The sketchmaster can be used for sketching at scales ranging from one-half to twice that of the photograph.

Simplicity, compactness, and portability make the sketchmaster an excellent instrument for use in field offices to transfer planimetric and soil data from the field sheets to a manuscript map. It

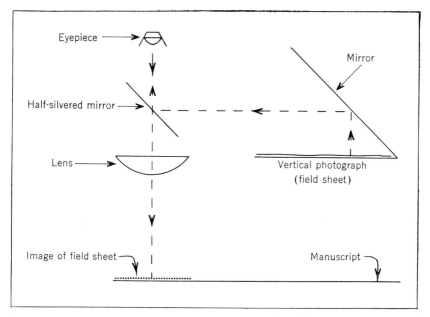

Figure 1.—Diagram showing the principles employed in a common type of sketchmaster used for transferring map data from a photograph to a manuscript map.

may be used for overlays and other field sheets as well as for aerial photographs.

Sketchmasters may be vertical or oblique. The vertical sketchmaster is used with vertical aerial photographs and the oblique is used with oblique aerial photographs. Since the vertical aerial photograph is used mainly in soil mapping, only the vertical sketchmaster concerns us here. The same general techniques are used with overlays of vertical aerial photographs or plane-table sheets.

In working with the sketchmaster, a framework of control is first indicated on the manuscript map, and into this framework planimetric detail is transferred from the photograph. This framework assists the operator to orient his instrument and thus to transfer the map data to their correct position on the manuscript. The framework may consist of photogrammetric stations, or culture and drainage, along with established section lines or other land lines.

If the manuscript map is a standard topographic or planimetric map, only soil boundaries and symbols, and revisions in culture and drainage need to be transferred.

An operator uses a sketchmaster about as follows:

   (1) After inspecting the aerial photograph to make certain that the detail is clearly delineated, it is inserted in the frame so that it is perfectly flat and all detail is shown.

(2) The instrument is placed on the manuscript map. Looking through the eyepiece, the operator orients the instrument so that the image reflected from the instrument is near the correct position on the manuscript.

(3) Among the lenses furnished with the instrument one is selected that removes practically all the parallax at the scale to be used. With a low rig, for example, a large numbered lens is used. If a point on the manuscript moves in a direction opposite to that of the eye of the operator, a smaller numbered lens should be selected.

(4) The instrument is adjusted for scale by lowering or raising the frame on all three legs. The final leg adjustment is made with the screw feet. Correction for any tilt in the photograph may be made by adjusting the length of one or two legs.

(5) The detail on the manuscript should coincide with the detail reflected to it from the aerial photograph.

(6) The detail on the aerial photograph is now ready to be transferred to its correct position on the map manuscript. The eye is shifted slightly to bring individual controls into exact register as the detail in their vicinity is being traced. When tracing a stream, for example, the operator holds to the control on or near it. If there is no control on a feature, a skilled operator can properly orient nearby points in order to locate boundaries correctly. Transferring can be extended out to the edges of the vertical photographs.

Good light is required. The mirrors should not be touched with the hands since the salt in perspiration decomposes the chemical coating of the mirror and spoils it.

SOIL-SAMPLING TOOLS

The soil scientist's most important tool is the humble spade, supplemented by the pick and the soil auger. For exposing soil profiles for morphological examinations, as in the initial work of preparing a mapping legend, for sampling, or for photographing, the spade is used almost entirely. For the more frequent routine examinations of soils in mapping, the spade is generally but not always superior to the auger. For example, where the chief differentiating characteristic between two soil types or phases is the depth to a deep underlying stratum of clay or is the color of the substratum, a soil auger may be better than the spade, both faster and more convenient. Perhaps the worst feature of the auger is its destruction of soil structure, so important in classification and identification. In dry, stony soils, the auger is difficult to use; nor can the spade alone be used rapidly; and the pick becomes the most useful tool. Whenever practical, the spade should be given preference over the soil auger, especially in excavating the upper part of the soil—the solum. Where the soil auger is used frequently in identifying soils, some exposed profiles of the soil types should also be examined in order to check the results.

Spades and picks.—For use in collecting samples, especially after the preliminary excavation has been made, the flat square-pointed spade (fig. 2, A) is most convenient. The best generally useful spade, however, for ordinary use in mapping, is a modified post hole spade (fig. 2, B and C). The sharp corners of the post hole spade are removed for best results. The common tiling spade tapers somewhat too much at the end, although it is a useful tool for some soils and generally superior to the post hole spade for

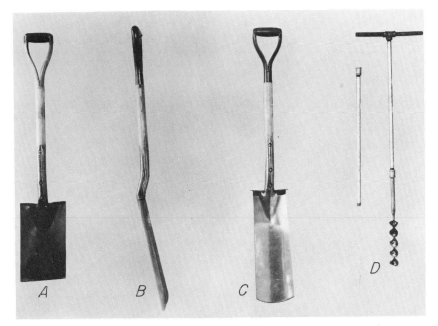

FIGURE 2.—Soil-sampling tools: *A*, Square-pointed spade, especially useful in collecting samples; *B*, side view, and *C*, front view of post hole spade, the most generally useful sampling tool; and *D*, soil auger with extension.

gravelly soils. Where deep holes are required, as in examining irrigated Alluvial soils, the long-handled irrigator's shovel is useful. It may be necessary to supplement this shovel with a heavy crowbar to penetrate dry cemented and compact layers.

The pick should always be at hand, especially for making holes in hard, dry, stony, or gravelly soils. In some soils a small trench pick will serve satisfactorily, but commonly a heavier pick with a long handle is better. One prong should be sharply pointed and the other made as a chisel. A heavy chisel-pointed bar is useful for penetrating strongly cemented or indurated hardpans.

A geologist's hammer, or small hand pick, one end of which can be used as a hammer, is also useful in examining rocks and the soil in cuts along roadsides. For moist soils and those containing many woody roots, a chisel-pointed hammer is better; whereas for dry soils a sharp-pointed hammer is better.

Augers.—The screw, or worm, type of soil auger (fig. 2, *C*) consists essentially of a 1¼- or 1½-inch wood auger, from which the cutting side flanges and tip have been removed, welded to a steel rod or iron pipe with a crosspiece at the top for a handle. The worm part should be about 7 inches long, with the distances between flanges about the same as the diameter, 1¼ to 1½ inches. If the distance between flanges is narrower, it is difficult to remove the soil with the thumb. For ordinary use augers are 40 to 60 inches long, with provisions for adding extra lengths for deep boring. An auger for continual use is made solidly throughout, and another extension auger is used for deep borings. In clay soils an auger with a 1-inch bit may be more convenient than the larger one. It is convenient to have a scale marked on the shaft of the auger from the tip.

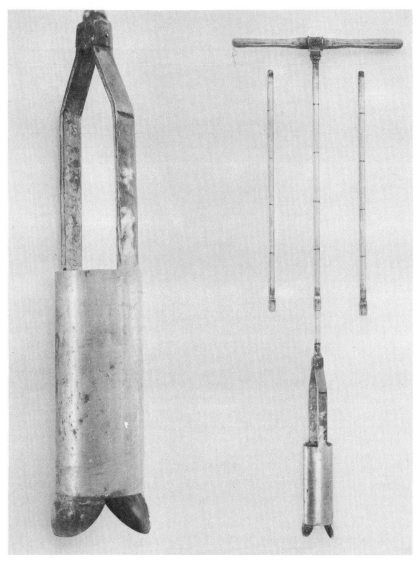

FIGURE 3.—Core type of soil auger: Left, a close view of the bit; right, a view of the whole auger, with extensions, marked at 6-inch intervals.

Generally, the core, or post hole, type of soil auger shown in figure 3 is better than the older screw type. The core type is especially favored in dry regions, and the screw type in wet ones. The core type gives a larger and less modified sample. It works well in loose dry sand and in compact soils. The cylinder is about 2 to 4 inches in diameter, commonly 3½ inches. The cutting blades are so constructed that the soil is loosened and forced into the cylinder of the auger as it is rotated and pushed into the soil. Each filling of the cylinder corresponds to a penetration of 3 to 5 inches. Although both ends of the cylinder are open, the soil becomes packed enough to stay in it while the auger is removed. If the cylinder is only partly filled, or if the soil is very dry and sandy, it may need to be tamped with a stick thrust through the upper end of the cylinder before it will stay in the auger when pulled out of the hole. Small cylinders are best for very sandy soils. A few taps of the cylinder on the ground or on a board usually loosens the soil for removal.

The core-type auger disturbs the soil, but less so than the screw-type auger. A better view of soil structure, porosity, consistence, and color can be had with the core auger, but even so, excavations are necessary for proper morphological studies. The core-type auger is not well suited to use in wet clay soils. Generally, with soils that are naturally moist for much of the year, the screw-type auger is faster.

Although soil augers are simple in design and somewhat crude in appearance, considerable skill is required to use them effectively in making dependable observations of the soil profile.

Peat sampler.—Examinations of deep deposits of peat are made with a special sampler. Although several devices are used, the one most common in the United States is the Davis peat sampler or some modification of it, as shown in figure 4. The instrument consists of 10 or more sections of steel rods, each 2 or 4 feet long, and a cylinder of brass or duraluminum, approximately 14 inches long with an inside diameter of three-fourths inch. The cylinder is provided with a plunger, cone-shaped at the lower end, and with a spring catch near the upper end. The sampler is pressed into the peat until the desired depth is reached for taking a sample; then the spring catch allows withdrawal of the plunger from its enclosing cylinder. With the plunger withdrawn and locked in that position, the cylinder may be filled with a solid core of the organic material by a further downward movement. The cylinder protects the sample completely from any contamination and does not destroy its structure when the instrument is removed.

Beginning at the surface, samples of peat are taken consecutively at intervals of 6 inches or 1 foot. The lengths of steel rods used allow an easy estimation of the depth of each sample. For very deep deposits, extra 2- or 4-foot rods are used. Each rod is threaded at one end to screw into a small coupling on the reverse end of another rod. For light work, the rods may be screwed and unscrewed with pliers; for heavy work in deep deposits, small pipe wrenches are used.

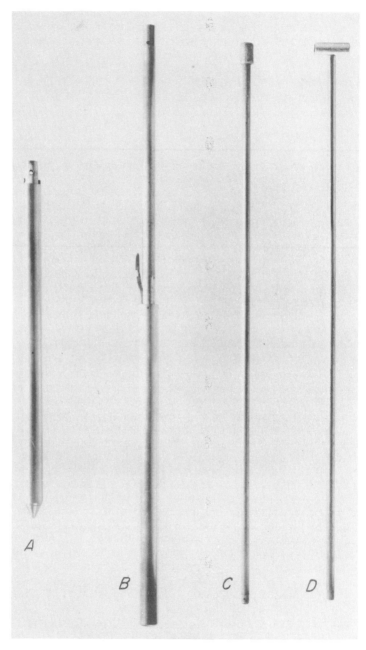

FIGURE 4.—Peat sampler: *A*, The head closed, ready for pushing into the peat; *B*, the head extended, as just prior to taking a sample; *C*, one 2-foot extension rod; and *D*, the top extension rod.

Other sampling tools.—Power augers, mounted on the rear of a truck or on a trailer, some custom made and others obtainable from manufacturers, are used in some soil surveys, either for special studies or for cutting through cemented or very compact dry soils. Some of these are of the core type, either similar to the hand core auger already described or so constructed as to obtain an undisturbed core of a complete soil profile.[2] Others are of the screw type. Further experience is needed with power augers. A custom-built one in use is shown in figure 5.

FIGURE 5.—Custom-built power soil auger: *A*, Mounted on a pick-up truck in position to operate; *B*, in position for transport; and *C*, close view of bit.

Another tool used little in routine soil mapping but of use in collecting soil samples is the King soil tube, or a modification of it, which consists of a long, narrow tube that can be driven into the soil. It is used primarily in collecting soil samples for moisture and bulk-density (or volume-weight) determinations. A short, wide tube is used for collecting samples from soil horizons for bulk-density determination. An angled cold chisel is convenient for cutting out blocks of compact or cemented soil. An ordinary

[2] For a description of a power auger see KELLEY, O. J., HARDMAN, J. A., JENNINGS, D. S. A SOIL-SAMPLING MACHINE FOR OBTAINING TWO-, THREE-, AND FOUR-INCH DIAMETER CORES OF UNDISTURBED SOIL TO A DEPTH OF SIX FEET. Soil Sci. Soc. Amer. Proc. 12: 85–87., illus. 1947.

trowel is used for sampling thin horizons and for filling sample sacks. A special trowel for this purpose consists essentially of an ordinary curved garden trowel with about one-half of the blade cut away (longitudinally) and sharpened. A straight-bladed steel fern trowel is also a good tool. A handy tool for examining soil profiles is a small steel pick of the type used by French workmen in laying slate roofs. The head of this tool has a broad-bladed chisel on one prong and a small hammer on the other. Finally, every soil morphologist needs a strong knife.

FIELD TESTING APPARATUS

Several suitable field kits for pH determinations are available. Where soils are very low or very high in pH, are highly organic, or are salty, an electrical field kit is better than the simpler colorimetric ones. Carbonates may be tested for with 10-percent hydrochloric acid solution in a small dropping bottle.

The sections on Soil Reaction and Estimation and Mapping of Salts and Alkali in the Soil should be read and appropriate apparatus obtained as required.

Besides these tests, manganese dioxide may be tested for by using a 10-percent solution of hydrogen peroxide in a dropping bottle. This is not a test for total manganese, and effervescence is not necessarily correlated with toxic concentrations. The peroxide test is useful in the field as a partial indicator of boundaries among some lateritic and latosolic soils.

No kits for chemical "quick tests" for available or soluble plant nutrients in soils are recommended. In some areas, particular ones may be useful if well standardized by field plot tests.

PLOTTING AND ASSEMBLY OF FIELD DATA

The plotting and assembly of field data are discussed early in the *Manual* because of their importance to preparation for field work, but some points may not be clear until later chapters dealing more specifically with soil classification and mapping units are studied.

AERIAL PHOTOGRAPHS IN SOIL SURVEYS
Characteristics of aerial photographs

The kinds of aerial photographs have already been described. First of all, an aerial photograph is not a map but a perspective view of a portion of the earth's surface. Like all perspectives, it does not present a true scale, and precise measurements of distances and directions cannot be made on it. In addition to the distortions of a perspective, there are those created by tilt, differences in elevation, and inherent errors of photography. Yet in contrast to maps made by ground methods, aerial photographs show more ground detail, permit a three-dimension view of the features, and afford an economical method for obtaining base material rapidly for large or inaccessible areas. From them, accurate planimetric and topographic maps can be made. For most soil mapping, there is no better medium than the aerial photograph.

Oblique photographs are taken with cameras (often hand held) pointed down at an angle such that the longitudinal axis of the camera forms an angle of less than 90° with the ground. They are classified as (1) *high oblique*, which show the horizon, and (2) *low oblique*, which do not show the horizon. The high oblique shows a large area of the terrain in panorama, whereas the low oblique shows only a small area of the ground. Although obliques serve many purposes and are useful in reconnaissance surveys as an aid to the identification of boundaries, they are not readily converted to maps and are not so satisfactory for soil mapping as vertical pictures.

Vertical photographs are taken with fixed-level cameras pointed straight down from the aircraft so that the longitudinal axis of the camera is perpendicular to the horizontal plane of the ground. Three broadly defined types are (1) the continuous-strip photograph, (2) the multiple-lens, and (3) the single-lens.

The strip photograph is a continuous-strip exposure. Strip photographs may be taken from low altitudes at high speeds by synchronizing film motion with the ground speed of the aircraft. In this way good pictures can be taken with poor light. Strip photographs so taken have little use in soil mapping because of their large scale and small coverage.

Multiple-lens photographs combine vertical and oblique camera angles. The cameras usually have three, five, or nine lenses. One lens takes a vertical view, and the others obliques. With a transforming printer, the obliques are transformed to the plane of the vertical picture to produce a composite vertical photograph composed of the center vertical picture and the transformed obliques. The multiple-lens camera is widely used where rapid and economical coverage of large areas at small scale is needed. Although the pictures are occasionally used in soil mapping, they are not recommended if single-lens pictures are available. The usually small scale, necessity for transforming prints, and difficulties of map construction make them less satisfactory than single-lens pictures. Multiple-lens photographs are also obtained through the use of multiple cameras, arranged and mounted to make vertical and oblique exposures. The tri-metrogon photograph is an example.

71

Single-lens photographs, which are taken in a series of independent over-lapping exposures, are recommended for soil mapping. They have convenient size for field use and map construction, permit stereoscopic study, give excellent detail of ground features and also have satisfactory ranges of scale.

In discussing the use of aerial photographs in this *Manual*, single-lens vertical aerial photographs, made to the specifications of the Department of Agriculture, are assumed unless otherwise stated. Where it is necessary to use other types of photographs or single-lens photographs of lower standards, the Cartographic Section of the Division of Soil Survey will advise the soil scientists about methods to use and their specific weaknesses. Excessive tilt, insufficient overlap, and other deficiencies may make it impossible to use the pictures stereoscopically or to construct accurate maps from them.

Flight lines and overlap.—Most aerial photography in this country is flown north and south. Flight lines are as near straight and parallel as possible; they should not deviate from the true direction by more than 5 degrees. Flight lines are usually continuous across the area, with the first and last photograph on each flight line falling entirely outside the area boundary.

In line of flight, consecutive photographs should overlap an average of 60 percent, with no overlap less than 55 percent nor more than 65 percent. Overlap in line of flight is referred to as *endlap*. The overlap between adjacent flight lines, or *sidelap*, should average 30 percent, with none less than 15 percent nor more than 45 percent. (See figure 6.)

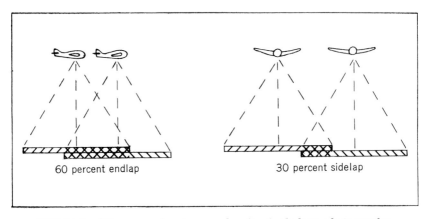

60 percent endlap   30 percent sidelap

FIGURE 6.—Diagrams showing overlap in single-lens photographs.

Adequate overlap is essential for stereoscopic study in the field and for the photogrammetric processes used in map construction. Where alternate photographs—every other photograph in line of flight—are used, the overlap of standard pictures averages only 20 percent.

Full stereoscopic coverage should be obtained for soil mapping, even though the soil boundaries are plotted only on alternate photographs.

Scale.—The scale of aerial photographs is not always accurate nor uniform like that of a good map. The scale varies between photographs because of varying altitudes of the aircraft, differences in ground elevations, or tilt of the camera. The sketch in figure 7 shows that a photograph taken at camera station A will not be the same scale as a photograph taken at station B because the aircraft is at different altitudes at the times of exposures. Thus, the 20-acre field C will not measure the same as the 20-acre field D because of the elevation differences within the photograph.

The scale given for photographs is the approximate average scale computed from the mean altitude of the entire area flown, from that of a

film and papers. These errors are reduced to the minimum in modern aerial photography where only precision mapping cameras, excellent laboratory equipment, and special aero film and paper are used.

Code numbers.—Aerial photographs are marked when taken and processed to permit indexing and rapid selection. Although organizations indicate different information in various ways on their aerial photographs, the following are usually shown: (1) Date of flight, (2) time of day, (3) owner of film, (4) scale of negative, (5) project or area, (6) film roll number, and (7) exposure number. Some also show altitude, focal length of camera, type of camera, and the like.

Each aerial photograph made for the United States Department of Agriculture bears a code letter designating the project or area and individual numbers to designate the roll of film and exposure. These are in the northeast corner for north-south flights and in the northwest corner for east-west flights. The code number for the area is limited to three letters; the roll of film is indicated by number, beginning with one and continuing unbroken; and numbers indicate the exposures, beginning with one for each roll of film and continuing unbroken. For example, in the designation ABC–46–122, ABC indicates the county or area, 46 the roll of film in that county or area, and 122 the exposure in that roll. In the adjacent corner are numbers for the month, day, and year the exposure was made. On the first and last exposure in each roll of film appears the abbreviation for the organization owning the film, the approximate scale of the negatives, and the time of day the exposures were made. The organization abbreviation and approximate scale precede the usual area symbol, as BPI–1:20,000–ABC–46–122. In the adjacent corner, immediately following the date, the time of day is placed, as 6–15–48—11:30.

Photo indexes.—Aerial photographic indexes are prepared for large areas. Without an index the user of photographs is seriously handicapped in selecting the photograph for a specific area or in locating adjacent photographs in adjoining flights. Photo indexes are prepared by laying the overlapping photographs so that the index numbers of each print are visible. Standard specifications usually require the index to be in sheets 20 by 24 inches at an approximate scale of 1:63,360. The soil survey party should have the photo index of the area to expedite the location of individual photographs.

Stereoscopic vision

Although individual aerial photographs are flat in appearance, overlapping pairs can be viewed under a stereoscope and the topography of the ground becomes apparent: hills and valleys appear, buildings and trees stand up, and the slight depressions of drainage can be seen. Thus viewed, the aerial photograph looks like a detailed relief model. The soil scientist can study the ground before going into the field. Drainage and trails that are obscure on the flat photographs can be outlined in advance. Travel routes can be selected. Stereoscopic study of the pictures, both before and after the mapping, helps him to see the relations between kinds of soil and land forms.

Theory of stereovision.—In normal vision, the observer sees objects in three dimensions, namely length, width, and depth. The ability to see depth depends on sight with two eyes, each at an equal distance from the object but viewing it from a different position, or angle. Each eye registers a slightly different image. These images are fused or combined by the optic nerves and brain to give depth perception or a third dimensional view of the object. The distance between the eyes is so short that the angle and difference becomes so small at great distances that it is difficult to register depth perception.

When viewing two overlapping aerial photographs under the stereoscope, one sees the same ground area from widely separated positions. The right eye is viewing the area in one photograph, the left eye the same area in another photograph. The effect is the same as if a person were viewing the area with one eye located at one camera position and the other eye at the next camera position. The brain so fuses the images that one sees the relief in the photograph, or the third dimension.

The average person with normal vision should have little difficulty with stereoscopic study of aerial photographs. Occasionally a person with apparently normal vision is unable to use the stereoscope. This may be expected of older persons whose eye muscles are not flexible. Some feel eyestrain when first using the stereoscope.

Stereoscopic vision requires some practice. At first it may be difficult to adjust the photographs and fuse the images; yet after practice this can be done rapidly with little or no eyestrain.

Types of stereoscopes.—Stereoscopes are constructed on two basic principles. Those most commonly used in the study of aerial photographs are (1) the mirror type, which utilizes the principle of reflection, and (2) the lens type, which makes use of the principle of refraction. A third type, less commonly used, is the prism stereoscope. In this type prisms serve as reflectors, much as mirrors do in the mirror stereoscope. Designs of all types vary widely.

The mirror stereoscope has four mirrors fastened in a frame and arranged to transmit the photographic image to the eye by reflection (fig. 12). Since these stereoscopes are usually large and bulky, they are not easily portable and are used mainly for office work where plenty of table space is available. Some mirror stereoscopes are designed to fold up and fit in a small case that can be carried in a large pocket. Even these are too bulky to carry in the field while mapping.

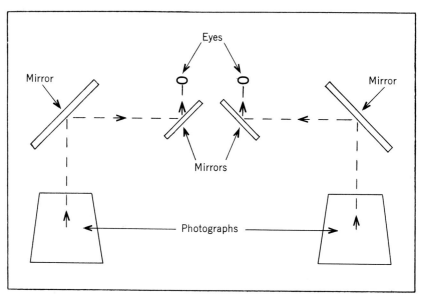

FIGURE 12.—Sketch showing the essentials of the design of a mirror stereoscope.

The mirror stereoscope gives an image nearly free of distortion. It has a wide field of vision—wide enough for one to view an entire photograph. The wide separation of the mirrors allows the photographs to be viewed without overlapping, which makes adjustment and fusion of the picture simple. Many instruments have a horizontal adjustment of the outer mirrors which allows them to be placed at various distances from the eyepiece. With this adjustment, larger scale photographs can be viewed than with the conventional lens-type stereoscope. Owing to the great optical distance between the eye and the photograph, the fused image appears to be reduced.

This is a disadvantage in studying fine detail, especially on small scale photographs. The disadvantage may be overcome by fitting the stereoscope with magnifying lens, but this increases the size and cost of the instrument.

The mirror stereoscope is especially good for the office study of aerial photographs. It is simple for the beginner to use and requires little practice.

Lens stereoscopes have two magnifying lenses mounted in a frame and supported on a stand so that the photographs are viewed directly through the lenses, or eyepieces. The lenses are ground so that the lines of sight are bent outward (fig. 13). These instruments are usually small, compact, and light. Many are designed for field use and fold into a small unit that can be carried easily by the soil mapper in the field. Most use, however, is in the field headquarters.

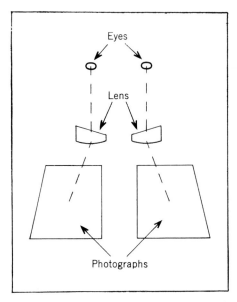

FIGURE 13.—Sketch showing the essentials of the design of a lens stereoscope. The thin edges of the lenses are inside.

The lens stereoscope gives a distorted image. It has a small field of vision, and only part of the photograph can be viewed at one time. The close spacing of the lenses, combined with direct vision, makes it necessary to place the photographs very close together or even to overlap them. Thus adjustment of the photographs and fusion of the images are somewhat difficult. For the same reason, large-scale photographs cannot be viewed satisfactorily except at the margins. Despite these disadvantages, the lens stereoscope is a useful tool for the soil scientist.

The lens stereoscope magnifies, which is a definite advantage, especially when studying minute detail or very small-scale aerial photographs. It emphasizes the relief, which is helpful in viewing nearly flat terrain.

The lens stereoscope is helpful for the field study of aerial photographs where the scale is small enough to permit its ready use. Appropriate models are light, compact, and relatively cheap.

Care of stereoscopes.—Stereoscopes are generally of rugged construction and will withstand a reasonable amount of hard use; but they are optical instruments and should be treated accordingly. "First-surface" mirrors are used in stereoscopes. In these the silver is applied to the front of the glass and not to the back. The silver coating is highly susceptible to scratching and corrosion and should not be touched. All first-surface mirrors should be protected with a soft cloth or chamois covering when not in use.

A first-surface mirror may be cleaned with soft clean cotton and alcohol. The cotton needs to be free from any grit that might scratch the silvered surface. The silvered surface is wiped gently with just enough pressure to remove the dirt. Fingerprints should be cleaned off immediately, since their residues corrode the mirror.

The lens type of stereoscope should be cleaned and cared for like a pair of glasses. Stereoscopic lenses are usually ground with one side thinner than the other in order to reflect the light rays outward. Such lens must be placed in the frame with the thick edge outward and the thin edge inward.

Use of the stereoscope.—To use the stereoscope in studying aerial photographs one must first acquire the knack of adjusting the photographs and accustoming the eyes to stereoscopic vision. This ability may be acquired in different ways.

One of the simplest methods is to place a small cross on two separate sheets of paper. With each sheet of paper under the lens, or mirror, of the stereoscope, one may look directly through the eyepieces of the stereoscope and focus the eyes on the crosses. Unless the crosses by chance are fused, one sees two crosses. After the eyes are focussed, one sheet is held firmly and the other moved slowly. The crosses move either nearer or farther from each other. The sheets are slowly shifted until the two crosses coincide and appear as one. During the operation, the eyes are not shifted nor the focus changed.

Once the crosses coincide, the sheet is moved until the image separates into two crosses again; then again the sheets are shifted until the crosses appear as one image. This practice is continued until "fusing" can be done rapidly. When the crosses are fused, the approximate location of the sheets with reference to the lens or mirrors is noted. The sheets are removed and then replaced to try focussing the eyes and fusing the crosses rapidly. When the operation can be performed quickly and accurately, one is ready to attempt stereoscopic vision with two aerial photographs.

To start, one may select two stereo-pairs of terrain with moderate relief and a distinct pattern of ground features. The photographs should be of equal tone and scale. The center of the photograph—its optical center—is located at the intersection of lines drawn between collimation marks, usually appearing as small ticks at the center of each margin, and marked with a cross. The picture centers are transferred to the overlap area in each adjoining picture, and the two crosses on each picture connected with a line. The photographs are placed under the stereoscope with the overlapping detail approximately in coincidence and the lines on the photographs parallel to the eye base. The shadows should fall toward the observer and both photographs need to be well and uniformly illuminated.

The photographs are shifted horizontally and adjusted until the crosses and connecting lines are fused. Then the relief can be seen. One of the photographs should be shifted until fusion is lost, and later recovered. With practice, images may be fused rapidly. As skill develops, the observer fuses the images by observing the physical features and less by watching the crosses and connecting lines.

After skill in these exercises has been obtained, it is time to try two photographs without the centers marked and connected. Two such pictures are placed under the stereoscope with the index finger of each hand just under the same selected physical feature in the overlap area on each photograph. The eyes are focussed and the pictures shifted until the fingers approximately coincide. The fingers are moved away and the images slightly separated. Then they are adjusted until they again coincide. This practice needs to be continued with other stereo-pairs. Once the knack of placing the photographs and adjusting them until they fuse has been acquired, the operator is ready to use the stereoscope in the study of aerial photographs.

Lenses need to be focussed properly. Many stereoscopes have an adjustment for varying the spacing of the eyepieces, so that they can be separated to the correct interpupillary distance of the observer's eyes.

Generally, on aerial photographs man-made features appear in geometric patterns—with straight lines, sharp angles, and circles.

Natural features, generally, have irregular and curved lines, as in twisting streams, curving shore lines, and the like.

For interpretation of size one needs to know the approximate scale of the photograph. A round image may represent a silo on a large-scale print, and one of the same size, a large gas storage tank on a small-scale print. Size is sensed by comparison among the ground objects.

The tone, or shade, in which various features appear on an aerial photograph is due mainly to the amount of reflected light. The amount of reflected light depends upon the texture of the surface of the object and the angle at which the light is reflected. An object that reflects a large amount of light appears in a light tone on the photograph. If little light is reflected, the object appears dark.

Because of differences in the angle of reflected light, the tone of an object may be different on two consecutive photographs, especially if the surface is smooth and a good reflector of light. Thus, in one photograph, with the light rays reflected from the water to the camera, a water area appears light; in an adjoining photograph, with the angle of reflection away from the camera, the same body of water appears dark. Most natural features, however, reflect light in all directions and appear in intermediate tones, for some of the reflected light finds its way to the camera lens.

For stereoscopic study, the light should be good and each photograph should be equally illuminated, but without glare. Where possible, the observer should face the source of the light. Of course, these lighting conditions cannot always be arranged in the field.

The photographs are placed under the stereoscope in such a way that the one taken to the left of the overlap area is viewed by the left eye, and the one to the right of the overlap by the right eye. If the position of the photographs is reversed, and the left eye views the right photo and the right the left, the image of relief appears in reverse. In such an arrangement, points of low elevation appear high, and points of high elevation low. This is commonly called a pseudoscopic image.

Photographic characteristics.—Certain characteristics of aerial photographs are the basis of stereoscopic interpretation. The most important ones are the shape and size of features, the tone in which the features appear on the photographs, and the shadows cast by the features.

The shape of features is important in the interpretation of ground detail from aerial photographs. The observer needs to study the shape of ground objects as they appear on the vertical photographs in comparison with how the same features look on the ground. Frequently the tone of objects appears darker or lighter in photographs than their contrasting ground colors would suggest.

Shadows on aerial photographs often reveal the size, shape, and identity of objects. The shadows suggest the heights of objects, which are not revealed by the horizontal dimensions alone. A one-story building, for example, may look like a five-story one in the picture except for the shadow. But shadows can be deceptive. If the ground under the object slopes abruptly, the shadow may be distorted. The height of the sun at the time of exposure also affects the length of the shadow. Yet many objects with little width, like fences, flagpoles, and chimneys, are difficult to identify except by their shadows.

Interpretation.—Most field scientists become proficient in photo interpretation by using the photographs in the field where opportunities are continually offered to compare ground features with their photographic images.

Study of the photographs of the area to be covered a day or so in advance can be helpful. The accuracy of interpretations is checked by observations of the ground detail. Images that are unidentifiable in the office can be identified in the field. With such practice, the soil scientist can rapidly train himself in aerial interpretation. It must always be recalled, however, that accurate photo interpretation depends on familiarity with ground conditions. Ability to interpret pictures accurately in one area is not necessarily followed by similar accuracy in another area with different conditions.

The time of day and season of the year in which photographs are taken influence interpretation. In order to have good light, most photography is taken under ideal weather conditions and during the middle part of the day. The length of shadows naturally depends upon the height of the sun. Shadows on photographs taken in summer are shorter than those on photographs taken in winter. Similarly, shadows appear much longer on photographs taken a few hours before or after noon than on those taken at noon.

Features appear differently on aerial photographs in the different seasons. Cultivated fields vary from season to season. In wet seasons, streams appear large and many small ponds may be visible. In the dry season, the same area may have no ponds and the streams may be dry beds. During summer, deciduous forests present a mass of treetops that obscure the ground detail. In winter, pictures of the same area show a confusion of tree trunks, emphasized by shadows, and trails, small drains, and other ground detail are clear. Snow on the ground obscures much of the detail. The experienced photo interpreter takes all of these factors into consideration when studying the photographs.

A few of the characteristics of some major features as they appear in aerial photographs may be helpful in acquiring skill in photo interpretation. With experience, the soil scientist can broaden his information.

Streams.—Streams are usually identified by their irregular widths and winding courses, frequently emphasized by the growth of brush and trees along the banks. In heavily wooded areas, small streams are difficult to detect. Water in stream beds is suggested by dark or light lines, depending on the angle of the reflected light. Dry stream beds are easily recognized in the open and usually appear in light tones.

Bodies of water.—Ponds and lakes appear lighter or darker than the adjoining shore, depending on the reflected light. Furthermore, they are flat. The shore lines are sharply defined and appear as irregular outlines. One end of a large lake in a photograph may appear light and the other end dark.

Marshes.—Swamps and marshes have a blurred appearance. Many display very winding channels, or small bodies of open water. Very wet areas or those partially covered with water usually appear darker than the surrounding ground.

Forests and brush.—Wooded areas appear as dark masses with irregular outlines. The intensity of tone for deciduous cover varies with the season. In summer the tone is very dark; in winter it is lighter. Coniferous forests appear dark in tone, regardless of the season. Brush areas have a dark tone in summer and a lighter one in winter, but shadows are lacking. Stereoscopic inspection suggests the height.

Cultivated areas.—Cultivated fields are readily identified by their contrasting tones and their boundaries. Many field edges are well defined by fences, hedges, trails, or roads. Terraces, contour strips, and other patterns show clearly.

Some crops can be identified by planting patterns and tone or shade. Fields with heavy standing crops or grass appear dark. Fields from which crops have been harvested recently appear lighter. During harvest of crops such as hay, wheat, and corn, fields acquire a distinctive pattern. Shocks appear as dark-colored, regularly spaced dots against a lighter background. Because of the rough surface and damp soil, freshly plowed fields are usually very dark. The pattern of plowing is frequently visible on the photograph. Orchards, vineyards, and similar plantings are readily identified by their distinctive spacing.

Roads, trails, and paths.—Roads usually appear as light lines. Cement concrete roads have well-defined edges and appear light except for streaks of oil drop in the center of each lane. Bituminous concrete or other black-surfaced roads may seem dark. Most improved roads are identified by long straight stretches, gentle curves, and regular width. Unimproved roads are more irregular, have sharper curves, and vary in width.

Trails meander and often follow the contour. Paths are even more indistinct and irregular. If used a great deal, paths and trails appear as light streaks.

The appearance of roads, trails, and paths changes with the season because of shadows cast by trees and partial covering by overhanging vegetation.

Railroads.—Railroads appear much like roads on the photographs but are usually darker and narrower. They have long straight stretches and smoother curves than roads. The roadbed material affects the tone appearance of the railroad. Large cuts and fills, water tanks, spur lines, and stations are distinct along the right-of-way.

Buildings.—Buildings are readily identified on aerial photographs. Their size is suggested by their relation to the scale of the photograph; and comparative heights can be estimated from the shadows. Isolated buildings often have roads or trails leading to them. Individual buildings in groups may be indistinct because of the collective shadows.

Land form.—With practice, land form may be suggested from the photographs. In fact, land forms may be clearer in aerial photographs than on any map or from the ground. As a start, the soil scientist may consult some of the standard texts on this subject.[1]

USING THE AERIAL PHOTOGRAPH

Techniques of using aerial photographs in soil mapping differ from those of using maps because measurements of courses and distances are less precise. Even though the vertical aerial photograph looks like a map, it is not an accurate plan of the ground surface.

Stereoscopic interpretation and delineation.—To begin with, the soil survey party should study the photographs of the survey area. Each mapper needs to be familiar with the film-roll and picture numbers, the sequence of flight lines, and direction of flights. Study of the photo index will also serve to give a view of the whole area and of the conditions to be met during the survey. Such study can be helped by laying out photographs for parts of the area on a table top as a sort of rough unassembled mosaic.

Once the survey is under way, it is helpful to study the photographs with the stereoscope before going into the field. Preliminary interpretations of features can be made and the scientist can familiarize himself with the ground conditions.

It is frequently helpful to delineate in advance certain ground features. Drainage can be accurately plotted on the photograph. The plotting of drainage features in heavily wooded areas is especially helpful to field orientation. Trails and obscure paths can be marked for reference. Possible places where streams may be crossed and routes through rough terrain can be tentatively selected. Buildings that might otherwise be overlooked can be marked for checking in the field. Such features as gullies, areas of eroded soil, pasture or idle land, and forests can be tentatively outlined and the time of scientists in the field thereby conserved. Delineations should be made in pencil, to be inked after confirmation in the field. Rivers, lakes, and other prominent water fea-

---

[1] See, for example, SMITH, H. T. U. AERIAL PHOTOGRAPHS AND THEIR APPLICATIONS. 372 pp., illus. New York. 1943.

tures can usually be inked in advance. Clearly defined stream courses can be inked as dashed lines, and after field inspection the dashes can be closed, or dots inserted, to indicate either perennial or intermittent streams.

Match lines and matching.—A *match line* is an arbitrary line drawn in the overlap area of a photograph to serve as a boundary for the mapping on the photograph and is to be matched by a similar boundary drawn through identical points on the adjoining photograph.

When stereoscopic pairs of photographs are used in mapping soils, the match lines should be placed to limit the plotting of data to the central parts of the pictures where distortion is least. If alternate photographs are used, match lines must be placed near the outer limits of the photographs in the narrow margin of overlap. Necessarily, a match line so placed includes the least accurate outer edge of the photograph. Thus using alternate pictures may increase the difficulty of plotting soil boundaries accurately, of matching soil boundaries from one sheet to another, and of transferring soil data to the base map, and decrease the accuracy of area measurements.

Match lines can be placed on photographs either with or without the stereoscope. In the stereoscopic method, a line is placed approximately midway in the overlap area of a photograph. This photograph and its adjoining mate are placed under the stereoscope, the images fused, and the match line transferred to the adjoining picture. This process is continued through the line of flight and between adjoining flights.

In placing a match line without the stereoscope, two distinguishable features are selected along the outer edge of the area to be mapped on the photograph and connected by a straight line. The same features are identified on the adjoining photograph and connected. The process is continued throughout the area.

If it is helpful in soil mapping, the match lines may follow some prominent ground feature, like a road, railroad, or river, even though it is irregular or curving. In sectionized areas, match lines may coincide with the land lines.

The colors of match lines should contrast with those of other lines. Green ink is frequently used for match lines.

Although the placing of match lines requires time, they are a necessity for good mapping. They avoid mapping of duplicate areas on adjoining photographs, facilitate the transfer of soil boundaries from one photo to another, and simplify the cartographic transfer of soil data from the aerial photograph to the base map.

Soil boundaries and other mapping should be broken sharply and precisely at the match line when inked. Soil symbols should be kept within the match line if possible.

The matching of the mapping on one photograph with that on another can be done in several ways. The mapped photograph and an adjoining unmapped photograph can be placed under the stereoscope and the images fused. The mapping along the match line of the completed photograph can then be transferred stereo-scopically to the adjoining unmapped photograph, although this is not good practice. It is better to join sheets *after* mapping as a check on the uniformity of the work being done by individual members of a soil survey party.

If adjoining photographs are at the same scale, a strip of trans-parent paper or plastic can be placed along the match line of a mapped photograph. The marginal mapping is marked on the transparent strip. This strip is then placed along the match line of another mapped photo for checking or of an unmapped photo for transfer of the soil boundaries to the match line.

Another method, which is particularly useful when adjoining photographs vary in scale, is to transfer boundaries by reference to photographic images. Along the match line one observes the relationship of the soil boundaries to such features as isolated trees, clumps of bushes, field corners, and the like. The same features are located along the match line of the adjoining photo-graph and the boundaries checked or transferred to their same position of relationship to that feature. Difficulty is had if dis-tinguishable ground objects are few.

One could scarcely overemphasize the need for care in match-ing the mapping on one photograph with that on others, both for joining of lines and for checking of the classification. Roads and streams need to be continuous from one photo to another. Special care is needed at the corners where four photographs come to-gether. Without a systematic method, it is easy to make errors that will make later interpretations of the mapping difficult or doubtful.

A record should be maintained of the matching of adjoining photographs. This is especially useful where a number of soil scientists are working in the survey area. A transparent overlay over the photo index makes a good means of keeping such a record. As the photographs are matched, the overlay can be marked. Some place the letters N, S, E, and W on each sheet and cross them out as the sheet is joined on the north, south, east, and west.

Inking on the photograph.—After completing the survey on a photograph in pencil, with boundaries matched to previously completed and adjoining photographs, the field sheet should be inked. For clarity and checking, it is helpful to ink the three major classes of features in contrasting colors that have good photo-graphic qualities. For example, roads, railroads, buildings, and other cultural features may be in red, drainage features in blue-black, soil boundaries and symbols in black, and section lines and numbers in red or green to avoid confusion with roads.

Each group of features can be inked in a separate operation. Culture can be inked first in red, for example, and the classifi-cation of roads and other features checked. Drainage can then be inked in a blue-black and inspected to see that individual drains are properly joined, matched, and classified. Soil boundaries can be later inked in black. When inking the soil boundaries, it is best to close each individual area as one proceeds, or to ink the soil boundaries up to some specific line, like a road or field boundary. As a soil area is closed, the symbol should be placed as near the center as practicable. If the soil area is long or irregular, additional symbols should be added for easy reading of the mapping, but no more. Soil symbols should be placed to be read from the same direction throughout the survey and should be approximately parallel. Where soil areas are so small that the symbol must be placed outside the area, it must carry a pointer to the area to which it applies. Place names are usually the last to be inked. These can be in black or in the same color as the feature to which they apply. By leaving them to the last, they can be placed where they will not obscure soil symbols and other detail. Place names need to be arranged in ways that leave no question about which features they designate. Names of railroads, rivers, and other features that continue across a number of photos need not be repeated on each one—only enough for clarity. Care should be used in the placing of stream names so that no confusion arises as to which branch of a stream a name applies.

The inking of the major features on a soil map separately, and in contrasting colors, permits the checking of each group of features individually. This usually results in fewer mistakes. The colors also facilitate the interpretation of the original field sheet by other users. If all plotted data are inked in one color, the field sheets appear congested and it is harder to check and to interpret them.

Inking on overlays.—Inking on overlays is done in the same way as inking on photographs. Opaque inks should be used, as overlays are frequently reproduced by direct printing methods. If standard waterproof drawing inks are used on plastic overlays, they should be coated lightly with a plastic spray to seal in the ink and prevent chipping.

Orientation of the aerial photograph.—One of the advantages of the aerial photograph is the rapidity with which it may be oriented in relation to the local detail and the unusual ease with which the soil scientist can locate his position on the photograph. Normally in field use, the photograph is oriented by locating features on the ground having images readily identifiable on the photograph.

In relatively flat areas with scanty detail, orientation is more difficult. In some places it is helpful to mount the photograph on a plane table set up over an identifiable point. The photograph may be oriented toward a second identifiable point with the plane table oriented by its compass. Then short traverses may be run in the area. Since variations of scale within the photograph make some difficulty, it is necessary to tie the traverse to all identifiable landmarks along the route. Long unbroken lines of traverse are rarely necessary. Nearby rather than distant features should be used for orientation because of scale variations within the photograph.

Heavily wooded areas present problems in both orientation and location. These can sometimes be overcome by running short traverses into the wooded area from the identifiable features on the outskirts of the area. Stereoscopic delineation of drainage features on the aerial photograph before going into the field often helps a great deal, and stereoscopic study of the relief while in the field contributes to orientation and location in wooded areas, especially in hilly districts.

Sometimes it is necessary to carry the orientation forward from one photograph to another. This is done by overlapping the photographs. The photo centers are first marked by drawing intersecting lines from the tick marks on the sides of the photographs and transferring the center of the rear photograph to the forward photograph and that of the forward photo to the rear one. The photographs may then be laid over each other so that the centers are superimposed in the overlap area. With a compass, a magnetic north line may be placed on a photograph that has been properly oriented by identifiable features. Then the north line is transferred to adjacent overlapping photographs either by association of identifiable features or stereoscopically, and the second photograph is oriented by using the compass.

The aerial photograph may be oriented with respect to true or magnetic north when it is used with a detailed map of the area. Two matching and identifiable points should be selected on both the photograph and the map, preferably along a line near the center of the photograph. The compass bearing of the line through the points on the map can be measured with a protractor and the photograph oriented accordingly. When the orientation is made with a compass, the points selected should be easily identifiable on the ground. Unless the land is too heavily wooded, a plane table with compass is better than a hand compass.

Shadows on the aerial photographs serve to give rough compass orientation provided one knows the time of the year and day at which the photograph was taken.

Plotting soil boundaries.—Plotting of soil boundaries is largely a matter of keeping oneself properly located with relation to the detail of the photograph and drawing the soil boundaries in relation to the identifiable images on both the photograph and the ground. Keeping himself accurately located on the picture is the first requirement of the soil mapper. Soil boundaries are plotted in relationship to easily identified landmarks, such as field boundaries, streams, buildings, edges of forests, isolated trees, roads, and similar features. With abundant detail, compass orientation and measurement of distances are not necessary and the soil scientist is not tied to a traverse. He is free to move about and examine the soil types as necessary. As measurements are not necessary, the difference in scale within the photograph or between photographs are of little or no significance.

New features that need to be mapped and that have been established since the photos were taken should be located by survey *resecting*: intersecting lines, as nearly as possible at right angles to each other, from identifiable positions, locate a new position. Measured distances from identifiable features will give the location of such features. Usually the intersection of two measured distances will be accurate enough for this purpose.[2]

When one has become thoroughly familiar with the soils of the area and their relationships to the features of the landscape, many soil boundaries may be visible on the photographs. These boundaries can be plotted on the photographs and verified as the survey progresses.

On photographs of heavily wooded areas or others with few identifiable features, it may be necessary to measure directions and distances in order to plot the soil boundaries accurately. This is best accomplished by using the photograph on the plane table. If the photograph is oriented by the compass and its scale is known, measurements of directions and distances are largely a matter of correcting for distortion. Every attempt should be made to tie to identifiable images as often as possible and to use the local scale for that portion of the photograph when measuring distances.

Corrections.—Corrections on aerial photographs need to be made carefully. If the photographic emulsion is broken or scratched, ink will run and smear so that symbols and lines will not be legible. Corrections of ink lines should be made with a soft eraser or with cotton and alcohol. If a photograph is so damaged that it cannot be reinked legibly, it is best to superimpose a thin sheet of transparent plastic over the area and reink the data on this. The plastic overlay should be securely fastened to the photograph.

HORIZONTAL CONTROL FOR AERIAL PHOTOGRAPHS

To transfer the soil boundaries and symbols from an aerial photograph to a compilation base, a planimetric map of good quality is required. In areas having no adequate map, it is necessary to construct a base from the aerial photographs.

The scale of the map, its accuracy, and orientation and placement on the earth's surface depend on horizontal ground control. This control is the framework of a map and comparable to the foundation and steel frame of a large building. After completion, the frame is hidden from view.

A horizontal ground-control station is a precise point on the earth's surface, the position of which has been accurately determined by field survey methods in relation to certain parallels of latitude and meridians of longitude. Many such stations are scattered throughout the United States. These have been and are being established by the United States Coast and Geodetic Survey, the United States Geological Survey, the Corps of Engineers of the United States Army, the Lake Survey, the Mississippi River Commission, and, to a limited extent, by private mapping and engineering firms. The positions and descriptions of these stations are readily available from the records of the establishing agency.

---

[2] See also Appendix I. Map Preparation with the Plane Table.

Distribution and extent.—Soil survey parties are not equipped to establish ground control and depend upon and use the control already established by other agencies. Using these control stations as a base, the Cartographic Section of the Division of Soil Survey establishes photogrammetric control points between widely spaced ground points by a process commonly known as radial triangulation. These photogrammetric control points (also called supplemental control) are then used on the map base for the proper orientation and placing of each aerial photograph in order that all culture, drainage, and soil boundaries may be shown in their true positions on the soil map.

The density of established horizontal ground controls in the United States varies from 2 to 3 miles between stations in highly developed areas to 75 miles in some of the Western States. It is general practice for the Cartographic Section to utilize all established horizontal ground-control stations immediately adjacent to an area that is being mapped, because they add to the accuracy and simplify the preparation of the soil map.

With the radial triangulation method, the distribution of ground-control stations ideal for accuracy is one in approximately every 16 square miles of area, plus points in the near vicinity of all map corners, and points in every 3 to 5 photographs along the boundaries of the area. Unfortunately, these conditions seldom exist. Either too few points have been established or they are not distributed proportionately. Thus, in most survey areas it is necessary to use each control station. Where sufficient ground control is lacking within the area, it is necessary to use control stations up to 5 miles beyond its border. Aerial photographs are needed for the station and for the intervening area. Established ground control is so sparse in some mapping areas that it is necessary to use surveys of railroads, highways, and utility companies and the General Land Office. These, of course, provide a lower degree of accuracy than proper control stations.

Description of control stations.—Horizontal ground-control stations fall into three general classes: (1) Monuments, (2) landmarks, and (3) road and fence intersections.

The first is most important. Monuments are permanently established by geodetic triangulation and traverse with a high degree of accuracy. The exact point located is marked by a concrete block, galvanized pipe, or cut stone with a bronze station marker imbedded in the top. Some of the older stations are marked by triangles or crosses cut into stone monuments or on natural rock outcrops. Many of these have bronze markers cemented in drill holes in the rock. Most of these stations are described at length so that they may be readily recovered. The descriptions include distances and directions from two or three towns, a route description to the station site from some town, ownership of the property on which the station is located, distances from nearby objects to the station, and angles and distances to reference, witness, and azimuth marks.

Landmarks used as ground-control stations include church spires, smokestacks, water towers, air beacons, lighthouses, flagstaffs, and sharp mountain peaks. Their positions are obtained through triangulation and they usually have a high order of accuracy. Short descriptions are available, including date of their location.

Third, and of a lower order of accuracy, are such ground points as the intersections of the center lines of roads, intersections of the projections of fence lines with the center lines of roads, railroad intersections, road and railroad crossings, and intersections of roads or railroads with section lines. These stations are obtained along the route of a transit traverse, and their position and a short description are available from the establishing agency. They are of relatively lower accuracy than others because they are not marked in any way on the ground and the recovery of the precise point established by the traverse is problematical.

Methods of locating and identifying stations.—With the initiation of a soil survey in an area, the Cartographic Section of the Division of Soil Survey obtains positions and descriptions of all established ground-control stations that exist in and adjacent to the area. The stations are then plotted on some type of existing map, and aerial photographs are obtained that will completely cover not only the area of the soil map, but also adjacent ground-control stations that need to be used for control purposes. Attempts are made in the Cartographic Section to identify each control station on a photograph. This is a very exacting task because the basic construction of the compilation depends on *all* points being identified precisely. A large percentage of points are identified in the office with certainty. Those in doubt or which cannot be identified are then referred to the soil scientist for recovery and identification in the field.

The exactness and care required of the soil scientist in the recovery and identification of ground control on aerial photographs cannot be overemphasized. The misidentification of a control station on an aerial photograph, if not detected in the radial assembly of the photographs or in the compilation, will cause distortion in the scale of the base and displacement of all planimetry and soil boundaries in the area governed by the station. Even when the misidentification is found, the station cannot be used, which weakens the accuracy of the radial triangulation or of the secondary control points. The field party should use every care possible when requested to recover and identify ground-control stations on photographs.

In requesting the information, the cartographers furnish the party chief with the photograph covering the general area of the station and with the approximate location of the station indicated on the face of the photograph by a red triangle made with a grease crayon. A copy of the description of the station is attached to the photograph

The landmark or intersection class of station is not usually described at length because it is easily recovered. Perhaps the major factor in recovery and identification is for the soil scientist to be positive of the identical point described in the original control survey. Some intersection stations such as water tanks, church steeples, and airway beacons are moved, and consequently their new location on the ground would not be represented by the old survey position. The date of the survey in the description of each such station enables the soil scientist to find out from local residents whether or not the station has been moved since the control survey established its position. After the soil scientist is positive of the recovery of the station, he identifies it on the photograph furnished him for that purpose. A small penciled circle, preferably in red crayon, about one-fourth inch in diameter, should be drawn around the station on the face of the photograph. On the reverse side, a slightly larger concentric circle should be placed directly opposite the first one and the name of the station written nearby in medium-hard black pencil. Ink should not be used on the face of the photographs used for control identification. It is not necessary for the soil scientist to locate the point on the photograph by pricking it; the exact location will be determined later in the office with the aid of a stereoscope and pricked with a fine needle. If the field man judges that the cartographer will have difficulty in pricking the point stereoscopically, he should include a sketch on the back of the photograph showing the ground detail immediately around the station.

Monumented stations present more of a problem in field identification than either of the two previous types, because many cannot be accurately identified on the photograph even with the aid of a stereoscope. The monumented stations fall into three classes: First are those stations that may be accurately pricked with a fine needle when viewed through a stereoscope or magnifying glass. The surveyor should circle the pricked point on the back of the photograph with a medium-hard pencil, write the name of the station, and, if necessary for clarity, make a small sketch of the ground and objects immediately adjacent to the station. He may give a short note on the accuracy of the identification.

Second are those stations that cannot be identified directly because they are located either in open areas nearly free of detail or in sparsely wooded areas. With these, the field scientist should obtain measurements from identifiable objects, such as roads, fences, buildings, and small trees in the vicinity of the station. These *tie points* should be as nearly at right angles to each other from the station as possible, for this will provide the most accurate position of the station when it is plotted on the photograph. Three tie points are sufficient and they may be as much as four or five hundred feet from the station. The surveyor should be cautious in his selection of tie points, for fences and buildings may be moved or rebuilt, roads may be changed, and small trees may have grown since the photographs were taken. Usually the soil scientist can tell whether or not a tie point existed at the time the photographs were taken by referring to the date in the upper left-hand corner. The tie points should then be pricked with a needle, and a small red crayon circle placed around each. On the back of the photograph, opposite the area of the tie points, a sketch should be made, in black pencil, showing the general positions of the tie points, the station, other pertinent detail, and the measured distances from the station to each tie point. The name of the station should be written and a north arrow for direction included. Although the sketch does not need to be drawn to scale, it should be carefully done, because from it the Cartographic Section will identify the true position of the station.

Third are monumented stations established in heavily wooded areas where no tie points are available and the station cannot be identified directly. With these, the soil scientist is limited to recovering the station on the ground from the description furnished him and by making a careful study of the area on the photographs with a stereoscope. When he is satisfied that his identification is the best he can do, he should prick the location, circle it on the front and back of the photograph, and otherwise handle like the first group.

The designating characters stamped into the bronze station markers should agree with the description of the station. The United States Coast and Geodetic Survey generally places two or three reference markers in the near vicinity of the station. These markers are stamped with an arrow pointing toward the station, and the station itself is stamped with a triangle. Along some traverses, monumented stations are set in pairs, usually over 500 feet apart, and the soil scientist should take care that he does not identify the wrong station.

In the examination of photographs in the field for control purposes, a stereoscope should be used whenever possible. If one is not available, then a magnifying glass should be used for pricking all points.

USE OF AERIAL MOSAICS AND PHOTOMAPS

Aerial mosaics and photomaps are generally used in soil surveying much like individual aerial photographs, except they cannot be used for purposes requiring stereoscopic vision. If the mosaic or photomap is uncontrolled, its use will parallel that of the photographs. If it is well controlled, it can be used much like a well-constructed planimetric map. Since mosaics and photomaps cannot be studied stereoscopically, more care is needed to locate accurately drains and other features in densely shadowed areas, and thereby avoid errors in plotting soil boundaries. Isolated buildings and trails may be overlooked or inaccurately identified.

A set of stereoscopic photographs may be used, however, along with a mosaic. These can be retained in the field office, studied before going into the field, and the necessary interpretations and delineations made. These interpretations can be transferred to the mosaic before taking it into the field. In transferring any changes in cultural features to the mosaic, one must be sure to

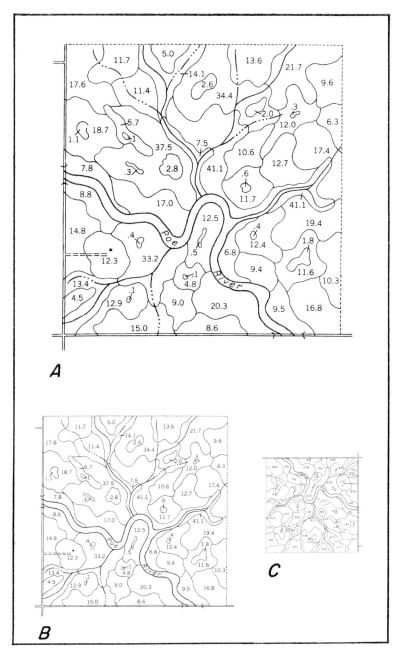

FIGURE 15.—Copies of the same soil map at different scales: *A*, 3 inches equal 1 mile; *B*, 2 inches equal 1 mile; and *C*, 1 inch equals 1 mile. The number within an individual area gives the acreage of the area. (Compare with fig. 14.)

ing requires ability to visualize the mapped detail at its publication scale and to follow definite rules about which areas must be combined or omitted. A helpful guide is a sheet of transparent acetate on which are outlined areas of minimum size for the scale of publication. This can be placed over the field sheet and shifted here and there to determine whether or not areas are too small for publication.

Table 1 gives a general idea of the smallest sized areas, at various field mapping scales, that may be shown at different publication scales. In this, only isolated or scattered areas are considered. If a large part of the total area were mapped in this maximum detail, it would be impossible to show it at the scales indicated.

TABLE 1.—*Minimum size of areas that can be shown on published maps of various scales from field sheets at different scales*

FIELD SURVEY SCALE OF 8 INCHES TO 1 MILE (1:7,920)

Ground area		Size on field sheet (inches)	Possible publication scale (inches to 1 mile)
Acres	Feet		
0.45	100 x 200...	0.15 x 0.30	4
0.86	150 x 250...	0.22 x 0.38	3
1.35	200 x 300...	0.30 x 0.45	2

FIELD SURVEY SCALE OF 4 INCHES TO 1 MILE (1:15,840)

0.45	100 x 200...	0.075 x 0.15	3
1.35	200 x 300...	0.15 x 0.23	2
3.44	300 x 500...	0.23 x 0.38	1

FIELD SURVEY SCALE OF 3.168 INCHES TO 1 MILE (1:20,000)

0.86	150 x 250...	0.09 x 0.15	2.5
1.33	200 x 300...	0.12 x 0.18	2
3.44	300 x 500...	0.18 x 0.30	1

If it is not feasible to combine small areas directly on the original field sheets, this can be done on reproductions of the sheets or on a transparent acetate overlay. Only the necessary symbols and soil boundaries are copied. If no need exists to keep the field sheets as they were originally mapped, the combinations may be made directly on them. Where made directly on the aerial photographs or copies of them, combinations should be indicated in a bright color that contrasts with the background of the photograph.

Especially where the soil scientist has difficulty in visualizing the field sheet at publication scale, it may be reproduced to the approximate scale for publication, and he can then make the consolidations on the small-scale reproductions. This method is costly.

All such schemes are expensive makeshifts. If the survey is properly planned in relation to both field and publication scale, they should be unnecessary. Office consolidations are never completely satisfactory. If complexes must be shown, their boundaries should be drawn in the field.

If unpublishable detail is to be mapped—and it is often necessary to do so—plans for handling it should be made at the start of the survey. Such detail may be shown (1) on the master map with special colors, provided this does not obscure or confuse the boundaries, planimetry, and symbols to be used on the published map; (2) secondary sheets may be used for the material not to be published; or (3) two manuscript maps may be drawn as the field work progresses, one showing all details and one showing only the material to be published. Commonly this last is the most economical alternative. Small areas of strikingly contrasting conditions may be shown by conventional signs.

Where much selection is required from the field sheets, arrangements should be made to have this work done by a skilled soil scientist familiar with the area, preferably the party chief, and the estimated cost should be included in the *Soil Survey Work Plan.* (See p. 43.)

INSPECTION OF FIELD WORK

Each field party is visited several times during the progress of the survey by the soil correlator in charge. He inspects the field work and consults with the party chief. Besides examination and revision of soil classification in the descriptive legend, the field maps themselves are checked in the field for legibility and accuracy of soil identification and placement of soil boundaries.

Special attention is given to legibility of soil symbols and place names, closure of soil boundaries, accuracy of classification and symbolization of cultural and drainage features, systematic placing of match lines, accurate matching of sheets, neatness of line work, and other items that influence the accuracy of the field work and the ease with which it can be used in map construction.

Party chiefs should continually check and advise the members of the party in order to insure neat and accurate inking of the field data. New employees especially need help until they are acquainted with the standards required in soil surveys. They should not be left to their own devices.

FINISHED FIELD SHEETS

The finished field sheet is the final product upon which the work and reputation of the scientist depends. It should be accurate, neat, and legible. It serves many other users and must be easily and accurately interpreted.

CONVENTIONAL SIGNS

The various mapping agencies of the Federal Government have developed and agreed upon standard symbols for most ground features. These standards are generally accepted for soil maps and should be used when practical.

Some special maps require symbols not normally found in the standard series. Such special symbols may be necessary because of the scale of the map or the data to be emphasized, but none should be used that may be confused with the standard ones.

In soil mapping, few such additional conventional signs are necessary.

For published soil maps the standard conventional signs are used almost exclusively. Such symbols are placed on the map according to rigid specifications as to weight of lines, sizes and spacing of dots and dashes, and the size and style of lettering. In field mapping, the standard symbols should be used, although exactness of line work is not so important.

Although some conventional signs used in the field mapping of soils do not conform to the general standards, it is still necessary that they be standardized. In the broad program of soil mapping throughout the country, standardization of as many techniques and methods as possible increases efficiency.

The cultural and natural features, other than kinds of soil, plotted in soil surveys throughout the United States are sufficiently similar to make the standardization of conventional signs practical. With a set of standard symbols, soil scientists do not need to learn new ones for each survey. By using the same symbols over and over, mappers develop skill in making them neatly and rapidly. The use of a standard set of conventional signs for natural and cultural features greatly facilitates the work of the cartographer. Obviously, the symbols for the thousands of different kinds of soil cannot be standardized.

To insure standardization at a range sufficiently wide to cover most features besides soils, a series of standard symbols for use by soil scientists are shown in plates 1 to 5. These standards include some alternatives. One set corresponds to those used on the finished soil map and closely approximates the symbols adopted generally by Federal mapping agencies. The other group represents a simplified form of the same symbols. This simplified set of symbols is solely for the convenience of the soil scientist in inking field sheets. It eliminates such symbols as double-line roads and substitutes a single line in color, and simplifies the spacing and dots for other signs. This simplified set of signs may not be appropriate in cooperative surveys if another organization plans to use the field sheets as base maps.

Signs and symbols are shown in the plates and are discussed under major classes as follows:

Works and structures

Roads.—On field sheets, roads are indicated according to the following distinctions:

1. First-class or good public motor roads are shown by solid lines. These include those public roads that may be used for automobiles at medium speeds and for hauling the greater part of the year and include all Federal, State, county, or other public roads in condition for such travel, all main or through roads in passable condition in sparsely settled sections, and all city streets and park drives open to the public.

2. Second-class or poor public motor roads and all private roads, regardless of condition, are indicated by dashed lines. Secondary roads include those public roads which, through disuse or neglect, are either impassable for automobile travel and for hauling or cannot be traveled without risk to an automobile, except at low speeds. Public roads that are passable for wagons but are not good for motor use are classed as poor motor roads.

Public roads are shown by solid or dashed lines, according to their condition; whereas private roads are shown by the dashed symbol, irrespective of condition. Public roads are those built or maintained by a public highway agency. Private roads include neighborhood roads in rural districts (except those of sufficient length and importance to be regarded as through routes, as defined above), lanes and stub roads to farms, country houses, or institutions, cemetery drives, and race tracks, and roads built or maintained by private or neighborhood funds.

Wagon roads winding through timber and other unimproved roads used principally in farm operations ordinarily are not shown on the published map. In sparsely settled country, however, such unimproved roads are shown if they offer to the public the only access to important places or to a large area of country. Occasionally, in unsettled areas, pack trails impassable to wagons or motorcars may offer the only opening to a region and should appear on the final map. It is convenient to indicate all traverses on the field sheets, but roads or trails that are not to appear on the published map should not be inked.

The class of road should be shown on the field sheets with the appropriate symbol rather than by figures. It is not convenient to indicate with figures precisely where one class of road ends and another begins, and the surveyor is apt to omit figures in a few places. In highly detailed surveys, especially where the soil map is used as a basis for detailed land classification, the class of primary roads must be subdivided according to the type of surfacing. All-weather roads may be shown with one line heavier than the other, and other primary roads by the conventional symbol. By appropriate modification, different symbols may be used for graveled roads and for paved roads where this distinction is necessary.

Buildings in general.—The map shows such permanent buildings as dwellings, public buildings, shops, factories, and other industrial establishments. Uninhabited dwellings, whether farmhouses or miners' and lumbermen's cabins, are shown only where they are important landmarks in sections of sparse culture. The conventional black square is used for all buildings except those exceeding the size of the symbol when their dimensions are plotted to scale. Houses should not be shown right next to roads unless the distance that separates them from the edge of the right of way is so small that it cannot be plotted to scale. Symbols for dwelling houses should be inked square and of uniform size on the field sheets. They are best made by outlining in ink an open square with sharp corners, and afterward filling in with ink. If houses are shown too small, it becomes difficult to make the symbols square, and, unless these are inked square and sharp, their identification as symbols for houses becomes uncertain. If it is important to distinguish houses from summer or winter cottages, the latter may be shown by leaving the square open. These symbols are used on published soil maps only where recreational land use is especially important and their use is specified in the work plan for the survey, otherwise the ordinary house symbol is used.

House blocks.—In towns of 2,500 population and under, individual houses, churches, schools, stores, factories, warehouses, and similar buildings are shown, except in business districts where buildings are constructed wall to wall and are shown as single block symbols.

In cities with population over 2,500, only prominent landmark buildings, like schools, churches, universities, colleges, and city halls are shown. Schools and churches are shown by the conventional symbol, and other buildings should be named. No other individual buildings are indicated within the city limits.

Churches and schoolhouses.—A church is distinguished by a cross, and a schoolhouse by a pennant attached to the house symbol at right angles to the roadway. A building used as both a school and a church bears the school symbol.

Railroads.—Railroads, whether operated by steam, electricity, gasoline, or other motive power, including all railroad lines listed in the Office Guide of the Railways, are shown by the broad-spaced symbol representing a railroad of any kind.

Electric trolley lines in urban areas or beyond city limits are shown by the standard railroad symbol and are designated by operating name and type, such as "Philadelphia Rapid Transit (electric)."

Double tracks, railroad yards, spur tracks, and switches are shown so far as the scale allows. Adjacent parallel tracks of two railroads are shown by staggered tie symbols and both lines are named. Adjacent tracks of one line are shown by extending the tie symbols across both tracks.

Railroads or electric trolley lines within a roadway are shown by fine cross lines having the same spacing as that on the corresponding line outside of the road. In such instances it is necessary to use the double-line road symbol on the field sheet instead of the usual single line.

In railroad yards with parallel spur tracks, only as many tracks should be inked as can be engraved legibly at publication scale, as too many tracks make difficult inking, illegible field sheets, and impracticable engraving. Where switches and sidings occur alongside single tracks, both the main track and the side tracks are inked in finer lines than the main track elsewhere; these fine lines are inked first and the extension of the main track inked afterward in a heavier line, in order to make clear copy.

Crossings at grade are shown by continuous railroad and road symbols; at grade separations, crossings are indicated by a break in the symbol for the lower crossing. A railroad crossing over a road is shown by a broken road symbol, and a road crossing over a railroad by a broken railroad symbol. (The words "overhead" or "underpass" should not be used.)

Railroad-station buildings.—A railroad-station building is shown like other buildings, except that its symbol is carried conventionally across the track to indicate the location of a train stop if this is not clear from the culture. The conventional station symbol is not drawn across the track where there is no station building; and its use is generally confined to small villages.

Bridges.—Symbols are used to show bridges across streams more than 300 feet wide, other bridges if named, and bridges in sparsely settled sections wherever the existence of a bridge is vital to the use of the road. Bridge ends are not shown for viaducts over railroads, railroad yards, roads, or streams. Names of large viaducts are given, however.

Drawbridges on roads and railroads are shown by separate symbols. Ordinary bridges and trestles on railroads are omitted. Wherever its presence would reduce the legibility of the map, the bridge symbol also is omitted.

The footbridge symbol is rarely used—only where the bridge is isolated and an important way into a large area.

Ferries.—Ferries are shown by symbol wherever the stream is wide enough to allow; where it is too narrow, the word "Ferry" is written. Names of ferries are placed on the map.

Fords.—The symbol for a road ford is similar to that used to represent a private road. The names of important fords appear on the map.

Trails.—The mapping of trails depends on their relative importance. In mountain and desert regions and in heavily wooded areas, especially where sparsely settled and where traveling is done largely along trails, important trails should be mapped and named. In the more densely populated districts where railroads and roads are plentiful, only trails such as those leading up mountains or through unimproved areas otherwise not readily accessible are shown. A mere "way through" not regularly traveled does not constitute a trail.

Steamboat routes.—Steamboat routes on lakes and rivers, over which regular public service is maintained by ferries or passenger boats, are indicated by fine dashed lines and the words "Steamboat route."

Canals and ditches.—Canals, whether for navigation, irrigation, or drainage, are shown by a double-line symbol if their actual width can be indicated at the scale employed, otherwise by a single blue line. Abandoned trunk canals constituting prominent topographic features are indicated by the long-dash symbol.

In the mapping of irrigation ditches, both mains and important laterals are shown. The mains are so designated. Canals and ditches are inked in blue.

Canal locks.—The lock symbol should point up current. The symbol for canal locks is inked only insofar as it can be engraved legibly at the publication scale, and the upper and lower gates are inked separately only where both gates can be shown legibly.

Aqueducts, water and oil pipes.—Only the principal aqueducts and pipelines are shown.

Power-transmission lines.—The alignment of high-voltage (100,000 volts or more) trunk power-transmission lines should be obtained in the course of the field survey and shown on the field sheets. Sections of power-transmission lines within corporate limits and lateral distribution systems should be omitted. Trunk lines are usually built on private right-of-ways and, in most parts of the country, are placed on steel towers. Power lines should be inked in red. They are not shown in sections of heavy culture.

Tunnels.—Tunnels of all kinds, whether for railroads or canals, are shown by tunnel symbols. The route of the tunnel is indicated by broken lines. Railroad or road tunnels are inked in black, aqueduct tunnels in blue.

Dams.—Permanent dams in streams, lakes, or reservoirs are indicated by a heavy line. Where a road follows the top of the dam, the road is shown in its correct place, and the road line on the upstream side is thickened to represent the dam. The dam should be inked to its mapped length and labelled "dam." The important ones are named.

Reservoirs.—The shore line used to represent a reservoir should correspond to the normal full state of the reservoir that is controlled by the dam. Artificial reservoirs surrounded by dams on all sides are not enclosed by the dam symbol, but are outlined in blue, like lakes and ponds. Small reservoirs are further emphasized by a blue water lining.

Levees.—Levees are shown on United States Geological Survey topographic quadrangles by hachures or contours printed in brown, and when these sheets are used as a base map, this symbol is used. The symbol to be used on other sheets is shown on plate 2 and should be inked in black.

Wharves, and so on.—Wharves, docks, jetties, breakwaters, and similar structures should be indicated by firm sharp lines and shown in such detail as the scale of mapping allows. These structures are inked in black, in outline only, as plotted to scale in the field. A narrow wharf or pier, however, is represented conventionally by a double line about the width of a narrow road. Jetties and breakwaters are inked in single heavy black lines.

Lighthouses, and so on.—All lighthouses and lightships are located on the map and shown by their respective symbols.

Lifesaving stations.—Lifesaving stations in general are shown by the house symbol, followed by the letters LSS; but lifesaving stations of the Coast Guard are shown by the same symbol followed by the letters CG.

Cemeteries.—Cemeteries are shown with their actual outlines; the name is inserted if the cemetery is a well-known landmark and if there is space; otherwise a cross is placed within the outline, or the letters CEM alongside it. Private cemeteries that are too small to plot to scale may be shown conventionally by a small square enclosing a cross, but they are omitted unless they constitute landmarks in a thinly settled country.

Airports and landing fields.—Boundaries of airports and landing fields are indicated, including those of municipal, commercial, and private airports; Federal intermediate landing fields; marked auxiliary landing fields; army airfields; and naval air stations. The symbol used for the boundary is that shown for a cemetery or small park on plate 5. The name is added, or the word "airfield."

Mines and quarries.—Mines and quarries are indicated by the pick-and-hammer symbol, together with the word "coal," "limestone," "granite," or other as appropriate. In sparsely settled sections with little culture, isolated mines, quarries, and even prospects (sawbuck cross) that constitute landmarks and are widely known are shown, together with their names.

Gravel pits are shown by the pick-and-shovel symbol. Large ones are outlined and indicated by either the symbol or by the words "gravel pit."

Oil and gas wells.—Producing oil and gas wells are indicated by a special symbol. Where such wells are so numerous as to be practically indistinguishable, only the approximate outline of the field (by dashed lines) is shown.

Furnaces and smelters.—No additional conventional sign other than that for a house is used to represent furnaces, and in many areas it is not practicable to name them. In sparsely settled sections, however, the furnaces may be the most important landmarks, and they may have well-recognized names which cling to the localities even after the practical disappearance of the furnaces themselves. In such areas, it is helpful to give the names, even though nothing remains but a ruined stack. The same rule applies to smelters, except that those shown on the map should be restricted to smelters in active or prospective operation.

Coke ovens.—Only coke ovens connected with mines in operation are shown on the maps.

Drainage

Tidal shore lines.—On soil maps the line of mean high tide ordinarily is taken as the shore line. The shore line bordering mangrove swamps, however, may be lower than mean high tide. In determining the margin of mean high water, the highest (semimonthly) tides are excluded and an average taken of the usual high tides as generally marked by the limits of vegetation. The charts of the United States Coast and Geodetic Surveys are frequently useful in checking the position of shore lines.

Shore lines of all waters should be inked in a firm continuous blue line and not broken for wharves, piers, and similar structures that may be built over the water. Such structures are inked in black. Sea and retaining walls that are simply artificially constructed parts of the shore lines are inked in blue.

Marshes in general.—Where large areas of fresh-water and salt-water marshes are recognized as soil types or soil phases no special symbol is used. Large areas designated as a land type may carry the special symbol or not, depending upon whether it will improve the readability of the map. Small areas are shown by their respective symbols, defined as to the acres represented by each one. Only small detached areas of marsh similar to adjacent larger bodies of marsh carry these symbols. Other wet spots are shown by the wet-spot symbol, *q.v.* Most marshes on low coasts are traversed by a network of tidal channels. Unlike the rills in mud flats, these channels are fairly permanent in location, and those that exist at mean high tide are mapped individually insofar as the scale allows.

Submerged marsh.—Marshlands that are partly submerged for many months each year are differentiated from ordinary marshes. Small areas are represented by inking grass tufts in blue (no horizontal lines between symbols) on the water surface.

River shore lines.—The mapping of broad braided rivers offers a perplexing problem, because these rivers are subject to periodic fluctuations and changes in width. As a general rule the width shown corresponds to the normal stage, defined as that water level remaining nearly stationary for the greater part of the year. This excludes stages of relatively short duration resulting from floods, whether periodical or out of season, and low-water stages. Generally, the normal stage exists for about 9 to 11 months for most streams in the relatively humid sections. If any stage of water other than the normal has been mapped by other government agencies, instructions should be sought as to the availability and best use of such cartographic material.

In areas where the flow of rivers, though active for brief periods, dwindles or ceases altogether for many months, the normal or prevailing stage is very low. Thus, rivers like the Platte and much of the Missouri are normally braided and are represented as such on the map. Where the streams have wide bottoms of unstabilized sediments, the land is shown as sand or riverwash and the principal channels are indicated as intermittent or perennial streams, double line or single line as may be required. Other bodies of land within the normal flood plain, having trees or other stabilizing vegetation, or cropland, are shown as soil types or phases. Rock outcrops are shown appropriately as such. Except in brief periods, many rivers in desert areas are no more than broad sandy washes, and they are shown by strips of sanding.

Natural lakes.—The shore line of a natural lake or pond is that corresponding to the normal stage of water. It is not necessarily the exact shore line found at the time of the survey, for the survey may have been made during a period of flood or extreme drought. An effort should be made to ascertain the shore line of the normal stage, as usually marked by a line of permanent land vegetation. The shore line used to represent a large lake subject to a gradual rise or fall over long periods is that line found at the date of survey. This date should be indicated on the water surface in ink.

Artificial lakes.—The shore line of an artificial lake is the line that represents the margin of the water surface at the full normal stage of the lake, as controlled by the dam.

Island shore lines.—The shore line of an island is that corresponding to the stage of water used for determining the adjoining mainland shore line. Islands exposed only at a stage of water below that accepted for the mainland shore line should not be mapped.

Drainage classification.—Field sheets need to indicate clearly and accurately all perennial and intermittent streams. On detailed soil surveys the pattern should be complete, partly because this pattern helps greatly in reading the soil map, especially where detailed topographic maps are unavailable. With soil types and phases well defined in terms of classes of soil slope and with the detailed drainage pattern, the length, shape, and direction of slopes are suggested to the experienced map reader.

In practice, it is well to indicate the drainage by dashed pencil lines on the photographs in advance by stereoscopic study. The lines must be confirmed and classified in the field.

Perennial streams are ordinarily inked as solid lines, but dashed lines are sometimes used instead. Since much advanced use is made of photographic copies of soil survey field sheets, the mapper should attempt to make it possible to distinguish streams from soil boundaries by form as well as color. Where a great deal of such advanced use is anticipated, perennial streams should be inked in long dashed lines with a few arrows, not enough to clutter the map, but enough to indicate the direction of the stream and help to distinguish it from adjacent soil boundaries.

Intermittent streams are classified on detailed soil surveys. Those crossable with agricultural machinery are shown with one dot between dashes, and those uncrossable are shown with two dots between dashes. Unclassified intermittent streams, as on reconnaissance soil surveys, are shown with three dots between dashes.

Perennial streams.—A perennial stream is one that flows throughout most of the year except in years of extreme drought. It is represented on the field sheet by a solid blue line or a blue line with long dashes, as just explained. It is important that the perennial character of streams thus shown be reasonably well established, especially in semiarid and arid regions where the water in these streams is vitally important to the use of the soil. In dry regions, streams having perennial water holes in their beds, even though water is not flowing everywhere on the surface during dry periods, are shown as perennial streams on the soil map. In some instances, local inquiry is necessary to supplement field observations.

Wide streams are shown by two lines drawn to scale. The double line should be used only when the actual width of the stream can be represented to scale without exaggeration. Narrower streams are shown by solid blue or dashed lines, increasing in width with the size of the stream. Stream lines taper toward the source, but should remain deep and strong to the very head.

Intermittent streams.—An intermittent stream is one that is dry for a large part of each year, ordinarily for more than 3 months. In arid and semiarid regions, intermittent streams are not reliable sources of water for stock, in contrast to perennial streams. The general standard symbol for unclassified intermittent streams is a dashed line with three dots between each pair of dashes. This symbol is ordinarily used for all intermittent streams in reconnaissance soil surveys. In detailed soil surveys, however, it is important to distinguish clearly between streams that are crossable with the usual agricultural machinery in the area and those that are not crossable. Thus, it is necessary in soil mapping to make a slight departure from the standard symbol.

Those intermittent streams that can be crossed with agricultural machinery are shown with the conventional dashes and one dot between them. Those intermittent streams that cannot be crossed with the ordinary farm machinery are shown by dashes with two dots between each pair of dashes. *Thus a detailed soil map should have no three-dot, or unclassified, intermittent streams.*

All clearly observable and mappable intermittent drainage should be shown and classified on detailed soil maps, even though a little of it may have to be omitted on published maps. (This should not be interpreted to mean that all insignificant rills and shallow gullies are shown individually.) The complete drainage system has an important relationship to the pattern of soil types and phases and assists greatly in reading and interpreting the soil map. Aggraded flats and valley floors without well-defined stream channels or scars are properly shown as miscellaneous land types or as strips of sand.

Disappearing streams.—Some streams, especially in areas underlain by limestone, disappear abruptly into caverns and may continue their courses for long distances through subterranean channels. The points of disappearance and reappearance should be located accurately, but only the surface drainage is shown.

Springs.—Only large and important springs are shown on the soil map in well-watered areas. In arid and semiarid regions, springs should be located with great care because of their vital importance to soil use. These springs usually have names that should appear on the soil map. Intermittent springs or those having salty or otherwise undrinkable water should be so designated on the map or in supplemental notes. Walled-in springs are shown like wells, by blue circles; but a spring that is a source of a stream is shown by a blue circle from which the outlet stream is plotted. The symbol for a spring needs to be made very clearly to be read distinctly.

Wells and water tanks.—As with springs, the importance of wells and water tanks depends upon their relative importance to soil use in the area. In arid and semiarid regions, both wells and tanks are shown. Artesian wells are so designated. They may or may not be flowing at the surface. In regions of few wells, all should be shown; but in thickly settled areas with many nonflowing artesian wells their presence may be explained in the report without showing them individually on the map.

Intermittent and dry lakes.—Shallow lakes and ponds that are dry for many months of each year are characteristic of arid and semiarid regions. Some of these are shown on the field sheets as specific kinds of soil. Other dry salt lakes and old playas, although not intermittent in the usual sense, are so closely akin to intermittent lakes in appearance and formation that they are shown by the same symbol. Those of large size and importance should also be described in supplemental notes.

Relief

Important mountain ranges, plateaus, bluffs, basins, valleys, and gulches are indicated on the map, generally, by the position of their names as well as by the soil conditions. Bluffs, cuts, depressions, fills, mine dumps, and narrow steep ridges are shown either by the standard symbols or by means of other conventions described in the text.

Depressions.—Natural depressions or sinks, like those common in limestone areas, are indicated on the field sheets by hachures, or by the standard symbols.

Mine dumps.—The symbol is used when mine dumps are not extensive enough to justify the inclusion of a miscellaneous land type in the mapping legend.

Boundaries, marks, and monuments

Boundaries, marks, and monuments to be shown on soil maps are indicated by the standard symbols or by other conventions described in the text.

Civil boundaries.—All civil boundaries, whether National, State, county, district, civil township, reservation (including National or State parks, forests, monuments, and bird and game preserves, and Indian, military, or lighthouse reservations), land grants, corporations (city, town, or borough), parks, and cemeteries, are shown on the map by their respective symbols.

Since these boundaries cannot be identified from aerial photographs in the office, the field scientist needs to plot them. Boundary monuments and other definite evidences of civil boundaries should be plotted, since they help in map compilation.

Necessary descriptions, survey notes, and plats of important boundary lines should be consulted. Data on National or State reservation boundaries can be obtained from headquarters prior to the beginning of the field work. Data on minor civil subdivisions can be obtained locally while the survey is in progress. Many boundaries are obscured or obliterated by natural causes or artificial works; some were indifferently marked when established; and others have lost some or all of their marks. Information from local settlers may prove of value and save time and effort in the search for obliterated lines. The word of a resident cannot be taken as authoritative, but merely as supplementing information from official sources.

Even though established land lines, as section lines, may have been placed incorrectly on the original survey, they are accepted as the *de facto* lines to be shown on the maps according to their actual position on the ground. Although some of the old Government Land Office plats may show sections to be regular, they may be irregular and must be shown on the finished map as nearly as possible according to the actual location of section corners on the ground.

Some civil boundaries are defined by statute to follow natural boundaries, such as streams or divides between drainage basins. Boundaries following large rivers should be given special attention, for they may be variously defined, as at the middle of the stream, its main current, or one of the banks. United States Geological Survey Bulletin 689 may be consulted for State boundaries. Although the field mapper is to identify the boundary line on the ground and then plot it on the map, ground conditions are sometimes found to be uncertain or lines indefinite or unmarked; for example, they may lie in streams that have shifting channels or banks difficult to determine. Again the line may not have been accepted by those living on both sides of it or by the proper county or State authorities; its location may be in dispute or even under litigation in court. The location of the State boundary line, therefore, should be subject to special attention.

The following general principles may be helpful: (1) A line marked on the ground and once accepted by competent authority is the real boundary, regardless of a statute (apparently) to the contrary. (2) Where the description of a particular bank or point in a stream is indefinite in wording or difficult of application, past practices or rulings must be sought. (3) Early Supreme Court decisions have ruled that a boundary moves with a gradually shifting channel or bank, but does not follow sudden shifts or cut-offs, and these rulings have generally been followed in recent decisions. (4) If a statute defines a boundary line as coincident with some channel or other part of a river, the location of the river itself at the time the statute became effective should govern, unless there has been a gradual change in the position of the river, as just indicated. If it is necessary to know the generally accepted location of a river at some past time, say at the time a law was enacted that made the river a State boundary, refer to General Land Office plats that were made at about the time in question. Supreme Court rulings must govern if they have been made, but few decisions that affect the details needed on soil maps have been handed down by the Court.

Civil boundaries should be verified before inking, as a precaution against errors in the interpretation of penciled field copy. Where civil boundaries of different classes coincide for a distance, the symbol of the major subdivision takes precedence, except in instances where greater clarity will be attained by another procedure. Where it is obvious that a civil boundary follows a stream or road for a short distance, the boundary symbol may be omitted to avoid confusion. In some places, however, clearness may be increased by placing the boundary symbol (in red) immediately alongside the stream or road.

County subdivision.—Only such county subdivisions are shown on soil maps as appear reasonably permanent in character and location. Those subject to frequent changes at county elections are excluded.

In general, counties are divided into small units. These bear different designations in different States, or even different designations within different counties of the same State. In the States organized from the public domain and surveyed under the public-land system, one or more of the so-called congressional townships has usually been taken as the unit of organization. In New England, and in other parts of the country affected by New England migration, are found town units, in which are vested many of the powers that in the South and in the newly settled West pertain to the county. Some counties in Maine, New Hampshire, and Vermont, in addition to the towns and cities—the only regular subdivisions—have partly organized or unorganized territory laid off by these States as plantations, gores, grants, purchases, locations, and islands.

The following summary, taken from census reports, gives the names of the primary divisions of the county, or its equivalent, in the several States and Territories:

Alabama .... Election precincts.
Alaska .... Recorders districts.
Arizona .... Election precincts.
Arkansas .... Townships.
California .... Judicial townships.
Colorado .... Election precincts.
Connecticut .... Representative districts.
Florida .... Election precincts.
Georgia .... Militia districts.
Hawaii .... Election districts.
Idaho .... Election precincts.
Illinois .... Townships and election precincts.
Indiana .... Townships.
Iowa .... Townships.
Kansas .... Townships.
Kentucky .... Magisterial districts.
Louisiana .... Police jury wards.
Maine .... Towns and cities.
Maryland .... Election districts.
Massachusetts .... Towns and cities.
Michigan .... Townships.
Minnesota .... Civil townships, townships, and ranges.
Mississippi .... Beats.
Missouri .... Townships.

Montana	School districts, townships, and election precincts.
Nebraska	Townships and election precincts.
Nevada	Townships and election precincts.
New Hampshire	Towns and cities.
New Jersey	Townships.
New Mexico	Election precincts.
New York	Towns and cities.
North Carolina	Townships.
North Dakota	Civil townships, election precincts, school townships, and school districts.
Ohio	Townships.
Oklahoma	Townships.
Oregon	Election precincts.
Pennsylvania	Townships, cities, and boroughs.
Puerto Rico	Barrios.
Rhode Island	Towns and cities.
South Carolina	Townships.
South Dakota	Civil townships, election precincts, school townships, and school districts.
Tennessee	Civil districts.
Texas	Commissioners' precincts and justices' precincts.
Utah	Election precincts.
Vermont	Towns and cities.
Virginia	Magisterial districts.
Washington	Election precincts.
West Virginia	Magisterial districts.
Wisconsin	Towns.
Wyoming	Election districts and election precincts.

Public-land lines.—In the so-called public-land States, all lands that have at any time been subdivided or "sectionized" by the General Land Office must be shown on finished soil maps by indicating such township and section lines as have been run and have been approved by the Land Office and are not under suspension. Theoretically, all corners are marked on the ground, but in practice many are difficult or even impossible to find.[5]

In well-settled parts of the country, where land lines often become property lines and sections are generally marked by roads and fences, the construction of a public-land survey net is comparatively simple. But in unsettled country or in settled areas where the roads or fences seldom conform to section lines, it is necessary to find on the ground and to locate on the map enough section corners to enable the cartographer to construct a land net built up from the Land Office plats and notes and tied to the located section corners. In some instances the old Land Office surveys are inaccurate, and the plats in no way conform to the actual section corners on the ground; therefore as many corners should be located as possible.

For map compilation it is not essential to ink the section lines on aerial photographs if they can be accurately drawn in the office from the pattern of roads and fences and from located section corners plotted on the pictures. Many users of the photographic copies of the field sheets, however, desire the lines drawn for their convenience, and the section numbers placed at the centers of the sections in figures distinctly larger than those used as soil symbols. Township and range numbers are placed on the outer edges of the sheet.

In order to avoid confusion with other cultural features, public-land survey lines are inked on the field sheets with a fine line in black or, preferably, in red or green, except where roads or canals are coincident with them. Township and range lines are made heavier. Only those township and section lines and parts thereof that have been surveyed and approved by the General Land Office, are not under suspension, and are indicated on the land plats by solid lines, should be inked on the maps. The fractional distances for section lines less than a mile are usually found

[5] For a description of the public-land survey system, see Beaman, W. M. TOPOGRAPHIC MAPPING. U. S. Geol. Survey Bul. 788: 161–378, illus. 1928.

on the land plats, and where accurate plats are available, such distances afford a means for plotting fractional land lines. Land lines broken at water surfaces on account of shore meanders should be broken as shown on the plats. Meander lines are not plotted or inked, and section lines are not drawn across meandered streams or lakes or across meander land.[6]

Search for public-land corners.—The time warranted in search for obscure corners is determined by the probable regularity or irregularity of the net and the proximity of corners already found. The less local information there is at hand, the greater the necessity for pioneer hunting for the needed land ties. In districts with few evidences of section lines, diligent search needs to be made on the ground for enough corners to prepare an accurate grid, because many users of soil maps locate themselves in relation to the public-land lines.

In a region where there are few roads on section lines, assistance in finding corners may be had by using an oversheet of tracing paper or cloth, upon which has been laid out to field scale either a single typical township or an entire land net covering the area to be mapped, built up in advance from the Land Office plats and notes. Such a tracing, placed in position over a field sheet as soon as the first land corner has been plotted, indicates graphically the *theoretical* location of other corners; and as more corners are found, the further placements of the tracing become more serviceable as a guide.

The field mapper should be familiar with the system of rectangular land surveys and the intricacies peculiar to it. Acquaintance with the standard monuments used for the several classes of land corners, their marks, and their bearing trees, as well as knowledge of the manner in which blazes on trees become overgrown with bark, will prove most useful both in searching for corners and in determining their authenticity where this is in doubt. Public-land corners that have been found in the course of field work are inked in red with the symbol for found-land corners. The map compiler is better served by having the location of the corners plotted than by the drawing of the lines themselves.

Township and range numbers.—Township and range numbers are placed along the margin of the map opposite the middle of each township, with the township numbers along the right and left and the range numbers along the upper and lower margins.

Triangulation stations and transit-traverse stations.—The triangulation stations and transit-traverse stations which have been tied to a traverse are indicated accurately on the field sheets in red ink with the open triangle and dot symbol. They are shown on aerial photographs as already explained in the discussion of horizontal control for aerial photographs.

Level bench marks.—Level bench marks are not to be shown on the field sheets, as their positions have not been determined geodetically. Field mappers need to distinguish triangulation stations, transit-traverse stations, and level bench marks one from another. Figures 16 and 17 show the standard markings of tablets used by the United States Coast and Geodetic Survey and the United States Geological Survey, respectively.

SPECIAL SYMBOLS

Several special symbols for soil maps are shown in plates 6 and 7. Most of these are for areas of soil phases or miscellaneous land types that are too small to enclose with boundaries and are yet large enough to influence soil use and management significantly. Definitions for these land types and phases are given in appropriate sections of the *Manual.*

---

[6] Meander land is unsurveyed land, usually between a former lake and shore or stream border at the time of cadastral survey and the present shore or border, commonly at a lower elevation.

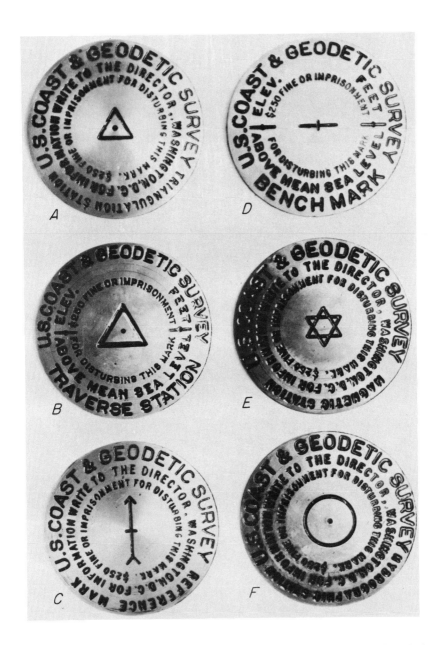

FIGURE 16.—Standard station marks of the United States Coast and Geodetic Survey: *A*, Triangulation station mark; *B*, traverse station mark; *C*, reference mark; *D*, bench mark; *E*, magnetic station mark; and *F*, hydrographic station mark. (Courtesy of Coast and Geodetic Survey.)

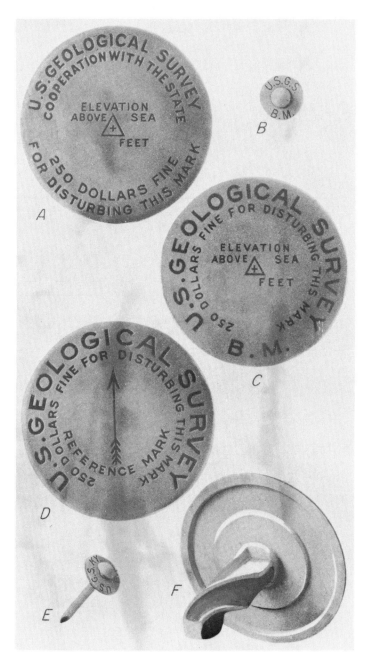

FIGURE 17.—USGS station marks: *A*, Triangulation or transit-traverse (marked "TTR" and numbered). *C*, Level bench mark, which may be later used as transit-traverse station, marked "TTR" and numbered. *D*, Reference tablet for triangulation, with arrow to station. *B* and *E*, Copper temporary level bench marks. *F*, Reverse side of *A*, *C*, or *D*. (Courtesy of USGS.)

to the adjoining new ones, but often this is bad practice. By studying the differences in mapping of individual members of the party at such margins, the party chief has a good check on the consistency of the mapping. In fact, many good party chiefs avoid giving individuals blocks of photographs for this very reason. By having match lines near roads, differences can be most conveniently adjusted. This scheme perhaps leads to some more work in joining but the ultimate objective of developing an accurate and consistent soil map is more nearly attained.

Omission of adequate boundaries to close all classified areas is a common error. Some typical examples of failures to close soil boundaries, thus leaving uncertainty of classification, are shown in figure 20.

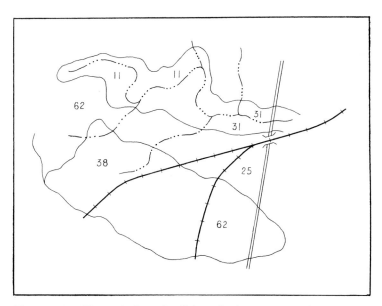

FIGURE 20.—The omission of soil boundaries causes serious errors.

To avoid such errors in closing boundaries, it is best to ink, individually, the drainage and culture first. Then the delineated soil areas are inked; each area is completely closed and its soil symbol placed before proceeding to the next one.

Areas without symbols, or with questionable or incorrect ones, occur in various forms. An area may be closed without a soil symbol; symbols may appear on the field sheet that do not appear in the accompanying legend or are unnamed; and illegible symbols may result from careless lettering or poorly made corrections. Listing each new symbol as soon as it is used, eliminates the appearance of symbols on field sheets that do not appear in the legend. When any new symbol appears to be required and is used temporarily, it should immediately be taken up with the chief of party for approval. If disapproved, the temporary symbol should be replaced before inking. This applies to *combinations* of letters and numbers used to indicate individual soil areas, not simply to the individual letters and figures in such combinations.

Practice and care in lettering, judgment in placing symbols, and careful erasures and reinking of corrections will reduce illegibility to the minimum. A carelessly made 91 may be read as 11, 71, or 77. Corrections should not be made by marking over the old symbol.

Incorrect interpretation of drainage or cultural features can seriously reduce the accuracy of soil maps. In figure 21, the

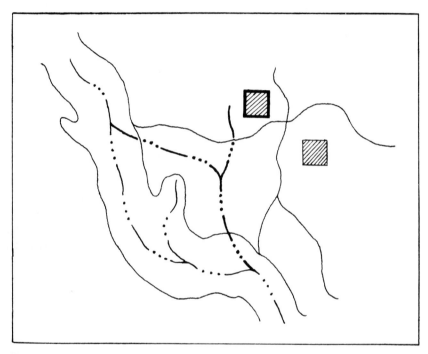

FIGURE 21.—Due to heavy woods, the positions of a fire tower and stream, light shade, were misinterpreted in contrast to their true positions, heavy shade. Consequently other drainage and soil boundaries are seriously in error.

locations of a stream and fire tower were misinterpreted due to heavy timber and the dark tone of the aerial photograph. Heavy lines indicate the true position of these features, light lines their mapped position. Because the soil boundaries were located in relationship to these two outstanding features, the result is incorrect soil classification of the area; and the necessary adjustment will affect the soil boundaries of adjoining areas. Had a careful study of the aerial photograph been made with a stereoscope, this error would not have occurred. Such instances can be greatly reduced by careful observation in the field, a study and understanding of photographic interpretation by the sur-

WORKS AND STRUCTURES

		PUBLISHED MAP	FIELD SHEET
Roads	Good motor		
	Poor motor or private		
Trails	Good pack or foot		
Railroads	Single track		
	Double track		
	Narrow gage		
	In road or street		R.R.
	Abandoned		
Railroad crossing	Grade - RR above - RR beneath		
Tunnel (railroad or road)			
Bridges	General symbol		
	Drawbridges		
	Foot		F.B.
Ferries		FERRY	FERRY
Fords	Road		
	Trail		
Dam			DAM
Canal or ditch			
Canal abandoned			
Flume			
Canal lock (point upstream)			
Aqueduct			Aqueduct / Aqueduct
Aqueduct tunnel			
Water pipeline			

WORKS AND STRUCTURES - CONTINUED

		PUBLISHED MAP	FIELD SHEET
Power-transmission line			
Buildings in general			
Summer or winter cottage			
Railroad station of any kind			
Church			
Schoolhouse			
Creamery			
Windmill			
Sawmill			
Cotton gin			
Forest fire or lookout station			
Cemetery			
Fort			
Gravel pit	Small		
	Large	GRAVEL PIT	GRAVEL PIT
Mine or quarry	Small		*Show kind, limestone, coal, or other*
	Large	QUARRY	QUARRY
Prospect		X	X
Shaft			
Mine tunnel	Opening		
	Showing direction		
Oil or gas wells			
Oil or gas pipeline			
Oil or gas storage tanks			
Levee			
Airway beacon			
Lighthouse			
Coke ovens			
Breakwater, wharf, dock, jetty			

DRAINAGE

	PUBLISHED MAP	FIELD SHEET

Perennial streams

Preliminary, prior to field classification

Intermittent streams:

   Crossable with farm machinery

   Not crossable with farm machinery

   Not classified

Falls and rapids

Probable drainage, unsurveyed

Lake or pond in general

Intermittent lake or pond

Spring

Wells or water tanks

Artesian wells

Wet spot

Swamp or marsh
(small isolated areas)

Marsh
(large grass or timbered areas)

Tidal marsh
(salt or fresh water)

Submerged marsh

RELIEF

	PUBLISHED MAP	FIELD SHEET
Escarpment, other than bedrock		
Bedrock escarpment		
Prominent hills or mountain peaks		
Sink holes and depressions: Easy to cultivate across		
Difficult or impossible to cultivate across		
Containing water most of the time		
Sand wash (riverwash)		
Mine dump		
Sand dunes (dune land)		

BOUNDARIES, MARKS, AND MONUMENTS

	PUBLISHED MAP	FIELD SHEET
National, State, or Province line		(Red or green)
County line		(Red or green)
Civil township, district, precinct, or barrio		(Red or green)
Reservation line		(Red or green)
Land-grant line		(Red or green)
City, village, or borough		(Red or green)
Cemetery, small park, etc.		(Red or green)
Township line		(Red or green)
Section line		(Red or green)
Township and section corners, recovered		
Boundary monument		
Triangulation point or primary-traverse station	△	△
Permanent bench mark (and elevation)	BM × 1232	B.M. 1232 ×
Supplementary bench mark (and elevation)	× 1232	× 1232
Any located station or object (with explanatory note)	⊙	⊙
Location of major soil samples (not published)		Ⓢ

SPECIAL SYMBOLS

	PUBLISHED MAP	FIELD SHEET
Rock outcrop	v	v
Stoniness ⎰ *Stony*	⌂	⌂
⎱ *Very stony*	⌂	⌂
Gravel	∴	∴
Chert fragments	◁	▷
Clay spot	✕	✳
Clay butte	⍦	⍦
Gumbo or scabby spot (truncated solodized solonetz)	∅	∅
Sand spot	∴	∴
Lava flow	⸨⸨⸨ɛ	⸨⸨⸨ɛ
Made land	≋	≋
Blowout	‿	‿
Moderate wind erosion	⅄	⅄
Severe wind erosion	≙	≙
Wind hummocks	◮	◮
Overblown soil	◠	◠
Kitchen midden	#	#

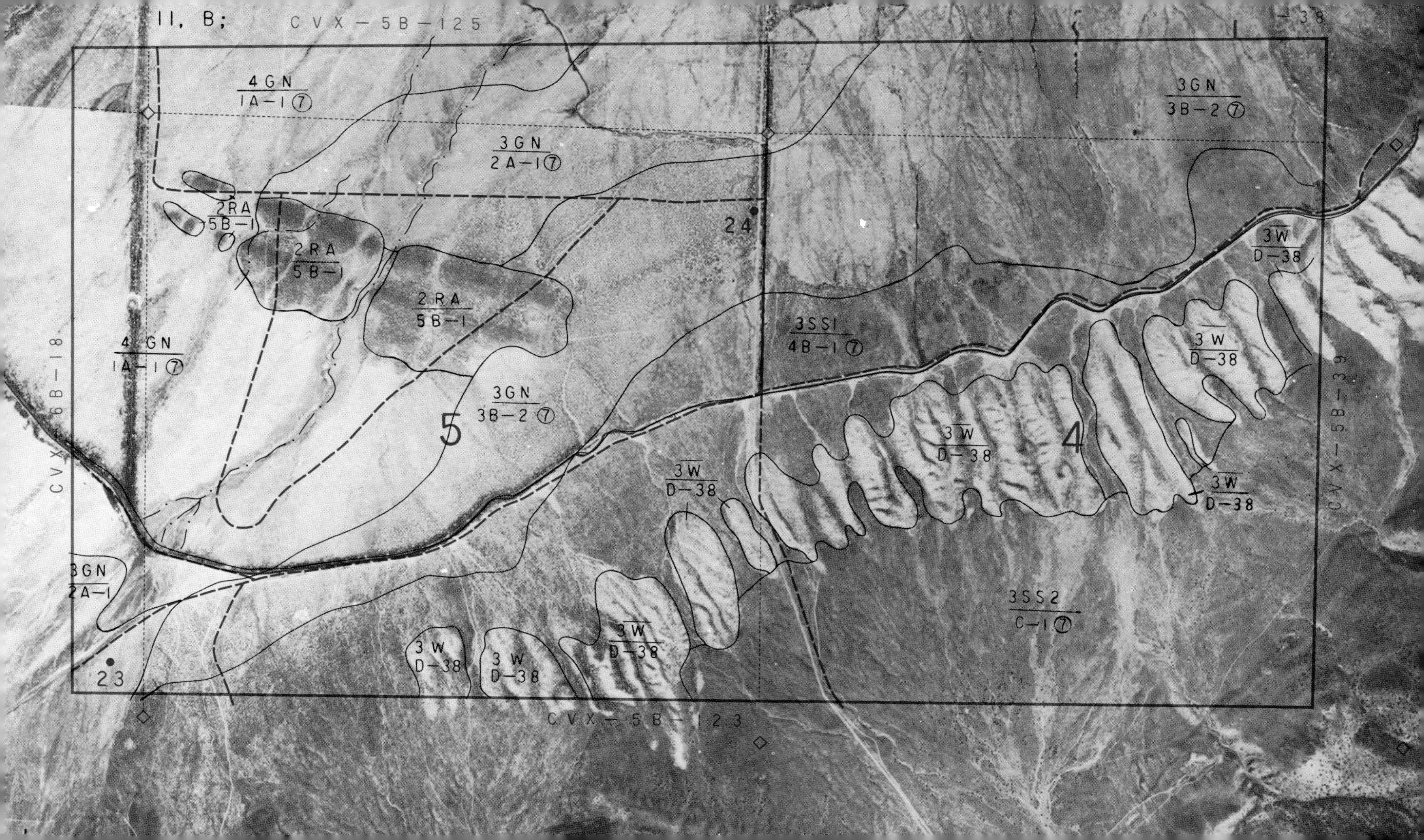

LEGEND FOR PLATE 9, *A* AND *B*

A sample photograph and field sheet in a characteristic general farming area of the eastern Middle West—Bartholomew County, Ind. The scale is about 1 : 20,000. The zonal soils belong in the Gray-Brown Podzolic group. Besides types and phases of these, there are types in the Humic-Gley and Alluvial soil groups. Only parts of the pattern of light-and-dark in the fields correspond to boundaries between Gray-Brown Podzolic and Humic-Gley soils. The soils have developed from Pleistocene valley-train materials, partly overlain by more recent alluvium and some wind-blown fines. The relief is nearly level to gently undulating. On the whole, drainage is good. Some of the boundaries separate soil-slope phases. The soils are used for general mixed farming in units of medium size. Corn and soybeans are prominent on the Alluvial soils. Here many local reference points—houses, isolated trees, field lines, road corners, and wood-lot boundaries—help the mapper to keep himself located. Yet it will be noted that the boundaries of the low-lying Alluvial soils (all those numbers ending with 73, 74, or 76) do not coincide with those of the woodland along the streams. A low sand dune in the northwestern part of the map does not show clearly in the photograph (area 605 on the map).

LEGEND FOR PLATE 10, *A* AND *B*

Sample photograph and field sheet in a mixed forested and farming area in Franklin County, N. Y. The scale is about 1 : 20,000. The land is undulating to gently sloping. The zonal soils are Podzols, but the dominant soils in this area are imperfectly and poorly drained Gray Hydromorphic and Humic-Gley soils. The large wooded area includes poorly and very poorly drained soils from sandy material of marine origin and some small spots of well-drained soils. The open farm land is used mainly in long leys ; only about 10 percent is plowed annually. The soils are developed on late Wisconsin drift of low relief. The photograph was taken in September at a time when the soils were moist and color contrasts among them were at a minimum. It will be noted that few reference points for location guide the mapper in the wooded area. Within it, the individual soil types and phases make such an intricate pattern that they are included in a defined complex as the mapping unit. Even the land-use boundaries cannot be drawn from the photograph alone in the cleared places. Although very useful to the soil mapper as a base, this photograph is an example of one from which little about the soil can be interpreted correctly in the office.

LEGEND FOR PLATE 11, *A* AND *B*

A sample photograph and field sheet in a semiarid, treeless region of Sierozem soils, Utah County, Utah. The scale is approximately 1 : 16,000. A large irregular area of sloping eroded soil, developed from an old terrace remnant of Lake Bonneville, stands out distinctly as a light pattern in the lower right-hand corner of the photograph. A gently sloping, shallow, gravelly soil shows plainly as a dark pattern in the upper left-hand part. Elsewhere, patterns on the photograph fail to give reliable clues to the soil boundaries, and they must be "dug for."

veyor, and the effective use of the stereoscope. If the drainage pattern is penciled on the aerial photograph before commencing mapping by using the stereoscope, it will serve the surveyor continually as a means of orientation in heavily wooded or rough terrain.

Figure 22 shows how the location of place names is sometimes **confused.**

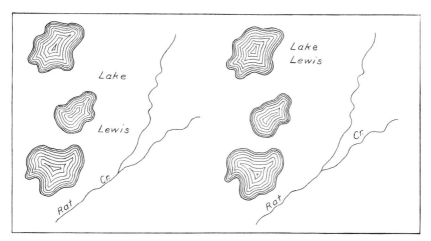

FIGURE 22.—Location of place names: Left, confusing; right, correct.

Transmittal letters.—Since the field and office work necessary to complete and to publish a soil survey continues over a considerable period and field sheets need to be shipped from one office to another, it is important that a complete record be made of all material transmitted. Even though it takes some time to check and to list large numbers of aerial photographs and other field sheets, it must be done. Shipments need to include a transmittal letter that itemizes the material. Such lists may be attached to the transmittal letter, with copies in each package.

The code, roll, and individual picture numbers should be given for aerial photographs; topographic quadrangles should be listed by name; and plane-table sheets should be assigned a number. Other maps or mosaics should be listed by name or assigned a number for identification. Supplementary material, such as photographic indexes and legends, should also be itemized.

Upon receipt of such material in any office, it should be immediately checked against the transmittal lists and receipt acknowledged. Any discrepancies need to be traced at once so that missing materials can be located.

Special instructions.—All the base-map material transmitted should be accompanied by an index map showing the location of the individual sheets and their relation one to another. Photographic indexes are ideal for aerial photographs. If photo·

graphic indexes are unavailable, a suitable one can be made by plotting the approximate center of the flight lines on a suitable base map and placing the photo numbers along the flight line in relation to the center of the pictures.

For topographic quadrangles or other base maps, an adequate index can be laid out on a small-scale map of the area. Such indexes should be marked with the name of the quadrangle or some identifying number or letter.

Overlay material, whether used with aerial photographs or other base material, is marked in the same manner as the base material. When overlays are transmitted with the base material, a specific statement that such overlays are included is needed. If corrections and additions are made on a separate set of maps, these maps are named or numbered like the sheets bearing the soil data and plainly marked and referred to as "correction sheets."

To help in locating specific sheets and in checking the material, separate items should be in order. Aerial photographs are kept in sequence by code symbol, roll number, and print number. Other base material is arranged by either name or number.

Marginal data.—Each field sheet should bear the name of the area or county, the State, the date of the survey, and the name of the soil scientist, or names, if more than one is responsible for the mapping on that particular sheet. Names of others who inked or checked the plotted data should be indicated. The scale of the field sheets should be shown. Commonly the full notes can be put only on the back of the sheet. Where they can be put on the front, they should be, so they will then appear on photographic copies of the field sheets. At least the date and the initials of the mapper should be placed on the front where they will not obscure the photograph numbers.

For use in the marginal lettering of the published map, the full name of the cooperating State agency, the name of its head or director, and the name of the soil scientist in charge of the State soil survey should be furnished. The names of both Federal and State soil scientists participating significantly in the survey are needed.

[For more detail on base map preparation see: SWANSON, L. W. TOPOGRAPHIC MANUAL PART II. U. S. Coast and Geod. Sur. Spec. Pub. 249, 570 pp., illus. 1949.]

EXAMINATION AND DESCRIPTION OF SOILS IN THE FIELD

Two essential elements of a soil survey require intensive field research: (1) Complete descriptions of the mapping units and (2) the location and plotting of soil boundaries. We shall review generally the problem of developing a complete mapping legend before discussing in detail the many individual items that enter into descriptions of soil units—the descriptions that serve as a fundamental basis for soil identification, classification, and interpretation.

Following the decision to make a soil survey of an area, a work plan should be prepared that sets forth the scale of mapping, the general methods to be used, the names of the scientists in the party and its organization, administrative arrangements for transportation, materials, and laboratory service, and the like, together with full descriptions of the uses to be made of the field results, insofar as they can be anticipated, and of all available maps, soil data, and aerial photographs. Where two or more research organizations are cooperating in the soil survey, their relationships need to be defined. (See pp. 43 to 48.)

A descriptive legend, as complete as possible, including *all* soil separations and *all* symbols that are to appear on the soil map, except for the standard symbols given in plates 1 to 5, should be prepared and made available to each member of the field party before any plotting of soil boundaries is undertaken. The first duty of the party chief in a new area is the preparation of such a legend, with at least skeleton descriptions of the mapping units. As the work progresses, especially in a new and undeveloped region, this legend needs to be revised from time to time.

On entering the area to be surveyed, the party chief should scout it thoroughly to get a general picture of the soils, geology, vegetation, and agriculture. Wherever possible this should be done in company with the regional supervisory scientist and the representatives of interested State and local agencies. Frequently, however, it is necessary for the party chief to undertake this work on his own responsibility. He should, of course, obtain the help of any competent and interested soil scientists available.

It is helpful for the party chief to reach the area in advance of his assistants so that he may familiarize himself with the soils, collect the preliminary data, prepare a preliminary field legend, and plan the work program. Toward this end, he must first have clearly in mind the objectives of the soil survey. His problem will be to determine how the soil mapping units and other features may be defined and shown on the map, clearly and definitely, without oversimplification on the one hand and without excessive detail on the other. First, the party chief must

123

determine the mapping units and symbols to be shown. Next, these units must be examined carefully at several places and clearly described. It is desirable that all soil units be examined and described in advance of any mapping. Where this is impractical, all the principal soil units may be defined, together with the subordinate ones in part of the area, leaving the others to be determined later as work progresses.

Where a new soil survey area lies adjacent to areas already mapped, representative examples of soil types already established and described should be examined in them. Full use should be made of any soil maps and reports available within the same general region or for like soil regions in other parts of the country. Usually, the party chief will find it extremely helpful to establish a small working library of soil reports and books or bulletins describing the geology, vegetation, and agriculture of the area.

CLASSIFICATION IN FIELD LEGEND

The setting up of a legend for a detailed soil survey requires first of all the identification and definition of the individual taxonomic units—soil series, soil types, and soil phases. These are sets of soil characteristics that are determined from the examination of sample areas. No soil type or phase can be *identified* on just two or three features alone, although one may be *separated* from a similar soil type or phase on the basis of one of two differences only.[1] Many fail to appreciate this distinction. In our minds we comprehend soils by comparison. Until we compare the soils of widely different climatic and biologic zones, we often fail to appreciate how very many characteristics most of the soils in a local area may have in common.

In a detailed soil survey enough taxonomic units—sets of soil characteristics—must be established and defined to permit the clear recognition and identification of every significant area of each soil in the project. The characteristics in each set are not precisely fixed; some range from the norm, or central standard, of the unit is allowed. In establishing these permissible ranges, no characteristic can be allowed so great a range that the fundamental nature of the unit, as a soil landscape, differs significantly from place to place in morphology, genesis, or behavior under use. Nor should the range in any characteristic be fixed narrower than its significance to the unit as a whole. In the present state of soil science, at least, it is impossible to lay down general quantitative rules about individual characteristics, because the influence of any one characteristic, or of a change in any one, depends upon the others in the set. That is, with one profile combination of clay minerals, exchangeable bases, texture, and structure and with a given land form, slope ranges within the set should be held narrowly, say between $\frac{1}{2}$ and 2 percent of slope. With

---

[1] A soil phase may be separated from the typical soil type or another phase of the same soil type on the basis of a difference in a single feature, such as slope; but a phase in one soil type is separated from a phase in another soil type on the basis of a set of characteristics.

other combinations of characteristics, the slope range may be 3 to 7 percent, 3 to 10 percent, 30 to 50 percent, or any one of a great variety. Small differences in clay content are critical in some sets of characteristics and not in others. The same may be said for any characteristics of soil horizons or array of soil horizons within the profile. Arbitrary combinations of "single-factors" are bound to lead to absurd results.

In defining soil units we must rely on experience and judgment in selecting allowable ranges for any set of soil characteristics. The practical purpose of the soil map must be served, and morphologically unlike soils must be separated.

The individual soil units need to be sufficiently homogeneous to permit making those differential predictions about their behavior and use that the principles and data of soil science permit us to make. We should go further toward narrower ranges in characteristics *only where sound scientific evidence shows that such differential predictions can be expected after further research.* Whatever classification is established in the field, the party chief should continually test it against the results of other research and against the experience of land users. Unnecessary separations reduce the value of his map.

As methods of measuring soil characteristics are refined, and with experience in the field, the soil scientist can establish and recognize continually narrower ranges in soil characteristics. We must guard against establishing narrower ranges just because our methods permit it. It is nearly as bad an error to split up soil types or phases into units not significantly different from one another as it is to include two significantly different units, inadvertently, within one. Furthermore, it is important that the boundaries between the units come at the place of greatest significance in terms of the sets of soil characteristics as a whole. As a simple illustration, we may think of stoniness: Let us say that areas of one soil type are similar in all differentiating characteristics except stoniness and that the range in stoniness extends from a low degree, where the soil can be cultivated, to a high degree, where it cannot be cultivated. In defining phases, or subdivisions, of this soil type, the main point of separation should be that critical place above which the land cannot be cultivated and below which it can be cultivated. On another soil type, this same separation may be neither significant nor necessary because other soil characteristics make it unsuitable for cultivation, regardless of stoniness. It would be as great an error to define stoniness narrowly in the second example as it would to omit the subdivision in the first.

Unreasonably detailed soil classifications, where they occur, commonly result because the soil correlator, the party chief, or both, have failed to face the job of classification. Many experience a real temptation to avoid the mental effort required. A common way of evading the problem of classification is that of setting up arbitrary classes of selected soil characteristics, such as texture, structure, color, and the like, along with arbitrary depths, classes of slope, accelerated erosion, and stoniness, and then letting combinations of these fall where they may. The soil scientist can shrug his shoulders and say: "We have recognized the facts." But the job of the scientist is not only one of gathering facts. He should gather the *relevant* facts and present them in ways whereby they may be readily interpreted. That is the purpose of classification. The details of soil analysis and morphology go into the notebook, not on the map. Between the detailed descriptions and the map lies the problem of soil classification.

Under a scheme devised to avoid classification, if class intervals are selected that will show significant differences in soil characteristics where the allowable range in these characteristics is narrowest, the intervals selected will certainly be much narrower than significant for places where the allowable range of characteristics is wider. The final result is an enormous number of arbitrarily defined separate units (really undefined as soils and even sometimes identified only by local numerical symbols without names that tie them into a standard system of soil classification!), the large majority of which are not really significantly different from one or more other units. In the application of such a scheme, despite the large number of separations—perhaps 2,000 where a proper system of classification would require only 150—some of them will still be too heterogeneous for making practical predictions, either because the arbitrary class intervals for some soil characteristics were not narrow enough in a few instances, or because of exclusion from consideration of characteristics relevant in only a part of the soil units. Such a scheme leads inevitably to poor soil mapping. For one thing, soil boundaries can be plotted accurately only if they come at a *significant* place in the landscape. Besides that, if soil mappers have a large number of boundaries to draw, they are less likely to get any of them accurately placed than they are if they have a smaller number of really significant boundaries.

As explained in detail in subsequent chapters, each separate observed characteristic of a soil horizon—as color, structure, texture, and pH—should be described in notes with standard terms for class intervals. Insofar as possible, standard terms should be used for inferred qualities, even though such qualities cannot be combined arbitrarily into meaningful soil types and other classificational units. The reader will note that some class intervals have slightly flexible ranges so they may be accommodated to specific sets of soil characteristics. Occasionally, class intervals for single characteristics need to be subdivided; often two or more need to be combined.

The normal soil.—First the classifier needs to study the relationships between the soil profiles in his area and the various combinations of environmental factors—slope, parent material, land form, vegetation, climate, and the like. He learns these relationships by comparison. As a general standard of comparison he should, if possible, define the *normal* soil (or soils). In the sense used here, a normal soil is one having a profile in equilibrium or nearly in equilibrium with its environment, developed under good but not excessive drainage from parent material of mixed mineralogical, physical, and chemical composition, and expressing the full effects of the forces of climate and living matter.[2] The typical representatives of the zonal great soil groups are normal soils. If the survey area lies within one principal climatic and physiographic region, one normal soil may serve as a standard for the whole area; otherwise each distinct region within the area will need to be considered separately.

The normal (or zonal) soil may not be the most productive nor the most extensive. Indeed, examples of zonal soils are not always found within the survey area. All the soils may be young, as in an active flood plain, or wet, as in swamps, or extremely limy, or very hilly, or because of some other combination of characteristics, development of a zonal soil has not occurred. In such a soil survey area all of the soils are members of intrazonal and azonal groups. Yet even in such areas, it is helpful to study similar climatic regions and to visualize what the zonal soil would be, if the appropriate landscape were present.

Frequently, several soil types in one area may all occupy normal positions but vary from one another in significant ways. That is, several soil types may satisfy all the requirements defining normal soils and belong to the same zonal great soil group, yet be developed from different mixtures of parent materials the natures of which are significantly reflected in the respective soils. In such a situation one may define the normal soil—the estimated normal soil—by orderly abstraction from the characteristics of those in the group.

A working concept of the normal soil, even in a survey area lacking one, can be a helpful standard for orderly study and arrangement of the other soils and for understanding their morphology and genesis.

Selection of sample areas.—The locating of sample areas should be directed toward one basic aim—to establish a standard for each unit against which other soil units can be compared. It must be emphasized that phases of soil types can be accurately defined and established only in relation to the defined standards for the soil types. The descriptions of some soils also take account of the effects of such processes as the silting of sandy soils being irrigated with muddy waters or flooded with water from glacier-fed streams, or the erosion of sloping hillsides, or the heavy fertilization of soils naturally low in nutrients, or the effects of long grass leys on podzolic soils. Still, the description should be objective and the conditions observed should be clearly apart from predictions of change that are expected to result from processes going forward.

Examinations of soil profiles may be made from road cuts during mapping, but detailed examinations for type descriptions

---

[2] Of course, it may be said that every soil is "normal" in the sense that it reflects its own history.

(and especially for important soil samples) should not be made in such places unless the road cuts are unusually fresh. Exposure of the soil in a road cut to freezing-and-thawing and to wetting-and-drying leads to great changes in soil structure. Layers of dust may accumulate on the soil along roadsides. In woodland areas the much greater light intensity along the roads favors the growth of grasses and other herbaceous plants that change the character of the upper soil horizons. At times dust from road-surfacing material is highly calcareous and changes the pH of upper layers of podzolic soils, after which other changes follow.

Having selected a representative place for a type description, an excavation is made extending through the solum and into the parent material. It is necessary that the excavation have at least one smooth vertical wall that is wide enough to show the entire profile clearly. It is important that this wall be as uniformly illuminated as possible and that the excavation be large enough to allow an examination of the soil in full depth. With Ground-Water Podzol, Tundra, solodized-Solonetz, self-swallowing soils, and other soils having well developed microrelief, it is helpful to have a trench dug in order that an accurate description can be made throughout both swale and mound.

Mapping units.—After establishment of the taxonomic units, the mapping units are defined. In a detailed soil survey most but not all of the taxonomic units—soil types and phases of soil types—are also mapping units. Even when plotting soil boundaries on aerial photographs of large scale, say 1:20,000 or 1:10,000, the pattern of some taxonomic units may be too intricate to be shown accurately and clearly. These intricate areas need to be combined into a soil association or soil complex[3] and shown as one mapping unit, defined in terms of the taxonomic units making it up (which are, in turn, defined as are any other taxonomic units), their proportions, and their pattern. Usually such areas bear a compound name derived from the names of the individual members of the complex. Solodized-Solonetz and associated soils must often be shown together in complexes. Ground-Water Podzols, Half Bogs, Bogs, and sandy Podzols are also often shown together in complexes on detailed maps.

A complex may consist of two phases of a single soil type that are taxonomically distinct but not mappable as separate units; it may consist of two or more soil types in the same series, or of two or more types in different families, great soil groups, or orders.

No definite rules can be laid down for deciding exactly what level of intricacy in soil pattern should be selected for the change from the mapping of each unit separately to the mapping of defined complexes. The uses of the map and the character and pat-

---

[3] The term "complex" is used in detailed soil mapping for those soil associations or parts of soil associations that are shown together because of necessity for clear cartographic presentation. The individual members of all soil associations are shown separately in detailed soil mapping where it is cartographically feasible to do so. (See section on Units of Soil Classification and Mapping.)

tern of the soils need to be taken into account. If the contrast in response to management among the soils is very great, every effort short of confusing cartography should be made to separate them. In some instances this means separating soil areas of only one-half acre or even less on very detailed maps where soil use is intensive. If the soils are similar in many characteristics, or if they are all unresponsive to management anyway, defined complexes should be used where appreciable savings in time can be made without reducing the prediction value of the map. If the soils in an intricate complex must ·be treated alike in fields, mapping of the individual components may not contribute anything to the prediction value of the map, and the highly intricate pattern may confuse the ordinary user.

The use of complexes does not relieve the scientist of the necessity of accurately describing the profiles of all their components. Data from the laboratory can be used only to characterize individual taxonomic units in the complex. This is also true of carefully planned experimental plots. Data on use experience by fields, however, can be used only to characterize the complex as a whole. Yield estimates and management requirements are needed for the defined complex as a whole.

Exceedingly intricate soil maps are less serviceable to most users than those where complexes are used as mapping units rather than the individual taxonomic units. On the other hand, where complexes are used without careful definitions of the individual taxonomic units and of their proportions and patterns, the maps cannot meet the requirements of a detailed soil survey. Complexes should be used sparingly on detailed soil maps for potentially arable soils.

Most reconnaissance soil surveys are far more useful if the individual taxonomic units are defined exactly as in a detailed soil survey and then combined into defined soil associations or soil complexes for mapping than if more broadly defined taxonomic units, with undefined inclusions, are used as mapping units.

Yet even on detailed soil maps of large scale, mapping units named in terms of a single taxonomic unit are bound to include small portions of other taxonomic units and of intergrades with other taxonomic units—say up to 15 percent.

DESCRIPTION OF SOIL UNITS

The value of soil descriptions depends upon the representativeness of the site selected, their objectivity, their completeness, and their clarity. Since making soil surveys is a very large activity, necessarily involving a great many scientists, the need of standard terminology can scarcely be overemphasized. Soil descriptions by different individuals within the same soil survey party, in different parts of the country, and even in different countries, need to be compared and correlated so that relationships may be established. The field descriptions are used by the regional supervisory scientists, the laboratory scientists, and others. Furthermore, a field party chief may need to turn over his notes and maps to a successor before the project is completed.

Great efforts toward standardization of terminology have been made in recent years. Improvements have been truly remarkable, partly because of the large amount of earlier work already done and partly because of the recognized need. These changes are among the most important ones reflected in this *Manual* over the earlier edition. Standardization can, however, be carried too far. Soils are anything but simple. Our terminology must be broad enough and flexible enough to permit accurate descriptions of all relevant features in all significant detail. We must find a reasonable position between extreme orthodoxy, on the one hand, and the sloppy or irresponsible use of terms on the other. Blind following of standard terminology may lead the soil scientist to overlook important features or to ignore fine but significant distinctions in special sets of soil characteristics.

Despite the improvements made, there is much farther to go in improving terminology. Responsible soil scientists are not in complete agreement on some of the terms used in this *Manual*. Some nearly arbitrary selection has been necessary. With further study and more refined measurements, some definitions will doubtless be changed. Furthermore, individual scientists may wish to use supplementary terms and classes. This should be done by all means where judgment indicates a real need. Usually, however, it is possible to define soils within the framework of terminology suggested in this *Manual*, so that the results can be understood by all.

Before taking up the details of each item in subsequent sections of the *Manual* it may be well to glance briefly at the principal items included in a proper soil description.

THE TAXONOMIC SOIL UNIT

Having established the normal soil as a standard set of characteristics for comparison, each unique local unit, resulting from a unique set of genetic factors, is defined. All the definitions should fit together, with no overlaps or gaps. These are the basic units of classification—soil types and phases of soil types.

Since the soil of the earth is a continuum, the units often merge into one another with gradual changes in characteristics through transitional belts several yards or more wide. Although divisions between units may have to be arbitrary, several characteristics usually change together. The outer limits of the definition of any one unit are bound to coincide with the outer limits of one or more other units. Thus, at the margins between two different soil units, the soils are more like one another than the soil near the margin of each is like the standard for that unit. Some field workers become disturbed over this obvious fact, especially where the transitional belts are broad. They may attempt to set up a new unit for the transition between the two. Often, however, this results in vagueness and overlapping, with two boundaries to define and recognize instead of one, each of which is as difficult as the first.

Each soil unit is a particular kind of landscape. It is defined by its land form and profile, and ranges in each. An individual soil profile occupies a very small place, essentially a point. Thus a soil area has an almost infinite number of profiles. Just as no two white pine trees are entirely identical, neither are any two soil profiles; but all trees called white pine have certain differentiating characteristics in common, as do all the soil profiles included in one named soil type. Each soil unit must be examined and described at several points in order to establish the modal profile and the allowable range in profiles. With experience and skill the soil scientist learns to associate soil profiles with the corresponding land form and can choose the proper places for the most useful examinations. The number of examinations required to establish a unit cannot be fixed. With a little preliminary examination in road cuts or with soil augers,[4] a skillful scientist may be able to prepare a good description from three major profiles, but usually more are required. As the work progresses, these descriptions need to be tested again and again in other areas of the unit. The final soil description is that of a three-dimensional soil-landscape.

In the field notes, observations must be clearly separated from conclusions and speculations. The condition of growing crops is an observable fact, but statements about soil productivity are inferred. The scientist may observe that the soil material is nearly uniform silt loam, rich in silt, low in clay and sand, and without coarse fragments. These are observable facts, whereas the interpretation that the soil is formed from loess is an inference from these and other observable facts. In making observations the soil scientist is guided by principles of genesis, by known relationships between soils and other features of the landscape, and by principles of soil management. These principles are helpful in making decisions about the significance of observable features.

This is not to suggest that speculation about the genesis and use capability of the soil are out of place. Quite the reverse. Such speculations are to be encouraged, but they should be clearly separated from observations. The descriptions of morphology, vegetation, land form, and geology should be as objective as possible. Any experienced soil scientist can testify to the great value of complete, objective original field notes. One can scarcely overemphasize their great usefulness. Many exceedingly important interpretations and relationships have been discovered after the descriptions were prepared—when they were being studied with other descriptions or with data from the laboratory—relationships that were not in the minds of the field men when the observations were being made and recorded. Above all, the features of the soil or landscape should not be left to memory alone.

---

[4] The auger, of course, should not be used for major profile studies, nor should road cuts unless they are fresh.

Many soil scientists have difficulty in describing the obvious. Without the exercise of care, the soil scientist may return from a survey area or exploratory trip with complete notes and good photographs of the uncommon soils, crops, and farms but without clear objective descriptions of the common ones. Unless an adequate description of the norm is available, all notes taken lose accuracy and significance.

Whenever practical, basic and detailed studies should be made of virgin soils. Only in these can the upper layers be properly defined. Yet, some companion descriptions of cultivated soils are needed, because many soils change a great deal with cultivation in ways quite apart from deterioration due to erosion, loss of structure, or depletion of organic matter and nutrients. Podzols, for example, may have a thick organic mat, often destroyed in burning and clearing, that is a definite part of the natural profile and essential to an understanding of its genesis. The natural surface horizons of many soils have exceedingly low bulk-densities, which increase greatly after a few years of cultivation. To illustrate, good examples of Subarctic Brown Forest soils may have surface organic layers (A_{00} and A_0) 3 to 6 inches thick over a solum some 19 inches thick. After normal clearing and cultivation the whole solum may be 15 inches thick, due to normal losses of organic matter and increases in bulk density, without any soil removal by erosion or blowing. To make comparisons, one needs a clear concept of the standard cultivated soil as well as of the virgin soil.

Every reasonable attempt should be made to locate undisturbed virgin areas in order to describe and sample the very upper layers. Even though these are always mixed in cultivation, they are very important to an understanding of soil genesis. In them occur the most active biological processes that influence soil genesis in a natural landscape. Thus, the uppermost 1 or 2 inches of the solum may provide exceedingly important clues to genetic processes. Furthermore, forest fires or grazing may alter the surface of podzolic soils considerably. Fence rows are also to be avoided, since they often have an unusual flora and commonly have received accumulations of organic and mineral dust from adjacent fields. It is not at all uncommon for the A_1 horizons of podzolic soils to be thickened from 2 or 3 inches to 6 or 7 inches in old fence rows under grass.

The search for virgin examples of a soil unit should not, however, become an obsession that leads the scientist to something far different from the modal soil. In many survey areas it will not be possible to find good examples, especially of the productive soils, in virgin sites. It is far better to develop a cultivated standard from several good examples than to use an unrepresentative virgin one. Wherever possible the management history of these sites should be described. In many countries no good examples of the productive soils exist except in cultivated fields, orchards, or pastures. Even in our own country, virgin areas of Prairie and Chernozem soils are exceedingly scarce. Some of those that can be found may have something unusual about them that makes them suspect for use as standards. Where cultivated standards are used, every reasonable attempt needs to be taken to establish a norm for both management history and for the soil itself.

Perhaps this point deserves emphasis. Some soil scientists have what amounts to an obsession for basing soil classification on virgin soils, even to the neglect of cultivated soils, especially of those that have been markedly altered by long agricultural use. In long-cultivated landscapes, some man-made or anthropic soils are sufficiently different from the original virgin soil to require separate series designation for proper classification and interpretation, either to understand the genesis of the soils or to predict their crop adaptabilities and management requirements.[5] For such soils, the definitions must be sought in the cultivated fields. Sometimes virgin counterparts may be found for comparison and sometimes not.

By grouping all items needed in a soil description in the same way, soils can be compared easily, and several descriptions of the same soil type may be abstracted into one that is standard for the type. A suggested grouping is that given in the seven numbered paragraphs following.[6]

1. **Land form, relief, and drainage.**—First of all, a description is needed of the relief—the gradient, length, and shape of slopes, and their pattern. This can be usefully supplemented by brief descriptions of the kind of land form—dissected terrace, active flood plain, esker, drumlin, old plain of coalescing fans, and the like. Since these terms are primarily the responsibility of physical geologists and geomorphologists, their definitions and use should be followed. Where soil scientists need supplementary terms for finer distinctions, these should be consistent with the major definitions.

Relief and drainage need to be mentioned separately. Although runoff (or external soil drainage) is closely related to slope, internal drainage depends upon the permeability of the soil and of the material beneath it. Thus a permeable soil may be well-drained on a gentle slope, whereas a slowly permeable soil may be imperfectly or even poorly drained on the same slope. Relationships between slope and permeability cannot be defined broadly for all soils in terms of drainage. One must also take into account the character of the soil itself in assigning to it a drainage class. The climate influences drainage relationships. In a cool climate with nearly continuous rainfall, poorly drained soils may be found on steep slopes.

Where differences in elevation are significant these should be recorded, either from the topographic survey, if the map is available, or by approximate measurement with a barometer. Evidence of flooding or of recent showers of volcanic ash need to be

---

[5] For some excellent examples see EDELMAN, C. H. THE SOILS OF THE NETHERLANDS. 177 pp., illus. (Maps). Amsterdam. 1950.

[6] Only brief statements are given here of items discussed in full later.

noted. Where significant, the exposure of the site to wind or sun needs to be observed. Near the boundary between plant associations, a difference in wind or exposure may determine the association. Where moisture is limiting, north-facing slopes contrast sharply with south-facing slopes in both vegetation and soil. In northern Europe, east-west sand ridges often have Podzols on the north slopes and Brown Forest soils on the south slopes. In dry regions of the northern hemisphere south slopes may have Sierozem soils or even Lithosols, and the north slopes, Brown or Chestnut soils.

2. **Parent material.**—The first requirement is a clear description of the parent material itself—its texture, structure, color, consistence, and any other significant features, including depth and stratification. Its approximate mineralogical composition should be given insofar as it can be determined in the field. Often supplementary laboratory determinations are needed. Suggestions should be added regarding the rock source of the material, such as granite, basalt, sandstone, limestone, and so on, or mixtures of several kinds of rock. The manner in which parent materials originated should be suggested: weathering of rocks in place, wind-deposited material, glacial till, mud flow, local alluvium, general alluvium, and so on. Many terms that relate to mode of origin, such as glacial till, loess, and alluvium, are too general for soil descriptions although they are useful as supplements. Important suggestions about probable or possible differences between the substratum (as C horizon) and the original material from which the solum itself has been developed may be helpful.

3. **The soil profile.**—After the excavation has been made for the study of the soil profile, the major horizons should be located first. If these can be given letter designations, as A, B, C, and their subdivisions, well and good. Often this is not possible without some laboratory study. Generally, however, it is best to make an estimate of the letter designation and indicate uncertainties with a question mark. Where great uncertainty exists, the horizons may simply be numbered from the surface on down to the parent material.

With the horizon boundaries located, the depth and thickness of each are recorded, together with the character of the boundaries between them. The zero point for measurement is usually the top of the A_1 horizon. After measurement, each horizon is described with special attention to the following items:

> *Color:* The color names and mathematical (Munsell) notations are taken from the standard color charts. Where the soil is streaked or mottled with contrasting colors, or where the outsides of aggregates are unlike the interiors, the principal colors are noted separately. Any relevant notes on moisture conditions may be added. Colors of moist soil are usually given in soil descriptions. In addition the authors recommend that the colors

of air-dry samples be noted, especially for comparing soils in widely different locations.

Texture: Soil class is observed in the field by feeling the soil with the fingers. In former years the many disparities existing between soil class as determined in the field and by the old standard triangle were ignored. Recently these have been adjusted and the correspondence is now fairly close. In all cases of doubt, special samples should be forwarded to the laboratory for immediate attention so that the soil survey party may have a uniform basis for soil class determination.

Structure: Soil structure needs careful attention, partly because of its importance to soil productivity, soil permeability, and root growth, and partly because of its great significance in soil genesis. This latter fact emphasizes the importance of the upper layer of virgin soils, even though they may be destroyed in tillage.

Porosity.

Consistence.

Reaction and effervescence: Several useful kits are available for making these determinations.

Concretions and other special formations.

Organic matter and roots.

Chemical and mineralogical composition: Kinds and amounts of clay minerals, exchangeable bases, plant nutrients, and the like can be obtained only from laboratory examinations of samples representative of each genetic horizon. Where uncertainty exists about the uniformity of any particular horizon, it may be subdivided arbitrarily and samples taken from the several subdivisions.

4. **Stoniness.**—Where stones are present, notes on their number and size and their distribution in the profile are essential in evaluating the use capabilities of the soil, and in correctly establishing phases for stoniness within soil types.

5. **Erosion or truncation.**—Most sloping soils have at least some erosion. In areas of recent uplift, gullies and other evidences of erosion may be conspicuous natural features of the landscape. Mainly, however, severe erosion has followed changes in plant cover that have permitted greatly accelerated erosion over that normal for the type. Such features are noted and their relationship to use and the other factors of the environment suggested. It is exceedingly important to differentiate between natural erosion, however severe, and accelerated erosion. Notes on the accelerated erosion, where it exists, should be accompanied with the best possible estimate of the previous use history of the soil.

Notes on erosion, and especially on its effects, are needed for two somewhat different purposes: (1) To estimate the erosion hazard of the soil unit under different uses and management systems, and (2) to provide a basis for establishing proper classes of eroded soils and finally eroded soil phases within the soil type. Eroded soil phases need to be defined for each soil type in such a way that the definitions can be related to differential land-use predictions.

Besides truncation, the effects that erosion or soil blowing have in covering soils need to be noted.

6. Vegetation.—The principal plants are noted, both dominant and associate, and comments made about the cover generally. For example, it may be observed that a soil has a second-growth cover after cutting or fire, is revegetating after over-grazing, is now severely overgrazed, is in virgin hardwood forests, or the like.

7. Land use.—The principal crops and their condition, and the type of farming, are noted. Detailed studies of yield and soil management practices are made separately, not as a part of individual soil profile studies.

NOTEBOOKS

The soil scientist takes a great many notes in the field accurately and rapidly. So many notes are needed that methods should be systematic and simple. If the scientist sets up an over-elaborate system, he may find it too much trouble. He must provide for soil descriptions at major sites of soil examination, for observations made between sites and during mapping, for photographs, for interviews with farmers and others, and for his usual travel records. In a survey area it is usually best to keep these classes of notes, and perhaps others, in separate books.

Individual preferences vary so much that no attempt has been made to standardize the size and format of notebooks. It is important that standard terms and symbols be used and that notebooks be legible so that other men may use them, as when one party chief or soil correlator is replaced by another.

Some prefer large notebooks with pages about 8 by 10 inches. These are easy to write in and have plenty of space for sketches as well as writing. Where working out of a car, these are best for detailed soil profile descriptions. So much equipment is needed anyway that their extra bulk is insignificant.

Some prefer smaller notebooks, 3 to 5 inches wide and 5 to 8 inches long, that may be carried in the pocket, especially for notes made while mapping. The more neatly a man writes, the smaller the notebook he can use satisfactorily.

Loose-leaf notebooks have the great advantage that individual descriptions may be filed together. Many prefer them, with standard forms similar to those illustrated on page 138. Although some use bound notebooks, for the greatest number of soil scientists, loose-leaf notebooks are probably best for soil descriptions. With notebooks having six or more rings, the loss of individual sheets is rare.[7]

Some sort of form is helpful in making soil descriptions, especially for beginners. With a definite outline, important items are less likely to be omitted. Just one omission may seriously reduce the value of a description, even spoil it altogether; and a great many items need to be noted. This is not to say that good notes cannot be taken without forms. Some prefer blank pages with finely ruled lines. It is easier to accommodate the description to the peculiarities of the soil. Important features may be described at length without trying to squeeze them into a form. Some who use plain notebooks paste or write a checklist of the items on the inside cover to aid their memories.

The important thing is that each soil scientist train himself to keep complete, accurate, standard notes. Perhaps his biggest job is to learn to note the commonplace—the common soils, vegetation, crops, farms, and farming practices. Most of us are inclined to accept these, unconsciously, as "norms." Since the mind comprehends by comparison, unless we train ourselves, we shall only note and photograph departures from the norms. Then, when we attempt to develop a descriptive legend or report, our notes will be inadequate. First we must describe the normal—our bench marks.

SUGGESTED OUTLINE FOR NOTEBOOK PAGE

A uniform system for describing soils can be helped with special notebooks that provide places for all the principal items that need to be noted. By using conventional abbreviations for the defined classes of the various features, as outlined in specific sections of this *Manual*, it is possible to get descriptions into a small space. Outline pages for such notebooks are shown in figure 23. It is most convenient to have these outlines printed on opposite sides of the same sheet for a loose-leaf notebook. The individual sheets may be removed and filed under the soil names. These sheets can be as small as 3¾ by 6¾ inches and punched along one of the long margins for use in a ring-binder pocket notebook; or they may be placed in a bound notebook. A similar outline can be used for a larger page, say about 7½ by 9½ inches, with an additional column in which to make a sketch of the profile and more space for remarks and discussion. A great advantage of using such a scheme lies partly in the use of standard

[7] When working intensively within an area, for soil descriptions, some prefer loose leaves or sheets of large size (8 by 10½ inches), held in a tatum holder or clip board. These can be filed by taxonomic units and conveniently summarized. Sheets held in a metal tatum holder are easy to write on and the metal gives good protection. Losses of notes may be held to the very minimum, since sheets can be removed and filed at the field headquarters each evening. For study in large areas, some prefer small bound notebooks, partly to avoid the danger of losing sheets and partly to reduce the equipment to be carried on planes and trains. Dangers of loss, through losing the whole notebook, are increased, however.

Soil type		Date	Stop No.	
Classification		Area		
Location			Elev.	
N. veg. (or crop)		Climate		
Parent material				
Physiography				
Relief	Slope		Erosion	
Drainage	Gr. water		Permeability	
Moisture	Salt or alkali			
Stoniness	Root distrib.			
Remarks				

Soil type

File No.

A

Hori-zon	Depth	Thick-ness	Bound-ary	Color — Check. D(ry) or M(oist)	Tex-ture	Struc-ture	Con-sistence	Reac-tion	Spec. Feat.
				D M					
				D M					
				D M					
				D M					
				D M					
				D M					
				D M					
				D M					
				D M					
				D M					
				D M					

B

FIGURE 23.—Outline for standard notebook pages for soil descriptions: *A*, front side of sheet; *B*, reverse side of sheet.

notations, which makes it possible to abstract several descriptions of the same taxonomic unit into a general one for the unit as a whole.

For the outline shown in figure 23, *A* and *B*, the following abbreviations and notations are suggested. They are also useful as a check list when using a plain notebook.

Horizon: Use the standard horizon nomenclature. (See pp. 173 to 188.)

Depth: In inches or centimeters from the top of A_1, or surface mineral horizon, except for the surface of peat or muck in Bogs and Half Bogs. (See p. 185.)

Thickness: Average thickness and range, as 6 (4–8).

Boundary[1]: Horizon boundaries are described as to distinctness: Abrupt—a; clear—c; gradual—g; diffuse—d; and according to topography: Smooth—s; wavy—w; irregular—i; broken—b. An abrupt, irregular boundary is ai.

Color: Soil colors are indicated by using the appropriate Munsell notation, such as 5YR 5/3. The spaces in the suggested notebook page under color are left open, except for checking whether dry or moist, in order to accommodate the small space to the need of the descriptions of individual horizons. If the soil mass is one solid color, only one notation is required. If the outsides of aggregates differ significantly from their interiors, both colors are needed. The description of mottled soil horizons needs to include the color of the matrix and the color, or colors, of the principal mottles plus a description of the pattern of mottling.

Mottling: A description of the mottling in soil horizons requires a notation of the colors and of the pattern. Colors can be given in terms of the Munsell notation or in their linguistic equivalents, since exact measurement is neither possible nor necessary. The pattern may be noted as follows:

Abundance:
few .... f
common c
many .... m

Size:
fine 1
medium 2
coarse 3

Contrast:
faint .... f
distinct ...... d
prominent .... p

Thus a medium-gray soil horizon mottled with yellow and reddish brown could be noted as: 10YR 5/1, c3d, 10YR 7/6 and 5YR 4/4 (or) 10YR 5/1, c3d, yellow and reddish brown.

Texture: The following notations are suggested:

gravel .... g
very coarse sand... vcos
coarse sand....... cos
sand .... s
fine sand .... fs
very fine sand..... vfs
loamy coarse sand. lcos
loamy sand .... ls
loamy fine sand ... lfs
sandy loam .... sl
fine sandy loam.... fsl
very fine sandy loam vfsl
gravelly sandy loam gsl

loam l
gravelly loam .... gl
stony loam .... stl
silt .... si
silt loam .... sil
clay loam cl
silty clay loam.... sicl
sandy clay loam... scl
stony clay loam... stcl
silty clay .... sic
clay c

Structure: The terms used follow the outline given on page 228.

Size or class:		Form or type:	
very fine[2]	vf	platy	pl
fine	f	prismatic	pr
medium	m	columnar	cpr
coarse	c	blocky[3]	bk
very coarse	vc	angular blocky	abk
Grade or distinctness:		subangular blocky	sbk
structureless	0	granular	gr
weak[4]	1	crumb	cr
moderate	2	single grain	sg
strong	3	massive	m

Thus, the structure of the B horizon of a solodized-Solonetz may be c3cpr; that of the A$_1$ of a Gray-Brown Podzolic, mlcr; and that of the B$_2$ of a Reddish Chestnut, m2abk. Horizons having a mixed structure require two notations. The B$_1$ of a Red-Yellow Podzolic may be f1sbk or m2sbk.

Consistence: The notation of consistence varies with moisture content. (See pp. 231 to 234.)

Wet soil:		Dry soil:	
nonsticky	wso	loose	dl
slightly sticky	wss	soft	ds
sticky	ws	slightly hard	dsh
very sticky	wvs	hard	dh
nonplastic	wpo	very hard	dvh
slightly plastic	wps	extremely hard	deh
plastic	wp	Cementation:	
very plastic	wvp	weakly cemented	cw
Moist soil:		strongly cemented	cs
loose	ml	indurated	ci
very friable	mvfr		
friable	mfr		
firm	mfi		
very firm	mvfi		
extremely firm	mefi		

Reaction: Use pH figures.

Indicate effervescence with HCl **as:**

slight	e
strong	es
violent	ev

Special features:

Concretions, for example, as:

lime	conca
iron	consir
siliceous	consi
Krotovinas	k

Other special features may be included under *"Remarks."*

Soil type: Name, as Memphis silt loam, plus field mapping number, if any.

Classification: Especially great soil group, if known.

Native vegetation (or crop): Such as: oak-hickory; short grass; wheat; apple orchard.

Climate: Such as: humid temperate; warm semiarid.

Parent material: Such as: residuum from basalt; mixed silty alluvium; calcareous clay loam till.

Physiography: Such as: high terrace, till plain; alluvial fan; mountain foot slope. Add names of formations, where known.

---

[1] In an outline, the lower boundary of a horizon is noted.
[2] Read "thin" and "thick" for platy instead of "fine" and "coarse."
[3] Unrecommended synonyms for subangular blocky are subangular nut and nuciform.
[4] "Very weak" and "very strong" may be noted as v1 and v3, respectively.

Relief: Give letter designation or name of soil slope class and indicate concave or convex, single or complex slopes. (See p. 161.)

Slope: Give approximate gradient of soil slope.

Erosion: Use appropriate class name and number. (See p. 261 *et seq.*)

Drainage: Use appropriate class name for soil drainage. (See p. 170 *et seq.*)

Ground water: Give depth to ground water or indicate "deep."

Permeability: Use appropriate class name. (See p. 168.)

Moisture: Indicate present soil moisture as (1) wet; (2) moist; (3) moderately dry; (4) dry.

Salt or alkali: Indicate concentration of either or both as slight, moderate, or strong.

Stoniness: Use appropriate class name and number. (See p. 217.)

Root distribution: Indicate depth of penetration as "deep" or to a certain depth or horizon; and abundance as "abundant," "plentiful," or "few."

Remarks: Include additional detail on listed items or include additional items, such as relative content of organic matter, evidence of worms, insects, or rodents, special mottling, and stone lines.

PHOTOGRAPHS[8]

Good photographs of profiles of the representative soil types, of characteristic landscapes, both natural and cultural, of evidences of soil processes, and of important practices, crops, and structures related to soil use and development are especially helpful. Such photographs are needed in published reports to supplement descriptions and recommendations and to give the reader a more direct "feeling" of the soils, landscapes, and agriculture. Many published soil surveys contain too few photographs of the soil and landscapes for the clearest presentation of the results of the research.

Besides their use in publications, photographs are a useful part of the record. Especially in a reconnaissance or exploratory soil survey where time is limited, photographs become an essential part of the field notes. Often one can take a picture more quickly than he can describe a landscape accurately.

Although both black-and-white photographs and color transparencies have their place, the greater need is for the former, especially since they can be reproduced easily and used as illustrations. The color transparencies, however, serve better in a record, especially for soil profiles[9].

The suggestions that follow are intended as general guides to soil survey party chiefs and others taking photographs for use primarily in soil survey reports and monographs presenting the results of the field work. During the progress of a soil survey, nearly ideal conditions of lighting may be selected; whereas on exploratory surveys many photographs need to be taken when the observer happens to be on the spot, regardless of weather, season, and time of day. Scientists vary individually in their flair for photography but with care and attention to a few simple

---

[8] The use of photographs, drawings, and maps as illustrations in published reports and monographs is dealt with in the section on The Soil Survey Report.

[9] The Committee on the Exchange of Soil Pictures and Soil Profiles of the Soil Science Society of America issues detailed suggestions from time to time for making color transparencies.

principles, most can get useful black-and-white pictures under good conditions. Sometimes professional photographers may be available, but only a few have enough appreciation of soils to compose photographs that bring out the important relationships.

General requirements.—Some of the important requirements of black-and-white pictures for publication are as follows:

(1) Photographs must be clear and distinct if they are to be most useful. This means that the subject should be well lighted and in sharp focus. Every photograph loses some part of its sharpness in reproduction; consequently publication of a photograph may reduce rather than enhance the value of an otherwise good text unless the original is clear and has adequate contrast.

(2) Field notes for each photograph should include the date, the location, and a description with soil names. These notes can be transferred to a permanent record after the film is developed. Unless an orderly system of numbering, describing, and filing is used, time, film, and equipment are essentially wasted.

(3) Emphasis should be given the most important soils, crops, and farms, and especially the normal soil. As with the making of complete notes, most soil scientists need to train themselves to photograph the commonplace. Unconsciously, one tends to accept the norm and to describe and to photograph the outstanding departures from it, forgetting to record the norm itself. Unless he plans his photographs carefully, the beginner may finish his survey with photographs of all the unusual things but with none of the dominant soils and farms. Partly, too, this is because buttes, gullies, beaches, and the like, are easier to photograph than common undulating landscapes. The beginner is more tempted to photograph an outstanding set of farm buildings or a settler's makeshift cabin than the ordinary farm layout.

(4) A useful photograph brings out one or more important points about the characteristics of the soil, its important relationships to other soils, land form, vegetation, or geology, or its use and management. No matter how clear they are, simple "views", unrelated to the soil descriptions or soil maps, should be discarded. When a photograph is used to present an idea of a soil management practice or the yield of a specific crop, for example, it should be tied down to an actual soil mapping unit, described in the text, and to defined management practices. Many pictures can serve two or more purposes at once; for example, a photograph may show a sprinkler irrigation system, a type of terrace, or a special crop adapted to several soil types, and also its use on a particular soil type. Relief and land-use pattern may be shown in one photograph. Yet one should avoid getting too much in one photograph, lest all the points become obscure. This is especially true of a broad or distant landscape view. These rarely reproduce successfully unless they are simple and unusually clear. It is generally best to make just one point in a photograph and make it clearly.

(5) A great many pictures taken for soil survey reports are too small in scale—the photographer was much too far from the

center of interest. One should be as near the soil profile, the growing crop, the farmstead, or any other center of interest as good composition makes possible.

(6) Good composition is essential for a first-class photograph. Where convenient and other factors are considered, the center of interest should be a little off center, preferably a little to the left and a little below the actual center of the photograph. Unsightly telegraph poles, fence posts, commercial signs, and other things irrelevant to the story of the photograph should be avoided, especially in the foreground. Often the observer is concentrating so intensely on the soil or other feature while exposing the film that he fails to see things that ruin the picture. Good pictures, both published and unpublished, are useful for many years. Automobiles, women's apparel, men's hats, or other items that drastically change style and "date" the photograph should be avoided since they distract the reader from the main story.

(7) Many photographs need some sort of reference scale to give a correct idea of dimensions. For close-ups, a rule of natural wood or plain white with black figures is better than a pick, shovel, watch, or the like.

(8) A great many pictures are poorly illuminated and "flat." Black-and-white pictures taken with the sun directly back of the camera are rarely good. Many taken at high-noon in summer, "when the bushes have their shadows tucked beneath them," lack enough contrast. Usually the sun should be at an angle to the subject in order to get good contrast. Photographs to show microrelief, for example, need to be taken nearly crosswise to the sun in early morning or late afternoon. For color transparencies these contrasts of light and shadow are less important than is adequate light.

(9) Generally better pictures can be taken from a tripod than without one. The composition can be better planned, the lens can be more conveniently shaded, and the aperture can be reduced to permit greater depth of focus. Use of a tripod is especially important when the light is poor. A tripod will also permit more critical focussing, which is of special importance in making pictures of soil profiles.

(10) All parts of a picture important to its story should be in sharp focus. This seems obvious indeed but it deserves special emphasis. Most of the pictures needed in soil survey notes or publications are more effective if they have the maximum depth of focus obtainable. Most can, therefore, be made more satisfactorily with a small aperture and a long exposure in order to have the greatest possible part of the view in focus. Small openings are generally better for landscapes and for soil profiles but cannot be used with rapidly moving objects. Relatively few of the photographs needed in soil survey reports, however, must include moving objects.

Soil profiles.—Soil profiles are not easily photographed. It is especially difficult to get clear black-and-white pictures that bring out the significant contrasts in structure and color among the soil horizons. Yet only those that do bring out these contrasts are useful. Some general points to observe in taking pictures of soil profiles are the following:

(1) A representative site needs to be chosen. Usually it will be necessary to prepare a soil profile in a road cut because of the difficulty of making a pit large enough to have adequate lighting of all the horizons. The photographer must avoid the temptation of taking photographs where they may be made easily in cuts where the soils are not really representative.

(2) After a vertical cut has been made with a spade, the profile needs to be cleaned and dressed to bring out the structure and other features without interference of loose roots. Beginning at the top, fragments of the soil may be broken off with a large knife or fork to eliminate spade marks. Dust and small fragments may be blown away with a small tire pump. Brooms are also used but may leave streaks. It may be helpful to moisten the whole profile or parts of it with a hand sprayer for uniformity of moisture content and comparability of contrast. Moist soils are somewhat darker than dry ones and often the colors are more intense. If the whole profile is dry, it may be useful to moisten one-half, vertically, to show the contrast between the dry and moist soil.

(3) For scale, a 60-inch rule of unvarnished and unpainted wood, $1\frac{1}{2}$-inches wide, and $\frac{1}{2}$-inch thick, with large clear black figures at 1-foot intervals, is satisfactory. White rules with black figures have also been used successfully. Large ticks or half-lines can indicate the 6-inch intervals and small ticks the 2-inch intervals. Such a rule may be made in two or three sections held together by dowels or hinges. An ordinary folding bricklayer's 6-foot rule with clear figures can be used for very large scale pictures. The zero point of the ruler should always be exactly at the top of the A_1 horizon. The unused part of the ruler can be buried at the lower end of the profile.

Good scales not only help the reading of the individual picture but also make it possible to bring several pictures to a common scale by differential enlargement.

(4) For black-and-white pictures some prefer indirect lighting to avoid shadows. Others prefer to have the sun shining directly on the profile. Strong sunlight may give unnatural results because of shadows from the structural aggregates, pebbles, and root ends.

For color transparencies direct sunlight and bright sky are preferred by some, although good results may be had with indirect lighting if it is strong. Good lighting is so important that adequate color transparencies of soil profiles usually can be made only during the middle of the day from late spring to early autumn in most parts of the United States.

(5) Photographs of soil profiles are rarely good unless the camera is close to the profile, say within 4 to 8 feet, or at the very most, 12 feet. This means careful focussing for which a tripod is usually necessary in order to use the small opening required for

from their weathering products and from those of interbedded sedimentary rocks.

Metamorphic rocks.—These have resulted from profound alteration of igneous and sedimentary rocks through heat and pressure applied to them. General classes important as sources of weathered parent material for soils are gneiss, schist, slate, marble, quartzite, and phyllite.

MATERIALS PRODUCED FROM SOFT ROCKS

Another group of materials, those produced from soft rocks, falls more or less intermediate between the group of mineral parent materials derived from hard rocks through residual weathering and the group derived from materials that have been transported.

Ash, cinders, and other volcanic ejecta may be regarded as unconsolidated igneous rocks; but they have been moved from their place of origin and usually they are immediately more or less reworked by wind and water.

Also included with the soft rocks are the unconsolidated equivalents of the sedimentary rocks already listed: marl, sand, silt, clay, and gravel. Usually such formations are described most appropriately within the categories that follow, but semi-indurated rocks are found that are intermediate in hardness and consolidation between those clearly recognized as hard rocks and those that are essentially unconsolidated. Chalk, for example, is one of these. It may be defined as an earthy limestone with a hardness less than 2.

Caliche is a very broad term for secondary calcareous material in layers near the surface. As the term is used, caliche may be soft and clearly recognized as the C_{ca} horizon of the soil; or it may exist in hard thick beds beneath the solum or exposed at the surface, especially in warm-temperate and warm regions of relatively low rainfall. The hardened form is also called *croûte calcaire*.

In this intermediate class are deposits of diatomaceous earth formed from the siliceous remains of primitive plants called diatoms.

TRANSPORTED MATERIALS

Taking the world as a whole, perhaps the most important group of parent materials is the very broad one made up of materials that have been moved from the place of their origin and redeposited during the weathering processes or during some phase of those processes, and which consist of or are weathered from unconsolidated formations. The principal groups of these materials are usually named according to the main force responsible for their transport and redeposition. In most places sufficient evidence can be had to make a clear determination; elsewhere the precise origin is doubtful.

In soil morphology and classification, it is exceedingly important that the characteristics of the material itself be observed and described. It is not enough simply to identify the parent material as alluvium, loess, or glacial till. Such names are used to supplement the descriptions of the material; and if doubt or uncertainty exists as to the correctness of the name, this fact is mentioned. For example, it is often impossible to be sure whether certain silty deposits are alluvium, loess, or the result of residual weathering in place. Certain mud flows are indistinguishable from glacial till. Some sandy glacial till is nearly identical to sandy outwash. Such hard-to-make distinctions are of little importance.

MATERIALS MOVED AND REDEPOSITED BY WATER

Alluvium.—The most important of the materials moved and redeposited by water is alluvium. It consists of sediments deposited by streams. It may occur in terraces well above present streams or in the normally flooded bottoms of existing streams. Remnants of very old stream terraces may be found in dissected country far from any present stream. Along many old established streams are a whole series of alluvial deposits in terraces—young ones in the immediate flood plain, up step by step, to the very old ones. Then too, recent alluvium often covers older terraces.

Generally, the alluvium may be divided into two main groups according to origin: (1) Local alluvium, like that at the base of slopes and along small streams flowing out of tiny drainage basins of nearly homogeneous rock and soil material, and (2) general alluvium of mixed origin, as that along major stream courses.

Colluvium.—The distinction between alluvium and colluvium is somewhat difficult and arbitrary. Some authorities hold that colluvium is strictly the material moved primarily under the influence of gravity, only imperfectly sorted, if sorted at all; and they include under alluvium all materials moved primarily by water. Generally, however, colluvium is used for the poorly sorted material near the base of strong slopes that has been moved by gravity, frost action, soil creep, and local wash. In the midwestern parts of the United States, for example, the established local usage by many soil scientists is to use the term "colluvium" for that part of the local alluvium at the base of slopes that has been moved into place through creep and local wash.

Lacustrine deposits.—These deposits consist of materials that have settled out of the quiet water of lakes. Those laid down in fresh-water lakes associated with glacial action are commonly included as a subgroup under glacial drift. Yet besides these there are other lake deposits, including those of Pleistocene times, unassociated with the continental glaciers. Some old lake basins in the western part of the United States are commonly called *playas* and may be more or less salty, depending on the climate and drainage.

Marine sediments.—These sediments have been reworked by the sea and later exposed either naturally or through the construction of dikes and drainage canals. They vary widely in lithological and mechanical composition. Some resemble lacustrine deposits.

Beach deposits.—These deposits, low ridges of sorted material, often gravelly, cobbly, or stony, mark the shore lines at old levels of the sea or lakes. Those formed on the beaches of glacial lakes are usually included with glacial drift, which is defined in another group.

MATERIALS REMOVED AND REDEPOSITED BY WIND

The wind-blown materials are generally divided into two classes, mainly in accordance with texture. Those that are mainly silty are called *loess*, and those that are primarily sand are called eolian *sands*, commonly but not always in *dunes*.[4]

It has been exceedingly difficult, both for geologists and soil scientists, to define loess precisely. Typically, deposits of loess are very silty but contain significant amounts of clay and fine sand. Usually, but not always, the material is calcareous. Most loess deposits are pale brown to brown, although gray and red colors are common. The thick deposits are generally massive, with some gross vertical cracking. The walls of road cuts in thick loess stand nearly vertical for years. Other silty deposits derived in other ways, however, have some or all of these characteristics. Then too, some wind-blown silt has been leached and strongly weathered so that it is acid and rich in clay. On the other hand, young deposits of wind-blown silty very fine sand, called loess, are exceedingly low in clay.

Characteristically, sand dunes, especially in humid regions, consist of sand, especially fine or medium sand, that is very rich in quartz and low in clay-forming minerals. Yet, nearly all transitions may be observed between the silty wind-blown materials called loess and the very sandy material in characteristic sand dunes. Especially in deserts and semideserts, the sand dunes may contain large amounts of calcium carbonate and of clay-forming minerals that would decompose to clay in a more humid environment. Examples may even be found of sand dunes, using sand in its purely textural sense, that consist almost wholly of calcium carbonate or of gypsum.

During periods of drought, and in deserts, local wind movements may pile up soil material of mixed texture or even materials very rich in clay. Piles of such material have even been called "soil dunes" or "clay dunes." It is better, however, to use an expression such as "wind-deposited materials" for local accumulations of materials of mixed textures moved by the wind than it is to identify them as loess or dunes.

MATERIALS MOVED AND REDEPOSITED BY GLACIAL PROCESSES

Several classes of materials moved and redeposited by glacial processes are as follows:

Glacial drift.—Glacial drift consists of all the material picked up, mixed, disintegrated, transported, and deposited through the action of glacial ice or of water resulting primarily from the

---

[4] Locally, loess is sometimes called "loam" regardless of actual texture. Relatively uniform wind-laid deposits of sand are sometimes called "cover sand."

melting of glaciers. In many places the glacial drift is covered with loess. Deep mantles of loess are usually easily recognized, but very thin mantles are so altered by soil-building forces as to be scarcely differentiated from modified drift.

Till or glacial till.—This includes that part of the glacial drift deposited directly by the ice with little or no transportation by water. It is generally an unstratified, unconsolidated, heterogeneous mixture of clay, silt, sand, gravel, and sometimes boulders. Till may be found in ground moraines, terminal moraines, medial moraines, and lateral moraines. It is often important to differentiate between the tills of the several glacial epochs. Often they underlie one another and may be separated by other deposits or old weathered surfaces.[5] Many deposits of glacial till were later washed by lakes, but without important additions. The upper part of such wave-cut till is uncommonly rich in coarse fragments as a result of the wave action in glacial lakes. *Drumlins* are long cigar-shaped low hills of glacial till, with a smooth sky line and with their long axes lying parallel to the line of movement of the ice.

Till varies widely in texture, chemical composition, and the degree of weathering subsequent to its deposition. Most till is slightly, moderately, or highly calcareous; but an important part of it is noncalcareous because no calcite- or dolomite-bearing rocks were contributed to the material or because of subsequent leaching and chemical weathering. In detailed soil classification one needs to recognize about five groups of till according to texture: (1) Coarse textured, loose, porous till, consisting mainly of a mixture of sand, gravel, cobbles, and boulders; (2) sandy till with some gravel and perhaps a few stones and a little clay; (3) medium textured, gritty till having a relatively even mixture of sand, silt, and clay, with or without stones and boulders; (4) medium textured silty till that is relatively free of gritty particles; and (5) fine textured till having a predominance of silt and clay.

Glaciofluvial deposits.—These deposits are made up of materials produced by glaciers and carried, sorted, and deposited by water that originated mainly from the melting of glacial ice.

The most important of these is *glacial outwash*. This is a broad term including all of the material swept out, sorted, and deposited beyond the glacial ice front by streams of melt water. Commonly, this outwash exists in the form of plains, valley trains, or deltas in old glacial lakes. The valley trains of outwash may extend far beyond the farthest advance of the ice.

Especially near the moraines, poorly sorted outwash materials may exist in kames, eskers, and crevasse-fills.

---

[5] In the Middle West, the term *gumbotil* is applied to tenacious clays, generally gray, plastic when wet, and hard when dry, which have been weathered from Nebraskan, Kansan, and Illinoian till during the interglacial periods.

Glacial beach deposits.—These consist of gravel and sand and mark the beach lines of former glacial lakes. Depending upon the character of the original drift, they may be sandy, gravelly, cobbly, or stony.

Glaciolacustrine materials.—These materials range from fine clays to sand. They are derived from glaciers and reworked and laid down in glacial lakes. Many of them are interbedded or laminated. The fine horizontal markings exposed in a section of glaciolacustrine clay, each related to one year's deposition and one season's glacial-ice melt, are called *varves*.

Fine examples of all the glacial materials and forms described in preceding paragraphs may be found. Yet in many places it is not easy to distinguish definitely among the kinds of drift on the basis of mode of origin and land form. In places, for example, pitted outwash plains can scarcely be distinguished from sandy till in terminal moraines. Often it is difficult to distinguish between wave-cut till and lacustrine materials. We must continually recall that these names connote only a little about the actual characteristics of the parent material. Certainly mode of origin of the parent material is not a sufficient basis, by itself, for separating soil classificational units.

MATERIALS MOVED AND REDEPOSITED BY GRAVITY

As strictly defined by some, *colluvium* is the unsorted or slightly sorted material at the base of slopes, accumulated largely as rock fragments that have fallen down the slope under the influence of gravity. In its extreme form this material is called *talus*. Rock fragments are angular in contrast to the rounded, water-worn cobbles and stones in alluvial terraces and glacial outwash. As mentioned before, colluvium is used generally for that part of the poorly sorted local alluvium that has accumulated at the base of slopes, in depressions, or along tiny streams, through gravity, soil creep, and local wash.

ORGANIC MATERIALS

In moist situations where organic matter forms more rapidly than it decomposes, peat deposits are formed. These peats become, in turn, parent material for soils. If the organic remains are sufficiently fresh and intact to permit identification of plant forms, the material is regarded as *peat*. If, on the other hand, the peat has undergone sufficient decomposition to make recognition of the plant parts impossible, the decomposed material is called *muck*. Generally speaking, muck has a higher mineral or ash content than peat, because in the process of decomposition the ash that was in the vegetation accumulates. Yet total mineral or ash content is not a dependable guide for distinguishing between peat and muck. Besides the accumulation of minerals through the decomposition of vegetation, large amounts of mineral matter may be introduced into peat formations by wash from surrounding uplands, by wind, and as volcanic ash. Nearly raw peat may contain 50 percent mineral matter as volcanic ash with only a small influence on the character of the peat.

The color, texture, compactness, and other characteristics of peat materials in soils need to be described. The principal general classes of peat, mainly according to origin, are (1) woody, (2) fibrous, (3) moss, (4) sedimentary, and (5) colloidal.

CHARACTERISTICS AND ORIGIN OF THE PARENT MATERIAL

Both consolidated and unconsolidated materials beneath the solum that influence the genesis and behavior of the soil need to be described in standard terms. Besides the observations themselves, the scientist should record his judgment about the origin of the parent material from which the solum has developed; yet the observed facts need to be separated clearly from inferences and, where important, an indication of the relative probability of the relationships suggested.

The hardness, lithological composition, and permeability of the material directly beneath the solum are especially important. Evidence of stratification of the material—textural banding, stone lines, and the like—need to be noted. Many soils have obviously developed from stratified parent material; others seem to have developed from uniform material like that directly beneath the solum, although one can rarely be certain without chemical, physical, and mineralogical data on samples of the horizons. As weathering and soil formation go forward on interbedded geological formations, with natural erosion, sola developed from materials weathered from one kind of rock, limestone let us say, are underlain by those weathered from another, say shale or sandstone. Commonly, the upper layers of outwash deposits were laid down from more slowly moving water and are finer in texture than the lower layers. Wind-blown fines and volcanic ash are laid down in blankets of varying thickness over other rock formations. The examples of such complications are nearly endless. Then, too, these geological changes often go forward along with soil formation. Where loess or ash are quickly dropped on old soils, buried soils may be well-preserved. Elsewhere the accumulation of mineral material on the top of the soil is so slow that the solum thickens only gradually. In such places the material beneath the solum was once a part of it and has now been buried beyond the influence of the biological forces.

Where hard rocks or other strongly contrasting materials lie near enough to the surface to affect the behavior of the soil, their depths need to be measured accurately; for the depth of the solum, or of solum and parent material, over such nonconforming formations is an important criterion for series and phase distinctions.

LAND FORM, RELIEF, AND DRAINAGE

Its land form is an essential part of a soil, conceived as a three-dimensional landscape resulting from the synthetic effect of all the materials and processes in its environment. Kinds of soil profiles are associated with kinds of land form that influence their genesis. Although, like other features of the soil, land form by itself is not always a sufficient basis for differentiating between soil series, it is usually associated with other differentiating characteristics. Important differences in both parent material and soil profile are commonly covariant with differences in land form.

Most soil series and types have a relatively narrow range in land form. Yet there are exceptions. Soils of two areas may be developed from deep loess, let us say, laid down on a ground moraine in one area and over a terrace in the other. Soil profiles, slopes, and other characteristics may be similar in the two areas, yet the land over the old terrace may have better water supplies in the substratum. In such an instance, the soil series should be subdivided into phases, the typical (phase) on the ground moraine and a *terrace phase* for the soil on the old terrace.

The importance of land form is being recognized increasingly by soil scientists in soil classification and interpretation. Materials in terraces, volcanic ash deposits, and other formations of differing ages and origins that appear to be similar in the field may have significantly different chemical compositions. Where substantial differences exist in texture, clay minerals, or calcium content, the materials themselves and the soils developed from them are easily distinguished; yet, differences in cobalt and other trace elements of great importance to soil use and management sometimes are not associated with other characteristics of the material recognizable in the field. In many such instances, geological origin is associated with land form, which, in turn, serves as the basis of prediction to farmers and agricultural advisers.

Other important examples, among many, that show the need for careful studies of land form may be found in areas of old valley fills made up of gently sloping coalescing fans of unlike origin and stratigraphy. A large part of the irrigated soils of the world are in such valleys. A dependable classification of these valley soils is greatly facilitated by a clear understanding of the origin of the various surfaces, especially as these relate to predictions of drainage conditions and problems that develop when water is supplied.

Land forms should be named and described in the standard terms used and accepted by physiographers and geomorpholo-

FIGURE 24.—Characteristic microrelief of the gilgai type: Upper, on Irving clay near Millican, Tex.; and lower, on Bell clay 15 miles southwest of College Station, Tex.

gists. Each soil survey party should use the most authoritative texts and monographs that apply to the survey area.[1]

RELIEF

Relief is sometimes used broadly to indicate simply the differences in elevation within an area or perhaps only the difference between the highest and lowest altitude of an area. More precisely, however, relief implies relative elevation and has been defined as the elevations or inequalities of a land surface considered collectively.

Microrelief refers to small-scale differences in relief. In areas of similar macrorelief, the surface may be nearly uniform or it may be interrupted by mounds, swales, or pits that are a few feet across and have significant differences in elevation of only 1 to 3 feet or even less (figs. 24 and 25).

FIGURE 25.—Characteristic microrelief of truncated solodized-Solonetz. The low places are sometimes called scabby spots. Western North Dakota.

Examples include (1) the relief of Ground-Water Podzols with characteristic cradle knolls, (2) truncated solodized-Solonetz with low bare spots, (3) puff Solonchak with mounds, (4) the small mounds, *coppice mounds,* of soil material stabilized around

[1] Some useful general texts are the following:
COTTON, C. A. CLIMATIC ACCIDENTS IN LANDSCAPE-MAKING. 354 pp., illus. Christchurch, New Zealand. 1942.
——— LANDSCAPE AS DEVELOPED BY THE PROCESSES OF NORMAL EROSION. Ed. 2, 509 pp. New York. 1948.
FENNEMAN, N. M. PHYSIOGRAPHY OF WESTERN UNITED STATES. 534 pp., illus. New York. 1931.
——— PHYSIOGRAPHY OF EASTERN UNITED STATES. 714 pp., illus. New York. 1938.
LOBECK, A. K. GEOMORPHOLOGY. 731 pp., illus. New York. 1939.
VON ENGELN, O. D. GEOMORPHOLOGY. 655 pp., illus. New York. 1942.

desert shrubs, and (5) the *gilgai*[2] microrelief of clays that have high coefficients of expansion and contraction with changes in moisture. Such microrelief consists of either a succession of enclosed micro-basins and micro-knolls in nearly level areas or of micro-valleys and micro-ridges that run with the slope.

Topography had a general connotation similar to relief, but has come to be used for the features disclosed on a contour map— even by some people for all the natural and cultural features considered collectively that are ordinarily shown on a topographic map. In soil descriptions the more specific terms—relief, physiography, land form, or soil slope—should be used rather than topography.

Soil slope refers to the incline of the surface of the soil area. It is an integral part of any soil as a natural body, not something apart from it. A simple, or single, slope is defined by its gradient, shape, and length. Depending upon the detail of mapping and the character of the soil areas, slopes may be defined as single or complex, or as patterns of slope classes.

RELIEF AND GENETIC PROFILES

Relief influences soil formation primarily through its effects upon drainage, runoff, and erosion,[3] and secondarily through variations in exposure to the sun and wind and in air drainage.

Theoretically, at least, the water falling on a perfectly level surface of permeable soil material is admitted until the material is saturated, or sealed, and then collects on the surface as a sheet. Uniformly flat and permeable soils are rare indeed. Rain water collects in depressions however slight, and penetrates some soils more rapidly than others. Because of runoff, strongly sloping soils receive less water than the average, and soils in depressions more.

The amount of water entering and passing through the soil depends upon the permeability of both solum and substrata, the relief, and the climate. In regions of nearly continuous rainfall, even strongly sloping soils may be very poorly drained. Nearly level soils on exceedingly pervious materials are excessively drained, even in humid climates, unless the water table is high. Thus, the specific relationships existing between relief or soil slope and soil genesis in one combination of climate and soil material cannot be applied to another significant combination.

In relation to soil genesis, four broad relief positions may be recognized. The definitions of these positions in terms of single or complex slopes vary among climatic regions and even on different geological materials within one region. Considering all

---

[2] The name *gilgai* is adopted from Australia, where this phenomenon is extensive and developed in extreme degrees, with microrelief up to 2 feet. Other common names with similar or overlapping connotations are hog-wallowed, crab-holey, hush-a-bye, buffalo-wallowed, Bay of Biscay, self-swallowing, self-plowing, self-mulching, tiger-striped, leopard-spotted, puffed, corrugated, and pits-and-mounds.

[3] In this discussion the reference is to water erosion, not soil blowing.

possible combinations of climate and parent material in the world, soils in each of these four relief positions have a rather wide range of slope. Within each, and between them, intermediate positions need to be recognized in detailed classification. The four broad relief positions are described in the numbered paragraphs following.

1. Normal relief.—In this position are sloping uplands with medium runoff. Under the native vegetation, normal erosion removes materials as the solum deepens, thus bringing relatively new minerals into the soil from beneath.[4] This is the relief position of the normal soil, including modal representatives of the zonal great soil groups. The actual soil slope, in quantitative terms, varies with different combinations of climate and parent material.

2. Subnormal relief.—In this position are the nearly flat to sloping uplands with slow to very slow runoff. Erosion under the native vegetation is so slow that in humid regions the leached materials accumulate on the surface. The solum is relatively fixed and does not gradually move down as in many soils in the normal position. Given the necessary time, claypans and hardpans generally form from materials of mixed chemical and mechanical composition. Soils in this position often have fluctuating water tables, or perched water tables, near the surface part of the time. Planosols and Ground-Water Laterite soils are typically found in this position. Soils characteristic of this relief position may be found on fairly strong slopes in very humid regions and on seepy slopes.

3. Excessive relief.—This is the relief position for hills and hilly uplands that have rapid to very rapid runoff and more erosion than areas in the associated normal position. Soil development is stunted because of rapid erosion, reduced percolation of the water through the soil, and lack of water in the soil for the vigorous growth of the plants responsible for soil formation. Lithosols and the lithosolic associates of other soils are characteristic of this relief position. Other things being equal, the minimum slope is relatively low on very slowly permeable materials in dry regions and relatively great on permeable materials in humid regions.

4. Flat or concave relief.—In this relief position are nearly flat or depressed lowlands with either very slow runoff or none at all, excess water all or part of the time, and no natural erosion. Such lands retain all or nearly all of the water that falls as rain and often receive a considerable additional amount from adjacent uplands. The hydromorphic and halomorphic intrazonal soils are

---

[4] The amount and character of natural erosion varies widely among the great soil groups. On Red Latosols, for example, it is relatively great, and on Chernozem relatively small or even insignificant. On some soils, like grassy Tundra, for example, natural erosion takes the form of a succession of slips rather than sheet wash. (See the first part of the section on Accelerated Soil Erosion.)

typically in this position. Soils characteristic of this position may be found on strong slopes in very humid regions of nearly continuous rainfall.

Within any soil zone one may find a group of strongly contrasting soil series that extend across all of the four relief positions described, yet are developed from similar parent material. Such a group of soil series is called a catena.[5]

Attempts have been made to develop uniformly defined stages or kinds of profiles, often indicated by numbers, according to evidences of natural drainage and land form or relief. Such schemes are appealing as guides to classification and for remembering characteristics, but they are not recommended. They are apt to be misused. Profile features result from such a wide variety of genetic factors that parallel analogs do not necessarily exist in different soil regions, or even on different parent materials within the same soil region. One catena can be adequately represented by four or five profiles, while another may need ten. If a uniform scheme has enough stages to accommodate the second catena, it may lead the field scientist to look for and to establish too many stages in the first catena, or to make the distinctions in the wrong places. Each catena needs to be defined by itself.

SOIL SLOPE CHARACTERISTICS

In defining soil classificational units, especially in detailed soil surveys, soil slope is given special attention. Within the permissible slope ranges of many soil types, phases need to be defined in terms of slope gradient that indicate differences significant to use and management. As with other important soil characteristics, the relative significance of differences in slope depends upon the other characteristics of the soil. Broad classes of soil slope, defined in terms of percentage alone without reference to other soil characteristics, have no consistent relationship to the capabilities of the soil for use. Thus, the definitions of slope classes must be adjusted among soil types, so that boundaries between soil areas are placed where the significant changes occur in soil slope for the particular kind of soil and so that insignificant boundaries are not added to the soil map.

Up to the present time, slope gradient—this one characteristic of soil slope—has perhaps been given undue emphasis over the other slope characteristics—shape, length, and pattern. The nomenclature for classes of soil slope does provide for recognizing units consisting (1) primarily of single slopes and (2) primarily of slope complexes. In actual practice, consideration is given to the relief of the terrain as a whole as well as to that of an individual soil area within it. That is, in a rolling terrain, the slope of a particular soil area is designated in the complex group

---

[5] In East Africa, catena is used in a somewhat broader sense for groups of soils over a range in relief, but from similar or unlike parent materials. See MILNE, G., in collaboration with BECKLEY, V. A., JONES, G. H. GETHIN, MARTIN, W. S., GRIFFITH, G., and RAYMOND, L. W. A PROVISIONAL SOIL MAP OF EAST AFRICA (KENYA, UGANDA, TANGANYIKA, AND ZANZIBAR) WITH EXPLANATORY MEMOIR. 34 pp., illus. London. 1936.

even though it is single if considered only by itself. In contrast, soil slopes on fans and mountain foot slopes are regarded as single.

Ranges in soil slope are described for each mapping unit. The significant features of soil slope cannot be worked into the nomenclature except as they are included in the description of the classificational units, especially those of series and types. Even though phases within different soil types or series are given the same adjective in their name, as for example "slope" or "sloping," this does not and cannot mean that there are no other important differences in slope characteristics between the two units or even that the two are entirely similar in the gradient of slope. Often slope characteristics even more important than gradient, such as shape, length, direction, and pattern of slopes, are implied by the soil series name rather than by the adjective used in the phase name that refers to soil slope alone. Thus, the slope classes must be looked upon simply as convenient units of slope gradient, arbitrarily limited in terms of percentage, and somewhat analogous, for example, to the classes defined in terms of pH, which are used for expressing the acidity of soil horizons as "medium acid," "strongly acid," and the like.

In studying and describing the soil, important practical aspects of soil slope, besides its relation to soil genesis, need to be given consideration under the probable conditions of use and management: these are (1) the rate and amount of runoff, (2) the erodibility of the soil, and (3) use of agricultural machinery. None of these varies as a linear function of slope gradient alone, except where other characteristics of the slope and other soil characteristics are similar. It is well known that some soils, if cultivated, are not subject to erosion at 1 percent slope but may be at 2 percent; whereas others, such as some of the highly pervious Latosols of the humid tropics, are not subject to significant accelerated erosion even with soil slopes of 40 percent or more. The use of machinery and the rapidity and amount of runoff also depend upon many other soil characteristics besides slope gradient. Thus, in arriving at the definition for any soil unit, or of a phase, in terms of percentage of slope gradient, all important soil characteristics in relation to all significant aspects of soil use must be evaluated.

Classes by soil slope gradient.—Soil slope is normally measured by the hand level (fig. 26) and expressed in terms of percentage—the difference in elevation in feet for each 100 feet horizontal. Thus, a soil slope of 45° is one of 100 percent since the difference in elevation of two points 100 feet apart horizontally is 100 feet.

Slope classes have been established with alternative minimum and maximum limits in terms of gradient, so that all soil slopes within a given class, as named, will fall within broad limits and yet allow enough flexibility to make narrow definitions and subdivisions as needed for specific application to different soil types.

The slope classes provide for the recognition of either single or complex slopes as appropriate. The distinction is not mandatory. Generally, the terms for single slopes are used except in

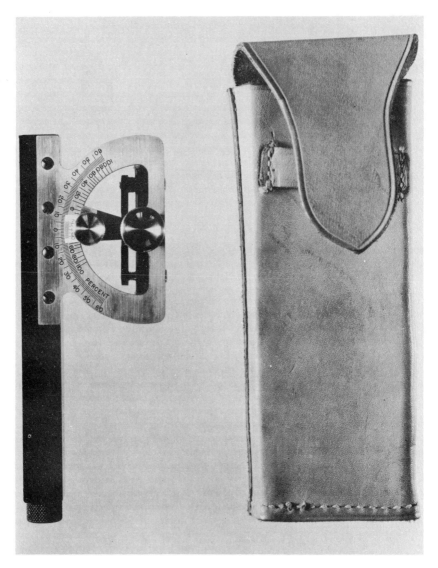

FIGURE 26.—Abney hand level with case.

areas where long established usage of terms for complex slopes make their use much more meaningful or where soil relief is very complex, as in areas of dunes and karst sinkholes. The soil slope classes are not always directly translatable into mapping units.

Slope classes are designated in the numbered paragraphs following.

1. *A class.*—In this class are level or nearly level soil areas on which runoff is slow or very slow. The soil slope alone offers no

difficulty in the use of agricultural machinery; nor is there likelihood of significant water erosion except possibly on very long slopes of highly erodible soils.

Limits	*Names*
Lower—0 percent. Upper—1 to 3 percent.	Single slopes—level; or level and nearly level.[1] Complex slopes—level; or level and nearly level.

[1] Where subdivisions are necessary in extremely detailed classification.

2. *B class.*—This class consists of gently undulating, undulating, or gently sloping soil areas on which runoff is slow or medium for most soils. All types of ordinary agricultural machinery may be used without difficulty, insofar as slope is concerned. Soils with B slopes vary widely in erodibility, depending upon the other soil characteristics. On some, erosion offers no serious problem; on many, relatively simple precautions are all that is needed; while for use under cultivation some very erodible soils need protection by terraces, or by other means, depending on the other features of the soil and the set of soil management practices.

Limits	*Names*
Lower—1 to 3 percent. Upper—5 to 8 percent.	Single slopes—gently sloping; or very gently sloping and gently sloping. Complex slopes—undulating; or gently undulating and undulating.

3. *C class.*—In this class are gently rolling, rolling, or moderately and strongly sloping soil areas on which runoff is medium to rapid for most soils. Insofar as slope is concerned, all types of farm machinery can be used successfully although some difficulty may be had in using the large and heavy types. Soils with C slope vary widely in erodibility under cultivation, depending upon the other soil characteristics and the management practices. On a few, erosion offers no serious problem, or else can be controlled by relatively simple practices; while others need careful management in which close-growing crops are used most of the time, with supplemental strip cropping or terracing where the soils are otherwise suitable.

Limits	*Names*
Lower— 5 to 8 percent. Upper—10 to 16 percent.	Single slopes—sloping; or sloping and strongly sloping. Complex slopes—rolling; or gently rolling and rolling.

4. *D class.*—This class is made up of very strongly sloping or hilly soil areas on which runoff is rapid or very rapid on most soils. Unless the slopes are very complex, most farm machinery can be used, but with difficulty, especially for the heavier types. Soils with D slopes are likely to erode under clean cultivation, except for the most pervious ones, like well-developed Latosols, for example. There are many exceptions, but the separation between those soils suited to ordinary rotations that include intertilled crops and those soils suited only to pasture or to rotations dominated by sod-forming crops commonly comes at the dividing point between C and D classes of soil slope.

Limits	*Names*
Lower—10 to 16 percent.	Single slope—moderately steep.
Upper—20 to 30 percent.	Complex slope—hilly.

5. *E class.*—In this class are steeply sloping or very hilly soil areas on which runoff is very rapid on most soils. Only the lightest types of agricultural machinery can be used. The arability of soils with E class slope varies widely. If the soils are highly fertile and permeable, they may support good grass, orchards, or even intertilled crops with a proper set of management practices. With many hilly soils, the distinction between areas useful for pasture and those suited only to forests coincides with the dividing point between the D and E classes of soil slope.

Limits	*Names*
Lower—20 to 30 percent.	Single slope—steep.
Upper—45 to 65 percent.	Complex slope—steep.

6. *F class.*—This class is used where the soils are unusually fertile and permeable and distinctions in soil slope above the E class therefore may be needed. Ordinarily, soils with such slopes are lithosolic and are included in the appropriate miscellaneous land type.

Limits	*Names*
Lower—45 to 65 percent.	Very steep.
Upper—None.	

The use of slope classes as a basis for phase distinction is discussed in a later section of this *Manual.* If properly defined, where variations in slope are significant, each slope class within a soil type can be given a specific set of yield estimates, productivity ratings, and management recommendations.

In the definition of detailed soil classificational and mapping units, the names for single slopes are more commonly appropriate than the names for complex slopes, although both need to be used, depending upon the features of soil slope besides gradient.[6] For soil associations, the names of the complex slopes are most commonly meaningful.

Other characteristics of soil slope.—In the description of soils in the field and in the definition of classificational units, the length and shape of slopes need to be described. Other things being equal, soils at the lower parts of long slopes are more likely to be gullied because of the concentration and velocity of the water. Concentration of water and other factors being equal, cutting is more likely on the convex slopes and filling on the concave slopes. For detailed description and definition of slopes and land form, the names and definitions employed by the geomorphologists are

---

[6] Except in highly detailed special soil surveys, however, it is not appropriate to have within one soil type two soil slope phases having the same slope class and differentiated on the basis of single versus complex slopes alone. For very highly detailed surveys in areas to be irrigated, the following distinctions according to shape of slope have been recognized: (1) Single slopes, (2) undulating, with short gentle slopes in all directions, (3) convex slopes, (4) concave slopes, and (5) concave-convex slopes on an incline, or inclined corrugations.

used. Regular patterns of slope are characteristic of most soil series, and especially of soil associations.

With accurate mapping and classification of intermittent drainage, a skilled reader of soil maps can visualize length and direction of soil slope from a detailed soil map.

ELEVATION

It is often necessary to observe the elevation where soils are studied, either from a topographic map or with a barometer, in order to correlate soil descriptions with each other and with the other observations of geology, land form, and climate.

EXPOSURE

In describing soils in the field, notes need to be taken of significant differences in exposure to wind and especially to sun that may have an important bearing on soil climate and vegetation at the particular spot. Near the critical limits of temperature, length of day, and moisture, quite different soils may be found on the north and south slopes of similar geological materials. Then too, near the critical boundaries between shrubs and trees or between grass and trees, strong winds favor the low vegetation. The skilled map reader can interpret exposure from a detailed soil map with well-defined units and a complete pattern of classified intermittent streams.

The climatic pattern of many mountainous regions is so variable within short distances that unless soil observations are carefully located in relation to elevation and exposure, they cannot be correlated with general climatic conditions.

SOIL DRAINAGE

Soil drainage, in a dynamic or active sense, refers to the rapidity and extent of the removal of water from the soil, in relation to additions, especially by surface runoff and by flow through the soil to underground spaces. Yet evaporation and transpiration contribute to water loss. Thus a nearly level Sierozem soil, having neither runoff nor percolation to the deep substratum, is well-drained because the water from all rains can distribute itself within the solum and move out by evaporation and transpiration without appreciable reduction in aeration of the soil material.

Soil drainage, as a condition of the soil, refers to the frequency and duration of periods when the soil is free of saturation or partial saturation. Such conditions can be accurately measured, although the field scientist shall need to estimate them by inference.

Accurate appraisals of the drainage conditions of soils are necessary in both soil descriptions and definitions. The problem is far more complicated than it may first appear to be. One may observe certain direct evidences of drainage or a lack of it, such as saturated soil at various times after rains or after additions of irrigation water, water-table levels, pools of surface water, and the like. Variations in soil drainage can be related by inference to differences in soil color and patterns of soil color. Mottling, the gray colors that accompany gleying, and the organic-rich material characteristic of many poorly drained soils are all good evidences, but not infallible ones. Other influences may cause similar evidences. Then too, soil slope and the texture, structure, and other characteristics of the horizons of the soil profile are useful as a basis for predicting permeability of the soil and drainage conditions. Here again, however, the scientist must consider climate, water-table levels, and other factors along with these evidences. Thus, the assessment of drainage is partly a matter of direct observation and partly a matter of inference from a large group of observations.

The concept of soil drainage is a broad one. Certain narrower aspects need to be defined first: (1) Runoff, (2) internal soil drainage, and (3) soil permeability. These last two are overlapping, but not identical qualities. That is, a slowly permeable soil may have medium internal drainage under the natural rainfall and slow internal drainage under irrigation. A soil of similar permeability may be regarded as having very slow internal drainage in a wet climate. The first quality, runoff, or external drainage, is closely related to soil slope; yet a rapidly permeable, nearly level soil may have slow runoff, as contrasted to rapid runoff on a slowly permeable soil of similar slope. A slowly permeable soil and rapidly permeable soil may both have very slow internal drainage because of a high water table. If this is lowered by tiling and ditching, the one may have slow internal drainage and the other rapid internal drainage after reclamation. It is important to be able to predict the *potential* internal drainage of poorly drained soils prior to reclamation.

Ordinarily, in soil descriptions, indication of the general soil drainage class, or that and permeability class, is sufficient. In detailed studies, however, and especially in predicting soil drainage under significantly changed conditions to be brought about through reclamation works for irrigation, drainage, and water control by dikes, separate indication of the classes of runoff and of internal drainage should be given also. An indication of the permeability of naturally poorly drained soils is essential to predictions of their suitability for use after artificial drainage.

RUNOFF

Runoff,[7] sometimes called surface runoff or external soil drainage, refers to the relative rate water is removed by flow over the surface of the soil. This includes water falling as rain as well as water flowing onto the soil from other soils. Where needed for clear descriptions, six classes are recognized on the basis of the relative flow of water from the soil surface as determined by the characteristics of the soil profile, soil slope, climate, and cover.

---

[7] Sometimes the term "runoff" is applied to whole watersheds to refer to all the water entering stream flow, including that from springs. If any possibility of confusion exists, the term "surface runoff" should be used instead of "runoff" in soil descriptions and interpretations.

0. *Ponded.*—None of the water added to the soil as precipitation or by flow from surrounding higher land escapes as runoff. The total amount of water that must be removed from ponded areas by movement through the soil or by evaporation is usually greater than the total rainfall. Ponding normally occurs in depressed areas and may fluctuate seasonally.

1. *Very slow.*—Surface water flows away so very slowly that free water lies on the surface for long periods or enters immediately into the soil. Much of the water either passes through the soil or evaporates into the air. Soils with very slow surface runoff are commonly level to nearly level or very open and porous.

2. *Slow.*—Surface water flows away so slowly that free water covers the soil for significant periods or enters the soil rapidly and a large part of the water passes through the profile or evaporates into the air. Soils with a slow rate of surface runoff are either nearly level or very gently sloping, or absorb precipitation very rapidly. Normally there is little or no erosion hazard.

3. *Medium.*—Surface water flows away at such a rate that a moderate proportion of the water enters the soil profile and free water lies on the surface for only short periods. A large part of the precipitation is absorbed by the soil and used for plant growth, is lost by evaporation, or moves downward into underground channels. With medium runoff, the loss of water over the surface does not reduce seriously the supply available for plant growth. The erosion hazard may be slight to moderate if soils of this class are cultivated.

4. *Rapid.*—A large proportion of the precipitation moves rapidly over the surface of the soil and a small part moves through the soil profile. Surface water runs off nearly as fast as it is added. Soils with rapid runoff are usually moderately steep to steep and have low infiltration capacities. The erosion hazard is commonly moderate to high.

5. *Very rapid.*—A very large part of the water moves rapidly over the surface of the soil and a very small part goes through the profile. Surface water runs off as fast as it is added. Soils with very rapid rates of runoff are usually steep or very steep and have low infiltration capacities. The erosion hazard is commonly high or very high.

SOIL PERMEABILITY[3]

Soil permeability is that quality of the soil that enables it to transmit water or air. It can be measured quantitatively in terms of rate of flow of water through a unit cross section of saturated soil in unit time, under specified temperature and hydraulic conditions. Percolation under gravity with a $\frac{1}{2}$-inch head and drainage through cores can be measured by a standard procedure involving presaturation of samples. Rates of percolation are expressed in inches per hour.

---

[3] R. D. Hockensmith, Soil Conservation Service, made valuable suggestions concerning soil permeability.

In the absence of precise measurements, soils may be placed into relative permeability classes through studies of structure, texture, porosity, cracking, and other characteristics of the horizons in the soil profile in relation to local use experience. The observer must learn to evaluate the changes in cracking and in aggregate stability with moistening. If predictions are to be made of the responsiveness of soils to drainage or irrigation, it may be necessary to determine the permeability of each horizon and the relationship of the soil horizons to one another and to the soil profile as a whole. Commonly, however, the percolation rate of a soil is set by that of the least permeable horizon in the solum or in the immediate substratum.

The infiltration rate, or entrance of water into surface horizons, or even into the whole solum, may be rapid; yet permeability may be slow because of a slowly permeable layer directly beneath the solum that influences water movement within the solum itself. The rate of infiltration and the permeability of the plow layer may fluctuate widely from time to time because of differences in soil management practices, kinds of crops, and similar factors.

Sets of relative classes of soil permeability are as follows:

		Possible rates in inches per hour[1]
Slow:		
	1. *Very slow*	less than 0.05
	2. *Slow*	0.05 to 0.20
Moderate:		
	3. *Moderately slow*	0.20 to 0.80
	4. *Moderate*	0.80 to 2.50
	5. *Moderately rapid*	2.50 to 5.00
Rapid:		
	6. *Rapid*	5.00 to 10.00
	7. *Very rapid*	over 10.00

[1] Very tentatively suggested rates through saturated undisturbed cores under a ½-inch head of water.

INTERNAL SOIL DRAINAGE

Internal soil drainage is that quality of a soil that permits the downward flow of excess water through it. Internal drainage is reflected in the frequency and duration of periods of saturation with water. It is determined by the texture, structure, and other characteristics of the soil profile and of underlying layers and by the height of the water table, either permanent or perched, in relation to the water added to the soil. Thus, a soil of medium internal drainage may be similar in permeability to one of slow internal drainage that has a more moist climate.

As needed, six relative classes of internal drainage are recognized and defined in the following paragraphs.

0. *None.*—No free water passes through the soil mass. In humid regions, the water table is at or near the surface most of the year. Even sandy or gravelly soils may have this natural drainage condition, but when they are drained—when the water table is lowered—they may become moderately or even rapidly drained internally.

1. *Very slow.*—The rate of internal drainage is much too slow for the optimum growth of the important crops in humid regions, and may even be too slow for the optimum growth of crops on soils of the semiarid regions. Soils may be saturated with water in the root zone for a month or two. Most soils of very slow internal drainage are blotched or mottled in nearly all parts of the profile, although some have dominantly gray surface soils and upper subsoils, and others have dark-colored surface soils that are high in organic matter. A high water table, or a very slowly permeable horizon, or both, may be responsible for very slow internal soil drainage.

2. *Slow.*—In slow internal drainage, the rate of movement of water through the soil is not so fast as in medium drainage but faster than in very slow drainage. Saturation with water occurs for periods of a week or two—long enough to affect adversely the roots of many crop plants. The rate of drainage is usually somewhat too slow for the optimum growth of the important crops[9] of the region. This is especially true in the humid temperate region, where most soils having slow internal drainage have black or gray A horizons. Mottling or blotching occurs in the lower A or upper B horizons as well as in the lower B and C horizons. Many soils with slow internal drainage have relatively high permanent water tables, or a fluctuating water table.

3. *Medium.*—Internal drainage is not so free as in rapid drainage but is freer than in slow drainage. Saturation with water is limited to a few days—less time than is required for it to injure the roots of crop plants. Internal drainage is about optimum for the growth of the important crops under humid conditions. Most soils of medium internal drainage are free of mottling and blotching throughout the A horizon and all or most of the B horizon.

4. *Rapid.*—The horizons somewhat restrict the movement of water through the soil as compared to very rapid drainage. Saturation with water is restricted to a few hours. Internal drainage is somewhat too rapid for the optimum growth of the important crops of the region.

5. *Very rapid.*—The rate of movement of water through the profile is very rapid, usually because of its high porosity, and the soil is never water-saturated. Internal drainage is too rapid for the optimum growth of most of the important crops adapted to the region. Most soils with very rapid internal drainage are free to a depth of several feet of those characteristic blotches or mottlings that suggest impeded drainage. The permanent water table is usually several feet beneath the surface.

SOIL-DRAINAGE CLASSES

On the basis of the observations and inferences used to obtain classes of runoff, soil permeability, and internal soil drainage,

---

[9] The reference to "important crops" is a general one, with exceptions for water-loving sorts like paddy rice.

general relative soil-drainage classes are described below. The soil-drainage class needs to be given in each soil description. Except in very young soils, the natural drainage conditions are usually reflected in soil morphology. Since their formation some soils have had their drainage markedly altered, either naturally or by irrigation or drainage structures. Seven classes of soil drainage are used in soil descriptions and definitions to describe the natural drainage under which the soil occurs.

In the numbered paragraphs following, each of the seven soil-drainage classes is defined first in broad general terms and then in terms of the morphological relationships existing among podzolic soils and among the dark-colored soils of the grasslands. Some relationships to the production of crops, especially of corn and small grains, are suggested. Examples of soil series that fall in each class are added in parentheses.

0. Very poorly drained.—Water is removed from the soil so slowly that the water table remains at or on the surface the greater part of the time. Soils of this drainage class usually occupy level or depressed sites and are frequently ponded. Very poorly drained soils in the podzolic soil regions commonly have dark-gray or black surface layers and are light gray, with or without mottlings, in the deeper parts of the profile. In the grassland regions, very poorly drained soils commonly have mucky surfaces with distinct evidences of gleying. These soils are wet enough to prevent the growth of important crops (except rice) without artificial drainage. (Portsmouth, Toledo, Brookston, Westland, Abington, Pamlico muck, and Everglades peat)

1. Poorly drained.—Water is removed so slowly that the soil remains wet for a large part of the time. The water table is commonly at or near the surface during a considerable part of the year. Poorly drained conditions are due to a high water table, to a slowly permeable layer within the profile, to seepage, or to some combination of these conditions. In the podzolic soil region, poorly drained soils may be light gray from the surface downward, with or without mottlings. Among the dark-colored soils of the grasslands, poorly drained soils commonly have slightly thickened dark-colored surface layers. The large quantities of water that remain in and on the poorly drained soils prohibit the growing of field crops under natural conditions in most years. Artificial drainage is generally necessary for crop production, provided other soil characteristics are favorable. (Henry, Waverly, Myatt, Melvin, Webster, Loy, Clermont, Bethel, Delmar, and Wehadkee)

2. Imperfectly or somewhat poorly drained.—Water is removed from the soil slowly enough to keep it wet for significant periods but not all of the time. Imperfectly drained soils commonly have a slowly permeable layer within the profile, a high water table, additions through seepage, or a combination of these conditions. Among the podzolic soils, somewhat poorly drained soils are uniformly grayish, brownish, or yellowish in the upper A horizon and commonly have mottlings below 6 to 16 inches in the lower A and in the B and C horizons. Among the dark-colored soils of the grasslands, somewhat poorly drained soils have thick, dark A horizons, high in organic matter, and faint evidences of gleying immediately beneath the A horizon. The growth of crops is restricted to a marked degree, unless artificial drainage is provided. This is the lowest drainage class in which a zonal soil retains enough of its characteristics to be classed in that order. Many soils with this drainage class cannot be placed in the zonal order. (Taft, Calloway, Pheba, Fincastle, Lawrence, Crosby, Vigo, and Odell)

3. **Moderately well drained.**—Water is removed from the soil somewhat slowly, so that the profile is wet for a small but significant part of the time. Moderately well drained soils commonly have a slowly permeable layer within or immediately beneath the solum, a relatively high water table, additions of water through seepage, or some combination of these conditions. Among podzolic soils, moderately well drained soils have uniform colors in the A and upper B horizons, with mottling in the lower B and in the C horizons. Among the dark-colored soils of the grasslands, profiles have thick, dark A horizons and yellowish or grayish faintly mottled B horizons. (Grenada, Tilsit, Richland, Muscatine, Gibson, Bronson, Bedford, and Ellsworth)

4. **Well-drained.**[10]—Water is removed from the soil readily but not rapidly. Well-drained soils are commonly intermediate in texture, although soils of other textural classes may also be well drained. Among the podzolic soils, well-drained soils are free of mottlings (except for fossil gley), and horizons may be brownish, yellowish, grayish, or reddish. They may be mottled deep in the C horizon or below depths of several feet. Among the dark-colored soils of the grasslands, well-drained soils have thick, dark A horizons, reddish, brownish, or yellowish B horizons, and C horizons that may or may not be mottled. Well-drained soils commonly retain optimum amounts of moisture for plant growth after rains or additions of irrigation water. This is the characteristic drainage of modal representatives of the zonal great soil groups. (Baxter, Ruston, Vicksburg, Cecil, Memphis, Tama, Fayette, Barnes, Williams, Miami, Russell, Cincinnati, and Holdrege)

5. **Somewhat excessively drained.**—Water is removed from the soil rapidly. Some of the soils are lithosolic. Many of them have little horizon differentiation and are sandy and very porous. Among podzolic soils, somewhat excessively drained types are free of mottling throughout the profile and are brown, yellow, gray, or red. Among the dark-colored soils of the grasslands, many profiles have relatively thin A horizons, brownish, yellowish, grayish, or reddish thin B horizons, and no mottlings within the solum. Only a narrow range of crops can be grown on these soils,

---

[10] A well-drained soil has "good" drainage.

and the yields are usually low without irrigation. (Bruno, Dickinson, Flasher, and Oshtemo)

6. **Excessively drained.**—Water is removed from the soil very rapidly. Excessively drained soils are commonly Lithosols or lithosolic, and may be steep, very porous, or both. Shallow soils on slopes may be excessively drained. Among podzolic soils, excessively drained types are commonly brownish, yellowish, grayish, or reddish in color and free of mottlings throughout the profile. Among the dark-colored soils of the grasslands, profiles commonly have thin A horizons (except for sand types that may have thick ones). Enough precipitation is commonly lost from these soils to make them unsuitable for ordinary crop production. (Guin, Muskingum, Hamburg, Plainfield, Coloma, and Chelsea)

ALTERED DRAINAGE

Notes on altered drainage are needed to indicate changed drainage conditions where there has been no corresponding change in soil morphology. Such changes are commonly due to reclamation, as in artificial drainage or irrigation, but they may also be due to a natural deepening of the stream channels or to the filling of depressions. Altered drainage conditions need to be described, as they affect potentialities for crop production. Usually the same relative terms can be used for altered drainage as those used for natural drainage.

Descriptions and definitions of altered drainage conditions may serve as the basis for the establishment of drained or waterlogged phases of soil types or series.

INCIDENCE OF FLOODING

The descriptions and definitions of soils subject to flooding need to include statements describing the frequency and regularity of flooding in as much relevant detail as the available evidence permits. The following general classes are suggested:

1. Floods frequent and irregular, so that any use of the soil for crops is too uncertain to be practicable.

2. Floods frequent but occurring regularly during certain months of the year, so that the soil may be used for crops at other times.

3. Floods may be expected, either during certain months or during any period of unusual meteorological conditions, often enough to destroy crops or prevent use in a specified percentage of the years.

4. Floods rare, but probable during a very small percentage of the years.

Issued May 1962

U.S. DEPARTMENT OF AGRICULTURE

Soil Conservation Service

Supplement to Agriculture Handbook No. 18

SOIL SURVEY MANUAL

(Replacing pages 173–188)

IDENTIFICATION AND NOMENCLATURE
OF SOIL HORIZONS

The description of a soil profile consists mainly of descriptions of its several horizons. A *soil horizon* may be defined as a layer of soil, approximately parallel to the soil surface, with characteristics produced by soil-forming processes. One soil horizon is commonly differentiated from an adjacent one at least partly on the basis of characteristics that can be seen in the field. Yet laboratory data are sometimes required for the identification and designation of horizons as well as for their more detailed characterization. The *soil profile*, as exposed in a cut or section, includes the collection of all the genetic horizons, the natural organic layers on the surface, and the parent material or other layers beneath the solum that influence the genesis and behavior of the soil.

Besides genetic soil horizons, many soils have layers inherited from stratified parent material. In making soil examinations, all distinguishable layers, or horizons, are separately described, regardless of genesis. These descriptions need to be completely objective and clearly able "to stand on their own," regardless of presumed genesis or nomenclature. Objective descriptions are the basic stuff of soil classification. Nothing can substitute for them. The more laboratory data there are available on collected samples, the more important the descriptions become; without them, the laboratory data cannot be safely interpreted, if indeed, they are relevant at all.

The profiles of numerous soils having properties quite unlike those of the original material have some characteristics due partly to inheritance from stratified parent material as well as to soil-forming processes, as in an alluvial terrace; or even partly to geological processes accompanying soil formation. That is, a soil with a well-developed profile may be gradually covered with volcanic ash, loess, windblown sand, or alluvium, for example, without seriously injuring the vegetation. The surface horizon becomes thickened and the lower part of the soil profile gradually passes beyond reach of active soil-forming processes.

Soil profiles vary in an almost endless number of ways. The important characteristics to be described have already been listed,

173

and separate sections of this *Manual* explain the classes and terms for describing each one. Soil profiles vary widely in thickness, from mere films to those many feet thick. Generally in temperate regions, soil profiles need to be examined to depths of 3 to 5 feet. Normal soils are thinner toward the poles and thicker toward the Equator. Yet even in temperate regions, deeper layers, say to 6 feet or more, may be so important to soil drainage that they need to be examined, especially in the study and mapping of soils to predict their response to reclamation through irrigation or drainage.

Soil profiles vary widely in the degree to which genetic horizons are expressed. On nearly fresh geological formations, like new alluvial fans, sand drifts, or blankets of volcanic ash, no genetic horizons may be distinguished at all. As soil formation proceeds, they may be detected in their early stages only by laboratory study of the samples, and then later with gradually increasing clarity in the field.

In describing a soil profile, one usually locates the boundaries between horizons, measures their depth, and studies the profile as a whole before describing and naming the individual horizons.

DESIGNATIONS FOR HORIZONS AND LAYERS

It is not absolutely necessary to name the various soil horizons in order to make a good description of a soil profile. Yet the usefulness of profile descriptions is greatly increased by the proper use of genetic designations, like A, B, and C. Such interpretations show the genetic relationships among the horizons within a profile, whereas simple numbers like 1, 2, 3, 4, and 5, or undefined letters like a, b, c, and so on, tell us nothing but depth sequence. The genetic designations make possible useful comparisons among soils. One cannot usefully compare arbitrarily defined "12- to 24-inch" layers of different soils, but B horizons can be usefully compared.

It is assumed that each horizon or layer designation used is merely a symbol indicating the considered judgment of the person describing the soil relative to kind of departure from the original material from which it has formed, including the zero degree of departure in the case of R and some C layers. This implies that each symbol indicates merely an estimate, not a proven fact. It implies that when reading a symbol one must reconstruct mentally the character of the parent material, for this was done when the designation was assigned. It implies that the processes that have caused change need not be known. It also implies that specific morphology need not be consistent from profile to profile and that morphology relative to an estimated parent material is the criterion for judgment. The parent material of the horizon in question, not the material in the horizon or layer designated by the symbol C, is used as the basis of comparison. Morphology is interpreted relative to this assumed parent material, not in terms of absolute values of properties.

CONVENTIONS GOVERNING USE OF SYMBOLS

1. Capital letter symbols include O, A, B, C, and R. They indicate dominant kinds of departures from the parent material. More than one kind of departure may be indicated by a single capital letter,

providing these departures are within the limits of the definitions given further along in this chapter.

2. In a description of a given profile, if a horizon designated by O, A, or B is subdivided, the subdivisions are indicated by placing an arabic number after the capital letter. Thus, symbols such as O1, O2, A1, A2, A3, B1, B2, and B3 are obtained. Each symbol derived in this way stands for an integral unit, and each unit requires its own definition. A given arabic numeral therefore has different implication when combined with different capital letters. Thus, the symbols O1, O2, A1, and A2 indicate specific kinds of O and A master horizons. The symbols A3, B1, and B3 are transitional horizons. Likewise, the symbol B2 indicates that part of the B horizon that is of a nature not transitional either to A or to C. Even if both B1 and B3 are absent, if the B horizon of a given profile is subdivided, the symbol B2, not B, is used. The symbols O, A, and B each indicate a unit that, according to need, can have several subdivisions or none. The symbol C, however, indicates a unit that is not subdivided in the manner of O, A, and B. If a horizon is subdivided, this is done only in the manner described in the following paragraph 3, and the arabic numeral assigned has no consistent meaning except vertical sequence.

3. Vertical subdivision within an otherwise undifferentiated horizon is indicated by primary or secondary arabic numbers assigned, in order, from the topmost subdivision downward. These are not used with O, A, or B without a primary arabic number. Thus, secondary numbers are used with O1, O2, A1, A2, A3, B1, B2, B3, and C. Primary arabic numbers are used with C and Ap. Thus, we use C1 and C2, Ap1 and Ap2, but A11 and A12, B21, B22 or B23, as needed, without consistence in meaning beyond the fact that we have made a subdivision. The reason for the subdivision may be indicated in the text of the description or by a lower case letter suffix.

4. Lower case letters are used as suffixes to indicate selected subordinate departures from the assumed parent material or to indicate selected, specific kinds of major departures from the definition assigned to the symbol O, A, B, C. These are regarded as alternatives to narrative statements of equivalent interpretations in the profile description. These suffixes follow the arabic number in the letter-number combined symbols discussed under item 2 above (A2g or B3ca), or they may follow the capital letter of a master horizon if it is not subdivided (Bt or Ap). These suffixes also follow arabic numbers used solely for vertical subdivision described under item 3 above, as A21g and A22g or C1ca and C2ca. An exception is made with the lower case letter p. This is used only with the letter A (Ap) and is comparable to the A1 or A2.

5. Roman numerals are prefixed to the master horizon or layer designations (O, A, B, C, R) to indicate lithologic discontinuities either within or below the solum. The first, or uppermost, material is not numbered, for the Roman numeral I is understood; the second contrasting material is numbered II, and others encountered are numbered III, IV, and so on, consecutively with depth. Thus, for example, a sequence from the surface downward might be A2, B1, IIB2, IIB3, IIC1, IIIC2.

A lithologic discontinuity is a significant change in particle size distribution or mineralogy that indicates a difference in the material from which the horizons have formed. A change in the clay content associated with an argillic horizon (textural B) does not indicate a difference in parent material. Appearance of gravel, or a change in the ratios between the various sand separates, will normally suggest a difference in parent materials. One purpose in identifying lithologic discontinuities is to distinguish between those differences between horizons that are the result of pedo-genesis and those that are geologic. Consequently, a designation with a different Roman number would not normally be used for a buried soil in a thick loess deposit. The difference between the properties of the buried soil and the overlying loess are presumably the result of pedo-genesis. But a stone line usually indicates a need for another Roman number. The material above the stone line is presumed to be transported. If the transport was by wind or water, one must suspect that during the movement there was some sorting of the material according to size.

6. An illuvial or B horizon (together with its overlying eluvial or A horizon if one is present) is called a sequum. If more than one sequum is present in vertical sequence, the lower sequum is given A and B designations with a prime accent, as A'2, B'2. The prime accents are not used however for buried soils. These carry the lower case letter b.

MASTER HORIZONS AND LAYERS

Organic horizons

O—Organic horizons of mineral soils. Horizons: (1) formed or forming in the upper part of mineral soils above the mineral part; (2) dominated by fresh or partly decomposed organic material; and (3) containing more than 30 percent organic matter if the mineral fraction is more than 50 percent clay, or more than 20 percent organic matter if the mineral fraction has no clay. Intermediate clay content requires proportional organic-matter content

The O horizons may be present at the surface horizon of mineral soils, or at any depth beneath the surface in buried soils, but they have been formed from organic litter derived from plants and animals and deposited on the surface. The O horizons do not include soil horizons formed by illuviation of organic material into mineral material, nor do they include horizons high in organic matter formed by a decomposing root mat below the surface of a mineral material.

Because organic horizons at the surface may be rapidly altered in thickness or be destroyed by fire or by the activities of man or other animals, the depth limits of organic horizons that are at the surface are always measured upward from the top of the underlying mineral material. Two subdivisions are recognized:

O1—Organic horizons in which essentially the original form of most vegetative matter is visible to the naked eye

Identifiable remains of soil fauna, or their excrement, may be present, and the horizon may be filled with fungal hyphae. The vegetative matter may be essentially unaltered, as freshly fallen leaves, or may be leached of its most soluble constituents and discolored. The O1 corresponds to the L and some F layers mentioned in literature on forest soils and to the horizon formerly called Aoo.

O2—Organic horizons in which the original form of most plant or animal matter cannot be recognized with the naked eye

Remains of parts of plants and animals commonly can be identified with magnification, and excrement of soil fauna is commonly a large part of the material present. The O2 corresponds to the H layer and some F layers described in literature on forest soils and to the horizon formerly called Ao.

The organic horizons in organic soils are not defined here. They are currently under discussion. The organic B horizons in mineral soils are defined under B horizon, along with the mineral horizons.

Mineral horizons and layers

Mineral horizons contain less than 30 percent organic matter if the mineral fraction contains more than 50 percent clay or less than 20 percent organic matter if the mineral fraction has no clay. Intermediate clay content requires proportional content of organic matter.

A—Mineral horizons consisting of: (1) horizons of organic-matter accumulation formed or forming at or adjacent to the surface; (2) horizons that have lost clay, iron, or aluminum with resultant concentration of quartz or other resistant minerals of sand or silt size; or (3) horizons dominated by 1 or 2 above but transitional to an underlying B or C

A1—Mineral horizons, formed or forming at or adjacent to the surface, in which the feature emphasized is an accumulation of humified organic matter intimately associated with the mineral fraction

The mineral particles have coatings of organic material, or the soil mass is darkened by organic particles; the horizon is as dark as, or darker than, adjacent underlying horizons. The mineral fraction may be unaltered or may have been altered in a manner comparable to that of A2 or B. The organic fraction is assumed to have been derived from plant and animal remains deposited mechanically on the surface of the soil, or deposited within the horizon without translocation of humified material through an intervening horizon that qualifies for a horizon designation other than A1.

A2—Mineral horizons in which the feature emphasized is loss of clay, iron, or aluminum, with resultant concentration of quartz or other resistant minerals in sand and silt sizes

Such horizons are commonly but not necessarily lighter in color than an underlying B. In some soils the color is determined by that of the primary sand and silt particles, but in many soils, coats of iron or other compounds, apparently released in the horizon and not translocated, mask the color of the primary particles. An A2 is most commonly differentiated from an overlying A1 by lighter color and is generally measurably lower in organic matter. An A2 is most commonly differentiated from an underlying B in the same profile by lighter color, or coarser texture, or both. A2 horizons are commonly near the surface, below an O or A1 horizon and above a B, but the symbol A2 may be used either above or below subsurface horizons; position in the profile is not diagnostic. For horizons at the surface that would qualify equally well as either A1 or A2, the designation A1 is given preference over A2.

A3—A transitional horizon between A and B, and dominated by properties characteristic of an overlying A1 or A2 but having some subordinate properties of an underlying B

No distinction is made between the different kinds of horizons that are transitional from A1 or A2 to different kinds of B; they obviously may be quite unlike one another, but the burden of characterization rests on the description of the transitional horizon, plus inferences that can be made after noticing the symbols assigned to the overlying and underlying horizons. The symbol A3 normally is used only if the horizon is underlain by a B horizon. However, where the profile is truncated from below in small places by rock, so as to eliminate the horizon that would be designated B, the symbol A3 may be used for the horizon that is above the rock. For example, in one part of a pedon, a horizon may be transitional between A and B, and thus appropriately designated A3. But, in another part of the same pedon, the same horizon rests on rock, and may appropriately be called A3, even though there is no underlying B.

The symbol A3 is confined to those kinds of transitional zones in which some properties of the underlying B are superimposed on properties of A throughout the soil mass. Those kinds of "transitional horizons" in which parts that are characteristic of A enclose parts characteristic of B are classified as A and B.

AB—A horizon transitional between A and B, having an upper part dominated by properties of A and a lower part dominated by properties of B, and the two parts cannot conveniently be separated into A3 and B1

Such combined horizons are normally thin; they should be separated if thick enough to permit separation.

A&B—Horizons that would qualify for A2 except for included parts constituting less than 50 percent of the volume that would qualify as B

Commonly, A and B horizons are predominantly A2 material partially surrounding thin, columnar-like upward extensions of the B or wholly surrounding small, isolated spheres, elipsoids, or other bodies that would qualify as B. In such horizons the A2 appears to be encroaching on an underlying B.

AC—A horizon transitional between A and C, having subordinate properties of both A and C, but not dominated by properties characteristic of either A or C

B—Horizons in which the dominant feature or features is one or more of the following: (1) an illuvial concentration of silicate clay, iron, aluminum, or humus, alone or in combination; (2) a residual concentration of sesquioxides or silicate clays, alone or mixed, that has formed by means other than solution and removal of carbonates or more soluble salts; (3) coatings of sesquioxides adequate to give conspicuously darker, stronger, or redder colors than overlying and underlying horizons in the same sequum but without apparent illuviation of iron and not genetically related to B horizons that meet requirements of 1 or 2 in the same sequum; or (4) an alteration of material from its original condition in sequums lacking conditions defined in 1, 2, and 3 that obliterates original rock structure, that forms silicate clays, liberates oxides, or both, and that forms granular, blocky, or prismatic structure if textures are such that volume changes accompany changes in moisture.

It is obviously necessary to be able to identify the kind of B before one can establish that a horizon qualifies as B. There is no common diagnostic property or location in the profile by means of which all kinds of B can be identified. There are, however, marginal cases in which a horizon might qualify as either of two kinds of B. In such cases, the horizon description should indicate the kind of B that characterizes the dominant condition, in the judgment of the person describing the soil. Laboratory work may be needed for identification of the kind of B, or even to determine that a given horizon is a B.

B1—A transitional horizon between B and A1 or between B and A2 in which the horizon is dominated by properties of an underlying B2 but has some subordinate properties of an overlying A1 or A2

An adjacent overlying A1 or A2 and an adjacent underlying B2 are essential to characterization of a horizon as B1 in a virgin soil. In a few instances the horizon may still be recognized in a truncated soil by comparing the truncated profile with a profile of the same soil that has not been truncated. The symbol B1 is confined to those kinds of transitional horizons in which some properties of the overlying, adjacent A1 or A2 are superimposed on properties of B throughout the mass of the transitional horizon. Those kinds of transitional horizons containing parts characteristic of B, separated by abrupt boundaries from parts characteristic of an overlying A2, are classified as B&A.

B&A—Any horizon qualifying as B in more than 50 percent of its volume including parts that qualify as A2

Such horizons commonly have many vertical tongues of A2 material that extend downward into the B from the A2 or they have thin horizontal bands of A2-like material, which lie between thicker bands of B and are connected with tongues extending from the A2. Tubes filled with A1 material, as in krotovinas or earthworm channels, in a B horizon should be described but should not be designated as B and A. Many B horizons have A2-like material in widely spaced narrow cracks. Such features should be described, but the horizon should be designated as B and A only if the A2 material constitutes more than 10 percent of the volume of the horizon.

B2—That part of the B horizon where the properties on which the B is based are without clearly expressed subordinate characteristics indicating that the horizon is transitional to an adjacent overlying A or an adjacent underlying C or R

This does not imply that the B2 horizon in a given profile must express to uniform degree the properties diagnostic of B or that it must be confined to a zone of maximum expression in the absolute sense. The horizon B3, which is transitional from B2 to C, commonly exhibits the subordinate properties of C by expressing in lower degree the properties of an adjacent B2. Before the designation B3 is justified, the degree of expression of B2 must be low enough that the properties of C are clearly evident. The definition does not imply that a given kind of B2 has the same degree of expression in all profiles. In some profiles the most strongly expressed part of the B horizon, which would be designated B2, may be as weakly expressed as B3 in other profiles. The designation B2 is used strictly within the frame of reference of a single profile and not in an absolute sense of degree.

B3—A transitional horizon between B and C or R in which the properties diagnostic of an overlying B2 are clearly expressed but are associated with clearly expressed properties characteristic of C or R

The designation B3 is used only if there is an overlying B2; this applies even though the properties diagnostic of B are weakly expressed in the profile. Where an underlying material presumed to be like the parent material of the solum is absent, as in A–B–IIC profiles, B3 is used below B2 in the sense of a horizon transitional to an assumed original parent material. Use of the symbol IIC involves an estimate of at least the gross character of the parent material of the horizons above it. B3 in such cases is based on this estimate of the properties of the parent material of the B. B3 is not used as a horizon transitional from IB2 to IIC or IIR.

> C—A mineral horizon or layer, excluding bedrock, that is either like or unlike the material from which the solum is presumed to have formed, relatively little affected by pedogenic processes, and lacking properties diagnostic of A or B but including materials modified by: (1) weathering outside the zone of major biological activity; (2) reversible cementation, development of brittleness, development of high bulb density, and other properties characteristic of fragipans; (3) gleying; (4) accumulation of calcium or magnesium carbonate or more soluble salts; (5) cementation by such accumulations as calcium or magnesium carbonate or more soluble salts; or (6) cementation by alkali-soluble siliceous material or by iron and silica

This definition is intended to exclude horizons that meet the requirements of A or B but to include certain kinds of alteration that, historically, have been considered to be little influenced by the activity of organisms. These alterations include chemical weathering deep in the soil. Some soils are presumed to have developed in materials already highly weathered, and such weathered material that does not meet requirements for A or B is considered C. Development of the firmness, brittleness, and high density characteristic of fragipans is, by itself, not a criterion of A or B. Fragipans that have distinct silicate clay concentrations are to be indicated as Bx or simply as B. Fragipans lacking such clay concentration, however, are considered to be within the definition of C and are designated Cx. Accumulations of carbonates, gypsum, or more soluble salts are permitted in C if the material is otherwise considered to be little affected by other processes that have contributed to genesis of associated horizons. Such horizons are designated as Cca, Ccs, Csa. Even induration by such materials is permitted and this can be indicated by the suffix m, as in Ccam. Induration by alkali-soluble siliceous material is also permitted and may be indicated by Csim. Induration by iron and silica does not exclude the horizon from C, and horizons or layers thus indurated would be designated Cm. Horizon C, as defined, is intended to include the diagnostic horizons indicated by ca, cs, and sa, and the alkali-soluble pans, the iron-silica pans, and the fragipans, provided these layers do not meet the requirements of B. The C horizon now includes the contrasting layers of unconsolidated material formerly designated as D. It also includes the former G horizon, if that horizon cannot be designated as A or B. Historically, C has often incorrectly been called parent material. In fact it is impossible to find the parent material from which the A and B horizons have developed; that material has been altered. For this reason, C never was parent material, but was merely presumed to be like parent material. As C is now defined, even this assumption is dropped.

The differentiation between C1 and C2 that was formerly made has been dropped because it is untenable when applied to the variety of conditions recognized as C. Deletion of C1 makes arabic numerals applied to C indicative only of vertical sequence within C.

R—Underlying consolidated bedrock, such as granite, sandstone, or limestone. If presumed to be like the parent rock from which the adjacent overlying layer or horizon was formed, the symbol R is used alone. If presumed to be unlike the overlying material, the R is preceded by a Roman numeral denoting lithologic discontinuity as explained under the heading

SYMBOLS USED TO INDICATE DEPARTURES SUBORDINATE TO THOSE INDICATED BY CAPITAL LETTERS

The following symbols are to be used in the manner indicated under the heading Conventions Governing Use of Symbols.

b—Buried soil horizon

This symbol is added to the designation of a buried genetic horizon or horizons. Horizons of another solum may or may not have formed in the overlying material, which may be similar to, or different from, the assumed parent material of the buried soil.

ca—An accumulation of carbonates of alkaline earths, commonly of calcium

This symbol is applied to A, B, or C horizons. Possible combinations are A1ca, A3ca, B1ca, B2ca, B3ca. A2ca is probably also possible where accumulation has occurred in an A2 formed under different conditions, but it is not common. The presence of secondary carbonates alone is not adequate to justify the use of the ca symbol. The horizon must have more carbonates than the parent material is presumed to have had.

cs—An accumulation of calcium sulfate

This symbol is used in a manner comparable to that of ca. Calcium sulfate accumulations commonly occur in the C below ca accumulations in chernozemic soils but may occur in other horizons as well. Before the symbol cs is used, the horizon must have more sulfates than the parent material is presumed to have had.

cn—Accumulations of concretions or hard nonconcretionary nodules enriched in sesquioxides with or without phosphorus.

The nodules indicated by the symbol cn must be hard when dry but need not be indurated. The horizon description should characterize the nodules. Nodules, concretions, or crystals do not qualify as cn if they are of dolomite or more soluble salts, but they do qualify if they are of iron, aluminum, manganese, or titanium.

f—Frozen soil

The suffix f is used for soil that is thought to be permanently frozen.

g—Strong gleying

The suffix g is used with a horizon designation to indicate intense reduction of iron during soil development, or reducing conditions due to stagnant water, as evidenced by base colors that approach neutral, with or without mottles. In aggregated material, ped faces in such horizons generally have chroma of 2 or less as a continuous phase, and commonly have few or faint mottles. Interiors of peds may have prominent and many mottles but commonly have a network of threads or bands of low chroma surrounding the mottles. In soils that are not aggregated, a base chroma of 1.0 or less, with or without mottles, is indicative of strong gleying. Hues bluer than 10Y are also indicative of strong gleying in some soils. Horizons of low chroma in which the color is due to uncoated sand or silt particles are not considered strongly gleyed. Although gleying is commonly associated with wetness, especially in the presence of organic matter, wetness by itself is not a criterion of gleying. The symbol g may be applied to any of the major symbols for mineral horizons and should follow the horizon designations, as A2g, A21g, A3g, B1g, B2g, B3g, and Cg. Bg may be used where B horizons cannot be subdivided into B1, B2, and B3.

No lower case letter is used as a suffix with horizon designations to indicate reduction of iron less intense than that indicated by g. Not given a special designation but described in detail is the condition generally associated with (1) common to many, distinct to prominent mottles on base colors of chroma stronger than 2 in unaggregated material, or (2) evidenced by base chroma greater than 2 with few to common, faint to distinct mottles on ped faces and common to many distinct to prominent mottles in ped interiors in well-aggregated material.

h—Illuvial humus

Accumulations of decomposed illuvial organic matter, appearing as dark coatings on sand or silt particles, or as discrete dark pellets of silt size, are indicated by h. If used, this suffix follows the letter B or a subdivision of B, as Bh or B2h.

ir—Illuvial iron

Accumulations of illuvial iron as coatings on sand or silt particles or as pellets of silt size; in some horizons the coatings have coalesced, filled pores, and cemented the horizon.

m—Strong cementation, induration

The symbol m is applied as a suffix to horizon designations to indicate irreversible cementation. The symbol is not applied to indurated bedrock. Contrary to previous usage, m is not used to indicate firmness, as in fragipans, but is confined to indurated horizons which are essentially (more than 90 percent) continuous, though they may be fractured.

p—Plowing or other disturbance

The symbol p is used as a suffix with A to indicate disturbance by cultivation or pasturing. Even though a soil has been truncated and the plow layer is clearly in what was once B horizon, the designation Ap is used. When an Ap is subdivided, the arabic number suffixes follow, as Ap1 and Ap2, for the Ap is considered comparable to A1, A2, or B2.

sa—An accumulation of salts more soluble than calcium sulfate

This symbol may be applied to the designation of any horizon and in its manner of use is comparable to that described for ca or cs. If the symbol is used, the horizon must have more salt than the parent material is presumed to have had.

si—Cementation by siliceous material, soluble in alkali. This symbol is applied only to C

The cementation may be nodular or continuous. If the cementation is continuous the symbol sim is used.

t—Illuvial clay

Accumulations of translocated silicate clay are indicated by the suffix t (Ger. ton, clay). The suffix t is used only with B, as B2t, to indicate the nature of the B.

x—Fragipan character

The symbol x is used as a suffix with horizon designations to indicate genetically developed properties of firmness, brittleness, high density, and characteristic distribution of clay that are diagnostic of fragipans. Fragipans, or parts of fragipans, may qualify as A2, B, or C. Such horizons are classified as A2, B, or C, and the symbol x is used as a suffix to indicate fragipan character. Unlike comparable use of supplementary symbols, the symbol x is applied to B without the connotative arabic numeral normally applied to B. Arabic numerals used with C to indicate only vertical subdivision of the horizon precede the x in the symbol, as C1x, C2x.

All lower case symbols except p follow the last arabic number used, as B3ca, A2g, A21g. If the horizon is not subdivided, the symbol follows the capital letter, as Cg, Bt. The symbol p is restricted to use with A because of the common difficulty of deciding which horizons have been included in the plow layer.

It will be noted that the connotation of the symbol m has been changed to prohibit its use with "fragipans" and that definitions of the other symbols have been modified or elaborated. The symbols si and x have been added, and the symbols r, G, D, M, and u have been dropped.

SUBDIVISION OF HORIZONS

In a single profile it is often necessary to subdivide the horizons for which designations are provided, for example, to subdivide Ap, A1, A2, A3, B1, B2, B3, or C so that detailed studies of morphology, sampling, and similar work can be correctly recorded. In some cases, such subdivision is arbitrary in relation to differences observable in the field; in others, it may be needed to differentiate within a horizon on bases not provided by unique horizon symbols. In all such cases, the subdivisions are numbered consecutively, with arabic numbers, from the top of the horizon downward, as B21, B22, B23. If the suffixes consisting of lower-case letters are being used, the arabic numbers precede all lower-case suffixes except p as B21t, C1g, C2g, but Ap1, Ap2.

LITHOLOGIC DISCONTINUITES

Roman numerals are prefixed to the appropriate horizon designations when it is necessary to number a series of layers of contrasting material consecutively from the surface downward. A soil that is all in one kind of material is all in material designated by the numeral I. This numeral therefore can be omitted from the symbol, as it is understood that all the material is I. Similarly, the uppermost material in a profile having two or more contrasting materials is always designated I. Consequently, for the topmost material, the numeral I can be omitted from the symbol because it is always understood. Numbering starts with the second layer of contrasting material, which is designated II, and each contrasting material below this second layer is numbered consecutively, III, IV, and so on, downward as part of each horizon designation. Even though a layer below a layer designated by II is similar to the topmost layer, it is given the appropriate consecutive number in the sequence. Where two or more horizons developed in one of the numbered layers, the Roman number is applied to all the horizon designations in that material.

Following are two examples of horizon sequences using this convention:

A1—A2—B1—B21—IIB22—IIB3—IIC1—IIIC2.

A1—A2—B1—B2—IIA′2—IIB′x—IICIx—IIIC2x—IIIC3—IVR.

In the first example, the first contrasting layer is unnumbered; the second layer, starting in the B2, is indicated by Roman II, as IIB22; the third, within the C, by the symbol IIIC. In the second example, the first contrasting layer is unnumbered; the second, starting at the top of A′2, is numbered II; the third, starting in the middle of the fragipan is numbered III, even though the fragipan is partly in C; and the fourth, starting below C, is indicated by IVR. Note that arabic numerals are used independently of the Roman numerals, in the conventional manner, both as connotative symbols and for vertical subdivision.

THE SOLUM

The solum may be defined simply as the genetic soil developed by soil-building forces. In normal soils, the solum includes the A and B horizons, or the upper part of the soil profile above the parent material.

Although the concept of *solum* is commonly understood by soil scientists, this definition is deceptively simple. Especially in some of the intrazonal soils, the actual sola are not easily determined; and in some soils their lower limits can be set only arbitrarily, say at 6 feet or 2 meters, or at the lower limit of plant roots. Used with such soils, the term "solum" may need to be defined in relation to the particular soil.

These difficulties concerning the solum arise mainly from the fact that the processes of soil formation often merge with broad geological processes. Although it is important to distinguish between geological and soil-forming processes, it is equally important to recognize that they usually go on together and that soils are being influenced by both. It is of little use to argue semantically about certain phenomena in the profile that are the result of combinations of the two sets of processes or that can be ascribed sometimes to one and sometimes to the other. These difficulties are illustrated by some common examples in the paragraphs following.

Croûte calcaire.—Croûte calcaire, or hardened caliche, is often found in thick masses overlain by only a few inches of soil. The common Cca horizons of Chernozems, let us say, are easily conceived as part of the soil profile, although they are not within the solum.[1] Their genesis and relationships to the solum raise no particular difficulties. It is another matter, however, to include some 10 to 25 feet of croûte calcaire under a Reddish-Brown soil as a part of its

---

[1] Admittedly this may appear to be somewhat arbitrary. In many Chernozems and Chestnut soils it may seem that the solum could be defined to include the Cca; but in some developed from materials low in calcium the Cca comes deep within the C, far below the solum.

profile. Doubtless this croûte calcaire is related to the solum and should be described in any description of the soil profile; but certainly broad long-time geological processes have been at work, as well as soil-forming processes.

Laterite.—Laterite includes the sesquioxide-rich, highly weathered clayey material that is hardened irreversibly to concretions, hardpans, or crusts when dehydrated, and hardened relicts of such materials more or less mixed with quartz and other diluents. Laterite is found in many soils and is a distinguishing feature of Ground-Water Laterite soil. In the profile of a Ground-Water Laterite soil one may designate the horizons easily as A1, A2, A3, and B1, down into the B2 or, perhaps, into the B3. The same material may continue practically without change for another 25 feet or so with no definite place for dividing the solum from the material underneath it. It would be unreasonable to exclude the upper part of the laterite from the solum; and it seems unreasonable to include the lower part, far removed from the influence of organisms.

Gleyed soil material.—Gleyed soil material may begin a few inches below the surface of hydromorphic soils and, in some instances, continue on down for many feet essentially unchanged. Such conditions can arise through the gradual filling of a wet basin, with the A horizon gradually being added to at the surface and being gleyed beneath. Finally the A rests on a thick mass of gleyed material, which may be relatively uniform, especially in sandy types. Obviously the upper part belongs in the solum, while the lower part does not. This illustration does not extend to all gleyed soils. In many the gleyed horizon is clearly a part of the solum and has a clear lower boundary with the C.

Permafrost.—Permanently frozen ground under soils of the arctic and subarctic regions is called permafrost. The upper boundary, or *permafrost table*, is said to be coincident with the lower limits of seasonal thaws. The upper boundary of frozen ground varies, of course, from month to month during the summer and from year to year, depending upon the season. The soil that freezes and thaws seasonally is above the permafrost table. The frozen ground may extend downward many feet, even several hundred feet. Here again, the morphologist may properly place some part of the frozen ground in the soil profile, or even in the solum, as a kind of "thermal" hardpan, especially if it contains organic matter and bears a definite relationship to the upper horizons or solum. In many soils with permafrost, the permafrost table is deep beneath the solum, within the C or below it.

Some soils have no solum at all although they support plants. Examples include very young soils from recent accumulations of volcanic ash, alluvium, or loess. At least some time is required after vegetation has become established before recognizable genetic horizons are formed.

POPULAR TERMS FOR SOIL LAYERS

Several popular terms have long been used to refer to certain soil horizons or groups of horizons—terms that are exceedingly difficult to define precisely. They are very old and have been used by laymen in widely different senses.

Topsoil is a general term that is used in at least four senses: (1) For the surface plowed layer (Ap) and thus as a synonym for surface soil; (2) for the original or present A1 horizon, and thus exceedingly variable in depth among different soils; (3) for the original or present A horizon; and (4) for presumed fertile soil or soil material, usually rich in organic matter, used to top-dress road banks, parks, gardens, and lawns.

The authors know of no way to settle on a specific definition that would make the term even reasonably clear in soil descriptions. It should be avoided except as a top-dress material.

Surface soil refers to the soil ordinarily moved in tillage, or its equivalent in uncultivated soil, about 5 to 8 inches in thickness. The depth varies among different soil regions. If the term is used without qualification, reference is made to the existing surface soil, regardless of origin. If reference is made to a former condition, the term needs to be modified to *original surface soil*, as in the statement, "50 percent of original surface soil has been lost by sheet erosion."

Subsurface soil refers to that part of the A horizon below the surface soil. In soils of weak profile development subsurface soil can be defined only in terms of arbitrary depths.

Subsoil refers to the B horizon of soils with distinct profiles. In soils with weak profile development, subsoil can be defined as the soil below the surface soil in which roots normally grow or in terms of arbitrary depths. It is a poor term inherited from the days when "soil" was conceived only as the plowed soil; hence that under it was "subsoil."

Substratum is any layer beneath the solum, either conforming (C or R) or unconforming.

MEASUREMENT OF HORIZONS

The designations and descriptions of several horizons of the soil profile follow their identification and location within the profile. The description of the profile as a whole can be aided greatly by a scaled diagram, sketch, or photograph on which the horizon boundaries are shown.[2]

DEPTH AND THICKNESS

The profile description needs to include for each horizon (or layer) both (1) thickness in inches (or centimeters) and (2) depth of horizon boundaries below the top of A1.[3] If both sets of figures vary widely, it will be necessary to give the two sets separately to avoid confusion.

---

[2] The reader will find many schemes for measuring horizons in various publications. The best ones are those coupled with conventional outlines of soil characteristics so that none is inadvertently omitted. C. C. Nikiforoff outlined an excellent scheme in his METHOD OF RECORDING SOIL DATA. Soil Sci. Soc. America Proc. 1: 307–317. 1936. The scheme he outlines needs only revision in classes and grades of horizon characteristics to bring it up to date with current practices. (See also p. 137.)

[3] This standard applies to all soils except Bogs and Half Bogs, in which the measurement begins at the top of the peat or muck, not counting fresh leaves or twigs. In other soils, if the A1 is missing, the measurement is taken from the top of the AP or other surface horizon, say the A2 in severely burned podzolic soils or the B2 of a truncated profile if it now lies at the surface.

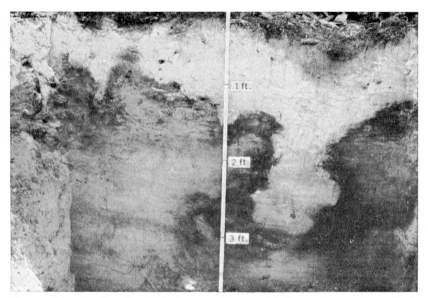

FIGURE 29.—Profile of a Podzol or sandy material illustrating an exceedingly irregular horizon boundary.

The upper boundary of a B2 horizon, for example, may lie from 10 to 18 inches beneath the top of A1, and the lower boundary from 20 to 32 inches below the top of the A1; while the thickness may vary from 8 to 16 inches, not 2 to 22 inches as might be interpreted from the figures for depth below the top of the A1. Even the figures for thickness and for depth do not describe very irregular horizons adequately. The main body of the A2 of a Podzol, for example, may be 5½ to 8½ inches thick, with an upper boundary ¼ to ½ inch deep, and a lower boundary generally 5 to 8 inches deep but with irregular tongues extending down to 18 inches. The lower boundary of the underlying B2 may vary similarly—as little as 10 inches deep to as much as 24 inches, but with a thickness of only 4 inches to not more than 12 inches.

In sandy Podzols with microrelief it is not unusual to find tongues of A2 actually bending under the B2 in such a way that a vertical cut into the soil will pass through A1, A2, B2, back into a bulging tongue of A2, then into B2 again, and finally through the B3 into the C. This example illustrates the need for a considerable trench for examining soil profiles and especially for taking samples, else serious errors may rise. Many soil horizons have similar tongues or other discontinuities, such as the common krotovinas of Chernozem and Chestnut soils, for example.

HORIZON BOUNDARIES

Horizon boundaries vary (1) in distinctness, and (2) in surface topography. Some boundaries are clear and sharp, as those between A2 and B2 horizons in most solodized-Solonetz and well-developed Podzols. Again they may be diffuse, with one horizon gradually merging into another, as between the A1 and A3 of Chernozem or the B2 and B3 of many Latosols. With these diffuse horizons, the location of the boundary requires time-consuming comparisons of small samples of soil from various parts of the profile until the midpoints are established. Small markers can be inserted until all horizons of the profile are worked out; then measurements can be taken; and finally the individual horizons can be described and sampled. Sampling can often begin with the lowest horizon to good advantage.

The distinction of the horizons to the observer depends partly upon the contrast between them—some adjacent ones are highly contrasting in several features—and partly upon the width of the boundary itself or the amount of the profile in the transition between one horizon and the next. The characteristic widths of boundaries between soil horizons may be described as (1) *abrupt*, if less than 1 inch wide; (2) *clear*, if about 1 to 2½ inches wide; (3) *gradual*, if 2½ to 5 inches wide; and (4) *diffuse*, if more than 5 inches wide.

The topography of different soil horizons varies, as well as their distinctness. Although observations of soil horizons are made in profiles or sections, and so photographed or sketched, we must continually recall that they are not "bands" (or literally "horizons" as that word is understood in everyday speech) but rather three-dimensional layers that may be smooth or exceedingly irregular. Horizon boundaries may thus be described as (1) *smooth*, if nearly a plane; (2) *wavy* or undulating, if pockets are wider than their depth; (3) *irregular*, if irregular pockets are deeper than their width; and (4) *broken*, if parts of the horizon are unconnected with other parts, as the B$_2$ in the limestone cracks of a truncated Terra Rossa.

HORIZONTAL VARIATIONS

The profiles of soils having well-developed microrelief cannot be satisfactorily described from pits. To describe such soils, or to understand how one soil profile merges into another at the soil boundary, a long trench is dug so that horizons may be measured, described, sketched, and sampled at appropriate horizontal intervals. Small stakes may be set on the margin of the trench at 6- or 12-inch intervals as reference points. Using one stake as a zero point, the relative elevations of the others can be measured with an ordinary surveyor's level or Y-level.

For the purpose of observing any horizontal cracking or patterns in the soil, it is often revealing to remove soil horizons, one by one from the top down, from an area of a square yard or more. One may, for example, discover gross hexagonal cracking of hardpans or claypans, unsuspected from the vertical cut alone, that suggest previous influences of freezing, moistening, or desiccation that have been interrupted by coverings now changed to a part of the solum.

In soil descriptions the mottling can be most conveniently described by describing the mottles as to abundance, size, contrast, and color, such as, ". . . brown silt loam with few, fine, distinct reddish-brown and dark-gray mottles."

In verbal descriptions of soil mottling intended for the general reader, part of the detail needed in detailed soil morphology and correlation may be omitted. Thus, starting with the classes according to abundance, descriptions may be written as follows:

1. *Few:* ". . . brown silt loam, slightly mottled with red and yellow."
2. *Common:* ". . . brown silt loam, mottled with red and yellow."
3. *Many:*
   (a) If the matrix is clearly apparent: ". . . brown silt loam, highly mottled with red and yellow."
   (b) If no clear matrix exists: ". . . mottled red, yellow, and brown silt loam."

If contrast is not clearly shown by the color names, "faintly" or "prominently" may be added. Faint mottling can be implied as ". . . brown silt loam, mottled with shades."

If size is important "finely" or "coarsely" may be added, as ". . . coarsely mottled red and yellow clay", or ". . . brown silt loam finely and slightly mottled with reddish brown." Usually such distinctions are more confusing than helpful to the lay reader.

In the description of soil color, special notice should be taken of any relationships between the color pattern and structure or porosity. Structural aggregates in the soil must be broken to determine whether the color is uniform throughout. The black or dark-brown surface color of soil granules is often due to a thin coating, though the basic color of the soil material is brown or yellow. When such granules are crushed, the mass of soil is lighter in color than the original surfaces of the aggregates. Marked contrast between the color of the soil aggregates and the color of the soil when crushed is common. Coatings of red color often cover structural particles or sand grains; and a gray color may be due to a thin film of leached soil around darker aggregates.

EFFECTS OF MOISTURE

Soil color changes with the moisture content, very markedly in some soils and comparatively little in others. Between dry and moist, soil colors commonly are darker by $\frac{1}{2}$ to 3 steps in value and may change from $-\frac{1}{2}$ to $+2$ steps in chroma. Seldom are they different in hue. Some of the largest differences in value between the dry and moist colors occur in gray and grayish-brown horizons having moderate to moderately low contents of organic matter.

Reproducible quantitative measurements of color are obtained at two moisture contents: (1) Air dry, and (2) field capacity. The latter may be obtained with sufficient accuracy for color measurements by moistening a sample and reading the color as soon as visible moisture films have disappeared. Both the dry and the moist colors are important. In most notes and soil descriptions, unless stated otherwise, colors are given for moist soils.

Comparisons of color among widely separated soils are facilitated by using the color designation of freshly broken surfaces of air-dry samples. Official descriptions for technical use, such as series descriptions, should include the moist colors, and preferably, both dry and moist colors if significantly unlike.

DETERMINATION OF SOIL COLOR

Soil colors are most conveniently measured by comparison with a color chart. The one generally used with soil is a modification of the Munsell color chart and includes only that portion needed for soil colors, about one-fifth of the entire range of color.[6] It consists of some 175 different colored papers, or chips, systematically arranged, according to their Munsel notations, on cards carried in a loose-leaf notebook. The arrangement is by *hue, value,* and *chroma*—the three simple variables that combine to give all colors. *Hue* is the dominant spectral (rainbow) color; it is related to the dominant wavelength of the light. *Value* refers to the relative lightness of color and is a function (approximately the square root) of the total amount of light. *Chroma* (sometimes called saturation) is the relative purity or strength of the spectral color and increases with decreasing grayness.

In the soil color chart, all colors on a given card are of a constant hue, designated by the symbol in the upper right-hand corner of the card. Vertically, the colors become successively lighter by visually equal steps; their value increases. Horizontally, they increase in chroma to the right and become grayer to the left. The value and chroma of each color in the chart is printed immediately beneath the color. The first number is the value, and the second is the chroma. As arranged in the chart the colors form three scales: (1) Radial, or from one card to the next, in hue; (2) vertical in value; and (3) horizontal in chroma.

The nomenclature for soil color consists of two complementary systems: (1) Color names, and (2) the Munsell notation of color. Neither of these alone is adequate for all purposes. The color names are employed in all descriptions for publication and for general use. The Munsell notation is used to supplement the color names wherever greater precision is needed, as a convenient abbreviation in field descriptions, for expression of the specific relations between colors, and for statistical treatment of color data. The Munsell notation is especially useful for international correlation, since no translation of color names is needed. The names for soil colors are common terms now so defined as to obtain uniformity and yet accord, as nearly as possible, with past usage by soil scientists. Bizarre names like "rusty brown," "tan," "mouse gray," "lemon yellow," and "chocolate brown" should never be used.

The soil color names and their limits are given in the name-diagrams, figures 30 to 36.

---

[6] The appropriate color chips separately, or mounted by hues on special cards (4¼ by 7¼ inches) for a loose-leaf notebook, may be obtained from the Munsell Color Company, Inc., 10 East Franklin Street, Baltimore 2, Md.

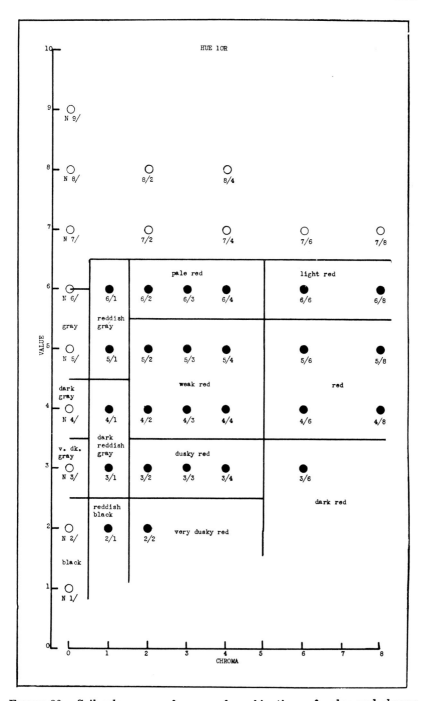

FIGURE 30.—Soil color names for several combinations of value and chroma and hue 10R.

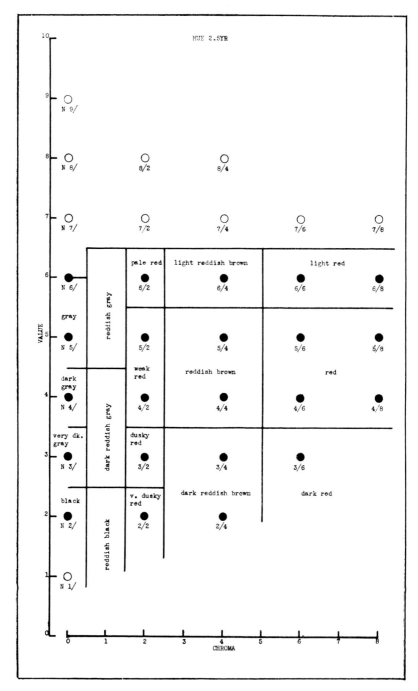

FIGURE 31.—Soil color names for several combinations of value and chroma and hue 2.5YR.

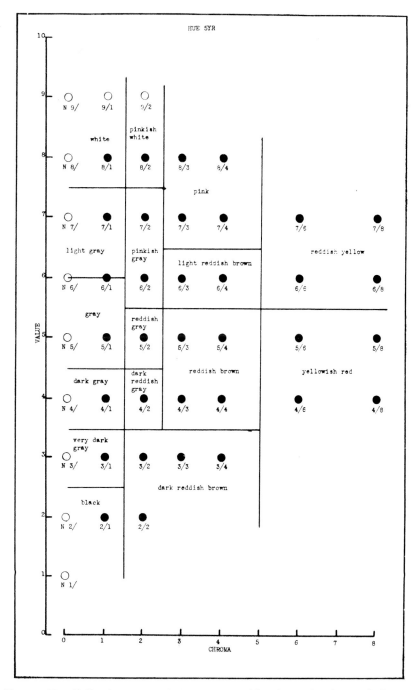

FIGURE 32.—Soil color names for several combinations of value and chroma
and hue 5YR.

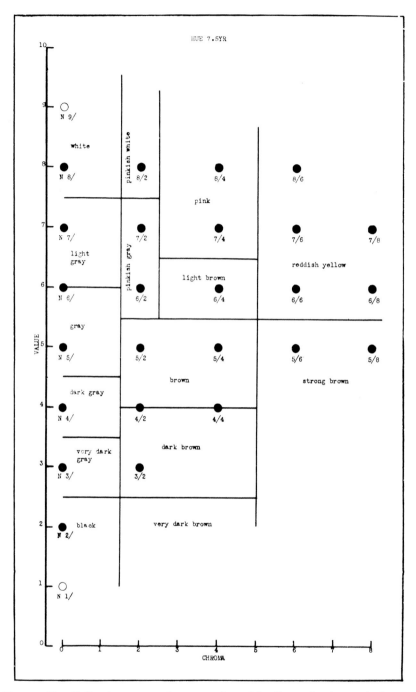

FIGURE 33.—Soil color names for several combinations of value and chroma and hue 7.5YR.

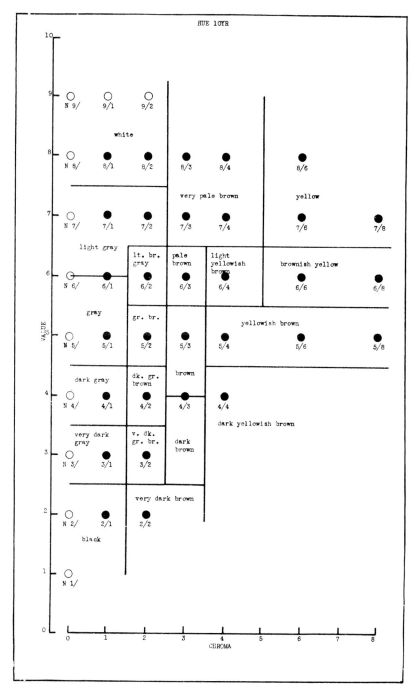

FIGURE 34.—Soil color names for several combinations of value and chroma and hue 10YR.

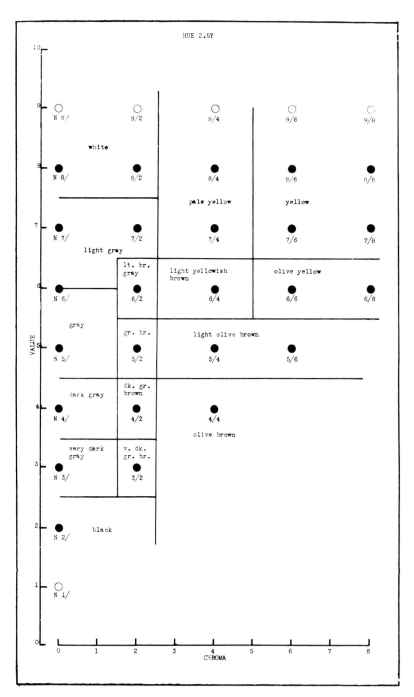

FIGURE 35.—Soil color names for several combinations of value and chroma and hue 2.5Y.

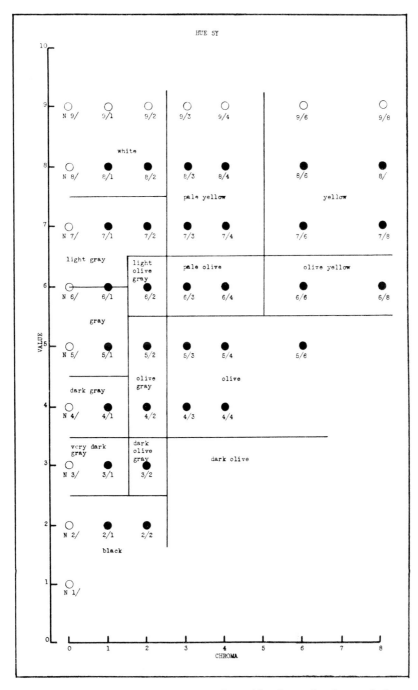

FIGURE 36.—Soil color names for several combinations of value and chroma and hue 5Y.

The Munsell notation for color consists of separate notations for hue, value, and chroma, which are combined in that order to form the color designation. The symbol for hue is the letter abbreviation of the color of the rainbow (R for red, YR for yellow-red, or orange, Y for yellow) preceded by numbers from 0 to 10. Within each letter range, the hue becomes more yellow and less red as the numbers increase. The middle of the letter range is at 5; the zero point coincides with the 10 point of the next redder hue. Thus 5YR is in the middle of the yellow-red hue, which extends from 10R (zero YR) to 10YR (zero Y).

The notation for value consists of numbers from 0, for absolute black, to 10, for absolute white. Thus a color of value 5/ is visually midway between absolute white and absolute black. One of value 6/ is slightly less dark, 60 percent of the way from black to white, and midway between values of 5/ and 7/.

The notation for chroma consists of numbers beginning at 0 for neutral grays and increasing at equal intervals to a maximum of about 20, which is never really approached in soil. For absolute achromatic colors (pure grays, white, and black), which have zero chroma and no hue, the letter N (neutral) takes the place of a hue designation.

In writing the Munsell notation, the order is hue, value, chroma, with a space between the hue letter and the succeeding value number, and a virgule between the two numbers for value and chroma. If expression beyond the whole numbers is desired, decimals are always used, never fractions. Thus the notation for a color of hue 5YR, value 5, chroma 6, is 5YR 5/6, a yellowish-red. The notation for a color midway between the 5YR 5/6 and 5YR 6/6 chips is 5YR 5.5/6; for one midway between 2.5YR 5/6 and 5YR 6/8, it is 3.75YR 5.5/7. The notation is decimal and capable of expressing any degree of refinement desired. Since color determinations cannot be made precisely in the field—generally no closer than half the interval between colors in the chart—expression of color should ordinarily be to the nearest color chip.

In using the color chart, accurate comparison is obtained by holding the soil sample above the color chips being compared. Rarely will the color of the sample be *perfectly* matched by any color in the chart. The probability of having a perfect matching of the sample color is less than one in one hundred. It should be evident, however, which colors the sample lies between, and which is the closest match. The principal difficulties encountered in using the soil color chart are (1) in selecting the appropriate hue card, (2) in determining colors that are intermediate between the hues in the chart, and (3) in distinguishing between value and chroma where chromas are strong. In addition, the chart does not include some extreme dark, strong (low value, high chroma) colors occasionally encountered in moist soils. With experience, these extreme colors lying outside the range of the chart can be estimated. Then too, the ability to sense color differences varies among people, even among those not regarded as color blind.

While important details should be given, long involved designations of color should generally be avoided, especially with variegated or mottled colors. In these, only the extreme or dominant colors need be stated. Similarly, in giving the color names and Munsell notations for both the dry and moist colors, an abbreviated form, such as "reddish brown (5YR 4/4; 3/4, moist)," simplifies the statement.

By attempting detail beyond the allowable accuracy of field observations and sample selection, one may easily make poorer soil descriptions than by expressing the dominant color simply. In all descriptions, terms other than the ones given on these charts should be used only in rare instances, and then only as supplemental expressions in parentheses where some different local usage is common.

SOIL TEXTURE, COARSE FRAGMENTS, STONINESS, AND ROCKINESS

Soil texture refers to the relative proportions of the various size groups of individual soil grains in a mass of soil. Specifically, it refers to the proportions of clay, silt, and sand below 2 millimeters in diameter.

The presence of coarse particles larger than very coarse sand (or 2 mm.) and smaller than 10 inches is recognized by modifiers of textural class names, like *gravelly* sandy loam or *cobbly* loam.

General classes of still larger particles—stones or rock outcrops—are defined in terms of the influence they have on soil use, and in specific physical terms for individual soil series. Although distinctions within a type, series, family, or great soil group according to stoniness or rockiness are *phases,* these are indicated in soil types by an additional adjective added to the soil class name. Thus, Gloucester stony loam and Gloucester very stony loam are two phases of Gloucester loam which could be written more accurately and more clumsily Gloucester loam, stony phase, and Gloucester loam, very stony phase.

Actually, of course, sharp distinctions among the size groups of particles are more or less arbitrary. They have been arrived at after many, many trials in developing classes that can be used consistently and conveniently to define soil classificational and mapping units in such ways that they can be given the most specific interpretations.

The discussion of particle size is therefore presented under three principal headings: (1) The designation of soil textural class based primarily upon the proportion of clay, silt, and sand; (2) the definition of groups of coarse fragments having diameters less than 10 inches that may be regarded as a part of the soil mass and modify the textural class; and (3) the definition of classes of stoniness and rockiness for stones over 10 inches in diameter and for bedrock not considered a part of the soil mass.

SOIL TEXTURAL CLASS

The texture of a soil horizon is, perhaps, its most nearly permanent characteristic. Structure can be quickly modified by management. Often the texture of the plowed layer of an arable soil is modified, not by changes within the surface layer, but by the removal of surface horizons and the development of a new surface soil from a lower natural horizon of different texture, or by the addition of a new surface horizon, say of wind-blown sand or of silt loam settling out of muddy irrigation water. Soil blowing during drought may change soil texture by removing the fine particles from the exposed soil, leaving the surface soil richer in sand and coarse fragments than before.

Although texture is a seemingly simple basic concept in soil science, its consistent application has not been easy. Texture is so basic that terms like sand, clay, and loam are very old indeed. Since both consistence and structure are very important properties related partly to texture, the textural terms, as used earlier, had some connotations of these qualities as well as of texture. As long as their use was confined to soils in Britain and in the eastern part of the United States, the lack of correspondence between field designations of soil textural class and actual size distribution as shown by mechanical analysis was not obviously great. Yet structure and consistence depend on the kind and condition of the clay as well as on the amount of clay, on other soil constituents, and on the living tissue in the soil. As soil scientists began to deal with all soils, many of which are quite unlike the podzolized soils of the temperate forested regions, it became clear that structure, consistence, and texture had to be measured separately. Then too, early dispersion methods were so inadequate that fine granules of clay were actually reported as silt or sand.

Common sources of confusion and error are the agricultural connotations that were associated with the soil textural class names as formerly used. Clay soils were supposed to be sticky and easily puddled; sand soils were supposed to be loose, structureless, and droughty. Such connotations do not hold generally, however, and must be dissociated from general soil textural class names. Among some soil groups, clay soils are sticky and easily puddled, but among others they are not at all. Many sand soils are loose, structureless, and droughty, but some are not. As with each other soil characteristic, no direct relationship that can be applied generally to all soils exists between soil textural class and fertility, productivity, or other inferred qualities. To make such inferences we must also know the other important soil characteristics. Unfortunately, these erroneous correlations are well fixed in some textbooks and other books about soils for farmers and gardeners. Within the universe that the authors of these books actually consider, say Britain and the northeastern part of the United States, the correlations may be approximately correct for most soils; but the writers do not thus clearly limit their universe. As applied to the arctic, the tropics, and the desert they are often seriously wrong, even for the principal soils. Standardization of soil textural class names in terms of size distribution alone is clearly essential if soils of widely different genetic groups are to be compared.

SOIL SEPARATES

Soil separates are the individual size-groups of mineral particles. Sometimes the large sizes—coarse fragments—are included, but usually the groups of particles below 2 mm. in diameter are the only ones called soil separates. Since so many of the chemical and physical reactions in soils occur mainly on the surface of the grains, the fine part is most important. Only 4 pounds of dry clay particles having a diameter of 0.001 mm. have a total surface

Silty clay loam.—Soil material that contains 27 to 40 percent clay and less than 20 percent sand.

Sandy clay.—Soil material that contains 35 percent or more clay and 45 percent or more sand.

Silty clay.—Soil material that contains 40 percent or more clay and 40 percent or more silt.

Clay.—Soil material that contains 40 percent or more clay, less than 45 percent sand, and less than 40 percent silt.

Necessarily these verbal definitions are somewhat complicated and, perhaps, not entirely adequate for unusual mixtures near the boundaries between classes. Some of the definitions are not entirely mutually exclusive, but the information needed to make them so is lacking. Departures from these definitions should be made only after careful joint research between field and laboratory scientists.

In addition to these basic soil textural class names, modified according to the size group of the sand fraction, other terms are also added as modifiers.

Muck, peat, mucky peat, and *peaty muck* are used in place of the textural class names in organic soils—muck for well-decomposed soil material, peat for raw undecomposed material, and peaty muck and mucky peat for intermediate materials. Former definitions have also specified a higher mineral content for muck than for peat. This cannot be followed, however, since many raw peats contain high amounts of mineral matter dropped from the air or washed in by water. The word "mucky" is used as an adjective on the textural class name for horizons of mineral soils, especially of Humic-Gley[4] soils that contain roughly 15 percent or more of partially decomposed organic matter. Horizons designated "mucky loam" or "mucky silt loam" are intergrades between muck and the soil textural class.

The terms for coarse fragments, outlined in the following section, are also added as adjectives to the soil class name and become a part of it. Thus a "gravelly sandy loam" has about 20 percent or more of gravel in the whole soil mass. The basic soil textural class name, however, is determined from the size distribution of the material below 2 mm. in diameter. That is, the percentages used for the standard soil class designations are net after the coarse fragments are excluded.

Phase names for stoniness and rockiness, although not a part of textural soil class names, are used to modify the soil-class part of a soil-type name, as for example, Gloucester *very stony* loam. In the descriptions of all soil horizons, particles larger than 10 inches are excluded from the soil textural class name. It needs to be recalled that classes of stoniness and rockiness are separate from soil class and have a separate place in soil descriptions.

Terms besides those herein defined, such as "wet," "ashy," "cindery," and the like, should be avoided in soil-class names or as modifiers of soil class in soil-type names.

---

[4] Tentative name for soils now included with Wiesenboden and for some included in Half Bog.

FIELD DETERMINATION OF SOIL TEXTURAL CLASS

The determination of soil class is still made in the field mainly by feeling of the soil with the fingers, sometimes supplemented by examination under the hand lens. This requires skill and experience, but good accuracy can be had if the field scientist frequently checks against laboratory results, especially for each soil varying widely from other soils of the area in structure, consistence, and content of organic matter. Moist soil feels different to the fingers than dry soil. Frequently clay particles are grouped into small hard aggregates that give a feel of silt or sand when dry. Because of differences in relative size within the clay fraction itself, soil horizons of similar total clay content vary in physical properties. Variations in kind of clay or in other constituents may give a soil unusual hardness, suggesting a high amount of clay, or an unusual granulation, suggesting a low amount of clay. The soil must be well moistened and rubbed vigorously between the fingers for a proper designation of textural class by feel.

For many years, the field determination of soil textural class actually took precedence over the results of mechanical analyses, which served only as general guides. Some 25 years ago the late Professor C. F. Shaw[5] worked out the following definitions of the basic soil textural classes in terms of field experience and feel:

Sand: Sand is loose and single-grained. The individual grains can readily be seen or felt. Squeezed in the hand when dry it will fall apart when the pressure is released. Squeezed when moist, it will form a cast, but will crumble when touched.

Sandy loam: A sandy loam is a soil containing much sand but which has enough silt and clay to make it somewhat coherent. The individual sand grains can readily be seen and felt. Squeezed when dry, it will form a cast which will readily fall apart, but if squeezed when moist a cast can be formed that will bear careful handling without breaking.

Loam: A loam is a soil having a relatively even mixture of different grades of sand and of silt and clay. It is mellow with a somewhat gritty feel, yet fairly smooth and slightly plastic. Squeezed when dry, it will form a cast that will bear careful handling, while the cast formed by squeezing the moist soil can be handled quite freely without breaking.

Silt loam: A silt loam is a soil having a moderate amount of the fine grades of sand and only a small amount of clay, over half of the particles being of the size called "silt." When dry it may appear cloddy but the lumps can be readily broken, and when pulverized it feels soft and floury. When wet the soil readily runs together and puddles. Either dry or moist it will form casts that can be freely handled without breaking, but when moistened and squeezed between thumb and finger it will not "ribbon" but will give a broken appearance.

Clay loam: A clay loam is a fine textured soil which usually breaks into clods or lumps that are hard when dry. When the moist soil is pinched between the thumb and finger it will form a thin "ribbon" which will break readily, barely sustaining its own weight. The moist soil is plastic and will form a cast that will bear much handling. When kneaded in the hand it does not crumble readily but tends to work into a heavy compact mass.

Clay: A clay is a fine textured soil that usually forms very hard lumps or clods when dry and is quite plastic and usually sticky when wet. When the moist soil is pinched out between the thumb and fingers it will form a long, flexible "ribbon." Some fine clays very high in colloids are friable and lack plasticity in all conditions of moisture.

---

[5] SHAW, C. F. A DEFINITION OF TERMS USED IN SOIL LITERATURE. 1st Internatl. Cong. Soil Sci. Proc. and Papers 5: 38–64. Washington. 1928.

Such definitions are suggestive only. None could be made in these or similar terms that would apply adequately to all soils. Variations in the kind of clay mineral and in the proportion of different exchangeable cations in the clay are too great among the great soil groups. Such kinds of definitions are limited to a group of similar soils.

The dependable definitions, the standards, are those developed from mechanical analyses. Each soil scientist must work out for himself the ability to determine soil class by feel, within each genetic soil group according to the standards established by mechanical analysis. In the progress of soil surveys, samples of soil horizons of doubtful texture should be forwarded to the laboratory and given high priority so that results may be sent back to the field at once to serve as guides. Soil scientists must recall that soil horizons of the same soil textural class, but in different great soil groups, may have a different feel. The scientist needs to adjust his field criteria, not the size-distribution standards.

GENERAL GROUPING OF SOIL TEXTURAL CLASSES

The need for fine distinctions in the texture of soil horizons results in a large number of soil textural classes. Often it is convenient to speak generally of a broad group of textural classes. Although the terms "heavy" and "light" have been used for many years, they are confusing, since the terms arose from the power required in plowing, not the actual weight of the soil. According to local usage in a few places, "light" soils are those low in productivity, including especially ones of clay texture.

An outline of acceptable general terms, in three classes and in five, in relation to the basic soil textural class names, is shown as follows:

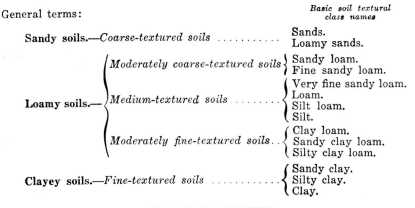

General terms:

Basic soil textural class names

Sandy soils.—*Coarse-textured soils* . . . . Sands. Loamy sands.

Loamy soils.—
- *Moderately coarse-textured soils* — Sandy loam. Fine sandy loam.
- *Medium-textured soils* . . . . — Very fine sandy loam. Loam. Silt loam. Silt.
- *Moderately fine-textured soils* . . — Clay loam. Sandy clay loam. Silty clay loam.

Clayey soils.—*Fine-textured soils* . . . . — Sandy clay. Silty clay. Clay.

COARSE FRAGMENTS

Significant proportions of fragments coarser than very coarse sand and less than 10 inches, if rounded, or 15 inches along the longer axis, if flat, are recognized by an appropriate adjective in the textural soil-class name. Such fragments are regarded as a part of the soil mass. They influence moisture storage, infiltration, and runoff. They influence root growth, especially through their dilution of the mass of active soil. They protect the fine particles from wash and blowing. They are moved with the soil mass in tillage.

Many names and standards have been proposed by geologists and soil scientists for these fragments. Fine distinctions are easily made (but not always easily mapped) because the fragments are easy to see; but finer distinctions than those set forth in table 3 have little or no real significance to soil genesis or behavior. Other variables, like the mineralogy of the clays or the nature of the organic matter, are far more important. The scientist must guard against making finer distinctions among the coarse fragments than those of real significance, simply because he can see them easily in the field.

The accepted adjectives to include in textural soil class names and the size limits of classes of coarse fragments are set forth in outline form in table 3. This table includes the probable maximum of detail required for detailed basic soil surveys. In situations where no useful purpose is served by developing separate mapping units to indicate the separate classes, the classes are grouped and a name given the soil type or soil phase that most clearly indicates the situation. Thus a cobbly loam or a stony phase may include other fragments also listed in the two right hand columns. In this section we shall concern ourselves only with fragments smaller than stones.

TABLE 3.—*Names used for coarse fragments in soils* [1]

Shape and kind of fragments	Size and name of fragments		
	Up to 3 inches in diameter	*3 to 10 inches in diameter*	*More than 10 inches in diameter*
Rounded and subrounded fragments (all kinds of rock).	Gravelly____	Cobbly_____	Stony (or bouldery). [2]
Irregularly shaped angular fragments:			
Chert_____	Cherty_____	Coarse cherty.	Stony.
Other than chert_____	(Angular) gravelly.	Angular cobbly.[3]	Do.
	Up to 6 inches in length	*6 to 15 inches in length*	*More than 15 inches in length*
Thin, flat fragments:			
Thin, flat sandstone, limestone, and schist.	Channery____	Flaggy_____	Stony.
Slate_____	Slaty_____	_____do_____	Do.
Shale_____	Shaly_____	_____do_____	Do.

[1] The individual classes are not always differentiating characteristics of mapping units.
[2] Bouldery is sometimes used where stones are larger than 24 inches.
[3] Formerly called "stony."

The adjectives listed in the first two columns of table 3 are incorporated into the soil textural class designations of horizons when the soil mass contains significant proportions of the fragments, above 15 to 20 percent by volume, depending upon the other soil characteristics. These class names become parts of soil-type names. Where the coarse fragments make up 90 percent or more of the soil mass by volume in the upper 8 inches, the land is classified in the appropriate miscellaneous land type.[6] If necessary to make distinctions of clear significance, another subdivision can be made of the coarse fragments at about 50 percent to give, for example, gravelly loam (20 to 50 percent gravel) and very gravelly loam (50 to 90 percent gravel). The other defined fragments may be handled similarly.

The recommended terms to apply to soil containing above 15 to 20 percent coarse fragments smaller than stones, and less than 90 percent, are defined as follows:

Channery: Soils contain fragments of thin, flat sandstone, limestone, or schist up to 6 inches along the longer axis. A single piece is a *fragment*.

Cherty: Soils have angular fragments that are less than 3 inches in diameter, more than 75 percent of which are chert; *coarse cherty* soils have fragments of 3 to 10 inches (fig. 39). Unless the size distinction is significant to the use capability of the soil, the *cherty* soil includes the whole range up to 10 inches. Most cherty soils are developed from weathered cherty limestone. A single piece is a *chert fragment*.

FIGURE 39.—Fullerton coarse cherty fine sandy loam in Jefferson County, Tenn.

[6] Formerly, some soils having a high proportion of gravel or pebbles in the surface 8 inches were given a textural class name of "gravel," as in Rodman gravel. It is recommended that such soils be classified as gravelly loam, gravelly sandy loam, or gravelly sand, if they have less than 90 percent pebbles, or with the appropriate miscellaneous land type if they have more.

Cobbly: Soils have rounded or partially rounded fragments of rock ranging from 3 to 10 inches in diameter. *Angular cobbly,* formerly included as stony, is similar to cobbly except that fragments are not rounded. A single piece of either is a *cobblestone* or *small stone.*

Flaggy: Soils contain relatively thin fragments 6 to 15 inches long of sandstone, limestone, slate, or shale, or, rarely, of schist. A single piece is a *flagstone.*

Gravelly: Soils have rounded or angular fragments, not prominently flattened, up to 3 inches in diameter. If 75 percent or more of the fragments is chert, the soils are called *cherty.* In descriptions, soils with pebbles mostly over 2 inches in diameter may be called *coarsely gravelly* soils, and those with pebbles mostly under one-half inch in diameter may be called *finely gravelly* soils. An individual piece is a *pebble.* The term "gravel" refers to a mass of pebbles.

Shaly: Soils have flattened fragments of shale less than 6 inches along the longer axis. A single piece is a *shale fragment.*

Slaty: Soils contain fragments of slate less than 6 inches along the longer axis. A single piece is a *slate fragment.*

Stony: Soils contain rock fragments larger than 10 inches in diameter, if rounded, and longer than 15 inches along the longer axis, if flat. Classes are outlined in the following section.

STONINESS AND ROCKINESS

Stones larger than 10 inches in diameter and rock outcrops are not regarded as part of the soil mass as defined by soil textural classes. They have an important bearing on soil use, however, because of their interference with the use of agricultural machinery and their dilution of the soil mass. In fact, stoniness, rockiness, or both, are the differentiating criteria between classes of arable soil and between arable and nonarable soil in many places. In large part the soils developed from glacial till, for example, especially where the till is thin, have characteristics that make them highly responsive to management, except for stoniness. Soil scientists have sometimes neglected this factor, perhaps in part because it is a difficult problem to deal with in the field. Several otherwise useful published soil surveys have failed in their objectives because of the failure to establish meaningful classes of stoniness. Although detailed attention was given soil color, texture, parent material, slope, erosion, depth, and the like, stoniness was so carelessly evaluated that the maps cannot be used to distinguish between potential cropland, pasture land, and forest land, in descending order of intensity.

The suggestions that follow differentiate between loose stones and fixed stones and provide classes within each as required in detailed basic surveys. Admittedly the suggestions are especially aimed to deal with the most complicated situations—where both loose stones and fixed stones exist and influence soil-use capability differently and where the soils are otherwise suitable for intensive use. Generally, loose stones are scattered over the soil area, while rock ledges are more concentrated in strips with relatively rock-free soil between. Such situations are most common in glaciated regions with thin drift, as in New England and parts of the northern Lake States.

Outside the glaciated regions, loose stones are less abundant, although by no means uncommon. In some sections of the country, soils containing fixed stones (rocky soils as here defined), some loose fragments 3 to 10 inches in diameter, and some stones have been called stony for many years. Where no useful purpose is served by dividing into additional types and phases, it should not be done. Thus the classes proposed for stoniness and rockiness may be grouped in the definition of any individual mapping unit.

STONINESS

Stoniness refers to the relative proportion of stones over 10 inches in diameter in or on the soil. The significance of a given number or amount of stones depends upon the other soil characteristics. That is, if a soil is not suited to cultivated crops anyway, the presence of enough stones to interfere with cultivation is not significant and should not be used as a basis for a soil phase separation. If a soil is exceedingly responsive to management for improved pasture, let us say, differences between even high degrees of stoniness are significant and may separate mapping units, as for example, an extremely stony phase of a soil type from the miscellaneous land type, Stony land.

The limits of the classes of stoniness are defined broadly in absolute terms and more specifically in terms of soil use wherever the other soil characteristics are favorable for crops or improved pasture. The able soil classifier avoids fine distinctions according to stoniness where they are not significant as clearly as he recognizes them where they are significant. This means that in the descriptive soil legend and in the soil survey report, stony phases need to be defined *within* the soil series and types. The classes of stoniness are used in definitions of all units of soil classification and may become one criterion for soil series as well as the sole criterion for distinctions among phases within the soil series or soil types.

Classes of stoniness are outlined as follows:

Class 0: No stones or too few to interfere with tillage. Stones cover less than 0.01 percent of the area.

Class 1: Sufficient stones to interfere with tillage but not to make intertilled crops impracticable. (If stones are 1 foot in diameter and about 30 to 100 feet apart, they occupy about 0.01 to 0.1 percent of the surface, and there are about 0.15 to 1.5 cubic yards per acre-foot.) (See fig. 40.)

Class 2: Sufficient stones to make tillage of intertilled crops impracticable, but the soil can be worked for hay crops or improved pasture if other soil characteristics are favorable. (If stones are 1 foot in diameter and about 5 to 30 feet apart, they occupy about 0.1 to 3 percent of the surface, and there are about 1.5 to 50 cubic yards per acre-foot.) (See fig. 41.)

Class 3: Sufficient stones to make all use of machinery impracticable, except for very light machinery or hand tools where other soil characteristics are especially favorable for improved pasture. Soils with this class of stoniness may have some use for wild pasture or forests, depending on other soil characteristics. (If stones are 1 foot in diameter and about 2.5 to 5 feet apart, they occupy about 3 to 15 percent of the surface, and there are about 50 to 240 cubic yards per acre-foot.)

FIGURE 40.—An area of soil having class 1 stoniness, near the margin between class 1 and class 2.

FIGURE 41.—This photograph illustrates class 2 stoniness on a productive soil. On other soils it might be included in class 3.

Class 4: Sufficient stones to make all use of machinery impracticable; the land may have some value for poor pasture or for forestry. (If stones are 1 foot in diameter and are about 2.5 feet or less apart, they occupy 15 to 90 percent of the surface, and there are more than about 240 cubic yards per acre-foot.)

Class 5: Land essentially paved with stones that occupy more than 90 percent of the exposed surface (Rubble).

It should be emphasized that these classes are for general application in soil descriptions. They may or may not be used as phase distinctions. In other words a mapping unit may be defined in terms of more than one class of stoniness. Some individual soils may be defined in terms of classes of stoniness, classes of rockiness, and classes of coarse fragments. Stoniness is not a part of the soil textural class. The terms "stony," very stony," or "exceedingly stony" may modify the soil textural class name in the soil type; but this is simply a brief way of designating stony phases.[7] Soil series descriptions need to include the range of stoniness in terms of classes 0, 1, 2, and 3.

Distinctions between classes 0 and 1 are commonly the basis for stony phases of soil types, and between classes 1 and 2, of very stony phases. Distinctions between soil series and the miscellaneous land type, Stony land, usually come between classes 2 and 3, but may come between classes 3 and 4 if the soil is otherwise unusually responsive to management practices for improved pasture or for forestry.

If differences in potential use for wild pasture or for forestry, related to the parent material, exist among kinds of soil having class 3 stoniness, class 3 stoniness may be called Stony land, (series name) material.

If the distinction between class 3 and class 4 stoniness has no significance, all the land of both classes should be included as one unit, Stony land. But if land with class 3 stoniness is separated from that with class 4 stoniness, either as an extremely stony phase or as Stony land, (series name) material, or if a real difference exists of importance to grazing or forestry, class 4 is called Very stony land.

Land having class 5 stoniness is always called Rubble land, which may, in turn, be part of a complex mapping unit.

Some idealized relationship between the spacing of stones, area covered by stones, and cubic yards per acre in the surface foot are set forth in table 4. These values will vary, of course, with unevenness in spacing and with different sizes of stones.

The relation of classes of stoniness and of rockiness to one another and to some soil classificational units is set forth in table 5.

Areas of the units too small to be enclosed in boundaries are shown on the map by separate stone symbols for each stony phase (see p. 296 *et seq.*) with each symbol defined in terms of the area it represents (pl. 6). Areas of a stony phase enclosed within

---

[7] See section on Units of Soil Classification and Mapping.

boundaries but too small in total area for a place in the map legend are shown on the published map by symbols.

TABLE 4.—*Approximate spacings of stones and cubic yards of stones per acre-foot at selected percentages of area covered*

Diameter of stones (feet)	Spacing of stones from center to center (feet)	Area covered with stones (percent)	Stones per acre-foot (cubic yards)
2	11 5 2.7	3 15 50	97 485 1,616
1	5.5 2.5 1.3	3 15 50	48 242 808
0.5[1]	2.7 1.2 .7	3 15 50	24 121 404

[1] Cobbles.

ROCKINESS

Rockiness refers to the relative proportion of bedrock exposures, either rock outcrops or patches of soil too thin over bedrock for use, in a soil area. "Rocky" is used, perhaps arbitrarily, for soils having fixed rock (bedrock), and "stony" for soils having loose detached fragments of rock.

The classes of rockiness, as of stoniness, are given broad definitions in absolute terms and more specific definitions in terms of soil use for those soils otherwise suitable for crops or improved pasture. Soil areas having the same definitions in terms of area of bedrock exposure may vary widely in the depth of soils between the rock outcrops. Such distinctions need to be made within the soil series definitions. As with stoniness, the classes of rockiness are used in soil series descriptions and can become one criterion for series distinctions or the sole criterion for phase distinctions. Two or more classes may be combined in one mapping unit. Some mapping units may also have classes of stoniness and of coarse fragments.

The relationships to soil use suggested in the definitions of the classes apply mainly to areas of soil in humid regions that are otherwise responsive to management. The definitions of actual soil phases must take account of the alternative management practices that can be used for seeding, harvesting, weed control, and the like.

In each descriptive legend and soil survey report, rocky phases need to be defined specifically within each soil series or type.

The classes of rockiness are as follows:

Class 0: No bedrock exposures or too few to interfere with tillage. Less than 2 percent bedrock exposed.

Class 1: Sufficient bedrock exposures to interfere with tillage but not to make intertilled crops impracticable. Depending upon how the pattern affects tillage, rock exposures are roughly 100 to 300 feet apart and cover about 2 to 10 percent of the surface.

Class 2: Sufficient bedrock exposures to make tillage of intertilled crops impracticable, but soil can be worked for hay crops or improved pasture if the other soil characteristics are favorable. Rock exposures are roughly 30 to 100 feet apart and cover about 10 to 25 percent of the surface, depending upon the pattern (fig. 42).

FIGURE 42.—Area of soil with class 2 rockiness.

Class 3: Sufficient rock outcrop to make all use of machinery impracticable, except for light machinery where other soil characteristics are especially favorable for improved pasture. May have some use for wild pasture or forests, depending on the other soil characteristics. Rock exposures, or patches of soil too thin over rock for use, are roughly 10 to 30 feet apart and cover about 25 to 50 percent of the surface, depending upon the pattern.

Class 4: Sufficient rock outcrop (or of very thin soil over rock) to make all use of machinery impracticable. The land may have some value for poor pasture or for forestry. Rock outcrops are about 10 feet apart or less and cover some 50 to 90 percent of the area.

Class 5: Land for which over 90 percent of the surface is exposed bedrock (Rock outcrop).

The distinctions between classes 0, 1, and 2 are commonly the bases for phases of soil types.[8] As with stony phases, these terms are added as adjectives to the soil textural class part of the soil-

[8] See section on Units of Soil Classification and Mapping.

TABLE 5.—*Relation of classes of stoniness and rockiness[1] to one another and to some soil classificational units*

	Stoniness			Rockiness	
Class	Approximate percentage of surface covered	Modification in name of classificational unit to indicate degree of stoniness	Class	Approximate percentage of rock-exposed surface[4]	Modification in name of classificational unit to indicate degree of rockiness
0	Less than 0.01	No modification. Example: Gloucester loam.	0	Less than 2	No modification. Example: Hagerstown loam.
1	0.01 to 0.1	Stony (phase).[2] Example: Gloucester stony loam.	1	2 to 10	Rocky (phase).[2] Example: Hagerstown rocky loam.
2	0.1 to 3.0	Very stony (phase). Example: Gloucester very stony loam.	2	10 to 25	Very rocky (phase). Example: Hagerstown very rocky loam.
3	3 to 15	Any one of following: Extremely stony (phase). Example: Gloucester extremely stony loam. Stony land.[3] Stony land (Gloucester soil material).	3	25 to 50	Any one of following: Extremely rocky (phase). Example: Hagerstown extremely rocky loam. Rock land.[3] Rock land (Hagerstown material).
4	15 to 90	Either of following: Stony land.[3] Very stony land.	4	50 to 90	Rock land.[3]
5	Above 90	Rubble land.	5	Above 90	Rock outcrop.

[1] This table is a general guide in detailed basic surveys where it is important to differentiate among several classes and between stoniness and rockiness. With soils having rockiness, stoniness, and some coarse fragments, and for which separation by classes serves no useful purpose, stony phases may be recognized.

[2] The word "phase" usually can be omitted; but, for example, Gloucester stony loam is simply a short way of naming the unit, Gloucester loam, stony phase. Theoretically, at least, if all areas of a soil type have one class name of stoniness, say class 2, "very stony" is a descriptive adjective of the type and there are no phases of stoniness.

[3] Commonly, the distinction between classes 3 and 4 is not necessary, and the whole range of both classes is included as *Stony land* or *Rock land*.

[4] Including soil too thin over rock for useful plant growth.

type name to give names like Hagerstown rocky loam, Hagerstown very rocky loam, or Hagerstown extremely rocky loam. These are three phases, plus the unnamed nonrocky phase, within the Hagerstown loam.

The distinctions between classes 2 and 3 or between classes 3 and 4 are commonly the dividing lines between the soil series and the miscellaneous land type, Rock land. If the soil is not responsive to management for improved pasture with rockiness greater than class 2, the distinction is made there; and land with class 3 rockiness is designated as Rock land. If the soil is especially responsive to soil management practices for improved pasture and can be tilled with very light machinery, the soil is named and placed in an extremely rocky phase. If the land cannot be used practicably for improved pasture but the distinction between several kinds of Rock land with class 3 rockiness is important, a unit is designated as Rock land, (series name) soil material.

If distinctions between classes 3 and 4 of rockiness are not significant, all the land in both classes is called Rock land. If the distinction between these two classes is significant, land of class 3 rockiness may be indicated as an extremely rocky phase of a soil type or as Rock land, (series name) soil material, and the term Rock land reserved for that having class 4 rockiness.

Land with class 5 rockiness is always classified as Rock outcrop even though a little soil may be found between the outcrops or the ledges.

The relationship of classes of stoniness to classes of rockiness, and of these to some soil classificational units, is shown in table 5.

Areas of rocky phases too small to enclose with boundaries are not shown on the map. Instead symbols for rock outcrops and for rock ledges are used (pls. 4 and 6). In each survey, the area that each represents needs to be defined.

COMBINED CLASSES OF STONINESS AND ROCKINESS

Frequently it is necessary to combine classes of rockiness and stoniness. In such instances the combined influence of the two conditions on soil use needs to be considered. Soils having class 1 stoniness and class 1 rockiness might be named as a very stony and rocky phase of a soil type, or simply as a stony phase. Land having both class 2 rockiness or higher and class 2 stoniness or higher would doubtless need to be put into a miscellaneous land type, as Stony rock land.

SOIL STRUCTURE

Soil structure refers to the aggregation of primary soil particles into compound particles, or clusters of primary particles, which are separated from adjoining aggregates by surfaces of weakness. The exteriors of some aggregates have thin, often dark-colored, surface films which perhaps help to keep them apart. Other aggregates have surfaces and interiors of like color, and the forces holding the aggregates together appear to be wholly internal.

An individual natural soil aggregate is called a *ped*, in contrast to (1) a *clod*, caused by disturbance, such as plowing or digging, that molds the soil to a transient mass that slakes with repeated wetting and drying, (2) a *fragment* caused by rupture of the soil mass across natural surfaces of weakness, or (3) a *concretion* caused by local concentrations of compounds that irreversibly cement the soil grains together.

The importance of soil structure in soil classification and in influencing soil productivity can scarcely be overemphasized. The capability of any soil for the growth of plants and its response to management depends as much on its structure as on its fertility. Generally, in the United States, soils with aggregates of spheroidal shape have much pore space between aggregates, have more rapid permeability, and are more productive than soils of comparable fertility that are massive or even coarsely blocky or prismatic. In other parts of the world, some soils are overgranulated. Some Latosols have such well-developed spheroidal peds that the moisture-holding capacity is low, too few contacts exist between roots and soil, and the soils are relatively unproductive.

Field descriptions of soil structure note (1) the shape and arrangement, (2) the size, and (3) the distinctness and durability of the visible aggregates or peds. Field terminology for structure consists of separate sets of terms designating each of these three qualities, which by combination form the names for structure. Shape and arrangement of peds is designated as *type* of soil structure; size of peds, as *class;* and degree of distinctness, as *grades.*[1] The structural pattern of a soil horizon also includes the shapes and sizes of pore spaces as well as those of the peds themselves.

There are four primary types of structure: (1) Platy, with particles arranged around a plane, generally horizontal; (2) prismlike, with particles arranged around a vertical line and bounded by relatively flat vertical surfaces; (3) blocklike or polyhedral, with particles arranged around a point and bounded by flat or rounded surfaces which are casts of the molds formed

---

[1] For a useful background discussion of these concepts, see NIKIFOROFF, C. C. MORPHOLOGICAL CLASSIFICATION OF SOIL STRUCTURE. Soil Sci. 52: 193–212, illus. 1941.

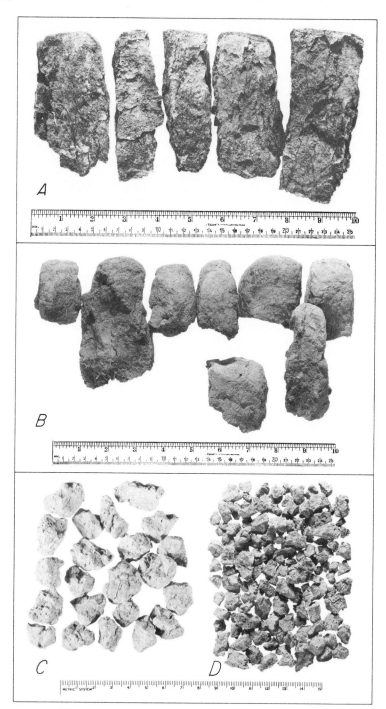

FIGURE 43.—Photographs of characteristic structural aggregates: *A*, prismatic; *B*, columnar; *C*, angular blocky; and *D*, subangular blocky.

by the faces of surrounding peds; and (4) spheroidal or polyhedral, with particles arranged around a point and bounded by
curved or very irregular surfaces that are not accommodated to
the adjoining aggregates. Each of the last three have two subtypes. Under prismlike the subtypes are *prismatic*, without
rounded upper ends, and *columnar*, with rounded caps. The subtypes of blocklike are *angular blocky*, bounded by planes intersecting at relatively sharp angles, and *subangular blocky*, having
mixed rounded and plane faces with vertices mostly rounded.
If the term "blocky" is used alone, angular blocky is understood.
Spheroidal is subdivided into *granular*, relatively nonporous, and
crumb, very porous. Each type of structure includes peds that
vary in shape, and detailed soil descriptions may require supplemental statements about the shape of the individual peds (figs.
43 and 44).

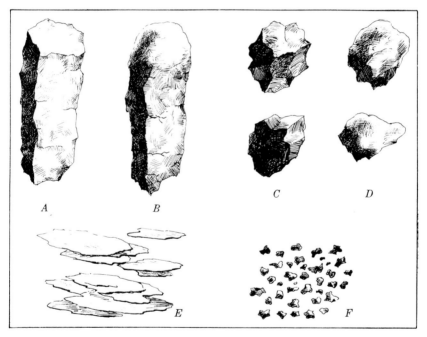

FIGURE 44.—Drawings illustrating some of the types of soil structure: *A*,
prismatic; *B*, columnar; *C*, angular blocky; *D*, subangular blocky; *E*,
platy; and F, granular.

The names in the preceding paragraph placed in italics are the
terms most used in descriptions of soil horizons. *Nut* has been
used for blocklike peds, but is not recommended; *nuciform* has
been an optional alternative for subangular blocky, but *subangular blocky* is recommended. It is difficult for many to dis-
associate a size connotation from terms like *nut* and *nuciform*. For
this reason some confuse very fine blocky with granular. Terms

TABLE 6.—*Types and classes of soil structure*

TYPE (Shape and arrangement of peds)

Class	Platelike with one dimension (the vertical) limited and greatly less than the other two; arranged around a horizontal plane; faces mostly horizontal.	Prismlike with two dimensions (the horizontal) limited and considerably less than the vertical; arranged around a vertical line; vertical faces well defined; vertices angular.		Blocklike; polyhedronlike, or spheroidal, with three dimensions of the same order of magnitude, arranged around a point.			
				Blocklike; blocks or polyhedrons having plane or curved surfaces that are casts of the molds formed by the faces of the surrounding peds.		Spheroids or polyhedrons having plane or curved surfaces which have slight or no accommodation to the faces of surrounding peds.	
		Without rounded caps.	With rounded caps.	Faces flattened; most vertices sharply angular.	Mixed rounded and flattened faces with many rounded vertices.	Relatively non-porous peds.	Porous peds.
	Platy	Prismatic	Columnar	(Angular) Blocky [1]	Subangular blocky [2]	Granular	Crumb
Very fine or very thin.	Very thin platy; <1 mm.	Very fine prismatic; <10 mm.	Very fine columnar; <10 mm.	Very fine angular blocky; <5 mm.	Very fine subangular blocky; <5 mm.	Very fine granular; <1 mm.	Very fine crumb; <1 mm.
Fine or thin.	Thin platy; 1 to 2 mm.	Fine prismatic; 10 to 20 mm.	Fine columnar; 10 to 20 mm.	Fine angular blocky; 5 to 10 mm.	Fine subangular blocky; 5 to 10 mm.	Fine granular; 1 to 2 mm.	Fine crumb; 1 to 2 mm.
Medium.	Medium platy; 2 to 5 mm.	Medium prismatic; 20 to 50 mm.	Medium columnar; 20 to 50 mm.	Medium angular blocky; 10 to 20 mm.	Medium subangular blocky; 10 to 20 mm.	Medium granular; 2 to 5 mm.	Medium crumb; 2 to 5 mm.
Coarse or thick.	Thick platy; 5 to 10 mm.	Coarse prismatic; 50 to 100 mm.	Coarse columnar; 50 to 100 mm.	Coarse angular blocky; 20 to 50 mm.	Coarse subangular blocky; 20 to 50 mm.	Coarse granular; 5 to 10 mm.	
Very coarse or very thick.	Very thick platy; >10 mm.	Very coarse prismatic; >100 mm.	Very coarse columnar; >100 mm.	Very coarse angular blocky; >50 mm.	Very coarse subangular blocky; >50 mm.	Very coarse granular; >10 mm.	

[1] (a) Sometimes called *nut.* (b) The word "angular" in the name can ordinarily be omitted.
[2] Sometimes called *nuciform, nut,* or *subangular nut.* Since the size connotation of these terms is a source of great confusion to many, they are not recommended.

used to designate types of soil structure refer *only* to shape and arrangement and do not specify size.

Five size classes are recognized in each of the primary types. The names of these and their size limits, which vary with the four primary types for shape and arrangement, are given in table 6.

Grade of structure is the degree of aggregation and expresses the differential between cohesion within aggregates and adhesion between aggregates. In field practice, grade of structure is determined mainly by noting the durability of the aggregates and the proportions between aggregated and unaggregated material that result when the aggregates are displaced or gently crushed. Grade of structure varies with the moistening of the soil and should be described at the most important moisture contents of the soil horizon. The principal description of the structure of a soil horizon should refer to its normal moisture content, although attention should be called to any striking contrasts in structure under other moisture conditions to which the soil is subject. If grade is designated at an unstated moisture content, it is assumed that the soil is nearly dry or only very slightly moist, which is commonly that part of the range in soil moisture in which soil structure is most strongly expressed.

With exposure, structure may become much altered, often much stronger. Old road cuts are not suitable places to determine the grade of structure, but they often afford a clue to the type of structure present where the grade is so weak that it cannot be identified in the undisturbed soil.

Terms for grade of structure are as follows:

0. *Structureless.*—That condition in which there is no observable aggregation or no definite orderly arrangement of natural lines of weakness. *Massive* if coherent; *single grain* if noncoherent.

1. *Weak.*—That degree of aggregation characterized by poorly formed indistinct peds that are barely observable in place. When disturbed, soil material that has this grade of structure breaks into a mixture of few entire peds, many broken peds, and much unaggregated material. If necessary for comparison, this grade may be subdivided into *very weak* and *moderately weak.*

2. *Moderate.*—That grade of structure characterized by well-formed distinct peds that are moderately durable and evident but not distinct in undisturbed soil. Soil material of this grade, when disturbed, breaks down into a mixture of many distinct entire peds, some broken peds, and little unaggregated material. Examples are the loam A horizons of typical Chestnut soils in the granular type, and clayey B horizons of such Red-Yellow Podzolic soils as the Boswell in the blocky type.

3. *Strong.*—That grade of structure characterized by durable peds that are quite evident in undisplaced soil, that adhere weakly to one another, and that withstand displacement and become separated when the soil is disturbed. When removed from the profile, soil material of this grade of structure consists very largely of entire peds and includes few broken peds and little or no unaggregated material. If necessary for comparison, this grade may be subdivided into *moderately strong* and *very strong.* Examples of strong grade of structure are in the granular-type A horizons of the typical Chernozem and in the columnar-type B horizons of the typical solodized-Solonetz.

The sequence followed in combining the three terms to form the compound name of the structure is (1) grade (distinctness), (2) class (size), and (3) type (shape). For example, the designation for the soil structure in which the peds are loosely packed and roundish but not extremely porous, dominantly between 1 and 2 mm. in diameter, and quite distinct is *strong fine granular*. The designation of structure by grade, class, and type can be modified with any other appropriate terms wherever necessary to describe other characteristics of the peds.

Many soil horizons have compound structure consisting of one or more sets of smaller peds held together as larger peds. Compound structures are so described: for example, *compound moderate very coarse prismatic and moderate medium granular*. Soil that has one structural form when in place may assume some other form when disturbed. When removed, the larger peds may fall into smaller peds, such as large prisms into medium blocks.

With increasing disturbance or pressure any aggregate breaks into smaller particles. These finer particles may or may not be peds, depending on whether their form and size are determined by surfaces of weakness between natural aggregates or by the place and direction of the pressures applied. Mere breakage into fragments larger than the soil grains without some orderly shape and size should not be confused with soil structure. Massive soil horizons, without structure, can be shattered into fragments—so can glass. Such fragments are not peds.

SOIL CONSISTENCE

Soil consistence comprises the attributes of soil material that are expressed by the degree and kind of cohesion and adhesion or by the resistance to deformation or rupture. Every soil material has consistence irrespective of whether the mass be large or small, in a natural condition or greatly disturbed, aggregated or structureless, moist or dry. Although consistence and structure are interrelated, structure deals with the shape, size, and definition of natural aggregates that result from variations in the forces of attraction within a soil mass, whereas consistence deals with the strength and nature of such forces themselves.

The terminology for consistence includes separate terms for description at three standard moisture contents (dry, moist, and wet). If moisture conditions are not stated in using any consistence term, the moisture condition is that under which the particular term is defined. Thus *friable* used without statement of the moisture content specifies *friable when moist;* likewise, *hard* used alone means *hard when dry,* and *plastic* means *plastic when wet.* If a term is used to describe consistence at some moisture content *other* than the standard condition under which the term is defined, *a statement of the moisture condition is essential.* Usually it is unnecessary to describe consistence at all three standard moisture conditions. The consistence when moist is commonly the most significant, and a soil description with this omitted can hardly be regarded as complete; the consistence when dry is generally useful but may be irrelevant in descriptions of soil materials that are never dry; and the consistence when wet is unessential in the description of many soils but extremely important·in some.

Although evaluation of consistence involves some disturbance, unless otherwise stated, descriptions of consistence customarily refer to that of soil from undisturbed horizons. In addition, descriptions of consistence under moist or wet conditions carry an implication that disturbance causes little modification of consistence or that the original consistence can be almost restored by pressing the material together. Where such an implication is misleading, as in compacted layers, the consistence both before and after disturbance may require separate description. Then, too, compound consistences occur, as in a loose mass of hard granules. In a detailed description of soils having compound structure, the consistence of the mass as a whole and of its parts should be stated.

A number of terms, including *brittle, crumbly, dense, elastic, fluffy,*[1] *mealy, mellow, soft, spongy, stiff, tight, tough,* and some

[1] As used in describing soils, *fluffy* denotes a combination of loose to very friable consistence and low bulk density.

others, which have often been used in descriptions of consistence, are not here defined. These are all common words of well-known meanings. Some are indispensable for describing unusual conditions not covered by other terms. They are useful in nontechnical descriptions where a little accuracy may be sacrificed to use a term familiar to lay readers. Whenever needed, these or other terms for consistence not defined in this *Manual* should be employed with meanings as given in standard dictionaries.

The terms used in soil descriptions for consistence follow:

I. CONSISTENCE WHEN WET

Consistence when wet is determined at or slightly above field capacity.

A. **Stickiness.**—Stickiness is the quality of adhesion to other objects. For field evaluation of stickiness, soil material is pressed between thumb and finger and its adherence noted. Degrees of stickiness are described as follows:

   0. *Nonsticky:* After release of pressure, practically no soil material adheres to thumb or finger.
   1. *Slightly sticky:* After pressure, soil material adheres to both thumb and finger but comes off one or the other rather cleanly. It is not appreciably stretched when the digits are separated.
   2. *Sticky:* After pressure, soil material adheres to both thumb and finger and tends to stretch somewhat and pull apart rather than pulling free from either digit.
   3. *Very sticky:* After pressure, soil material adheres strongly to both thumb and forefinger and is decidedly stretched when they are separated.

B. **Plasticity.**—Plasticity is the ability to change shape continuously under the influence of an applied stress and to retain the impressed shape on removal of the stress. For field determination of plasticity, roll the soil material between thumb and finger and observe whether or not a wire or thin rod of soil can be formed. If helpful to the reader of particular descriptions, state the range of moisture content within which plasticity continues, as plastic when slightly moist or wetter, plastic when moderately moist or wetter, and plastic only when wet, or as plastic within a wide, medium, or narrow range of moisture content. Express degree of resistance to deformation at or slightly above field capacity as follows:

   0. *Nonplastic:* No wire is formable.
   1. *Slightly plastic:* Wire formable but soil mass easily deformable.
   2. *Plastic:* Wire formable and moderate pressure required for deformation of the soil mass.
   3. *Very plastic:* Wire formable and much pressure required for deformation of the soil mass.

Consistence when moist is determined at a moisture content approximately midway between air dry and field capacity. At this moisture content most soil materials exhibit a form of consistence characterized by (a) tendency to break into smaller masses rather than into powder, (b) some deformation prior to rupture, (c) absence of brittleness, and (d) ability of the material after disturbance to cohere again when pressed together. The resistance decreases with moisture content, and accuracy of field descriptions of this consistence is limited by the accuracy of estimating moisture content. To evaluate this consistence, select and attempt to crush in the hand a mass that appears slightly moist.

0. *Loose:* Noncoherent.
1. *Very friable:* Soil material crushes under very gentle pressure but coheres when pressed together.
2. *Friable:* Soil material crushes easily under gentle to moderate pressure between thumb and forefinger, and coheres when pressed together.
3. *Firm:* Soil material crushes under moderate pressure between thumb and forefinger but resistance is distinctly noticeable.
4. *Very firm:* Soil material crushes under strong pressure; barely crushable between thumb and forefinger.
5. *Extremely firm:* Soil material crushes only under very strong pressure; cannot be crushed between thumb and forefinger and must be broken apart bit by bit.

The term *compact* denotes a combination of firm consistence and close packing or arrangement of particles and should be used only in this sense. It can be given degrees by use of "very" and "extremely."

The consistence of soil materials when dry is characterized by rigidity, brittleness, maximum resistance to pressure, more or less tendency to crush to a powder or to fragments with rather sharp edges, and inability of crushed material to cohere again when pressed together. To evaluate, select an air-dry mass and break in the hand.

0. *Loose:* Noncoherent.
1. *Soft:* Soil mass is very weakly coherent and fragile; breaks to powder or individual grains under very slight pressure.
2. *Slightly hard:* Weakly resistant to pressure; easily broken between thumb and forefinger.
3. *Hard:* Moderately resistant to pressure; can be broken in the hands without difficulty but is barely breakable between thumb and forefinger.
4. *Very hard:* Very resistant to pressure; can be broken in the hands only with difficulty; not breakable between thumb and forefinger.

5. *Extremely hard:* Extremely resistant to pressure; cannot be broken in the hands.

IV. CEMENTATION

Cementation of soil material refers to a brittle hard consistence caused by some cementing substance other than clay minerals, such as calcium carbonate, silica, or oxides or salts of iron and aluminum. Typically the cementation is altered little if any by moistening; the hardness and brittleness persist in the wet condition. Semireversible cements, which generally resist moistening but soften under prolonged wetting, occur in some soils and give rise to soil layers having a cementation that is pronounced when dry but very weak when wet. Some layers cemented with calcium carbonate soften somewhat with wetting. Unless stated to the contrary, descriptions of cementation imply that the condition is altered little if any by wetting. If the cementation is greatly altered by moistening, it should be so stated. Cementation may be either continuous or discontinuous within a given horizon.

1. *Weakly cemented:* Cemented mass is brittle and hard but can be broken in the hands.
2. *Strongly cemented:* Cemented mass is brittle and harder than can be broken in the hand but is easily broken with a hammer.
3. *Indurated:* Very strongly cemented; brittle, does not soften under prolonged wetting, and is so extremely hard that for breakage a sharp blow with a hammer is required; hammer generally rings as a result of the blow.

SOIL REACTION

Soil reaction receives special emphasis in soil classification, partly because of its direct importance but mainly because of other soil qualities, less easily determined, that may be inferred from it. Early field workers distinguished roughly between acid soils and alkaline soils by testing for carbonates with dilute acid and by the use of litmus paper and phenolphthalein. Since then, better field methods, based upon laboratory methods, have become available.

pH

The intensity of soil acidity or alkalinity is expressed in pH—the logarithm of the reciprocal of the H-ion concentration. With this notation, pH 7 is neutral; lower values indicate acidity; and higher values show alkalinity. Soil horizons vary in pH from a little below 3.5 to a little above 9.5.

The corresponding terms to use for ranges in pH are as follows:

	pH		pH
Extremely acid	Below 4.5	Neutral[1]	6.6–7.3
Very strongly acid	4.5–5.0	Mildly alkaline	7.4–7.8
Strongly acid	5.1–5.5	Moderately alkaline	7.9–8.4
Medium acid	5.6–6.0	Strongly alkaline	8.5–9.0
Slightly acid	6.1–6.5	Very strongly alkaline	9.1 and higher

[1] Strict neutrality is pH 7.0, but in field work those soils between pH 6.6 and 7.3 are called neutral. In the rare cases where significant, the terms very slightly acid and very mildly alkaline may be used for soils of pH 6.6 to 6.9 and 7.1 to 7.3, respectively.

Values for pH of the soil horizons are important in soil classification and in the identification of soils in the field.

Generally, pH reflects the base status of the soil. Acid soils are high in exchangeable hydrogen, and alkaline soils, high in exchangeable bases. The base status of the several horizons, taken with their other characteristics, tells a lot about the kind and degree of weathering, the composition of the parent material, the amount of leaching, and the influence of the vegetation. Since other factors, like the kind of clay, kind and amount of organic matter, the particular exchangeable bases present, and the soluble salts in the soil, influence pH, the relationship between pH and base status is not the same for all kinds of soil.

Then, too, pH is a measure of the intensity of acidity or alkalinity, not the capacity or total amount. Other things being equal, soils rich in clay or in organic matter have greater reserves of acidity or alkalinity than sandy soils or those low in organic matter. The reserves are very high in peat and muck. With the same clay content, Latosols or latosolic soils have less reserve than Podzols or podzolic soils. A soil with a high capacity or reserve is said to be well buffered.

A pH value much above 7 usually indicates the presence of some free carbonates of calcium, magnesium, or both, but not necessarily so. Some Solonetz soils of pH 8.5 show no test for carbonates in the field. On the other hand, a long-cropped cherno-zemic Wiesenboden may show tiny particles of carbonate that react to acid, although the soil horizon (A_p) as a whole has pH 5.5.

Soils having pH values higher than 8.5 nearly always contain significant amounts of exchangeable sodium; so do some soils below that pH, for example, those relatively high in exchangeable sodium and hydrogen but low in exchangeable calcium.

Plants are partly responsible for differences in soil pH. Some feed very heavily on sodium, which they return to the surface. The reaction of soil under such shrubs may be more than one whole pH unit more alkaline to a depth of 2 feet than that of soil only 2 feet away. Other plants feed very heavily on calcium, and the decomposition of their remains tends to keep the soil neutral. Still other plants feed very lightly on bases. The decomposition of their remains tends to produce acidity in the surface of the soil.

This relationship is mutual: Plants that leave acid-forming litter usually grow better where the soil is acid. Those requiring lots of lime fail to thrive on very acid soils. Yet, as with all other soil characteristics, the relationship between soil pH and plant growth varies with other soil characteristics. Some beech trees, for example, usually grow on soils well supplied with lime, yet if all of the other growth factors are favorable, they grow well and produce an acid litter where lime is scarce.

Plant nutritionists have investigated the ranges in pH for optimum growth of nearly all common plants. Such values are useful but are not specific for contrasting soils. That is, the soil pH range for optimum growth of red clover, for example, appears to be lower in Podzols than in Gray-Brown Podzolic soils. We must recall that soil pH is a sort of average, or statistical, value for many separate points within the soil horizon. The same pH value, say 6.5, for two soil samples, may represent the average of two quite different ranges in pH within the soil masses examined.

Besides its great importance in soil classification, soil pH is considered with other soil characteristics as a basis for predicting the lime needs of acid soils. For most crop plants, pH 6.5 is within the optimum soil pH range. Generally, the plant nutrients needed by crop plants are most likely to be available at around pH 6.5.

The party chief needs to gather the best available information about crop and soil requirements for liming in his soil survey area in order to make interpretations for the soil survey report. These should be reviewed in cooperating agricultural experiment stations. Table 7 suggests some general guides[1], although in most developed areas better local guides may be had. Better recommendations can be made with values for both pH and for exchangeable calcium than with those for pH alone.

---

[1] From EFFICIENT USE OF FERTILIZERS, Ignatieff, V., ed., as cited in the General Bibliography.

MEASUREMENTS OF SOIL pH

Methods for determining soil pH are either electrometric or colorimetric.[2] Electrometric methods are usually used in the laboratory. The pH meter with a glass electrode is the common instrument. If precise determinations are required in the field, especially where salts are likely to interfere, a field pH meter is available. A soil-water ratio of 1 to 1 is recommended for routine work. The suspension is stirred vigorously, allowed to stand for 30 minutes, and again well stirred immediately before making the measurement. For organic soils, a soil-water ratio of 1 to 5 is generally best, with a standing period of 2 hours.

Indicators or dyes that have different colors at different pH values are commonly used in the field. Only simple equipment is required.

TABLE 7.—*Approximate amounts of finely ground limestone needed to raise the pH of a 7-inch layer of soil as indicated*[1]

Soil regions and textural classes	Limestone requirements—		
	From pH 3.5 to pH 4.5	from pH 4.5 to pH 5.5	From pH 5.5 to pH 6.5
Soils of warm-temperate and tropical regions:[2]	*Tons per acre*	*Tons per acre*	*Tons per acre*
Sand and loamy sand	0.3	0.3	0.4
Sandy loam	....	.5	.7
Loam	....	.8	1.0
Silt loam	....	1.2	1.4
Clay loam	....	1.5	2.0
Muck	[3]2.5	3.3	3.8
Soils of cool-temperate and temperate regions:[4]			
Sand and loamy sand	.4	.5	.6
Sandy loam	....	.8	1.3
Loam	....	1.2	1.7
Silt loam	....	1.5	2.0
Clay loam	....	1.9	2.3
Muck	[3]2.9	3.8	4.3

[1] All limestone goes through a 2 mm. mesh screen and at least ½ through a 0.15 mm. mesh screen. With coarser materials, applications need to be greater. For burned lime about ½ the amounts given are used; for hydrated lime about ¾.
[2] Red-Yellow Podzolic, Red Latosol, etc.
[3] The suggestions for muck soils are for those essentially free of sand and clay. For those containing much sand or clay the amounts should be reduced to values midway between those given for muck and the corresponding class of mineral soil. If the mineral soils are unusually low in organic matter, the recommendations should be reduced about 25 percent; if unusually high, increased by about 25 percent, or even more.
[4] Podzol, Gray-Brown Podzolic, Brown Forest, Brown Podzolic, etc.

A number of satisfactory kits for field use can be obtained from firms handling scientific supplies.

[2] REED, G. F., and CUMMINGS, R. W. SOIL REACTION: GLASS ELECTRODE AND COLORIMETRIC METHODS FOR DETERMINING PH VALUES OF SOILS. Soil Sci. 59 (1): 97–104. 1945.

Methods using indicator dyes can give satisfactory results with mineral soils between about pH 4.5 and pH 7.5. That is, an experienced operator should expect results within 0.2 to 0.4 units of the pH values determined electrometrically. Such results require care in getting representative samples and the avoidance of contaminations from perspiration, dust, chemicals, and the like.

Common specific indicators used in the field and their pH ranges are as follows:

Indicator	pH range
Bromcresol green	3.8–5.6
Chlorphenol red	5.2–6.8
Bromthymol blue	6.0–7.6
Phenol red	6.8–8.4
Cresol red	7.2–8.8
Thymol blue	8.0–9.6

Some field kits contain mixtures of the indicators.

In many soil survey areas numerous pH measurements are required. A few mapping units are separated mainly on the basis of pH determinations in some part of the soil. A few duplicate samples should be collected from time to time for immediate determination in the laboratory as a check on the reliability of the field-determined value, especially of soils having low or high pH value, excess salts, or abundant amounts of organic matter.

For an accurate estimation of soil reaction, samples for test are needed from different parts of the soil horizon, especially in one having well-developed blocky or prismatic structure. In a columnar B_2 horizon, for example, the soil may have a pH of 7 or less between the columns to a depth of 20 or 24 inches, and a pH over 7.5 just under the caps in the interior of the columns.

FREE CARBONATES

The presence of free carbonates in the soil and parent material may be tested for with 10-percent hydrochloric acid. In testing very dry soils, the emission of air bubbles should not be confused with slight effervescence. The reaction is indicated as slight, strong, or violent effervescence.

Dolomite is more resistant to the acid than calcite. Some time needs to be allowed for the acid to react, or the presence of dolomite may be overlooked. In some rock materials, a test of the powdered rock or the use of hot hydrochloric acid is necessary for the reaction.

It may be useful to note whether the effervescence is due primarily to fragments of limestone, to accretions or concretions of lime, or to the fine earth itself. The exact boundaries of effervescing material in relationship to structural aggregates and to depth are important. The pattern of free carbonates in the soil profile and in the parent material is a useful criterion for deciding between soil series. Where the presence of carbonates is doubtful or where quantitative results are required, soil samples may be sent to the laboratory for carbonate determinations.

SPECIAL FORMATIONS IN SOIL PROFILES

Special formations include such features as concretions, pans, efflorescences, and krotovinas. These features are important because of their influence on alternative uses of soils or especially because they often indicate soil qualities that are not directly observable in the field.

CONCRETIONS

Concretions are hardened local concentrations of certain chemical compounds that form indurated grains or nodules of various sizes, shapes, and colors. They are commonly formed from local accumulation of calcite (calcium carbonate), iron, and manganese oxides. Other minerals, such as bauxite, will readily form concretions but are not common in soils.

Lime concretions.—Lime concretions usually consist of calcite along with other included soil constituents. Many are irregularly rounded (fig. 45, right) and vary in diameter from a millimeter

FIGURE 45.—The concretion on the left has been fractured to show concentric lamination. The center concretion has been broken to show its cavernous nature. The right concretion shows the irregularly rounded shape of the typical lime concretion.

or two up to as much as 2 feet. Some have more or less concentric laminations (fig. 45, left) ; others are cavernous (fig. 45, center). Yet lime concretions take many forms as spheres, ellipsoids, rounded shapes with pointed protuberances, rough and irregular forms, tubular or branched tubular forms, and rough plates.

The formation of lime concretions in soil is not perfectly understood, and care must be used in drawing conclusions from their presence. Since they presumably form when ground waters become supersaturated, they have often been considered characteristic of soils developed from calcareous parent materials under a subhumid or arid climate. Yet, they are not uncommon in soils of humid regions that have formed in postglacial times. Many Humic-Gley soils (Wiesenboden) in central and northern Illinois, for example, have horizons with abundant lime concretions of the cavernous type. Further, in drawing conclusions from the presence of lime concretions, it must be recalled that they may be forming now, under the present processes of weathering and soil formation, or they may simply be inherited from the parent material formed under other conditions. Loess is a parent material which frequently contains lime concretions.

Often lime concretions are found near or even on the surface. Commonly this indicates truncation through erosion or soil blowing, but not always. Burrowing animals may have brought concretions to the surface from considerable depths. Many soils, especially heavy clays in regions of alternating wet and dry seasons, are "self-swallowing." During the dry season great cracks open up; then, with the coming of the rains, any dry, loose soil in the immediate surface is washed down into the cracks before they close. As the soil moistens and the cracks close, the lower soil between them is pushed up. Finally soil from the lower layers, possibly including concretions, appears at the surface.

Iron and manganese concretions.—Accumulations of iron and manganese oxides occur in a great many soils. Those in the form of indurated and irregularly spherical pellets are called concretions, or pisolites. They also take nonspherical forms. In the solum they may vary in size from less than 0.05 millimeter to 10 millimeters or more. In deep layers they are occasionally much larger. The concretions usually show more or less concentric laminations. They are generally mixtures of soil materials cemented together by iron and manganese oxides. Roughly, the blacker the concretion, the higher is the content of manganese oxides. These concretions appear to develop under conditions of alternating reduction and oxidation; yet they are often present even in well-drained soils. Concretions are easily overlooked in field examinations of dark-colored soils, since they may be no larger than sand grains. The soil in clean-cultivated fields or on terraces may appear to have a higher concentration of small concretions than other similar soil simply because the beating rain has washed away the fine particles, exposing the concretions more clearly.

PANS IN SOILS

Horizons or layers in soils that are strongly compacted, indurated, or very high in clay content are often called "pans." They may be genetic, in the sense of having formed during and as a part of the present cycle of soil formation and weathering; or they may be relicts of earlier cycles of weathering and are thus essentially a part of the parent material of the present soil. Other types of pans, accidental in relation to the present environment, may occur as noted below. The presence of a pan is of great significance to the use of many soils. The possibility of eliminating an adverse influence on root and water penetration through management practices depends upon its characteristics. Then, like other prominent horizons, pans are important indicators of genetic processes.

Indurated or cemented pans.—Massive, indurated or cemented pans are characteristic of many soils. Indeed, pans are essential horizons of soils placed in certain great soil groups, like Ground-Water Podzol, for example. Yet relict pans may occur at random, in relation to the existing combination of genetic factors. Layers of hardened laterite thought to be of Cretaceous age, for example, underlie some soils in Kansas, Nebraska, and northern Iowa at shallow depths. The common cementing agents of pans are iron, iron and organic matter, iron and silica, silica, silica and lime, and lime. Several instances of podzolic soils developing from Ground-Water Laterites formed in earlier geological periods have been reported.[1] Some of the laterite pans still show the original structure of the rock, even though its physical and chemical properties have been altered drastically. Such pans may even weather into flattened concretions suggesting the original shape of unaltered rock fragments.

Cementation by iron.—Cementation by iron is characteristic of layers of hardened laterite formed by the lowering of the water table in Ground-Water Laterite soils. Roots and water may penetrate soft laterite without serious difficulty. Indeed many of the hardened layers of laterite are permeable to water, and roots can often find their way through cracks and other openings. Hardened laterite layers may be present in a very wide variety of soils in tropical regions as an accidental feature in relation to the present environment.

Cementation with iron and organic matter.—The formation of pans cemented with iron and organic matter, called "ortstein," is characteristic of the Ground-Water Podzols and some Podzols. (Horizons of accumulation of iron and organic matter not accompanied by cementation are called "orterde.") The formation of these horizons is thought to be due to the mutual flocculation of the negative organic colloids with the positive iron colloids. Although ortstein forms within the zone of a fluctuating high water table, evidence exists that it also forms in soils of good drainage. Hilly Podzols with well-developed ortsteins, for example, are found on dunes and sandy moraines in the northern Lake States.

Cementation with iron, silica, or both.—Large areas exist having soils underlain with pans cemented with iron, silica, or both together. These pans are massive and structureless, and usually underlie a horizon of accumulated clay that is neutral to mod-

---

[1] See, for example, STEPHENS, C. G. PEDOGENESIS FOLLOWING THE DISSECTION OF LATERITIC REGIONS IN SOUTHERN AUSTRALIA. Australia Council Sci. and Indus. Res. Bul. No. 206, 21 pp., illus. Melbourne. 1946.

erately acid in reaction. Pans cemented with iron and silica are common on the gently sloping alluvial fans formed from acid alluvium in California. Pans cemented with silica are found on nearly level areas in the semiarid parts of Australia and may occur in the United States as well. The pans inhibit water and root penetration unless broken by blasting or other means. Adequate explanations of the development of these pans are lacking.

Cementation with silica and lime.—In depressional areas of arid and semiarid regions some soils have pans that are cemented with a mixture of silica and lime. The pan frequently underlies an alkaline horizon of clay accumulation. The genesis of these pans has received little attention. Extensive and continuous pans of this sort are important because they must be broken before irrigation can be successful. They must be looked for in arid regions because the natural soil may show little evidence of impeded drainage that may become serious with irrigation. Some of the deep ones, however, are not so impervious to water as they may appear to be.

Cementation with lime.—In regions where the rainfall is too low to remove all the soluble minerals from the soil, lime usually accumulates in the lower part of the soil. In some soils, lime accumulates as a soft powdery mass; in others it accumulates in concretions; and in some it accumulates as a pan. The formation of the pan is often associated with an intermittent high water table; although after a pan is once formed it may persist indefinitely even though the water table is lowered. These pans vary widely in their effects on soil drainage. Some hard ones seem not to cause much reduction in water movement; others do, especially if deep in the soil. The indurated accumulations of lime are known as *croûte calcaire* or, more commonly in the Americas, as *hardened caliche* or simply *caliche*. Where the accumulations are prominent and thick, and not hardened, they are known as *soft caliche*. Calichelike layers are present in some glacial gravels in regions as humid as Illinois and Indiana. Where the caliche layers are extensive and continuous they may inhibit the penetration of water and roots. Such caliche in soils of humid regions is not always continuous, but may be interrupted at intervals of several inches or a few feet.

Commonly, in the United States, the soft layers of accumulated lime carbonate, characteristic of most Chernozem, Chestnut, and Brown soils, are called lime horizons rather than caliche. The latter term is most commonly applied to the generally deeper and thicker accumulations that occur in soils of hot regions or warm-temperate regions like the southern Great Plains.

Nonindurated pans.—In gently sloping or nearly level soils of humid regions pans occur which are not indurated. Many such pans are sufficiently compact and slowly permeable to interfere seriously with root and moisture penetration. The presence of a slowly permeable pan near the surface greatly increases the erosion hazard of a soil under cultivation. After rain has saturated the soil above the pan, more rain causes the soil to become viscous and to flow, even on gentle slopes.

The pans high in clay content have customarily been referred to as claypans, while those low in clay and high in silt have been referred to by some as "siltpans." Many of these so-called "siltpans" are, in fact, sandy. Some regard them as primarily compact rather than cemented; yet they are no more compact than the upper part of the C in some soils from glacial till. Redeposited silica may contribute to their density and brittleness. Thus the name *fragipan* (approximately equals "brittle pan") has been given to them.

Claypans.—Claypans are compact horizons or layers rich in clay and separated more or less abruptly from the overlying horizon. Horizons that are high in clay content, either because of illuviation or by inheritance from clay-rich parent material, but that are not separated abruptly from the overlying horizon, are not universally considered to be claypans, although some authors refer to them as claypans.

The origin of a genetic claypan is often suggested by the presence in the bleached A_2 horizon of small nodular remnants of an old B_1 horizon. Generally, the minerals in genetic claypans have been strongly weathered. Commonly soils with such claypans are low in one or more essential plant nutrients, and many claypans have a relatively narrow ratio of exchangeable calcium to exchangeable magnesium.

Soils developed in alluvial materials, however, may have horizons very rich in clay or even claypans that are inherited from a stratified parent material. While such pans may be as effective as genetic claypans in retarding root and water penetration, the associated soils are quite variable in their supply of plant nutrients. Soils having inherited claypans vary in their nutrient supply with differences in the parent material.

While blasting has proved effective in ameliorating most indurated pans, it has had little lasting effect on the claypans.

Fragipans.—Fragipans are found in many gently sloping or nearly level soils in humid warm-temperate climates. These are very compact horizons, rich in silt, sand, or both, and usually relatively low in clay. Fragipans may or may not underlie or overlie a horizon of clay accumulation. They commonly interfere with water and root penetration. When dry, the compact material appears to be indurated, but the apparent induration disappears upon moistening. It has not yet been generally agreed whether fragipans are merely an expression of extreme compaction or are reversibly indurated. Fragipans are found in soils developed from both residual and transported parent materials.

EFFLORESCENCE

Efflorescence of salts refers to the occurrence of various salts in crystalline forms, as crusts, coatings, or pockets. The efflorescences of carbonates, chlorides, and sulfates of calcium, magnesium, and sodium are common. The efflorescence may occur on the surface of the soil and on vegetative remnants on the surface; as films on the walls of cracks or structural particles; as pseudomycelium, or thin, irregular veins thoroughly penetrating the soil mass; or as nodules or nests. Efflorescences are most easily seen following long dry periods. The deposits of the soluble salts occur at places where water evaporates and are proportional to the salt in the soil water and the length of time evaporation is active. Often salts appear on the margins of cracks in very heavy soils during drought and are washed down with the first rains. This accounts for the low salt content of the upper sola of some heavy soils in arid regions and the concentrations beneath.

KROTOVINAS

Krotovinas are irregular tubular streaks within one horizon of material transported from another horizon. They are caused by the filling of tunnels made by burrowing animals in one horizon with material from outside the horizon. In the soil profile they appear as rounded or elliptical spots of various sizes. They may have a light color in dark horizons, or a dark color in light horizons, and their other qualities of texture and structure may be unlike those of the main body of soil in the horizon of their occurrence. Common animals responsible for the presence of krotovinas are rodents and crayfish (Astacidae). The burrows of rodents are usually found in well-drained situations, and the burrows of crayfish in poorly drained sites. Krotovinas are a common feature of Chernozem and other dark-colored soils developed under grasses.

ORGANIC MATTER AND ROOTS

Organic matter and roots are noted in descriptions of the soil profile. Exact amounts of organic matter can be learned only by analyses of samples in the laboratory.

ORGANIC MATTER

The nature and content of organic matter are important characteristics of soils. Organic matter and its formation influence soil properties in many ways. The magnitude of the influence is usually far out of proportion to the quantity of organic carbon in the soil. Products of the decomposition of plant and animal materials hasten the weathering of minerals in the soil; and the vertical distribution of different kinds of organic matter in the soil often has a marked influence upon horizon differentiation.

Amount and distribution of organic matter in soils.—The total amount of organic matter in soils varies widely. Gray Desert soils contain only a fraction of 1 percent of organic matter in the surface layers, while Bog soils (peat and muck) consist largely of organic materials. The quantity and distribution of organic matter in the several soil horizons is a major criterion in classification. Commonly, soils have the maximum amount in the surface layer and decreasing amounts beneath; but most Podzols and many soils with claypans show two maxima of organic matter accumulation, one in the surface and a second in the B horizon or claypan.

The plant residues from which most soil organic matter is formed by decomposition consist of (1) litter, or those plant materials deposited upon the surface of the soil, and (2) roots that are formed and decay beneath the surface of the soil.

Estimates of the quantity of litter deposited annually vary from a few pounds to a few hundred pounds of dry matter per acre on the soils of arid regions, 1 to 2 tons under grass or deciduous and coniferous forests in temperate-humid or subhumid climates, and 10 to 20 tons in soils under tropical rain forests.

Litter from grass and tropical rain forests is rapidly decomposed and mixed with the surface mineral soil. In spite of the great amount of litter from the tropical rain forests, there is seldom an accumulation of more than an inch or two. Forested soils of cool humid climates usually have a rather prominent surface layer of only partly decomposed organic matter. This is particularly prominent in Podzols. The classification of these organic surface layers is based largely on the amount of mixing of the organic matter and mineral soil and the degree of decomposition. The names suggested by Heiberg and Chandler are generally accepted by foresters and soil scientists. Forest humus layers are classified in two main groups: *mull,* which is a humus-rich layer consisting of mixed organic and mineral matter, generally with a gradational boundary to the underlying mineral horizon; and *mor*, which consists of unincorporated organic matter that rests with little mixing on the underlying horizon.

Mulls are subdivided principally on the basis of structure into coarse, medium, fine, firm, and twin mulls. Mors are subdivided on the basis of decomposition and structure into matted, laminated, granular, greasy, and fibrous mors. In general, mull is common in many Gray-Brown Podzolic and Brown Forest soils, and mor in most Podzols and Gray-Wooded soils.

Various schemes have been used to designate the layers of organic matter that lie on the surface of the soil. Some use L for the freshly fallen litter, F (fermentation layer) for partially decomposed litter still recognizable as to origin and age, and H (humus layer) for rather completely decomposed litter unrecognizable as to origin.[1]

In the standard system of horizon nomenclature, the freshly fallen litter is noted as the A_{00} horizon, and the partly decomposed litter as the A_0 horizon. In detailed work the latter may be subdivided into A_{01} and A_{02} according to decomposition. Other letters, like L, F, and H, already referred to, and the words "mor," "mull," and the like are for use in the descriptions of horizons, as appropriate.

The quantities of roots that die in the soil each year are also variable. Accurate estimates of root production in the soil are wanting, partly because of the transient nature of some roots. Studies at various seasons of the year indicate that grasses have large root systems. Total roots (dry) of mature prairie grasses in temperate subhumid areas run as high as 5 tons per acre in the plow layer of soil. The roots of cultivated grasses are somewhat less, 2 to 3 tons per acre for bluegrass and 1 to 2 tons per acre for alfalfa and sweetclover. Such crops as tomatoes and peas rarely yield more than 500 pounds of roots per acre.

The distribution of roots in the soil profile bears some relationship to the distribution of organic carbon, although the relationship is not always linear.

Kinds of organic matter in soils.—Most mature plant residues are composed of a number of rather well known chemical complexes for which the loci in the plant cell and chemical and physical properties have been extensively studied. These compounds have been grouped into the following broad classes: (1) Sugars, starches, and simple carbohydrates, most of which are soluble in water; (2) hemicelluloses, pectins, and the like; (3) celluloses; (4) lignins and tannins; (5) fats, waxes, oils, sterols, and fatty acids; and (6) proteins and their derivatives. The chemical and physical nature of the complex products formed by partial decomposition or by synthesis in the cells of the decomposing microflora is not well understood, but there are many similarities and differences between these latter products and those from mature plant materials.

[1] Heiberg and Chandler, and Lunt, as cited in footnote 2, p. 178.

Some mature plant materials decompose more rapidly than others. This results from (1) differences in proportions in the various organic constituents, (2) differences in quantity of mineral nutrients, and (3) variations in the physical properties of the plant residues. These differences influence their palatability to the soil fauna as well as the manner and extent of direct attack by microfauna, bacteria, and fungi. In general, litter from broad-leafed plants decomposes more rapidly than coniferous litter. The slower decomposition of coniferous needles results in part from the high resin content and the low water-absorbing capacity. Also, coniferous litter remains in a loose, well-aerated mass for a much longer period of time and does not pack with wetting. This makes the litter more susceptible to drying and results in frequent and extensive periods when decomposition is slow.

Some chemical constituents of plant materials are more susceptible to microbiological decomposition than others. In general, the water soluble constituents decompose most rapidly. The hemicellulose fraction, or those substances soluble in dilute acid or dilute alkali, also decomposes rather rapidly. The lignin fractions tend to be the most slowly decomposed of the major plant constituents.

The well-decomposed complex mixture of organic materials in soil is referred to as humus. This mixture represents the current point of equilibrium attained in a dynamic system in which decomposition is more or less continuous and in which periodic additions of fresh plant residues are made. It is quite unlikely that much of the original plant material exists in humus in an unchanged form except for a short period of time following the addition of fresh material. Most of the plant materials such as simple sugars, cellulose, hemicellulose, pectin, fats, waxes, and proteins completely disappear. Formed in the process of decomposition are numerous microbial cells and some other extraneous synthesis products, the chemical nature of which is in many ways different from the plant tissue. By far the greater part of the decomposed plant tissue is converted to carbon dioxide, water, and ash.

The decomposition process is strongly influenced by climatic factors. Optimum temperatures for mesophilic micro-organisms range from about 28 to 40 degrees centigrade. In general, plant residues decompose only one-sixth to one-third as rapidly at 12 as at 25 degrees centigrade.

The influence of moisture is likewise important. Dry plant residues will absorb 250 to 300 percent moisture. Decomposition is most rapid at these high moisture contents, provided the supply of air is optimum. Often under conditions of high moisture in the soil, air interchange is reduced and anaerobic conditions result. Under these conditions the rate of decomposition is slow.

Micro-organisms are not limited in activity at the same levels of moisture that limit plant growth. Reducing moisture to the wilting point for plants reduces the decomposition rate to only about one-third that prevailing under optimum conditions.

In studying the soil it is relatively easy to distinguish and to estimate the relative amounts of undecomposed and partially decomposed plant residues, particularly at the surface of the soil. It is much more difficult to estimate the total soil humus. Organic matter tends to impart characteristic colors to soils, but very serious errors may result if the amount of organic matter is estimated from the color of the soil alone. Within a small area where the kinds of organic and mineral matter are relatively uniform, color intensity may be used as a rough indication of the quantity of organic matter present. Between widely different climatic regions, however, color is not a useful criterion of organic-matter content.

The nature of the soil organic matter varies among the great soil groups. For example, the dark-colored organic matter of the Chernozem soils is high in lignin and protein and low in acid-extractable carbohydrates. The organic matter of these soils has a C–N ratio of roughly 10 to 12 and a high base-exchange capacity. In contrast, soils that may be equally high in organic matter but which have developed under forest vegetation in a humid or subhumid cool climate appear to have organic matter lower in lignin and proteins but higher in acid-soluble carbohydrates. (In plant analysis, the acid-soluble fractions include the celluloses and hemicelluloses.) The organic matter of these soils often has a light color and, in some soils, a strong chroma. Available evidence indicates a low base-exchange capacity. Variations in quality result partly from differences in the extent of decomposition. Generally, soils developed under forest vegetation in humid temperate climates have less organic matter than comparable soils developed under grass, although there are many exceptions; and the organic matter present usually has a wider C–N ratio.

Some important differences in degree of soil development seem to be related only to differences in vegetation. A Kauri Podzol of New Zealand, for example, with an unusually thick A_0, a very thick white A_2 horizon, and a dark reddish-brown ortstein, may be found only a few feet from a Brown Forest soil with no differences in genetic factors except the contrast between the kauri trees over the first and the broad-leafed trees over the second. Differences in the ash content of the litters hardly explain the effects; perhaps some powerful reducing compound is produced during decomposition of the kauri litter.

Relatively little is known about the composition of the organic matter in the soils of the humid tropics. They range in total organic matter from very high to very low. Some of the light-colored soils of the humid tropics are as rich in organic matter as many of the dark-colored Chernozem or Prairie soils of temperate regions, or even richer.

Organic matter and cultivation.—Many studies have been made of the influence of fresh organic matter on soil properties and crop yields. In general it is believed that the addition of fresh organic materials tends to increase aggregation and infiltration and to reduce erosion. The influence on crop yields depends on the crop, the kind of fresh organic matter added, and the amount of available moisture. Where materials high in available carbohydrate and low in nitrogen decompose, the nitrogen is temporarily immobilized by the soil microflora and crop yields may be reduced.

Systems of soil management have a strong influence upon the rate at which soil organic matter is depleted or accumulated. Plowing or other methods of distributing and mixing the soil to appreciable depths tend to hasten the decomposition of the organic constituents. The use of summer fallowing or other means of maintaining the soil at optimum aeration throughout the warm season provides optimum conditions for organic matter depletion. The culture of corn or other intertilled crops is nearly as destructive of organic matter as fallowing. On the other hand the growing of grass and deep-rooted legumes provides conditions which result in a higher stable level of organic matter. The favorable influence of grasses and legumes results chiefly because these plants provide large annual additions of fresh organic matter to the soil, which improves structure and nutrient balance, and because they permit leaving the soil relatively undisturbed for extended periods.

Exposure of the soil to the sun hastens the loss of organic matter, especially in the tropics.

ROOT DISTRIBUTION

Although a considerable body of knowledge exists about the distribution of plant roots in soils, it is inadequate for predictions about the needs of most cultivated crops. Certainly much more information is needed concerning the relation that the roots of many cultivated plants have to aeration, structure, compaction, and water- and nutrient-supplying capacity of the various soil horizons. Careful studies of plant roots in relation to detailed soil morphology are urgently needed as a basis for making better predictions concerning the adaptability of crop varieties to soil types.

To carry on their principal functions effectively, roots require soil horizons that are able to supply adequate water, air, and nutrients. Plant roots grow little in horizons lacking available moisture, or in horizons lacking nutrients, even if moisture is available elsewhere. The failure of plant roots to penetrate some soil horizons may be due to deficiencies of moisture, nutrients, or oxygen, or to extremely unfavorable physical conditions.

There are few soil horizons which some roots cannot penetrate. Ordinarily roots cannot penetrate the cemented pans, unless fractured, or the strongly developed fragipans. Although penetrated with difficulty by the roots of many plants, claypans do not prevent root development. Roots found in claypans usually follow cleavage faces and are often flattened by the pressures exerted by those faces. The failure of many roots to penetrate claypans is complicated by nutrient deficiencies and unfavorable pH.

A high proportion of the roots of most plants is in the upper soil horizons. With most grasses, from 65 to 80 percent of the roots live in the surface 6 inches, or plow layer. Some grasses are shallow rooted, and the roots are almost entirely in the upper part of the soil. Other grasses, although with a large proportion of their roots in the surface layer, have roots to depths of 6 to 10 feet, and in places, deeper. In general, the number of grass roots decreases with depth.[2]

The roots of many forest trees are also concentrated in the upper soil horizons. Some tree roots penetrate deeply, but with depth there is a gradual decrease in total root volume. The depth varies with species and soil. Some species, like oak for example, can penetrate deeply into soil that other species might find impenetrable. Generally the conifers have a higher percentage of roots in the very surface than hardwoods. In fact, in the Podzol region where the A_0 layer is thick, the roots of spruce and fir are concentrated largely in this layer and immediately under it. In cool moist regions these trees may be found growing on litter-covered hard rock.

The roots of plants have an important relation to soil structure. As the roots die, they leave food for bacteria and other micro-organisms that are important to the maintenance of granular structure. This is, of course, true of deep roots as well as shallow ones. Oak roots, for example, can penetrate very heavy B horizons, even in soils where they grow poorly. Their direct effects, plus the slight movements during heavy winds, help maintain a blocky, or mixed blocky and granular, structure. When such deeply rooted plants are removed and replaced with shallow-rooted plants, the soil may lose its structure and become massive. A few years after the beginning of cultivation such soils may gradually become imperfectly or poorly drained during moist seasons.

Given favorable conditions, some plant roots penetrate to much greater depths than commonly believed. Grass roots penetrate to depths of 6 to 10 feet or more. Even corn plants have been known to remove available moisture to depths of 5 feet or more. Alfalfa roots can penetrate to much greater depths and remove available moisture to depths of 25 feet or more.

ANIMALS IN THE SOIL[3]

Notes may need to be made of insects, worms, and even larger animals in the soil that have important influences in mixing, changing, or moving the soil material. Animals contribute greatly to the decomposition of plant remains. In some soils worms and insects are chiefly responsible for the mixing of material between soil horizons, say A_0 with A_1, or A with B. In extreme instances huge termite mounds occupy over one-quarter of the surface area. Rodents sometimes cause a great deal of mixing of the soil. Colonies of prairie dogs, for example, even cause the formation of a characteristic microrelief.

[2] SHIVELY, S. B., and WEAVER, J. E. AMOUNT OF UNDERGROUND PLANT MATERIALS IN DIFFERENT GRASSLAND CLIMATES. Nebr. Conserv. Bul. 21, 68 pp. 1939.

[3] For several interesting examples, see EFFECTS OF CERTAIN ANIMALS THAT LIVE IN SOILS, by James Thorp, Sci. Monthly 67: 180–191. 1949.

ACCELERATED SOIL EROSION

In a broad geologic sense, erosion means the wearing away of the earth's surface by the forces of water and wind. The Dakota Badlands, the Grand Canyon of the Colorado River, the dunes of the Nubian Desert, and the flood plains and deltas of streams are striking results of such erosion.

Erosion is constructive as well as destructive. Through erosion and redeposition, unconsolidated mineral parent materials of soils are accumulated. Perhaps one-third of the population of the world gets its food supply from Alluvial soils and from young soils developing on alluvium. Geologically, erosion is the chief agent responsible for the natural topographic cycles, as it wears down the higher points of elevation and constructs alluvial plains in the valleys. In these valleys are a large part of the world's most productive soil. Gradually, erosion cuts drainage systems into wet level areas, making it possible meanwhile for arable soils to develop. Under the natural vegetation, especially in humid forested regions, natural erosion serves to maintain a degree of youthfulness and fertility in many soils by removing leached materials from the soil surface while new materials are added to the soil profile from beneath. On steep slopes, especially where the rock material is impervious or vegetation scanty, this removal is so rapid that little true soil forms—not until the slope has worn down to or below its angle of repose. On nearly level soils and some sloping ones natural erosion may be so slow that the older leached materials accumulate in the surface, hardpans or claypans develop, and the soils become and remain unproductive.

Natural erosion in the natural landscape may be either a gradual process, with a soil cover on the land continuously, or a catastrophic one. Once started in a new cycle of erosion—initiated by uplift, changes in climate, showers of hot volcanic ash that kill the vegetation, or other causes—a large part of the solum, or even the whole of it, may be removed rapidly. Reconstruction and the formation of a new soil then follows the stabilization of the landscape again. One may find buried soils characteristic of a set of soil-forming processes unlike those responsible for the present soil. Often only patches of truncated remnants are found that suggest catastrophic removal of an old soil prior to the formation of the present one. Thus some soil landscapes have had significant gradual erosion over a very long period; others have had relatively stable periods with little natural erosion, separated by periods of catastrophic erosion.

Commonly, in applied soil science and agriculture generally, erosion is used in a restricted sense. The terms "erosion" and "soil erosion" are often used for accelerated soil erosion, or that erosion of soil resulting from disturbance of the natural landscape, usually by man, in contrast to the natural, or normal, erosion that takes place in the undisturbed landscape. Accelerated erosion can result from exposure of the soil to runoff through burning, excessive grazing, forest cutting, and tillage, any of which destroy or weaken the vegetation. Exposed soil may erode very rapidly if it is not managed according to its limitations and requirements.

The distinction between natural erosion and accelerated erosion is an important one in soil survey work. Natural erosion is an important process in soil development. Its effects are reflected in the units of the natural system of soil classification. On the other hand, accelerated erosion truncates the soil profiles formed in the natural landscape. Significant differences in soil caused by accelerated erosion are shown on soil maps by means of erosion phases—subdivisions within the natural units of the system of soil classification. The criteria must be found in the soil. These are selected to indicate differences of importance to soil use and management. Accelerated erosion may also have altered soils enough to require a change in their classification as natural units. By removal of the moderate textured A horizon, a Cecil sandy loam may be changed to Cecil clay loam, eroded phase. With plowing, a new surface soil (A_p) is developed partly from the B horizon, rich in clay. To avoid confusion, a clay loam type of this sort may need to be separated from a normal clay loam type in the same series, should it exist.

Natural erosion and accelerated erosion are so combined in some cultural landscapes that it is difficult to sort them out, especially where the accelerated erosion is only slight. In long-cultivated areas, special short steep escarpments, called *taluds* (from old French), are gradually formed at down-slope field margins against hedges or stone walls. As the talud forms with the slow accumulation of soil wash from above, the soil slope of course decreases. A talud can scarcely be regarded as strictly man-made, since the stone wall or hedge was usually built as a field line and only incidentally gave rise to the talud because of the natural and accelerated erosion above it. In areas having fairly erodible soils, with a pattern of small fields, erosion may now be reasonably well stabilized with taluds that act as terraces to reduce the slope gradient and hence reduce runoff and accelerated erosion.

Occasionally accelerated erosion may shift a soil from one series to another. Usually, the differences between any such series in their original state were confined to the upper parts of the sola, so that with deep truncation the original differences disappear. The Monona series differs from the Ida, for example, in having a thicker and darker colored noncalcareous surface soil and a weak B horizon. With deep accelerated erosion that removes both A and B and mixes the remaining horizons, the Monona may become indistinguishable from the Ida. In such situations, the soil should be classed with the series that best describes it.

With very severe erosion, soil may have become so truncated that its distinguishing characteristics have disappeared. Such areas are classified and named with the appropriate miscellaneous land type, say Gullied land or Rock outcrop, rather than with phases of a supposed original soil type. Rough land with only a thin soil may suffer accelerated erosion. Even where the results are dramatic in appearance, the actual loss of soil may not have been great nor the productivity of the soil much if any changed.

The soil scientist must guard fully as much against exaggeration of accelerated erosion as against failure to recognize it where it is significant. Some have assumed, for example, that all the rocky, thin, sloping soils of the Mediterranean region were once deep and highly productive of crops, whereas actually only an undetermined part of them have suffered severe erosion; probably many of them have always been rocky, thin, and stony.

Erosion[1] processes can be divided into two classes, water erosion and wind erosion, according to the moving agent. Wind erosion is important primarily, but not exclusively, in subhumid, semiarid, and desert regions. Although in such common use that it can scarcely be avoided, the term "wind erosion" is not a good one for soil removal alone. Either "soil blowing" or "soil drifting" can often be used as appropriately and with less chance of confusion.

WATER EROSION

Water erosion results from the forces of flowing water and abrasion when runoff passes over soil surfaces on which the vegetation is not adequate to prevent detachment of soil particles. A part of the process is due to beating raindrops that detach soil particles from the soil mass and suspend them in the runoff. Besides that, soil particles splashed upward by raindrops beating on a sloping soil do not fall back evenly; instead, they fall a bit down slope. Then too, frost helps push particles down slope. Very wet soils can creep down the slope without going into suspension, sometimes even without great disturbance of the surface horizons. Descriptions of slips, slip scars, and other evidences of soil creep are essential to the descriptions of soil types and phases where they occur. Predictions of their formation under alternative uses are included as well.

Sheet, rill, and gully erosion are three forms of water erosion, distinguished by the relative depth and stability of the channels cut by the runoff.

Sheet erosion.—Sheet erosion is the more or less uniform removal of soil from an area without the development of conspicuous water channels. The channels are tiny or tortuous, exceedingly numerous, and unstable; they enlarge and straighten with an increasing volume of runoff. Rill erosion of short duration, obliterated by tillage, is usually included with sheet erosion in soil classification and mapping.

---

[1] For brevity, the word "erosion" is used in the sense of "accelerated water erosion" in the remainder of this section, unless otherwise specified.

To untrained observers, sheet erosion is less apparent, particularly in its earlier stages, than other types; actually, it is the most widespread. Although the evidence varies among soil types, sheet erosion can be recognized by the thinning of the surface soil layers, appearance of "galled spots" from which all the surface soil has gone, or the mixing of the B horizon into the plow layer, and by the accumulation of freshly eroded materials at the foot of slopes, along field boundaries and in drainageways, and in the lower parts of fields.

Sheet erosion may be serious on unprotected soils of only 1 or 2 percent slope, as on some highly granular Rendzinas or on Planosols with nearly impermeable claypans. Usually, however, it affects more sloping soils. On the other hand, cultivated well-developed Latosols may have little such erosion on slopes of less than 25- to 50-percent gradient.

Rill erosion.—Rill erosion refers to the removal of soil through the cutting of numerous small but conspicuous water channels or tiny rivulets that are minor concentrations of runoff. Although rill erosion is intermediate between sheet erosion and gully erosion, it is included with sheet erosion in soil classification and mapping. The shallow channels are easily obliterated by tillage; yet in the process the solum is gradually truncated, or shortened.

Gully erosion.—Gully erosion is the most conspicuous form of water erosion, often dramatic and picturesque. The removal of soil results from the formation of relatively large channels or gullies cut into the soil by concentrations of the runoff. The gullies develop in exposed natural drainageways or other depressed irregularities in the soil slope pattern, in plow furrows, animal trails, wagon ruts, below broken terraces, and between rows of crop plants that run up and down the slope. In contrast to rills, they are not obliterated by ordinary tillage. Deep gullies are not even crossable with the common types of farm machinery and form barriers that subdivide fields into small units, frequently too small for efficient farming. Although gullies are conspicuous, frequently for long distances and especially from aircraft, and locally destructive, gully erosion affects a much smaller total area of arable soil and does less damage on most farms than sheet and rill erosion.

Although the gully patterns vary widely on different soil types, individual gullies are of two general shapes: (1) Perhaps most common are the V-shaped gullies that cut down in the soil more or less uniformly throughout their courses. These develop in soils having coherent materials throughout, like the Westmoreland, Wellston, Miami, and Cincinnati series. Maximum gully depth is governed mainly by the depth to bedrock or other relatively unerosive material. In lithosolic soils, like the Muskingum and Porters series for example, gullies are generally shallower than in the associated zonal soils. (2) Also common are the U-shaped gullies that develop in materials of relatively low coherence, especially by undercutting of soft substrata at the gully head. The undercut, or cavernous U-shaped gully, results from surface water first cutting through coherent soil material into loose incoherent substrata that erode very easily. As the substrata undercut, the material above falls into the gully channel in great chunks that readily disintegrate and wash away. Soils underlain by thick deposits of loess, water-laid sands, deeply weathered granite (saprolite), or similar incoherent materials are subject to this type of gullying. Some of the soils in the Cecil, Memphis, Ruston, and Orangeburg series are examples. Some U-shaped gullies reach tremendous size, such as ones developed in Ruston and Orangeburg soils near Lumpkin in Stewart County, Ga.

Gully patterns in a soil series are often distinctive. The gully pattern of the Grenada soils (an intergrade between Planosol and Gray-Brown Podzolic from moderately deep loess) can be cited: In their early stages the gullies are V-shaped. If uncontrolled, they branch and grow laterally rather rapidly. Numerous small columns or "spires" form along their sides at or near the contact of the fragipan with the horizon above it. Eventually the columns wear away, and the individual gullies merge to form a nearly smooth eroded area separated from the ungullied soil above by a kind of bench or nearly vertical bank that may still have numerous small columns along its face.

WATER DEPOSITS

Deposits of water-eroded materials on soils are a direct result of water erosion of other soils. The deposits vary widely in character and significance. Some deposition is apt to occur at any place that the velocity of the water is reduced—at the mouths of gullies, at the bases of slopes, along stream banks, on alluvial plains, in stream reservoirs, and at the mouths of streams. The most rapidly moving water, when reduced in velocity, drops stones, then cobbles, gravel, sand, and finally silt and clay. Fine clay settles out of still water. Deposits of coarse fragments or sand on productive lower lying soils injure them for crop production. Uniform layers of fine-textured materials, rich in plant nutrients, are beneficial; they maintain the high fertility of many Alluvial soils in stream bottoms and deltas.

WIND EROSION

With a few exceptions, wind erosion in humid areas is not important, except locally in unprotected very sandy soils and in large tracts of drained and cultivated organic soils. Yet even in fairly humid regions with strong winds during dry periods, the soil scientist may need to deal with wind erosion in exposed places, not simply as a factor in soil classification and mapping but especially as a hazard to be described in his reports.

In regions of low rainfall, however, wind erosion is widespread and serious on cultivated soils, especially during drought. Unlike water erosion, wind erosion is commonly greater on level soils than on sloping ones. The hazard is increased by destruction of the vegetation through overgrazing or clean tillage that exposes dry loose soil.

During high winds the finer, and commonly more fertile, particles are swept high in the air and are sometimes carried for great distances as dust storms; while coarser particles are rolled or swept along on or very near the soil surface to be piled into ditches, along fences, or behind obstructions. Once an area is blowing badly during drought, the sand may drift back and forth locally with changes in wind direction, while most of the silt and clay goes far away. After the serious drought of the thirties, soils in barren fields in the south-central Great Plains had loamy sand or light sandy loam surface layers, in contrast to sandy loam or loam before the drought.

Blowouts, or spots from which the surface soil has blown away, may be associated with spots of deposition in such an intricate pattern that the two conditions can be shown only as a complex or by symbols. Commonly the wind blows out the surface soil in some areas and piles it up in others.

ESTIMATING EROSION AND MAPPING ERODED SOILS

Standards, or norms, for each soil can be established for reference in the estimation of erosion losses. In the natural environment the individual horizons and the solum of each soil have characteristic ranges in thickness. These values should be determined as accurately as possible. If the standards are to be useful and reliable guides to erosion losses, several precautions must be taken.

First of all, cultivation causes great differences in the thickness of solum of many soils where no erosion has taken place or is even possible. The upper part of many forested soils has a very high content of roots, even to one-half the soil volume. When these decay, the soil shrinks. Then too, upper horizons of many forested soils have a low bulk density, which increases with tillage. Emphasis has already been given to the importance of measuring the horizon boundaries and solum depth from the top of the A_1 horizon. It is especially important in setting standards for classes of eroded soils. The A_{00} and A_0 horizons should not be counted in such standards.

The difference between solum depth in virgin and cultivated areas of the same soil type can be illustrated with a Subarctic Brown Forest soil. The A_{00} may be 4 or 5 inches thick, and the A_0 some 3 or 4 inches. The upper 10 inches of solum contain abundant roots and have an exceedingly low bulk density. A superficial examination of the virgin soil might indicate a total depth from the surface of the A_{00} down to a gravel substratum of, say, 24 inches. Yet where the soil had been cultivated normally under good management without erosion, the depth to the gravel would be about 12 inches. This latter figure should be the standard against which to measure erosion classes within the soil type.

Similar changes can be expected in heavily forested Podzols. Smaller but significant differences are found in many forested soils. Removal of many stones lowers the surface. In other soils, of course, cultivation may not cause much, if any, difference in solum depth.

The depth of surface soil (A_p) cannot be used as a yardstick, because as a soil erodes, the plow cuts progressively deeper into the profile and the depth of the plowed layer (A_p) maintains a relatively uniform thickness. Nor can the thickness of the A horizon be used as a yardstick on all soils, since the A is not equally significant in all arable soils. Among Prairie soils, for example, the A_1 horizon is commonly more than a foot thick. In Brown Podzolic soils, the whole A—A_1 and A_2 together—is commonly not more than 2 inches thick. To base erosion classes on differences in the thickness of the A horizon in such soils would lead to absurdities. Thus the thickness of neither A_1 nor A can be used generally in all soils.

Comparisons also need to be made on comparable soil slopes. Near the upper limits of the slope range of a soil type, and especially on convex slopes, the depth of solum is normally thinner than near the lower part of the range of concave slopes. Thus the standards of solum thickness for different slope classes within the permissible range of a soil type are slightly different. It is an error to call that part of a soil type having slopes in the C class as "eroded" if the difference in thickness between the soil with C slopes and that with B slopes is characteristic for the soil type.

In many well-settled areas it is not possible to find satisfactory examples of virgin areas of all soil types, especially of the most productive ones. The standards are established by examining areas of cultivated soils of known management history that have no evidences of significant accelerated erosion or deposition.

Roadsides, cemeteries, fence rows, and similar small, uncultivated acres need to be avoided. By using them, some classifiers have made serious errors, generally in the direction of setting the standards for surface soil thickness far too high, thus seriously overestimating the erosion in the whole area. In naturally treeless areas, or in those nearly cleared of trees, dust blowing from cultivated fields collects in the fence rows, roadsides, and other small uncultivated areas that are covered with grass or other stabilizing plants. Such dust is often fine and productive. In a relatively short time the A_1 may become thickened by several inches.

Especially on Lithosols and lithosolic soils, the soil scientist may have difficulty distinguishing between accelerated erosion and normal erosion. Deep gullies, landslides, and slips are normal features of many natural landscapes. Yet such features may also be increased or even initiated by overgrazing, fire, or clean cutting of trees. Climatic changes have initiated new erosion cycles by weakening the vegetation in formerly stabilized landscapes, as in North Africa and in the southwestern part of the United States. Again, a few dry years, followed by heavy rains, may cause abnormal slipping; then during a moist period plant vigor is restored and the slip scars heal.

On many kinds of soil, including especially soils developing from relatively soft materials like mudstone or volcanic ash on moderate to steep slopes, slips are characteristic features, even in the natural undisturbed landscapes. After the scars form they are healed by the reinvasion of vegetation. Careful inspection may disclose that many soil slopes are simply a mass of such restabilized slips and scars. In assessing the influence of heavy grazing, for example, the observer needs to differentiate between an increase in the formation of slip scars in contrast to a decrease in the normal revegetation of such scars. In such soils the slips may be caused primarily by excessive moistening, perhaps aided by frost; and subsequent erosion on the unprotected scars may be caused by running water and wind. The proper description and interpretation of such conditions require the establishment of the typical situations for each kind of soil, which vary widely, as bases for estimating or predicting departures related to use and management.

In a region of rapid uplift, an acceleration of natural erosion is inevitable. The hazard of gully formation in arable soils increases. The scientist needs to recognize that areas of like soil have a different erosion hazard depending upon whether the local erosion cycle, in a geomorphical sense, is in its early stage or is approaching quiescence. Apparently a new period of erosion cutting had begun in the Piedmont area of the southeastern part of the United States, for example, just before its occupation by farmers. Thus the clearing of the soil and its use for row crops added to the natural process already started. One might say that "the gun was loaded and clearing pulled the trigger." The Atherton Tableland in Northern Queensland is a less dramatic example, among many others, of the same thing.

All sorts of complications arise with soil management. Burning the brush off sloping soils to encourage grass, for example, may stimulate several kinds of erosion—sheet and gully wash or slips. Yet if the soils are otherwise suited to grass and need only heavy dressings of phosphatic fertilizers for maintaining a vigorous cover, burning *and* fertilization may actually reduce the normal erosion. Much of the conflicting evidence about the effect of fire is due to failure to take account of natural fertility or fertilizer management. Thus, on the same kind of soil, brush firing plus fertilization (and reseeding if needed) may be an excellent practice, whereas brush firing alone may be a ruinous practice. Dressings of fertilizers on hilly pasture lands may greatly speed up the reinvasion of slip scars by grass.

Increasing the water percolating down into the soil by terraces or by irrigation can increase soil slipping and landslides on some soils.

Stream-straightening in a fairly well stabilized landscape may stimulate gully formation and induce a serious local erosion cycle. If a winding stream at a nearly stable grade is reduced in length by straightening, it may seek a new grade by cutting. If the materials are soft, the cutting pushes up the stream branches and even out into the fields.

The few examples cited in previous paragraphs illustrate the importance of making geomorphological study along with soil study. Each soil survey area presents its own problems. To evaluate the erosion conditions, to estimate the hazards of accelerated soil erosion, and to suggest appropriate uses of the soil where such hazards exist, the soil scientist needs to have a clear picture of the general erosion cycle, how it is changing, and what factors influence it. Topographic maps and standard texts are helpful. Geomorphologists or geologists have made special studies of some areas; yet in many survey areas the party chief will need to work out the relationships himself. He should strive to distinguish clearly between natural erosion and accelerated erosion, and especially between the erosion that it is not practical to control and that which can be controlled.

Erosion differences and their significance can be evaluated only in relation to individual soil types. Since soil conditions due to erosion are classified and mapped primarily because of their significance to soil use and management, no erosion class or category can have the same quantitative limits in terms of inches or percentage of solum or of A horizon for all soil types. Memphis silt loam, for example, a deep, permeable Gray-Brown Podzolic soil with a high water-supplying capacity, is injured much less by the loss of a given amount of surface soil than one of its planosolic associates, Grenada silt loam, which has a very slowly permeable fragipan at depths of 24 to 34 inches. Rarely is the number of inches of soil lost at a particular point within an area enclosed by boundaries a useful measure of the total soil lost or of the significance of the loss to the use of the area. That is, the pattern of erosion conditions in soil areas of mappable size is normally complex. In classifying and mapping erosion conditions, the pattern is nearly as important as the estimated proportion of the upper soil horizons lost. The classifier must recall that all mapping units are areas, not points. It is the area as a whole that is classified and mapped. The degree of complexity within mapped areas depends on both the irregularity of the erosion and the scale of the map.

With soils having clearly defined horizons, significant differences due to erosion are comparatively easily and accurately determined by reference to the cultivated norm; and good mapping guides for the classes or phases can be set up in terms of the pattern of exposures of B and C horizons and the number and size of gullies. Guides for soils with little or no horizon differentiation are more difficult to set up and harder to follow in the field. Lithosols derived from shales are a good example: After the thin surface soil is gone, little remains to furnish a clue for estimating original depth and the degree of erosion. For guides the classifier needs to rely on the relative amount and physical condition of the parent materials in the plow layer, the appearance of the coarse fragments on the surface, the number and shape of gullies, and like evidence.

Most soil types, although by no means all of them, within which classes according to conditions caused by erosion need to be set up and mapped, have distinguishable soil horizons. In estimating erosion the *whole* profile needs to be considered. Obviously areas cannot be classified on the basis of what is gone—not there. The mapping standards and guides must be based on characteristics that can be seen. Within many soil types, for example, it can be established that a particular kind of B horizon is associated with an average original depth of A horizon and of solum.

Erosion classes used in mapping should show present conditions and not be confused with susceptibility to erosion. This distinction is very important. The several kinds of soil mapped may be grouped, by interpretation, according to their susceptibility to erosion. But this is a different matter. The soil type, including soil slope class, where the slope of the type ranges beyond the limits of one slope class, is the unit for indicating susceptibility to erosion, except for subdivisions in those instances where the erosion that has taken place may have changed susceptibility to subsequent erosion. Erosion classes are intended to indicate only the erosion that has already taken place that is significant to management practices and yields as contrasted to management practices and yields for the uneroded soil or other erosion classes. At the same time, however, determining the susceptibility of each soil to erosion under alternative uses and management practices, on the basis of the best evidence available, including the results of experimental work on similar soils outside the survey area, is a prime responsibility of the soil survey party and is to be dealt with in detail in the soil survey report.

Study of each soil area is needed in mapping to avoid confusing actual erosion differences with the effects of differences in management. Two areas of the same soil type may be eroded comparably, for example, but one may have been smoothed, is now farmed properly without erosion, and has a plow layer (A_p) well supplied with organic matter; whereas the other is still gullied, perhaps idle, poorly suited to crops in its present condition, and gives the appearance of having lost much more soil.

EROSION CLASSES[2] AND SYMBOLS

Since classes of accelerated erosion are established and eroded phases mapped primarily because of their significance to soil use and management, and since a given amount of erosion has a different meaning on different soil types and in different regions, erosion classes cannot be defined in precise physical terms applicable to all soils. The number of erosion classes to be recognized and their definitions depend on the objectives of the survey, the significance of the erosion to present agriculture, the mapping scale, and the dominant plant cover. For some immediate objective next year, it may be possible and useful to map existing conditions resulting from erosion in great detail, whereas on a published map, only the more permanent ones should be shown.

[2] Although the term "erosion class" is used for brevity, reference is, of course, to classes of eroded soil, based upon the effects of the erosion.

A condition resulting from slight erosion might exist for a long time on undulating areas of many soils, say Memphis silt loam, for example; whereas it would be transient on a hilly erosive soil, like hilly Decatur silt loam, if used for row crops. A general sod cover, as in grazing and pasture areas, reduces the detail of erosion conditions that can be mapped accurately.

In evaluating the effects of erosion on a given soil type, as a basis for establishing the limits of an eroded phase of the type, the classifier needs to recall that erosion is usually accompanied by other factors of soil depletion and that the erosion may be only partly responsible for poor yields. In fact, if continuing cultivation is assumed, generally, although not always, low soil fertility can be regarded as a main cause of the erosion. Land users unable or unwilling to follow systems of management that prevent harmful accelerated erosion usually fail to follow the other practices necessary for optimum sustained production.

FIGURE 46.—Class 1 erosion. Slight erosion is obvious although the soil has been little changed. Cotton plants have just emerged.

Classes of erosion by water.—In the following the four classes commonly used to distinguish soils having had different degrees of water erosion are defined:

Class 1:[3] The soil has a few rills or places with thin A horizons that give evidence of accelerated erosion, but not to an extent to alter

[3] In survey legends, where many numbers and letters are used, these classes may be lettered as m, n, p, and q, for example, instead of 1, 2, 3, and 4.

greatly the thickness and character of the A horizon. Except for
soils having very thin A horizons (less than 8 inches), the surface
soil[4] (A$_p$) consists entirely of A horizon throughout nearly all of
the delineated area. Up to about 25 percent of the original A horizon, or original plowed layer in soils with thin A horizons, may
have been removed from most of the area.[5] In most soils, areas with
this class of erosion are not significantly different in use capabilities
and management requirements from the uneroded soil. In a few
soils having very shallow sola over a nonconforming layer, or in a
few having a shallow A horizon over a claypan or hardpan, a
significant difference may exist (fig. 46).

FIGURE 47.—Class 2 erosion on Dunmore silty clay loam, Cocke County, Tenn.
The surface soil in the light-colored areas is made up mainly of the
original A, whereas the surface soil in the dark-colored areas is made up of
a mixture of the original A and some of the B.

    Class 2: The soil has been eroded to the extent that ordinary tillage
    implements reach through the remaining A horizon, or well below
    the depth of the original plowed layer in soils with thin A horizons.
    Generally, the plow layer consists of a mixture of the original A
    horizons and underlying horizons. Mapped areas of eroded soil
    usually have patches in which the plow layer consists wholly of the
    original A horizon and others in which it consists wholly of under-
    lying horizons. Shallow gullies may be present. Approximately 25 to
    75 percent of the original A horizon or surface soil may have been
    lost from most of the area (fig. 47).

---

    [4] Surface soil refers to that ordinarily moved in tillage, or its equivalent
in uncultivated soils, about 5 to 8 inches thick.
    [5] The figures used here and for the other classes are only suggestive.
Because of the great variations among soils in the thickness of their A
horizons and in other characteristics influenced by erosion, somewhat different values must sometimes be used to define appropriate classes. The plowed
layers of uneroded Brown Podzolic soils, for example, consist mainly of
B horizon.

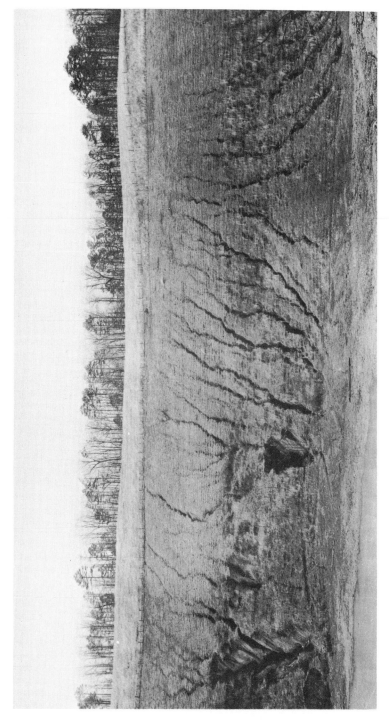

FIGURE 48.—Class 3 erosion. Gullies at the left require a gully symbol. Note the prominent rills that are obliterated in tillage. With further acceleration in erosion, these are likely to grow into gullies.

Class 3: The soil has been eroded to the extent that all or practically all of the original surface soil, or A horizon, has been removed. The plow layer consists essentially of materials from the B or other underlying horizons. Patches in which the plow layer is a mixture of the original A horizon and the B horizon or other underlying horizons may be included within mapped areas. Shallow gullies, or a few deep ones, are common on some soil types. More than about 75 percent of the original surface soil, or A horizon, and commonly part or all of the B horizon or other underlying horizons, have been lost from most of the area (figs. 48 and 49).

FIGURE 49.—Class 3 erosion. This photograph represents a soil area with very near the upper limit permitted within class 3 erosion. Knox County, Tenn.

Class 4: The land has been eroded until it has an intricate pattern of moderately deep or deep gullies. Soil profiles have been destroyed except in small areas between gullies. Such land is not useful for crops in its present condition. Reclamation for crop production or for improved pasture is difficult but may be practicable if the other characteristics of the soil are favorable and erosion can be controlled (figs. 50 and 51).

These four general classes need to be defined specifically and interpreted for each soil type. The significance of the change in soil characteristics depends upon the other soil characteristics. In ordinary basic detailed soil surveys, these classes are enough; although special needs may require subdivisions of a class. On the other hand, *individual classes should not be used as a basis for*

FIGURE 50.—Gullied land. This photograph illustrates the V-shaped gullies that develop in firm materials relatively rich in clay.

FIGURE 51.—Gullied land. This photograph illustrates the U-shaped gullies that develop in soils underlain with loose materials.

establishing phases unless the differences are significant to use and management.

In many instances, two classes are combined into one soil phase. For example, the four classes given are somewhat too narrow for defining phases of water erosion on most Regosols and Lithosols. Sheet erosion has little or no significance and is impossible to measure, even roughly, on very sandy Regosols. It is seldom practical, therefore, to map eroded phases of Regosols of this kind, but Gullied land may be defined and mapped for class 4; and elsewhere individual gullies can be indicated by symbols. For Regosols of heavier texture and for many, perhaps most, Lithosols, one eroded phase is generally adequate, since the lack of a well-defined B horizon makes it impractical to attempt to distinguish between erosion classes 2 and 3. In such soils, the eroded phase includes those areas of the soil unit from which most of the original A horizon has been lost and that have a plow layer consisting largely or entirely of material from underlying horizons.

With these and any other necessary modifications, erosion classes are used as a basis for eroded phases. For most soils, where accelerated water erosion is significant and all four classes need to be distinguished, the phase names of the first three classes are as follows:

Class 1—Slightly eroded phase.[6]
Class 2—Moderately[7] eroded phase.
Class 3—Severely eroded phase.

Class 4 erosion is not normally recognized as a phase of a soil type or series but as the miscellaneous land type, Gullied land; and, where hilly, as Rough and gullied land. If significant to use, the name of the soil or rock material is added in parentheses to the name, as Gullied land (limestone material) or Gullied land (Ruston soil material).

Individual erosion symbols are used to indicate areas of eroded soils too small to enclose with boundaries on maps of the scale used but which are significant to soil use. Symbols are used also to show eroded phases of soils which are so small in total extent that named eroded phases should not be established in the legend. Each symbol is placed to show the location of the eroded spot accurately. Each is defined to represent a specific acreage, depending on the mapping scale and objectives of the survey. In a detailed survey with a mapping scale of 1:24,000, for example, each symbol ordinarily represents an area of 1 to 2 acres.

Definitions of symbols (pls. 6 and 7) used to indicate accelerated water erosion are as follows:

The symbol S indicates sheet erosion significantly greater (one erosion class or more) than the average for the soil unit shown. For example, S in an area mapped Fullerton silt loam, hilly phase, indicates a moderately eroded inclusion.

The symbol SS indicates sheet erosion greater by more than one erosion class than average for the soil unit shown. Thus, an SS in an area

---

[6] The word "phase" may be omitted from the name except where useful for clarity.
[7] The word "moderately" usually can be omitted.

mapped Fullerton silt loam, hilly phase, or Fullerton silt loam, slightly eroded phase, indicates a severely eroded inclusion.

The symbol *G* indicates a moderately gullied inclusion. The gullies are relatively shallow and on most soils can be obliterated with heavy tillage implements.

The symbol *GG* indicates a severely gullied inclusion too small to delineate as Gullied land. The gullies are too deep or too numerous for practical reclamation with the common heavy tillage implements.

The symbol *SG* indicates an inclusion of combined sheet and gully erosion significantly greater than average for the soil unit shown.

A wavy red line is used to indicate individual large gullies long enough to plot at the scale of mapping used, except in areas shown as Gullied land. If not crossable with farm machinery, the line is solid; if crossable a broken line is used. On detailed soil maps having a scale of 1:24,000, gullies about 300 feet long or longer are thus shown.

Water-laid deposits.—Associated with accelerated water erosion are recent deposits of local and general alluvium over other soils. Some of these soil areas are properly classified as soil types, some as miscellaneous land types, and a few as phases of soil types. As a general guide, overwash phases may be recognized in areas where the original surface soil is significantly altered but not changed enough to require the recognition of a different soil series.

Classes of erosion by wind.—The following are the definitions of three classes commonly used to distinguish eroded soils having had different degrees of wind erosion:

Class 1: Wind has removed from the soil a sufficient amount of the A horizon that ordinary tillage will bring up and mix the B horizon or other lower lying horizons with surface soil in the plow layer. Rarely is this condition uniform throughout a mappable area, however. Usually the plow layer consists mainly of the original A horizon in some patches, while in others the original A horizon is removed. Generally, about 25 to 75 percent of the original A horizon (or surface soil in soils with thin A horizons) may have been removed.

Class 2: Wind has removed all of the A horizon and a part of the B or other lower lying horizon. The plow layer consists mainly of the original horizons below the A (or below the original plowed layer in soils with thin A horizons), although some patches having much of the original A horizon remain in the area. An occasional blow-out area may be included.

Class 3 (Blown-out land): The wind has removed most of the soil profile and the land is classified as a miscellaneous land type. Use of the land for ordinary agriculture is not feasible without extensive reclamation. Blowout holes are numerous and deeply carved into the lower soil or parent material. Areas between blowouts are deeply buried by soil material from the blowouts.

Besides these classes for removal, two classes are used to define areas on which significant amounts of material have been deposited by wind:

Class 1a (Overblown).—Recent deposits of wind-drifted material cover the soil in layers thick enough to alter its characteristics significantly up to 24 inches. When the class is used as a phase, the soil type takes its texture designation from the new surface layer. For example, Baca fine sandy loam, overblown phase, consists of a Baca soil with a surface accumulation of wind-deposited fine sandy loam less than 24 inches thick. Thicker mantles usually, but not always, require series differentiations.

Class 2a (Wind hummocky).—Recent deposits of wind-drifted soil material in a fine pattern of hummocks or low dunes. The relief is less bold than that of Blown-out land. The soil materials have been drifted only locally, as contrasted to wind erosion classes 1 and 2, from which considerable soil material has been swept out of the mapped area.

As with water erosion classes, these classes serve as general guides to phases of soil types or series. Each needs to be defined and interpreted according to its local significance. With many soils these classes become phases named as follows:

Class 1.... Wind-eroded phase (or blown phase).

Class 2.... Severely wind eroded phase (or severely blown phase).

Class 1a.... Overblown phase.

Class 2a.... Wind-hummocky phase.

In class 3, wind has removed so much of the soil that the areas are included in the miscellaneous land type, Blown-out land.

Standard symbols are used for small areas of phases too small to enclose with boundaries. Each needs to be defined in terms of the area it represents (see pls. 6 and 7).

Other erosion classes.—Although the classes presented are adequate for most eroded soils, special classes may be needed in the definition of soil series and even for eroded phases. These include slips, and combinations of slips with water erosion, or soil blowing, or both. The problem of defining such classes for detailed soil classification and mapping has not been studied sufficiently to suggest definitions. Yet the problem will arise in regions of grassy Tundra and elsewhere as detailed basic soil surveys are made.

EVALUATION OF EROSION EFFECTS

The soil scientist is not simply concerned to show on the map and assert in his report just what areas are eroded and how much. Erosion by itself, unrelated to the soil, means little or nothing. Tons or inches of soil lost through erosion have little general meaning in terms of soil productivity. The erosion of an otherwise productive soil shallow over bedrock, for example, seriously reduces its productivity and use capability; whereas certain deep soils may be deeply eroded without serious effects on crop production if the erosion is brought under control short of gullying. Many eroded soils were very poor for crops or pasture to begin with. The erosion of such soils does not greatly reduce their capability for use; yet the products from such erosion may contribute to stream silting, and the increased runoff may lead to local flood hazards.

Accelerated erosion has lowered the productivity of a great many soils. The effect is not necessarily permanent. Here again, the improvement of eroded soils, like uneroded ones, depends upon the soil type. Improved management not only restores the productivity in many instances but may also raise it above the level it had when first plowed. This is happening with many eroded soils in the United States and elsewhere.

It cannot be accepted that even dramatic-appearing erosion has destroyed the soil for crop production unless it has been established that the soil was suitable for crops before it was eroded. It may originally have been suited only to forest and may still be well suited to forest with proper management, even after it is eroded. Erosion is a symptom of poor soil use. Some have recognized the symptom and abandoned an impoverishing system of farming, say of row crops year after year, in favor of a system of sustained production with mixed farming and livestock. Since erosion results from poor soil use, it is usually accompanied by other factors of soil depletion that reduce productivity. Yields go down on uneroded soils, too, if they are mismanaged.

The development of tables giving predicted yields of adapted crops under an alternative, physically defined system of management is essential to a soil survey. Besides, the effects of these systems on the long-time productivity of each soil should be predicted. This matter is of special importance with soils subject to erosion.

Through farm study in the area and with the cooperation of other agriculturists, the chief of party needs to discover and explain in his report systems of farming or other uses under which accelerated erosion is avoided. Generally, the basic system of soil management—tillage, crop rotation, lime, and fertilizers— is of first importance; supplementary, where they are adapted, are strip cropping, contouring, use of terraces and small dams, and other practices for direct control of runoff and erosion. Soil erosion is treated most effectively when it is fully considered with all the other soil factors and management practices and least effectively when it is high lighted by itself or neglected.

EROSION HAZARD

It is commonly helpful to group soils according to their erodibility or the erosion hazard under defined sets of practices. Such a grouping is carried in soil survey reports in tables setting forth the principal characteristics and inferred qualities of the soils. Depending upon the information available and the detail that is significant, soils may be grouped according to erosion hazard into three classes as (1) none to slight, (2) moderate, and (3) high, or into five classes as (1) none, (2) slight, (3) moderate, (4) high, and (5) very high.

Meaningful groupings of soils according to erosion hazard are accompanied by descriptions of the sets of soil management practices and cropping systems adapted to them.

VEGETATION

Wherever possible the natural [1] vegetation should be recorded with the soil description. Correlations between vegetation and soil types or other soil classificational units have three important purposes: (1) For an understanding of soil genesis, since vegetation is one of the most important dynamic factors in soil formation; (2) for aid in recognizing soil boundaries; and (3) for making predictions about the kind and growth of natural vegetation from soil maps.

NATIVE PLANT ASSOCIATIONS

Where soil examinations are made, the dominant and associated species should be listed separately in the approximate order of their importance in the mixtures. [2] In forested areas, separate treatment is often necessary for (1) the forest trees, (2) the understory of small trees and shrubs, and (3) the ground cover of low bushes, herbaceous plants, mosses, and the like. Many soils have shrubs or low trees to be listed separately from the grasses and other ground cover. In describing forest trees an idea of the density of stand—as thin, medium, or dense—should be given. The range in size can be given in inches such as "6 to 12 inches dbh" (=diameter breast high), or "aspen 3 to 6 inches dbh with occasional seed trees of Norway pine 24 to 36 inches dbh."

In abstracting the separate descriptions into general ones for the soil type, series, or other unit, the appropriate name of the general plant association should be used, such as plains grassland, prairie grassland, desert shrub, oak-hickory forest, oak-pine forest, spruce-fir forest, tropical rain forest, and so on, together with the most important species of general occurrence. These descriptions should also include, where appropriate and useful, the descriptions of contrasting associations of successions related to cutting, fire, abandonment, and the like.

Common names of the plants may be used if such names are clear and specific. Yet many common names vary from place to place and are even used for different species in the same region. In areas of survey where the native plants are important to the use and interpretation of the soil map, lists of the plants mentioned in the soil survey report should be included that give both

---

[1] The term "natural" vegetation is used for wild plants in contrast to "cultural" vegetation, such as planted grains, grasses, and trees. Natural vegetation is a broad term for the associations of wild plants, and qualifying words are necessary to differentiate the "original natural vegetation" from successions following major geological changes, fire, plowing and abandonment, forest cutting, or severe grazing. Some use "native vegetation" in the same sense, and others limit this term to the indigenous species only.

[2] Emphasis is upon the important species only. In soil study, a few have a tendency to go further than necessary with the mere listing of both common and unusual plants.

common and scientific names. The plant identifications need to be checked by competent plant taxonomists, either in the field or from collected specimens.

Where a survey includes important areas of grazing or forest plants, the chief of party and his assistants need to learn both the common and scientific names of the principal plant species and the means of their identification. A temporary collection of identified grasses and other small plants and leaves from trees and shrubs can be maintained at field headquarters. Specimens can be placed between the leaves of large magazines and the names written on the margins of the adjacent pages.

RELATION TO SOILS

In soil survey reports and other reports of soil research, the characteristics of growth and the use of important native plants need to be described in relationship to the individual soil units and their management. The seasonal growth, rate and volume of growth, and palatability of the various species eaten by grazing animals are important. The results from research plots and the experience of ranchers are helpful in making such estimates by soil type or groups of similar soil types. The kinds and amounts of poisonous plants need special emphasis. These should be described in the soil survey report or references given to bulletins that do describe them. Present or potential invasions of weed plants on soil used for grazing should be explained.

Generally, close relationships exist between natural vegetation and soil types. Yet, there are important exceptions, especially among the azonal and intrazonal soils. Further, this relationship between vegetation and soil is complicated and confused by differences in cutting, grazing, fire, or management. *One cannot make a reliable soil map by studying vegetation alone, or even mainly.* Many are tempted to try because plants are far easier to observe than soil, especially where digging is difficult. With *both* careful soil study and plant study, excellent correlations have been established between natural vegetation associations and soil types, with adequately explained departures due to specific causes of interference, like fire and heavy grazing. But nearly worthless results have followed extensions of these correlations into other areas as a basis for making soil maps without thorough soil examinations.

Near the boundary between two plant associations, a seemingly minor factor in the environment may throw the association one way or another. Differences in exposure, wind, natural fires, and humidity are examples. Even only minor differences in soil or soil material sometimes, although rarely, account for important differences in the original plant cover.

Most important of all, the natural soil conditions under which the native plants are growing are often greatly unlike those that the farmer develops for crop plants. Differences in soils of great importance under irrigation, for example, may be little reflected in the native plants of the desert or semiarid grassland under

UNITS OF SOIL CLASSIFICATION AND MAPPING

The examinations of the soils provide the basis for placing them into taxonomic and mapping units. Each mapping unit is identified on the map by a symbol; and each must have an identifying name within the general system of soil classification. Consistent nomenclature is essential for understanding the relationships and differences among the mapping units and for correlating the soil units with those found elsewhere in order to make use of the whole body of existing knowledge about soil genesis and behavior. Mapping units are therefore named in terms of the units in the taxonomic classification.

TAXONOMIC AND MAPPING UNITS

A taxonomic unit is a creation in the mind of man to facilitate his thought about objects in numbers so great that he cannot comprehend them individually. At a single site, the soil is examined vertically and horizontally in one place. The observer digs deeply enough to examine each horizon, including the parent material and any underlying strata that influence the genesis and behavior of the soil. The soil examination extends horizontally, in the third dimension, far enough for sampling. In relation to the whole three-dimension soil area, the places examined are little more than points. The number of such places could be almost infinite. The scientist groups the soils examined at these points into taxonomic units that have specified limits of variation. Each unit should be thought of as consisting of (1) a central core or nucleus—a single modal profile representing the most usual condition of each property of all soils in the class, and (2) many other closely related profiles that vary from this central nucleus within precisely defined limits. The same kinds of horizons are present in all of the profiles of the group and they occur in the same sequence. Such properties of these horizons as thickness, texture, structure, color, consistence, and pH vary within defined limits.

A soil mapping unit that bears the name of a taxonomic unit consists of this defined taxonomic unit and sometimes also small inclusions of other soils that must be included because of the limitations imposed by the scale of mapping and the number of points than can be examined. In other words, any single soil name stands for a specially defined unit in the taxonomic system of classification; but that *same name*, applied to a mapping unit, stands for that defined taxonomic unit plus a small proportion of other units, up to about 15 percent, that cannot be excluded in practical cartography.

Some mapping units are defined in terms of two or more taxonomic units which may or may not be associated geographically. The *soil complex* is a mapping unit, used on detailed soil surveys, which consists of two or more recognized taxonomic units. These may be similar or contrasting but occur together in a more or less regular pattern, and are so intimately associated *geographically* that they cannot be separated by boundaries at the scale used. Two or more recognized taxonomic units that are *not* regularly associated geographically may also be mapped as a single unit—an *undifferentiated group*—if the differences between them are too small to justify separate recognition for the objective of the soil survey. The steep phases of two or more soil types, for example, may be so nearly alike, because of the dominance of steep slope over the other soil characteristics, that their indication as separate mapping units would add too little to the information conveyed by the map for the objective of the survey to justify separation.

Taxonomic units at any level of generalization may be used as mapping units, provided the scale is large enough. In detailed surveys the soil type or soil phase is most commonly the unit of mapping; taxonomic units at higher levels of generalization in the scheme of classification are rarely sufficiently homogeneous for the objectives of detailed surveys. It is entirely appropriate, however, for some objectives, to use soil series, soil families, or great soil groups as mapping units, or, more commonly, as taxonomic units in complexes or associations used as mapping units. In most landscapes the use of great soil groups as mapping units reduces the detail of the map far less than it reduces the length of the mapping legend. That is, a large part of the boundaries between soil types in many areas are also boundaries between great soil groups.

In the preparation of generalized maps at smaller scales than those used in detailed mapping, limitations imposed by the scale nearly always require inclusion of two or more taxonomic units in each defined soil association. Such mapping units are defined in terms of the kinds, relative proportions, and patterns of distribution of the taxonomic units included in them. The level of generalization for these *taxonomic* units is generally the soil series or higher.

These distinctions between mapping units and taxonomic units must be clearly in mind in building a soil mapping legend. Attempts to set up each taxonomic unit as a mapping unit may lead to such great complexity, especially where the soils are used together in fields, that the final map will be less useful than one showing defined complexes. Where complexes are used, the component taxonomic units need as careful sampling and definition as if they were mapped separately.

Each mapping unit in the legend needs to be clearly mappable on the scale used. That is, each needs to be so defined that competent soil mappers can recognize the boundaries accurately on the ground, under the practical conditions of the survey, and have sufficient space on their field sheets or aerial photographs to plot them without distortion or confusion.

GENERAL GUIDE TO DETAIL OF CLASSIFICATION

The level of detail to seek in soil classification is always a difficult problem. First of all, categorical detail—the narrowness of definition and homogeneity of the individual classification and mapping units—should be clearly distinguished from cartographic detail, or the relative size of individual areas shown on the maps and the accuracy of boundaries. Categorical and cartographic detail are somewhat related. That is, areas of highly contrasting soils are separated on a map in greater detail than are areas of soils that are similar.

The classification in a detailed soil survey area must separate soils that are unlike in characteristics significant to genesis or behavior. That is, the applied purposes of the work must be served and genetically unlike soils separated. Two soils may be alike in all characteristics of the solum that reflect their genetic origin and determine their classification as genetic types and still they may vary significantly in use potentialities under a changed environment. The deep layers (D layers) may be important in irrigation or drainage, for example, or slight differences in slope or stoniness may affect the use suitability of forested soils for cultivation. On the other hand, a Brown Forest soil and a Gray-Brown Podzolic soil may appear to behave alike, in terms of present knowledge and experience, yet they should be separated.

The soil classificational units need to be sufficiently homogeneous for making whatever significant differential predictions the available principles and data of soil science, and of related sciences, permit to be made. Finer distinctions should be made only where sound scientific evidence exists for expecting that differential predictions will come with further research. This rule needs to be interpreted for each survey area in terms of the soil conditions to be dealt with, the objectives of the survey, and the information available from experience and scientific research—both within the area and on similar soils elsewhere.

The detail of classification in a survey area in the Chernozem or Chestnut soil regions, for example, is greater if the map is to be used for planning irrigation and for guiding farm practices under irrigation than if the map is to be used for guiding farm practices without irrigation. Special emphasis is given to combinations of soil characteristics that influence the movement of water on, into, and through the soil and the hazards of salinity. Units need to be defined somewhat more narrowly in relief, microrelief, depth of solum, character of underlying strata, structure and texture of horizons, permeability, exchangeable bases in horizons, salts, and drainage. The classification must set forth clearly the soil areas significantly different from one another after irrigation as well as before, and also show definitely the soil areas that need special practices for drainage, salinity control, runoff control, fertility maintenance, and the like.

In survey areas that have special problems of drainage, runoff and erosion control, or fertilizer use, certain mapping units may need to be more narrowly defined than has been customary prior to the recognition of these problems or the development of methods for dealing with them.

THE SOIL SERIES

The *soil series* is a group of soils having soil horizons similar in differentiating characteristics and arrangement in the soil profile, except for the texture of the surface soil, and developed from a particular type of parent material. The soils within a series are essentially homogeneous in all soil profile characteristics except texture, principally of the A or surface horizon, and in such features as slope, stoniness, degree of erosion, topographic position, and depth to bedrock where these features do not modify greatly the kind and arrangement of soil horizons.

The soil series by itself is seldom used as a mapping unit in any survey. It is not sufficiently homogeneous in such features as soil slope and stoniness for the objectives of most detailed soil surveys; and it rarely occurs alone in areas large enough to serve as a unit of mapping on more generalized maps. The series name, however, is the key to the majority of soil characteristics possessed by the soil types and phases used in detailed mapping. The series brings the units of mapping together in an organized manner to help us remember soil properties and the relationships among soils.

Soil series are differentiated mainly on the basis of significant variations in the morphological features of the soil profile. These features include mainly the kind, thickness, and arrangement of horizons, and their structure, color, texture (except texture of the A horizon), reaction, consistence, content of carbonates and other salts, content of humus, and mineralogical composition. A significant difference in any one of these properties in any one horizon may be the basis for recognizing a different series. Very rarely, however, does one soil series vary from another in just one of these characteristics, for the characteristics are genetically related and several usually change together.

Since relief is one important genetic factor, partly responsible for the characteristics of the profile, and since shape is a property of the soil body, each soil series has a defined range in slope. This range is very narrow in some soil series and wide in others. The width of the permissible range in a soil series depends upon the range over which no important difference is reflected in the soil profile under the native vegetation. Where variations in soil slope have practical significance but no significant effect on the behavior of the soil in its natural environment, they are recognized as *phases,* defined later.

It is not easy to make a hard-and-fast rule covering reasonable variations in properties within the range of a soil series. If every single observable characteristic in two soil profiles had to be identical to permit placing the two in the same soil series, every profile examined would be a separate series, for no two profiles are identical in all respects. Some variation in thickness of the individual soil horizons must be expected. Some variation in every property must be allowed. From the point of view of applied soil science, it might be said that mappable differences of importance to the growth of native or crop plants should be recognized. Inasmuch as soil science does not have at its disposal complete knowledge of all of the relationships between soils and plants, however, this principle cannot be accepted as the only criterion, since soils with different potentialities would be put together. As applied soil science has progressed, the enormous practical importance of soil differences, thought to be only of academic interest a few years previous, have been demonstrated again and again. Moreover, the uses of soil survey information for purposes other than those associated with the growth of plants are increasing in importance. Soil characteristics important to engineering problems, for example, are becoming increasingly recognized; and not all of the properties important in engineering are equally important to the growth of plants.

The guiding principle in separating soil series might then be revised to include all differences in the soil profile. This cannot be accepted entirely, as some characteristics can be determined only with great effort and may not be worth the time and expense involved. To illustrate: Two soils in the Gray-Brown Podzolic group may have similar profiles except that the C horizon of one has a pH of about 7.5 due to the presence of calcium carbonate, whereas the C horizon of the other has a pH of about 5.8. These soils should be separated, even though some trouble is involved. Such a difference is important to the growth of some deeply rooted crops, and it is likely that this difference is also associated with other related accessory characteristics. From a practical point of view such a separation is important to applied soil science and agronomy. On the other hand, suppose a similar difference in pH exists between two soils associated with the normal Gray-Brown Podzolic soils but developed on subnormal relief and characterized by a deep claypan or hardpan above the parent material. With these soils the agronomic importance of the difference is less than that between the first pair, because plant roots probably could not penetrate to the underlying material. Moreover, the difficulty of making the examinations necessary to separate the two soils is greater. From a practical point of view the separation would probably not be justified if no consistent external feature could be associated with this internal characteristic.

A further restriction on the mapping of different soil series is that characteristics on which the differentation is based must be mappable. Some differences may be so difficult to determine that the time and expense involved in separating two soil series based upon them cannot be justified for the objectives of the survey. As hard-to-recognize characteristics become more important to the purposes for which the soil map is to be used, a correspondingly greater expediture of time and money for separating soils according to these characteristics becomes justified. In some soil regions only very skilled and experienced soil scientists can recognize consistently the soil differences that are obscure to the layman but that have great importance to soil management systems. Physical characteristics of the lower solum from which drainage and permeability may be inferred are examples.

From what has been said, it is clear that precise rules governing exactly what characteristics are considered differentiating between series, or exactly what ranges of these characteristics may be allowed within a series, cannot be laid down for all conditions. Generally, it may be said that those observable and mappable properties which are known to have, or are likely to have, significance in soil genesis, in the growth of native or crop plants, in soil management, and in soil engineering are to be considered. With field experience and with appreciation of the findings in plant nutrition, soil management, and other relevant fields of research, the judgment of the soil scientist becomes tempered. Some special considerations are discussed in the following paragraphs, but differentiation between soil series must depend upon the experience of the scientist and the advances in soil science.

All of the profiles within a series should be developed from similar parent materials. The parent material of soil is produced from rock materials through the forces of weathering. Similar parent materials may be produced from different geological deposits and in different ways, and unlike parent materials may be produced from the same rocks because of differences in weathering. It is the character of the parent material itself which is important. Still, significant characteristics of parent materials that cannot be seen in the field can sometimes be inferred from those of the parent rock. It is not necessary that the original rocks or the manner in which unconsolidated parent material is accumulated be uniform throughout a series. The mineralogical composition of the parent material is the most important characteristic, but in addition, such features as porosity, permeability, texture, and degree of assortment must be considered.

From the definition of a soil series, it might be assumed that texture could be allowed to vary within a series only in the A horizon. Strict adherence to that concept would mean that a very large number of series could consist of only one soil type, since a close relationship commonly exists between the texture of the parent material and the textures of other horizons in the solum besides the A. With a large number of monotype series, the usefulness of the series as a tool for understanding the relationships among soils and remembering characteristics becomes small. It is necessary, therefore, to allow some range in texture of parent material, and this is commonly reflected in a range of textures in the B horizons. The very great range in texture, even from sand to clay, that was at one time permitted within a series is no longer allowed. We know now that such great differences are generally associated with important differences in the other properties of the solum. Texture is a characteristic that carries with it many accessory properties, and the range of texture allowed within a series is governed by its effects on the magnitude of variation in other important characteristics.

It is difficult to set up a general guide to govern the number of series to be established mainly on the basis of texture of the parent material. Soil texture does not have the same significance in all soils. Differences of significance in well-drained soils may not be significant in poorly drained soils. Then too, differences in drainage, mineralogy, and other qualities are often associated with variations in texture. Three subdivisions within the range from sand to clay could be sufficient if the drainage is essentially the same and if the sands, silts, and clays are of similar mineralogical composition. These would be soils on very sandy parent materials, soils on medium-textured parent materials, and soils on very clayey parent materials. Yet such comparable conditions in the separates are rarely met over a wide range of texture.

The exact limits of textural classes included in any one series must be determined by the way in which the soils occur and the importance of texture and its co-varying accessory characteristics for the objective of the natural classification of soils.

Separate series have been established on the basis of land form alone. This has been done, for example, in glaciated regions as a means of differentiating between kames and outwash terraces that consist of similar materials. If the morphology of the solum is different in the two situations, recognition of two series is justified. If the sola and the properties of the parent material are similar, however, the soils should be recognized as members of the same series and differentiated as phases. That is, land form alone is not sufficient to separate soils into different series. Usually, however, other soil characteristics are associated with differences in land form.

The soil series names are place names taken from the area where the soil is first defined, such as Miami, Hagerstown, Mohave, and Houston. In the early days of soil surveying many soil series were given very broad definitions; in fact, so broad that after the soils had been more thoroughly studied and understood, it became necessary to split some series into two, or even several, series. For example, several soil series are now recognized for soils included with the Miami and Marshall series as first defined. Although the Marshall soils were first mapped in the Marshall area (Lyon County, Minn.), subsequent investigations have shown those soils to be significantly different in many ways from those given the same name elsewhere. Since the name had been used most widely in Iowa, Missouri, and Nebraska, it was retained for the soils in that region, and some of those in Minnesota were renamed Barnes. Similar situations have developed throughout the United States as our knowledge about soils has increased. This development has caused a certain amount of unavoidable confusion, as soils shown on the older maps do not comform to the later, more precise definitions.

In the American system, these proper names have been used rather than purely genetic terms, like "weakly podzolized loams from glacial drift," since no connotative name could be long enough to define the differentiating characteristics accurately enough for detailed classification and mapping without being hopelessly unwieldy. Then, too, changes in theories of soil genesis —and these have been substantial over the last 30 years—would cause confusion. The standards for series must be written in terms of the morphology of the profile and the landscape. These standards are implied in the series name. Genetic names in addition to the series names, subject to revision, are appropriate and helpful to supplement, but not to replace, the series name.

As the same place names frequently occur in several parts of the country, care must be taken in correlation to prevent the use of the same name for unlike soils. In the field-mapping legend, each proposed series is given a place name and the soil is defined. If a doubt exists about the identity of any of the series previously defined, local names are used during the progress of the work. In the final correlation soils belonging to previously established series are given their proper names.

As the number of series has increased, there has been a certain amount of resistance to the establishment of new ones. Where this reluctance has been based on consideration of sheer numbers alone, it has led to delay in recognition of new series where significant differences occur. Failure to recognize a new series on this basis alone only causes confusion. The variation in nature is fixed; failure to recognize it in no way reduces its magnitude, and the resultant units are rendered less useful by reason of their heterogeneity. There should be no hesitation in the establishment of a new series when needed. Every effort should be made, however, to differentiate at the level of the soil type or soil phase, rather than the soil series, provided such differentiation is based on sound principles of classification. It is only by making the fullest use of the type and phase that the soil series can serve its most useful purpose as a means of remembering characteristics and understanding relationships among soils.

ALLUVIAL SOILS[1]

Special problems arise in the definition of series of Alluvial soils, which do not have sequences of genetically related horizons. Materials laid down by water commonly have layers that differ greatly in such characteristics as texture, but the occurrence of those layers is governed by geological processes and is accidental insofar as genetic relationships of the soils to the present environment are concerned. If every difference in the occurrence of such layers were used as a basis for separating series, an almost infinite number of series could be recognized among Alluvial soils alone. This would defeat the purpose of the soil series. As

---

[1] Admittedly this is a poor term since it refers *not* to "soils from alluvium" but only to the young soils in flood plains and deltas actively in process of construction and which have no developed characteristics beyond those inherited from the alluvium itself. Perhaps it would be better to reserve the term for those people who wish to speak loosely of "soils from alluvium" and coin a new word for the soils referred to here.

a general rule, the differentiation of series on the basis of texture in Alluvial soils should be based on the texture of the material of the subsoil but not of the plowed layer or of the deep substratum. From three to five series are generally needed on otherwise similar materials to cover the entire range of textures of the subsoil. Where five series are required on the basis of the texture of the profile or permeability of the subsoil, the following classes may be used:

(1) Very gravelly or stony subsoil, generally nonarable.
(2) Gravelly and very rapidly permeable subsoils but with some fine materials.
(3) Coarse-textured rapidly permeable subsoils.
(4) Medium-textured moderately permeable subsoils.
(5) Fine-textured slowly permeable subsoils.

Where three series are adequate to cover the range, the following classes may be used:

(1) Light sandy loam and coarser subsoils.
(2) Heavy sandy loam to light clay loam subsoils.
(3) Heavy clay loam and clay subsoils.

Where significant among Alluvial soils, a soil in which the subsoil rests unconformably on material of different texture should be designated as a phase of the appropriate soil type of the recognized series, i.e., Huntington silt loam, moderately deep over sand. A soil in which an unconformable layer different in texture from that of the subsoil makes up the plowed layer should be designated as a type of the series.

Depth classes.—The upper limit and the lower limit of a depth class, applied to any one soil, are fixed in definite figures. These limits need to vary somewhat among soils depending on the other soil characteristics. Still, the words "shallow" and "deep" should have approximately the same meaning everywhere.

The following outline of depth classes, applicable to all soils, not simply Alluvial soils, gives the ranges within which the upper and lower limits of depth classes may be set:

	Ranges in limits	
	Upper (inches)	Lower (inches)
1. *Very shallow*	0	5–10
2. *Shallow*	5–10	20–30
3. *Moderately deep* (or moderately shallow[1])	20–30	30–50
4. *Deep*[2]	{ 30–50 or	50–60
	{ 30–50	60+
5. *Very deep*[2]	50–60	60+

[1] "Moderately shallow" is used where the contrasting layer is nearer the surface than typical for the kind of soil.
[2] The very deep class is rarely required. Where it is needed, the deep class has a lower limit somewhere between 50 and 60 inches.

Specific limits within these ranges are established for individual taxonomic units as required. In the description of a *mapping* unit, any necessary inclusions of soils ranging in depths beyond the established limits are described.

In the classification of Alluvial soils in **arid** and **semiarid** regions, absolute values in common use are *shallow*, less than 20 inches; *moderately deep,* 20 to 36 inches; and *deep,* more than 36 inches. In a few situations *very shallow,* 0 to 10 inches; or *very deep,* below 60 inches, are used.

Other characteristics.—Significant variations in mineralogical composition and reaction of the subsoil material are suitable criteria for differentiation among soil series in the Alluvial group. Differences in color and origin of soil material may be used as indications of such differences in composition if laboratory research confirms such correlations.

Differences in drainage that lead to distinct differences in morphology of the soil should be bases for differentiation of series. If they are not reflected in soil morphology but are important from the standpoint of land use and crop adaptation, they should be differentiated as drainage phases.

Concentrations of soluble salts may be used to differentiate among series where those concentrations have greatly affected the morphology of the soil and its consequent adaptation to reclamation or irrigation. If the physical morphology is not appreciably affected, such conditions may be differentiated as phases.[2]

Physiographic position, in itself, is not a satisfactory criterion for differentiation among series. Such features of the landscape may be important from the standpoint of frequency of flooding but they should be differentiated as phases. Even Alluvial soils commonly have some characteristics that reflect the climatic zone in which they occur, even though a well-defined sequence of genetic horizons has not developed. Where such distinct morphological characteristics as reaction or content of organic matter are reflections of differences in climatic zones, separate series should be recognized. Separate series should be set up only where distinct morphological differences occur.

SHALLOW SOILS AND LITHOSOLS

Shallow soils and Lithosols also pose special problems in the differentiation among series, partly because the thinness of their sola dominates over other characteristics. Where bedrock occurs near the surface, the entire sequence of horizons may be affected. Genetic horizons may be weakly expressed. Different series are recognized for the shallow and deep soils from similar kinds of parent material. In some soils, however, bedrock at shallow depth merely cuts off the profile at the bottom. The horizons characteristic of the upper part of deeper soils may be present and as well expressed in the shallow soils as in the soils on deep materials. In such series, the shallow soil should be recognized as a phase of the deeper soil, even though the horizon at the bottom of the typical solum is absent or partly lacking. Classes of soil depth are set forth in the preceding discussion of Alluvial soils, and the phase names to use are given on pages 297-8.

---

[2] See section on Estimation and Mapping of Salts and Alkali in the Soil.

THE SOIL TYPE

The soil type is a subdivision of the soil series based on the texture of the surface soil. The soil-type name consists of the series name plus the textural class name, determined primarily by the texture of the upper part of the soil. In soils with well-developed profiles the texture of the A horizon determines the class name. Where the A horizon is thin or poorly developed, the average texture of the upper 6 inches (or approximately equivalent to the cultivated surface layer of arable soils) is the basis for determining the textural class name.[3]

The class name of a type should not be determined by the texture of a horizon deep in the profile. Such a practice leads eventually to identical names for two soils that are quite different. For example, a soil on glaciolacustrine clays may be characterized by silty clay loam texture throughout the profile, but within the area, due to unconformable layers in the parent materials, a soil with a silty clay loam plowed layer and a silt loam subsoil may occur. The soil with silty clay loam texture throughout the profile would be named a silty clay loam on the basis of the texture of the plowed layer. To differentiate between this soil and the one with the silt loam subsoil, the second might be named incorrectly a silt loam. Then, should a third soil, with a silt loam plowed layer and a silty clay loam subsoil, be found, it would also be named a silt loam of the same series; but there would be significant differences between the two in use and management. The soil with the silt loam subsoil should be recognized as a separate series, or, if it is of small extent, as a *variant,* and named appropriately.

It is not suggested that no difference whatever other than the texture of the upper part of the solum exists between soil types within a series. The textural class names of two types in the same series are determined from the upper part of the solum, but at the same time the texture may vary somewhat elsewhere in the soil. To illustrate: the surface soils of Plainfield sand and Plainfield fine sand have sand and fine sand textures. The same textural differences commonly carry down through the sola, thus giving the Plainfield fine sand a slightly higher moisture-holding capacity than Plainfield sand. Except on stratified materials—and there are many of these—it is normal to expect that small differences in texture of the B and C horizons will be associated with differences in the texture of the A horizon. Such differences must not go beyond the allowable range for the series, except for variants.

Formerly, and perhaps even to some extent now, soils were placed in the same series and differentiated on the basis of texture, when actually the soils belonged in separate series. Miami silt loam and Miami loam, for example, have a silt loam and a loam texture, respectively, in the upper part of the sola. The B and C horizons of Miami loam have, on the average, a

---

[3] In some countries, New Zealand for example, the texture of the A horizon determines the textural class name of the type, even though thin.

288   U. S. DEPT. AGRICULTURE HANDBOOK 18

lower percentage of the fine separates than comparable horizons of Miami silt loam. For many years it has been assumed that the other characteristics of the soils are similar, except for differences in consistence commonly associated with the differences of texture indicated by the class names of the types. It seems now that the differences in structure and consistence, as well as in permeability and drainage, may be more important to soil use than formerly suspected. Not only that, the original parent material of the Miami soils, although mainly calcareous glacial drift, was partly calcareous glacial drift overlain by wind-blown silts. Thus, part of the Miami silt loam, according to the older definition, has the characteristic lower solum and parent material, and part of it has the lower solum and parent material characteristic of Miami loam developed from till without any covering of wind-blown silt. This example illustrates the great difficulties that will often arise in future soil correlations if series differences are designated as type differences within a broadly defined series.

In the early work, textural class names, or types, were used to separate soils that really belong in different series. This can be illustrated by the Norfolk series. This series, named from Norfolk, Va., was established about 1900. During the next 30 years it was mapped in all the states along the Atlantic and Gulf coastal plains from New Jersey to east Texas. It included deep sands with little or no horizon differentiation, shallow sands resting on sediments with some clay in them, and zonal soils with well-defined horizons. An effort to restrict the Norfolk series to yellow and gray sandy soils led to the redefinition of the Sassafras series in the late twenties.

Later, the Norfolk series was further restricted to well-drained Yellow Podzolic soils and Lithosols (Regosols) with yellow substrata. In the forties, the Norfolk was redefined and split into three series, since the range of soils included within it extended far beyond a series as then and now defined.

The Norfolk is now retained for soils of the Red-Yellow Podzolic group with sand to fine sandy loam upper sola and finer material at around 18 inches (or at 24 inches for thick surface-soil phases). Lakeland includes soils with sand to sandy loam textures down to fine material at 30 inches or deeper. Kershaw includes sands without underlying fine material of influence on the solum. Previously all of these were included in Norfolk, using both type and phase names to indicate conditions that are more properly series criteria.

Among soils developed from stratified parent materials, questions frequently arise as to what differences should be expressed by type or phase and what by series. For example, suppose a soil has developed mainly from lacustrine clay and, in places, is overlain by varying thicknesses of unconformable sand. Where the sand layer on top is about the thickness of the plowed layer, the soil should be indicated as a sandy type of the series that includes the soil that is clayey throughout. As the sand layer on top becomes thicker, however, the question arises as to how much of the soil must be developed from the sand before it is placed in a different series. In this example, since the outstanding characteristic of the series is the heavy clay, at least a significant part of the solum must be developed from the clay for the soil to be included as a type within the series.

With Bog soils, the textural class names used with other soils are not applicable, and there are no type designations in a strict sense. In Bog soils having well-decomposed surface soils, the designation *muck* is used after the series name; and those which do not have well-decomposed surface soils are called *peat*. This muck surface soil may be developed by soil-building forces from peat or may be inherited from parent material. Thus, the complete soil name of a Bog soil consists of the series name plus the word "peat" or "muck." Intermediate types are called *peaty muck* or *mucky peat*.

The soil type is the lowest and most nearly homogenous unit in the natural system of classification. A soil type may include defined variations in such characteristics as slope, stoniness, degree of erosion, or depth to bedrock or layers of unconformable material. To be allowed within the soil type, soils cannot vary in these features beyond the range of significance to the genesis of the natural soil under the native vegetation in the natural landscape. Yet within the permissible ranges in these characteristics of the soil type are variations of great importance to the use and management of soils. Consequently, the soils included within a soil type may range widely in their suitability for use or in their management requirements. One phase of a soil type may be suitable for intertilled crops, though a steep phase of the same type may be suited only to pasture. The soil type is a most useful unit in the classification of soils, for in it all of the important properties of genetic horizons are held to a minimum of variation; yet for making predictions to use in farm planning and for similar objectives, only those types that have no significant ranges in characteristics affecting use and management are satisfactory units for use in detailed mapping.

The importance in defining the ranges of *all* relevant characteristics permitted within both soil type and soil series can scarcely be overemphasized. Certain variations within soil types are shown by phase, but this should not cause the soil scientist to overlook these characteristics in the definition of series and types. The classes for slope, erosion, stoniness, depth, and the like apply in the definitions of series and types as well as in those of phase.

THE SOIL PHASE

The *soil phase* has been most commonly used as a segment of a soil type. Recently, the concept of phase has been broadened so that it may be defined as a subdivision of any class in the natural system of soil classification, but it is not itself a category of that system. Any class of any category, such as type, series, family, great soil group, suborder, or order, may be subdivided into phases. The basis of subdivision may be any characteristic or combination of characteristics potentially significant to man's use or management of soils. When used as a subdivision of a soil type, which is by far the common use, the phase is defined and shown on the soil map on the basis of all of the characteristics of the soil type, of which it is a part, but with a narrower definition in certain features of importance to soil use than are differentiating for the genetic soil type. Any subdivision of a soil type based on such features is the equivalent of a soil phase, whether or not it is recognized as such in the name, or whether the word "phase" is used in the name. Except for monophase soil types, the phase of a soil type on detailed maps is the unit about which the greatest number of precise statements and predictions can be made concerning soil use, management, and productivity.

Differences in the texture in the upper part of the soil sufficiently important to be recognized in mapping are indicated by textural class designations in the name of the soil type. Similarly, important differences in structure and other characteristics of the solum, including texture of the subsoil or parent material, are recognized by series definitions. The most common bases for differentiating among phases within soil types include variations in soil slope, degree of erosion, physiographic position, contrasting layers in the substratum, depth to bedrock, stoniness, and salinity that have not influenced soil morphology significantly.

The authors should like to give the reader the opportunity to consider other current suggestions about the relationships among soil series, soil type, and soil phase, even at the risk of introducing some confusion. Some have tentatively proposed that the units now called soil phases in currently published detailed soil surveys and in this *Manual* be called soil types. Thus a soil type could be any significant subdivision within a soil series, whether differentiated by texture of the surface soil, slope, stoniness, or any of the other features used to define phases as explained in the following pages.

In some ways this would simplify the nomenclature, as illustrated in the discussion of stoniness. It would be a great break in custom. Most people are accustomed to associate soil type with only the texture of the surface soil within a series. Much research is already reported on that basis.

The interested reader can study the question himself. Such a change would have little or no effect on the classification or mapping. It would change the nomenclature slightly and require redefinition of the traditional categories used in detailed soil classification.

SOIL SLOPE PHASES

Each soil type has its own characteristic range in slope. Any marked departures are associated with other characteristics that determine soil series. With some soil types or series, the permissible range in slope is narrow—within one slope class; with others, it is wide enough to include differences that are important to soil use and management. In these, the slope range of the type either extends beyond that of one slope class or the class itself may need to be subdivided in highly detailed mapping. Phases of soil slope are established to separate such parts of soil types or other classificational units.

The characteristics of soil slope are discussed in the section on Land Form, Relief, and Drainage. The classes, by soil slope gradient, are defined and named on pages 162-4, together with the limits of each class. These classes are used in describing all classification units, and the names are used as phase names when needed. In increasing order of slope gradient, the phase names are repeated here; names in parentheses are those to use where needed in very detailed mapping that requires subdivisions of the major classes.

A class: *Names*
    Single slopes .... *Level* (or *Level* and *Nearly level*).
    Complex slopes .... *Level* (or *Level* and *Nearly level*).
B class:
    Single slopes .... *Gently sloping* (or *Very gently sloping and Gently sloping*).
    Complex slopes .... *Undulating* (or *Gently undulating and Undulating*).
C class:
    Single slopes .... *Sloping*[1] or (*Sloping*[1] and *Strongly sloping*).
    Complex slopes .... *Rolling* (or *Gently rolling* and *Rolling*).
D class:
    Single slopes .... *Moderately steep.*
    Complex slopes .... *Hilly.*
E class:
    Single slopes .... *Steep.*
    Complex slopes .... *Steep.*
F class:
    Single slopes .... *Very steep.*
    Complex slopes .... *Very steep.*

[1] "Moderately sloping" may need to be substituted for "sloping" for clarity.

With soil types and series that have differences in soil slope significant to soil use and management, phases are separated at the *significant* gradient or percentage of slope for each unit. These definitions of specific slope phases vary widely among soil types, depending upon the other soil characteristics. That is, the sloping phase of one soil type may have soil slopes between 5 and 10 percent; another, slopes between 8 and 16 percent; and still others, slopes somewhere between. The phase names need to fall within the definition of the soil slope classes outlined on pages 162 to 164. Mapping units, including phases, may include two soil slope classes. Such soil slope phases carry compound names, as "level and gently sloping."

Soils vary widely, for example, in their erodibility on different slopes. The division lines among the slope classes, especially in relation to erodibility may not have the same values in terms of percentage of slope for different soils in the same region. Usually, however, it is not advisable to adjust the slope limitations to individual phases on the basis of any single quality, such as erodibility, alone. That is, the sloping phases of some soil types may be erodible under intertilled crops, whereas sloping phases of other soil types are not. The Decatur soils of Tennessee and Alabama, for example, are highly responsive to management but quite erodible—more so than the Clarksville soils, which are low in productivity. Thus for the phase names to be uniformly associated with the practices required for erosion control, the definitions of soil slope classes could be broader on the Clarksville than on the Decatur soils. On the other hand, and with nearly equal justification, soil slope classes might be more narrowly defined on the Clarksville than on the Decatur if the boundaries were chosen on the basis of the intensity, or inputs, of management needed for the optimum production that would return the costs for runoff and erosion control.

Although the soil classifier can make some adjustments of his phase definitions within the general classes of soil slope, he cannot hope to make all his slope phases bearing the same name similar in erodibility, in erosion hazard, or in management recommendations for the control of erosion. The erodibility of some soils increases as the degree of erosion increases. Thus the eroded phase of a soil type may be more subject to additional erosion than the uneroded phases. It simply is not possible to lay down any general rules for defining slope phases in general, beyond those given in the definitions of the major classes of soil slope already referred to. The soil classifier needs to weigh all of the characteristics of a soil type and all the available information about its response to management and make the definition so that mapping units will carry the most specific information and predictions.

Then too, he must consider the practical limitations of carrying on the soil survey work. It simply is not practicable in ordinary mapping to attempt accuracy within 1 or 2 percent of slope in rolling or forested country; nor is it practicable to have minor differences in definition of slope phases for similar soils. The party chief cannot count upon his assistants remembering an enormous number of such distinctions and mapping them accurately.

It is important that slope distinction among series, types, and phases be consistent with the natural conditions of soil slope. In the northeastern part of the United States, for example, the line between B and C slope classes comes at 8 percent in many soils. The major portion of the soil areas of a few soil types in this region falls below 3 percent in slope gradient, and the rest has a range from about 6 to 10 percent. With such soils, the 8-percent dividing line would result in a large number of soil areas with gradients only a little below 8 percent being placed in the B class and an equally large number of similar areas a little above 8 percent being placed in the C class. The differences in interpretation of the phases thus defined would not be consistently significant, partly because of the impracticability of measuring the slopes that closely. Thus the boundaries of the soil slope phases should be placed at 3 and 6 percent, with (1) areas below 3 percent of slope, (2) areas with 3 to 6 percent of slope, and (3) areas above 6 percent of slope to the permissible upper limit for the soil type.

In setting up all units, and perhaps more especially phases, the classifier must always remember the ultimate objective is producing a soil map that can be clearly interpreted for predicting crop adaptations and soil management practices. In humid regions, soils are used in three principal use groups: Cropping, grazing, and forestry, in the order of their decreasing intensity. Certainly the boundaries among soil areas having different potentialities for these uses need to be interpreted from a soil map. Soil slope is an important factor in defining these boundaries.

Some study of soil slope is required in advance of defining the soil types and phases accurately in terms of gradient. The definition of the classes must first meet the requirements of significance to the objectives of the survey. They must be defined so that boundary lines are readily recognized in the field. With the units definitely established, soil slope in percentage should be determined by means of a hand level (fig. 24) or other suitable instrument. When the range of slope of the unit has been determined, the slope limits in percentage are added to the definitions of each mapping unit and are used as criteria for differentiation during the progress of the survey.

In the final correlation of detailed soil surveys, slope phases are named as subdivisions of soil types. In addition to the phase names already outlined, it is usually helpful to add the actual limits of slope in percentage. Formerly, one slope phase of a soil type that extended over two or more classes of soil slope, generally the most extensive one, was selected as typical for the soil type and the fixed designation was omitted in the name of that unit. This makes it difficult for some to interpret the soil map from the legend alone, unless the figures for slope are given too, since the typical in some instances would have the least slope and in some the most. Further, the type name stands on the map for two units (1) the whole soil type with all its phases and (2) a slope phase within the type. On the map and in the report, the soil type name should stand for the entire type with all its phases. This does not mean, however, that the word "phase" needs always to be added. The word "phase" may be omitted from the name of the unit wherever that can be done without loss of clarity.

The classification of soil slopes provides for naming both complex and single slopes. Usually the distinction between these is inherent in the definition of the soil series. In only the most highly detailed soil maps for special purposes should attempts be made to separate phases within the same soil type and having the same slope class on the basis of one having complex slopes and one having single slopes.

ERODED SOIL PHASES

Significant differences within the natural soil classificational units—types, series, families, and great soil groups—brought about by accelerated erosion are recognized by phases of eroded soil. Where such erosion has destroyed the essential profile features of the soil, the area is, of course, classified in some other unit—some miscellaneous land type.

Conditions caused by normal or natural erosion, characteristic of the soil unit, are not shown in phases but are a part of the definition of the natural unit. Nor are eroded phases used to indicate erodibility or erosion hazard—a quality that depends on the whole set of soil characteristics that define soil series.

The determination of erosion in the field and the definition of the classes of eroded soil are explained in the section on Accelerated Soil Erosion. The translation of these classes, described on pages 261 to 268, into taxonomic and mapping units depends upon their significance to the use and management of each individual soil type. Most soils with class 1 erosion, for example, are not significantly different in use capability and management requirements from the uneroded parts of the soil types. Yet with a few soil types having thin sola over strongly contrasting material or thin A horizons over a claypan or hardpan, class 1 erosion may be significant, if all factors were favorable to intensive use and some of them have been changed by erosion.

The important guiding principle to the number of eroded phases and their definitions is the need to recognize mappable differences in soil use capability caused by the erosion that has already taken place, and not to make more phases than necessary to bring out these differences. If a tentatively established eroded phase turns out to have the same recommendations for use and the same estimated yields for the same crops as another phase or as the uneroded soil, it should be eliminated and the definitions redrawn to include it with a similar mapping unit. The principle is the same as it is with the translation of classes of stoniness or of soil slope into phases. Definitions of the phases need to be adjusted so that the boundaries on the maps will separate (1) soil areas of unlike use capabilities and (2) soil areas of unlike management response and requirements.

The classes described on pages 261 to 268 have been developed after long experience with widely different soil types. Within the general definitions, specific definitions of phases should be developed for each soil type. In any one soil survey area, of course, several soil types will turn out to have similarly defined eroded phases.

Symbols to use in the mapping legend for significant areas of eroded phases too small to be enclosed with boundaries are shown in the plates of standard symbols and explained in the section on Accelerated Soil Erosion. Each symbol needs to be defined in terms of both the conditions it represents and the area one symbol represents.

For a large part of the arable soils, the eroded phases are defined in terms of the classes of eroded soil. For very detailed soil surveys these phases may be subdivided if the need exists. Sometimes they need to be combined into complexes for the establishment of mapping units.

Water erosion.—Water-erosion phases of eroded soil are as follows:

Slightly eroded phase[4]: Used only for a few soils where the erosion has changed the soil enough to require a little but significantly different set of management practices for sustained production than that used for the uneroded soil. This is usually class 1 erosion.

Moderately[5] eroded phase: Used where erosion has changed a soil to such an extent that it requires a set of management practices different from the set used for the uneroded soils (or slightly eroded phase, if established) but where erosion has not changed the use-group capability of the soil for crops, pasture, or forestry. The distinction is made by comparing the management practices made necessary by the effects of the erosion with the practices needed to prevent erosion on the uneroded soil. Usually this is class 2 erosion, but sometimes, especially with lithosolic soils, classes 2 and 3 are combined.

Severely eroded phase: Used where erosion has so altered the soil that (1) it has a different use capability, say pasture instead of crops, or forestry instead of pasture or crops, or (2) it needs drastic treatment, such as improvement of tilth and substantial fertilization, and perhaps terracing or contouring, with or without the need of filling small gullies, to be maintained in the same use group as the uneroded soil. The distinction is guided by comparing the management practices made necessary by the effects of the erosion with the practices required to prevent erosion on the uneroded soil. This is commonly class 3 erosion, rarely class 2 erosion, rarely class 4 erosion, and sometimes classes 2 and 3 erosion combined.

Gullied land: Used for land on which the soil profile has been destroyed except for small patches between the deep gullies and which is not useful for crops and pasture without extensive reclamation. This land type may be subdivided by slope and by kinds of soil or parent material where significant. Gullied land, Decatur soil material, or Sloping gullied land, limestone material, are examples.

Wind erosion or soil blowing.—Phases of wind-eroded soils are as follows:

Wind-eroded (or blown) phase: The wind has removed soil to such extent that a set of management practices significantly different from the set used on the uneroded soil is required. Its use-group capabilities have not been substantially changed. If originally capable of use for crops, it can still be so used with proper management. Usually this is rated class 1 wind erosion.

Severely wind-eroded (or severely blown) phase: The wind has removed material to such extent that the soil can be used for crops only if it is extensively reworked and a set of management practices unlike that for the uneroded soil is used. It may be useful for permanent grasses or trees, depending upon the climate and the other soil characteristics. Usually this is class 2 wind erosion.

Blown-out land: The wind has removed nearly all of the solum. The land is barren or nearly so. It usually cannot be used for crops without extensive levelling and special management, but stabilizing trees or grasses, depending upon the other soil characteristics and the climate, may be established. Usually this is class 3 wind erosion. (See under the heading Miscellaneous Land Types.)

Depositions.—Phases for depositions are as follows:

Overblown phase: The deposit of wind-removed material lying on the soil is great enough to influence management but not great enough

---

[4] The word "phase" may be omitted from the name unless needed for clarity.
[5] The word "moderately" is omitted unless needed to differentiate between this phase and other eroded phases.

to destroy the essential characteristics of the soil series. Such a soil takes its textural class name from that of the overlying material. (See class 1a, p. 267.)

Wind-hummocky phase: Recent wind deposits lie on the soil in a fine pattern of hummocks that markedly alter management requirements of the soil but do not obliterate the essential characteristics of the soil series. (See class 2a, p. 268.)

Overwash phase: Deposits from water erosion lie thick enough on the soil to influence management requirements significantly but are not deep enough to destroy the essential characteristics of the soil series. Such a soil takes its textural class name from that of the overlying materials. These may be named *overwash phases, sanded phases,* or *rock-wash phases.* Ordinarily they are not needed on very young Alluvial soils.

PHASES OF STONINESS AND ROCKINESS

Stoniness and rockiness are discussed in detail in the section on Soil Texture, Coarse Fragments, Stoniness, and Rockiness. Coarse fragments are recognized as a part of the soil class names. Classes of stoniness and rockiness are phase distinctions. In order to reduce the length of the name, the terms indicating these phases are added to the textural class names as modifiers. The relationships among the classes of stoniness and rockiness, and between them and some phases are set forth in table 5, page 222.

For soil types with characteristics such that they are otherwise suitable for intensive use, except for stoniness and rockiness, the phases are listed in the following paragraphs. Some stony phases also include classes of rockiness and of coarse fragments 3 to 10 inches in diameter where the separation according to individual classes serves no useful purpose.

Stony phase: Sufficient stones to interfere with tillage but not enough to make intertilled crops impracticable. Usually this is class 1 stoniness on detailed surveys. In soils having coarse fragments, stoniness, and rockiness, if the distinctions among them are unimportant, the stony phase may have some of all three conditions.

Very stony phase: Sufficient stones to make tillage of intertilled crops impracticable, but not the tillage required for hay crops or improved pasture if other soil characteristics are favorable. Usually this is class 2 stoniness. In soils having coarse fragments, stoniness, and rockiness, if the distinctions among them are unimportant, the very stony phase may have some of all three conditions.

Extremely stony phase: Sufficient stones to make all use of machinery impracticable except for light machinery where other soil characteristics are especially favorable for improved pasture. In soils having coarse fragments, stoniness, and rockiness, if the distinctions among them are unimportant, the extremely stony phase may have some of all three conditions. If the other soil characteristics are not especially favorable for improved pasture, land of class 3 stoniness is included with Stony land—a miscellaneous land type—rather than in a phase of a soil type.

If the soil characteristics are such that the soil is not suited to intertilled crops anyway, the distinction between classes 0, 1, and 2 stoniness may be omitted and the range in stoniness described in the soil type definition. With such soil types it usually will not be necessary to establish stony phases; the soil conditions can be expressed adequately by allowing the soil type as the mapping unit to include classes 1 and 2 stoniness and Stony land to include classes 3 and 4 stoniness.

The same principles apply in translating classes of rockiness into rocky phases. These are as follows:

Rocky phase: Sufficient bedrock exposure to interfere with tillage but not enough to make intertilled crops impractical. With soil suitable for crops, this is class 1 rockiness.

Very rocky phase: Sufficient bedrock exposures to make tillage of intertilled crops impractical, but not the tillage required for hay crops or improved pasture, if the other soil characteristics are favorable. With soils otherwise suited to hay crops, this is usually class 2 rockiness.

Extremely rocky phase: Sufficient rock outcrop to make all use of machinery impractical, except for light machinery where other soil characteristics are especially favorable for improved pasture. Such a phase is used only for highly responsive soil having class 3 rockiness. If the other soil characteristics are not favorable for improved pasture, the land is included as Rock land and not as a phase of a soil type.

As with stoniness, the use suitability of the soil must be considered in using the above phases. If characteristics of a soil other than rockiness are not favorable to use for crops or improved pasture, phases are not used to show distinctions between classes 0, 1, and 2 rockiness, and class 3 rockiness is included along with class 4 in Rock land. Small rock outcrops are shown by the standard symbol. The area of land represented by one symbol on the map needs to be defined in each survey.

SOIL DEPTH PHASES

Soil depth phases are distinguished for variations in the total depth of the soil profile, including the C if present, which are significant to soil use and management, over bedrock or other strongly contrasting nonconforming rock material. The standard depth classes used are the same as those used in separating soil series, as set forth in the early part of this section on page 285.

Formerly, names were wholly relative to individual soil types. Thus shallow phases of soil types normally deep turned out to be deeper in inches than deep phases of soil types normally shallow. To avoid confusion for the map reader, broad classes of soil depth are recognized, within which there is sufficient flexibility to set depth limits at the significant places and still give the terms their usual significance when considered generally without reference to the detailed soil descriptions. The specific significance of soil depth phases in terms of soil use and management can be interpreted, however, only within the soil type definition.

The establishment and definition of each soil depth phase needs to be made in specific terms within the soil series definition and within the general guides set forth on page 285. No one soil series or type could be expected to cover the whole range. Depth phases should not be used to represent differences among natural units that are significant to their definitions as types or series. The phase names and their definitions are as follows:

Very shallow phase: The shallowest part of a shallow soil unit,° from 5 to 10 inches deep.

° In the category type, series, family, or great soil group.

Shallow phase: That part of a soil unit, typically deeper (or shallower), that is more than 5 to 10 inches deep but less than 20 to 30 inches deep.

Moderately shallow phase: That part of a soil unit, typically deeper, that is more than 20 to 30 inches deep and less than 30 to 50 inches deep.

Moderately deep phase: That part of a soil unit, typically shallower, that is more than 20 to 30 inches deep and less than 30 to 50 inches deep.

Deep phase: That part of a soil unit, typically shallower, that is (1) more than 30 to 50 inches deep but less than 50 to 60 inches deep or (2) more than 30 to 50 inches deep.

Very deep phase: That part of a soil unit, typically shallower, that is more than 60 inches deep. Ordinarily, this phase is unnecessary.

Besides definitions of the ranges in depth of the taxonomic unit, any necessary inclusions are mentioned in the description of a mapping unit. That is, as a mapping unit, *(series name)* silt loam, deep phase, may contain small percentages of moderately deep and shallow soil.

SOIL THICKNESS PHASES

Besides any variations in soil depth to nonconforming materials and differences due to accelerated erosion, some areas of a few soil units have thinner or thicker A horizons or sola than the typical. Where such differences within any soil type or other unit are significant to soil use and management, they are indicated as phases. No general class ranges are given. Each phase needs to be defined specifically in relation to the typical part of the soil unit. The thickness of the specific horizons or groups of horizons needs to be defined. Here again, the classifier is cautioned not to use thickness phases for insignificant differences or for soils that should be classified as separate series or as variants. Soil thickness phases are defined as follows:

Thick-surface phase: That part of the soil unit that has an A_1 or A horizon significantly thicker than the typical.

Thin-surface phase: That part of the soil unit that has an A_1 or A horizon significantly thinner than the typical.

Thick-solum phase: That part of a soil unit that has a solum significantly thicker than the typical.

Thin-solum phase: That part of a soil unit that has a solum significantly thinner than the typical.

OTHER PHASES

A few other phases are used but less commonly than the ones already described. The old published soil surveys cannot be used as guides, since formerly many soils were indicated by phases, some with nearly bizarre names, that are now indicated as separate soil series or as soil variants.

Drainage phases.—These may be used for other subdivisions within those soil units that extend over two or more classes of soil drainage as set forth in the section on Land Form, Relief, and Drainage, pages 109-72. The soil-drainage classes are guides to the establishment of all units, and any drainage phases should conform to these definitions and be given the same names as the specific soil-drainage classes. The use of drainage phases is confined to those relatively young soils, especially Alluvial soils, in which the differences in drainage classes are not reflected in the other differentiating soil characteristics.

Drained phases.—These are used for those areas of a taxonomic unit having improved drainage, usually by two or more drainage classes, brought about by recent natural processes or by drainage structures, and accompanied by little or no change in the other differentiating soil characteristics.

Physiographic phases.—These are sometimes needed to distinguish between soils within a taxonomic unit that are otherwise similar but have unlike relationships to the ground water or to flooding not already expressed by soil slope. On a deep covering of loess over a gravelly terrace, soils may be developed like those formed on a deep covering of loess over a till plain. If the former have a much better water supply in the deep underlying gravel, it may be necessary to separate them as a *terrace phase*.

More commonly, distinctions are made among Alluvial soils to separate out parts that may be less or more susceptible to flooding than the typical soil, as *low-bottom phase* or *high-bottom phase*. A *fan phase* of soils typically developed on terraces or in bottom lands is sometimes needed to indicate the important differences in water problems or potentialities.

Burned phases.—These phases are used for areas of organic soils that have had enough of the surface burned to alter their characteristics of importance to use capability.

Silted phases.—Silted phases are used for irrigated areas of soil units that have had sufficient amounts of silt added more or less uniformly to the surface through deposition from muddy irrigation water to alter their use capability but not enough to require the recognition of a different soil series.

THE SOIL VARIANT

A soil variant is a taxonomic soil unit closely related to another taxonomic unit, say a soil series, but departing from it in at least one differentiating characteristic at the series level, from which it derives its name as modified by the principal distinguishing feature. Many so-called phases of old soil surveys are now regarded as variants as herein defined. Variants are really separate soil series but of too small known extent to justify establishment as new series. Thus a soil may be recognized and defined as a variant in one survey area and later be designated as a separate series if found to be of important extent.

The variant is a convenient unit that permits the classifier to avoid establishing separate soil series for soils of minor extent and still keep his soil series definition as narrow as required. It makes it possible for him to hold strictly to the rule that each series description comprehends all types and phases within it. Unfortunately, this rule was not observed in some soil surveys, especially in setting up soil phases that did include soils outside the series definition. Serious confusion was inevitable, especially in using the soil series as a basis for grouping into families or other higher categories.

In older soil surveys, for example, the name Hayden loam, dark-colored phase, was used for what should be called Hayden loam, dark-colored variant. The Hayden loam is a Gray-Brown Podzolic soil developed on calcareous glacial till like that from which the Clarion of the Prairie group is developed. This variant is a transitional soil between the two, since found to be important enough for separate recognition as Lester loam.

Other examples of variants are as follows: Chastain silt loam, phosphatic variant; Angie sandy clay loam, calcareous-substratum variant; Flom silty clay loam, calcareous variant; and Bosket very fine sandy loam, gently sloping shallow variant.

These variants are not soils within the soil type named, but are specific departures from them. Some of the variants may be recognized as soil series later.

THE SOIL FAMILY

As this *Manual* is being prepared, the category "soil family" is still in process of definition and development. It is not possible to define the category precisely now, but tentative principles and criteria developed to date are presented for the guidance of those needing to use this unit.

The purpose of the category is to make the similarities and differences among the soils apparent at a level between that of the great soil group and that of the soil series. The category is more urgently needed now because the number of soil series is becoming too great to permit remembering all of them individually; and the great soil group is too heterogeneous to be used for very many objectives. The soil family should consist of similar soil series, and all soil series within one soil family should be members of the same great soil group.

The criteria used to differentiate among soil families must be chosen from among those characteristics that become homogeneous between the great soil groups and the soil series. Since differentiating characteristics accumulate from the higher to the lower categories, the criteria used to differentiate among soil series must include the distinguishing criteria of the soil family and all other categories above the series. The differentiating criteria of the family therefore, must be drawn from those characteristics which accumulate between these two levels—the great soil group and the series.

Soil series are described in terms of characteristics of single horizons, but no one of these can be used systematically to define the series, or a class of any category, because the significance of each one depends upon its combination with the other. The entire soil, with all of its horizons, must be defined as a unit. Neither the A or B horizon, by itself, defines a Podzol. Generally, the great soil groups can be defined in terms of kind and sequence of the master horizons—A and B—including all subdivisions as part of the whole. The Podzol, for example, is defined in terms of the acid, strongly leached, light-colored A and the underlying B with its characteristic form of iron and humus accumulation. Below the great soil group, characteristics such as the degree of expression of these master horizons, kind and arrangement of their subdivisions, and mineralogy of the solum accumulate as differentiating characteristics at the series level. It is from among characteristics such as these that the differentiating criteria of the category of families must be drawn.

First approximations of family groupings have been made for soils of Iowa, New York, California, Hawaii, and the Tennessee Valley. In these diverse soil regions, a combination of three or more of the following criteria has given tentatively satisfactory subdivisions of the great soil groups involved:

1. Kind and sequence of horizons within the master horizons that define the great soil groups. These identify the central concepts of great soil groups, and of intergrades between them, such as the modal horizons of intergrades between Gray-Brown Podzolic and Low-Humic Gley soils.

2. Relative degree of horizon differentiation—the degree of expression of master horizons that are characteristic of a specific great soil group.

3. Mineralogy of the solum—major mineralogical differences associated with strongly contrasting parent materials, particle-size distribution, or kind of clay, but within the limits of the great soil group.

4. Relative "size" of the solum—such as difference in thickness of solum not associated with degree of expression of the master horizons.

Criteria 1 and 2 provide homogeneity of kind, sequence, and degree of expression of the horizons. Criteria 3 and 4 may appear to belong below them in level of abstraction. In the trial groupings made, many of the characteristics dropped between the series and the family levels were primarily functions of parent material not reflected in the criteria listed above.

Although the primary function of the family is to help us remember characteristics and see relationships among soil series, other uses of soil families are important. Families should be so constituted that they can be used as primary classes for subdivisions in technical groupings for the objectives of applied soil science. It would be helpful, for example, if each family could be subdivided into phases on the basis of such characteristics as slope, stoniness, and degree of erosion, to provide groups sufficiently homogeneous for useful generalizations about soil use and management requirements. If properties such as slope or stoniness range widely, one cannot be precise about soil use and management of a family or a series, or even of a type, as a unit. To be precise, one must subdivide the type into phases on the basis of slope and similar criteria; one should also be able to achieve a moderately high degree of precision for applied objectives by subdividing groups of soil series in like manner. An effort to define the category of soil families at a level of generalization that will permit the use of the family for this purpose has been made in the Tennessee Valley and in Hawaii.

Two alternative systems for nomenclature of the soil family are possible. In one, the soil family could be given a geographic name, as with the soil series. The family might carry the name of a prominent constituent soil series. Such names are not connotative and may become confused with the constituent series name within the family. As a second alternative, coined names, preferably connotative ones, may be used. Combined syllables that are connotative of the suggested criteria may be thrown together into coined names. This has been done tentatively for some soils, but the suitability of the scheme and its clarity to users of soil maps are still uncertain.

COMBINED TAXONOMIC UNITS

The individual taxonomic unit cannot always be shown separately on detailed soil maps and usually not at all on reconnaissance, exploratory, generalized, or schematic soil maps of small scale. In the largest scale reconnaissance survey some of the taxonomic units can be shown separately. Depending on the scale of the map and its purpose, the soil map is often easier to read with understanding if well-defined groups of soils are shown on them rather than a very intricate pattern of taxonomic units. Rarely does grouping according to *taxonomic* similarity greatly reduce the complexity of the soil boundaries. The mapping unit needs to be defined in terms of a mappable pattern of geographically associated taxonomic units, defined in terms of the properties of the individually defined and named taxonomic units and their patterns.

Such groups are called, generally, *soil associations*. In detailed soil surveys the separate taxonomic members of soil associations are mapped individually if the scale permits. Otherwise they are mapped as *soil complexes*. To avoid confusion, the term soil complex is confined to units in legends of detailed soil surveys for soil associations of which the individual members are not mappable. The separate taxonomic units of most soil associations are unmappable in soil surveys of small scale. Since both soil associations and soil complexes are named by joining the names of two or three of the principal taxonomic units by hyphens, in detail-reconnaissance surveys having both units, the word "complex" or "association" needs to be added to all soil mapping units that contain two or more taxonomic units to avoid confusion.

Besides these mapping units, occasional need arises for mapping units of taxonomically similar soils that are not regularly geographically associated. Such a unit is called an *undifferentiated group* and is named by combining the names of the units with "and."

THE SOIL ASSOCIATION

The soil association is a group of defined and named taxonomic soil units, regularly geographically associated in a defined proportional pattern. It is the principal soil mapping unit shown on all small-scale maps, including original surveys and compiled maps. On relatively large-scale reconnaissance soil maps made in fairly well-known areas, the associations are defined in terms of the same kinds of taxonomic soil units as the ones mapped individually or in soil complexes in a detailed soil survey—series, types, phases, and variants. In broader scale mapping only the names, proportions, and definitions of soil series may be given. On maps of small scale, great soil groups, or soil families, or subdivisions of great soil groups according to parent material, with phases for relief and stoniness, may be the lowest units defined within the individual soil association.

The levels of grouping and the limits of homogeneity used in defining soil associations vary widely with the purpose of the map. These are outlined broadly in the following numbered paragraphs.

1. *Level of farm unit.*—The soil associations are defined in terms of combinations of soil types and phases that permit predictions of the potentialities of whole farm units, either existing or prospective ones that might be created by land subdivision or by consolidation of existing parcels. Such predictions include the adapted systems of farming, the principal problems of soil use and management, and the productivity of various sizes of farms.

This is the level of abstraction of soil association maps ordinarily required of the soil survey party chief. Soil association maps at higher levels of abstraction are sometimes useful.

2. *Level of rural neighborhood.*—The soil associations are defined in terms of combinations of soil series, and of phases where significant, that permit predictions concerning small groups of farms or potential farms, including systems of farming or forestry, potential density of the individual farms, and the broad problems of soil use and management in the area.

3. *Level of rural community and trading center.*—The soil associations are defined in terms of combinations of soil families or subdivisions of great soil groups, and of phases where significant, that permit predictions about the potentialities of existing or proposed rural communities and trading centers as to soil use potentialities for cropping, grazing, and forestry; the potentialities for rural community organization and development; and the broad problems of soil use and management.

The definition of a specific soil association consists of the definitions of its constituent taxonomic units, their proportions and patterns. In reconnaissance soil surveys, tentative soil associations and descriptions need to be tested and defined by detailed mapping of representative sample areas.

Examples of names of soil associations are as follows:

1. Great soil groups:
    Podzol-Bog
    Podzol-Half Bog (Calcareous till)
    Chernozem (loess)-Solonetz-Alluvial
2. Series:
    Miami-Crosby-Brookston
    Iron River-Adolph
3. Series and miscellaneous land types:
    Iron River-Rock land-Peat
4. Soil types:
    Kennan-Freer silt loams
5. Phases:
    Keenan-Freer stony silt loams
    Kennan stony silt loam, rolling-Adolph stony silt loam.

Associations of soils developed from one kind of parent material but differing in characteristics due to differences in relief and drainage are called *catenary*. That is, the Miami *catena* is an association of soils of which the soil series in the normal position is Miami, belonging to the Gray-Brown Podzolic group, along with others belonging to different great soil groups, and intergrades between them, and derived from similar parent material.

THE SOIL COMPLEX

The soil complex is a soil association, the taxonomic members of which cannot be separated individually in a detailed soil survey. Complexes are mapping units, not classes in the system of classification. Complexes should not be given separate series names; they are mixtures of soils and cannot be defined in terms of a modal profile and variations from it. Many of the Solonetz and Solonchak soils occur as spots within other soils and the two associates are so intimately mixed that the areas can be shown only as complexes, even on highly detailed soil maps. Intricate patterns of Bog or Half Bog soils with associated upland soil must be mapped as complexes.

The constituent taxonomic unit may be soil phases of different types, soil types of the same series, soil types of different series, or even two or more soil series.

The name of the complex should be the combined names of the principal constituents joined by a hyphen. If the textural class names in the type name, or the phase names, are the same for both constituents, the combined name may be shortened by using the plural. For example, a complex of Odessa silt loam and Schoharie silt loam may be designated as Odessa-Schoharie silt loams. This is a unit in which the entire range of both soil types is involved. If only one of their phases is involved, such as the gently sloping phases of each, the name is Odessa-Schoharie silt loams, gently sloping phases.

In parts of the northern Lake States, intricate patterns of Rubicon sand, Saugatuck sand, Newton sand, and Rifle peat are mapped as the Rubicon-Rifle complex. The naming of the two end members in this complex suggests clearly the presence of the two intergrades. In the Chestnut soil region, the solodized-Solonetz soil, Rhoades, so dominates the complex in association with several other soils that the unit is named simply Rhoades complex.

For the definition of a complex in the soil survey report, the same definitions of the taxonomic units are needed as if they were mapped individually, in addition to a description of the proportional pattern that they make in the complex. Such descriptions of complexes are enhanced by one highly detailed soil map of a representative area of a few acres.

The chemical and physical data obtained in the laboratory can be interpreted only in relation to the taxonomic unit; but the results from experimental plots and from farm fields can be interpreted in terms of the complex as a whole. Yield estimates, productivity ratings, and management requirements are given for the complex as a whole.

THE UNDIFFERENTIATED SOIL GROUP

Occasionally, it may be better to show two or more similar taxonomic units, which do not occur in regular geographic association, as one mapping unit. Such groups are called *undifferentiated soil groups*. Such mapping units are named in terms of their constituent taxonomic units and connected by "and." In some soil surveys the differences between the steep phases of two soil types of the same or of similar series, for example, may not be significant because slope is so important that it outweighs the other soil characteristics in terms of the objective of the survey. As a specific example, the Howard and Palmyra series are both Gray-Brown Podzolic soils on glacial outwash material. Both have calcareous substrata, but the calcareous material occurs about 20 inches deeper in the Howard soil than in the Palmyra. On the nearly level terraces this difference in depth of material is significant, but on slopes greater than 30 percent gradient, soil slope so outweighs the depth to calcareous material that a separation between the two soils has little significance. Similarly, the separation between the loam and silt loam types of the two series has little significance on such steep slopes. Thus the steep phases of Palmyra loam, Howard silt loam, and Howard loam can be included in an undifferentiated soil group as Howard and Palmyra loam and silt loam, steep phases. Other examples are Spaulding and Greenwood peats; Cloquet and Gogebic sandy loams; Clarion silt loam and Nicollet silty clay loam; Clarksville and Fullerton cherty loams, steep phases; and Clarksville stony loam, rolling, and Fullerton cherty loam, steep.

Such combinations may be set up in survey legends, but ordinarily it is better to make the separation in a detailed soil survey, especially if their use capabilities are uncertain. Since the individual types do not ordinarily occur together, combining them saves little time or no time in mapping. They may be combined later on a published map, however, if their differences are found to be insignificant. The prospect of such combinations on the published map should not encourage the party chief to set up many mapping units with a view to their later combination. If early in the work, any symbol or separation is found to be unnecessary, it should be eliminated, and any mapped areas given the proper symbols. If the mapping is far along, the symbol should remain in the legend, but its further use should be discontinued. The making of a large number of combinations in map compilation greatly increases the cost.

Although the use of undifferentiated soil groups reduces the length of the legend and of the soil survey report, it may not significantly reduce the number of lines on the map or the amount of time required in mapping. The use of soil complexes and soil associations as mapping units in place of individual taxonomic units does reduce the number of boundaries to be drawn.

MISCELLANEOUS LAND TYPES

Miscellaneous land types are used in soil classification and mapping for areas of land that have little or no natural soil or that are too nearly inaccessible for orderly examination, or where, for other reasons, it is not feasible to classify the soil. In practical mapping work, their recognition and definition depends partly upon the detailed required for the objective of the survey. They are named primarily in terms of land form and secondarily in terms of material. A miscellaneous land type may be part of a complex that includes one or more other miscellaneous land types or part of a complex that has one or more soil types in it. Small areas of some miscellaneous land types, as rock outcrop, for example, may be shown by defined symbols. Phases of miscellaneous land types should be avoided. Some classifiers are inclined to make unnecessary separations among miscellaneous land types, partly because the differences, although insignificant to the purposes of a soil survey, are obvious without digging.

Definitions of accepted classes and subclasses of miscellaneous land types are given in the following:

Alluvial land consists of areas of unconsolidated alluvium, generally stratified and varying widely in texture, recently deposited by streams, and subject to frequent changes through stream overflow. Subclasses include: *Sandy alluvial land, Gravelly alluvial land, Cobbly alluvial land, Stony alluvial land,* and *Bouldery alluvial land.* Several of these types may be included in one mapping unit as *Mixed alluvial land. Riverwash* is essentially barren *Alluvial land,* commonly sandy, exposed along streams at low water and subject to shifting during normal high water.

Although subject to change through periodic overflow, *Alluvial land,* except for *Riverwash,* has remained long enough for plants to become established. The deposits are too recent for soil profile development, although the material may be mottled. Drainage is variable, and shallow pools are common. *Alluvial land* has little agricultural value unless leveled and protected from overflow, although forests may grow on it. *Riverwash* has little or no vegetation. If necessary, subclasses can be recognized as *Riverwash (sandy)* and *Riverwash (cobbly).* Riverwash has no agricultural value.

Areas formerly classified as "Alluvial soils, undifferentiated" should be classified as named complexes of defined Alluvial soil series or types, such as "Eel-Sloan silt loams" for example, or as *Alluvial land.*

Badland is steep or very steep nearly barren land, ordinarily not stony, broken by numerous intermittent drainage channels. *Badland* is most common in semiarid and arid regions, where streams have entrenched themselves in soft geologic materials. Local relief generally falls between 25 and 500 feet. Runoff is very high, and geological erosion active. *Badland* has practically no agricultural value, except for small areas of soil with some value for grazing that may be included in the mapping unit. The relief is similar to that of *Rough broken land*, which has a cover of vegetation.

Beaches are sandy, gravelly, or cobbly shores washed and rewashed by waves. The land may be partly covered with water during high tides or stormy periods. *Coastal beaches* occur along the coasts of oceans and seas; *Lake beaches* occur along the shores of lakes or large ponds. *Old beaches* are no longer being washed and reworked by waves but retain their original form. Subclasses include *Coastal beaches (sandy)* and *Coastal beaches (cobbly)*. *Beaches* support little or no vegetation and have no agricultural value, although they may be sources of sand and gravel.

Blown-out land consists of areas from which all or most of the soil material has been removed by wind—a condition resulting from an extreme degree of soil blowing or wind erosion. The areas are shallow depressions that have flat or irregular floors formed by some more resistant layers, by an accumulation of pebbles or cobbles, or by exposure of the water table. Some areas have a small proportion of hummocks or small dunes. The land is barren, or nearly so, and generally useless for crops. Transient areas of *Blown-out land*, developed in loose deep sand, are included along with adjacent dunes in *Sand-dune land*. Small areas of *Blown-out land* are often called "blowouts" and are shown with symbols.

Colluvial land includes areas of unconsolidated recent colluvium—a heterogeneous deposit of soil material, rock fragments, or mixtures of the two—accumulated at the base of slopes primarily by gravity. Subclasses of *Colluvial land* are named according to the dominant textural class or kinds of rock material: for example, *Stony colluvial land* and *Cherty colluvial land*. Mapping units of *Colluvial land* commonly include small areas of soil creep and local alluvium.

Coquina land consists of shell fragments, mainly from the coquina clam but with lesser amounts from the conch, oyster, and other shell-bearing mollusks. This land is not useful for crops but commonly supports a few trees. The material has been used for building.

Ditches and spoil banks include areas of land occupied by ditches and by the rock-waste banks and dumps from their excavation. Often this type of land can be shown only with symbols.

Dumps are areas of uneven accumulations, or piles, of waste rock. Subclasses include (1) *Mine dumps*—areas of waste rock, with little or no segregation that came from ore and coal mines, quarries, and smelters; (2) *Placer diggings*—areas in which the original soil has been disturbed, overturned, or removed in placer mining, leaving an uneven or rough, eroded, and scarred surface; and (3) *Tailings*—areas of coarse debris from which finer material has been removed during mining operations.

Commonly dumps are so closely associated with pits that complexes of *Pits and dumps* or *Mine pits and dumps* are needed. *Dumps* is a miscellaneous land type having little or no agricultural value. Where smoothed, the areas are classed as *Made land*. Areas too small to be delineated on the map are shown by symbols.

Dune land consists of hills or ridges of sand-sized particles drifted and piled up by the wind and either actively shifting or so recently fixed or stabilized that no soil horizons have developed. *Active dune land* is still drifting, and *Stabilized dune land* is fixed by vegetation. Some areas mapped in the past as *Stabilized dune land* should be classed as a named soil. In places *Blown-out land* is associated with *Dune* *land;* although in mapping practice, transient areas of *Blown-out land,* developed in loose deep sand, are included in *Sand-dune land,* as are the areas of shifting sand that occur between dunes or on the slopes.

Gullied land is land so cut by recent gullies that it is nonarable, and the soil profiles have been largely destroyed. Where necessary, separations based on dominant slope of the original land surface may be made, as *Sloping gullied land.* It may or may not be feasible to convert gullied land to arable land by leveling, depending upon the kind and depth of the soil material. It is often useful to indicate the kind of soil material involved as in: *Gullied land (Ruston soil material)* or *Gullied land (deep acid sandy materials).*

Kitchen middens are sites of aboriginal human homes. They consist of mixtures of soil material, mollusk shells or fragments, ashes, charcoal, artifacts, and a few stones and bones. They are generally slightly higher than adjacent land and in some places form distinct mounds. Many are so small that they can be shown on the map only by symbols.

Landslides are masses of rock fragments, soil, or other unconsolidated materials that have slid down slopes in recent times, together with the scarred surfaces resulting from such movement. A common form of landslide is soil slump—the slow downward slipping of a mass of soil, or of several subsidiary masses, usually with some degree of backward rotation, on a more or less horizontal axis parallel to the slope. Such landslides of soil material commonly have an uneven concave-convex, or sigmoid, cross section with wide cracks. The surface may have the appearance of steps or small benches on a slope. Materials of the lower solum or substrata are exposed as scars where the soil mass broke away from its original position. Slumps are common in some clay soils of the uplands, particularly on steep slopes in the vicinity of recent faulting, or along contacts of differing geologic formations. The slippage takes place during or after long rains or near irrigation ditches, and may be accompanied by earth flow. Rapidly moving landslides—debris-slides or wet debris-avalanches —may be dangerous and damaging.

Lava flows include areas covered with lava rock, commonly basalt. These flows are geologically recent, especially those in humid regions. Most lava flows have sharp jagged surfaces, crevices, and angular blocks, although a few have relatively smooth surfaces. A little soil material may have blown into a few cracks and sheltered pockets. Vegetation is limited to lichens, occasional bunches of grass, and scattered shrubs and trees. With slightly more soil material this type merges into *Lava rock land. Lava flows* has no agricultural value, and, because of the commonly rough surface and sparse vegetation, it is avoided by livestock.

Made land consists of areas filled artificially with earth, trash, or both, and smoothed. It occurs most commonly in and around urban areas. Stabilized land areas with clearly developed soil characteristics or even those with young soils if definable and uniform enough to map, and especially if arable, should be classified as soils even though originally made or reworked by man.

Marl beds include areas where marl (an earthy crumbling deposit consisting chiefly of calcium carbonate mixed with clay or other impurities) is exposed or lies a few inches below the surface. Marl is usually formed in lakes or ponds. The calcium carbonate may have originated from the calcareous remains of the chara plant (chara marl), from mollusk shells (shell marl), or from simple precipitation from solution. These beds are commonly a good source of agricultural lime.

Marsh consists of wet periodically flooded areas covered dominantly with grasses, cattails, rushes, or other herbaceous plants. Subclasses include *Tidal marsh,* periodically inundated because of the tide; *Fresh water marsh,* which is influenced by fresh water and not by the tide;

and *Salt water marsh*, which is influenced by salty water but not by the tide. *Tidal marsh* may be subdivided into *Tidal marsh (salty)* and *Tidal marsh (fresh)*. *Tidal marsh* may be associated with *Tidal flats*. *Salt water marsh* generally occurs in wet salty flats along stream valleys. *Marsh* is mainly covered with grasses and grasslike plants, while *Swamp* is covered with trees.

Mine wash consists of accumulations of sandy, silty, or clayey material recently eroded in mining operations. *Mine wash* commonly originates in areas of *Strip mines*. It is distinct from *Slickens*, which consists of fine-textured material separated in placer-mine or ore-mill operations. *Mine wash* may clog stream channels and damage the land on which it is deposited.

Oil-waste land includes areas where liquid oily wastes have accumulated. This miscellaneous land type includes slush pits and adjacent uplands and bottoms affected by the liquid wastes, principally salt water and oil. The land is unsuited to agricultural purposes, although some of it can be reclaimed.

Pits are open excavations from which soil and underlying material have been removed. Several kinds of pits are recognized, including: *Borrow pits, Clay pits, Gravel pits, Mine pits, Quarries, Sand pits,* and *Strip mines*. Commonly *Pits* are closely associated with *Dumps*, making it necessary to map complexes, such as *Pits and Dumps* or *Mine pits and dumps*. Pits too small to be delineated on the map are shown by symbols.

Playas are essentially barren, flat, generally dry, undrained basins in arid and semiarid regions. They may contain water of shallow depth for short periods at infrequent intervals. Many of them are salty.

Rock land consists of areas having enough rock outcrop and very shallow soil to submerge other soil characteristics. The upper limit of rock outcrop is 90 percent of the mapped area and, unless the other features place the land in some other miscellaneous land type anyway, the lower limit is ordinarily 25 percent. The word "rock" may appear in the land type names if only 3 percent of the area is rock outcrop: for example, *Stony rock land* or *Rough broken land and rock land*. Where a mappable area contains more than 90 percent rock outcrop, the whole is classed as *Rock outcrop*. Several kinds of *Rock land* are named according to the kind of rock material, including: *Limestone rock land, Sandstone rock land, Lava rock land, Quartzite rock land,* and *Granite rock land*. Usually such distinctions are not necessary.

Rock land may offer some light grazing. Tree growth is usually sparse and scrubby even where the climatic and other conditions are favorable. If a soil type has prominent soil features despite more than 25 percent rock outcrop, a very rocky phase of the soil type may be defined with 25 to 50 percent rock outcrop.

Rock outcrop consists of exposures of bare bedrock. Although very rarely needed, subclasses can be named according to the kind of rock materials, including: *Chalk outcrop, Limestone outcrop, Sandstone outcrop,* and *Shale outcrop*. Commonly, areas of *Rock outcrop* are too small to be delineated on the map and are shown by symbols.

Rough broken land consists of very steep land, ordinarily not stony, broken by numerous intermittent drainage channels. It is used for grazing and for timber. It has a cover of vegetation, as opposed to *Badland*, which has sparse vegetation or complete lack of cover. Stony areas are classed as *Rough broken and stony land*. *Rough broken land* is deeply dissected by narrow V-shaped valleys and sharp torturous divides. Local relief is generally between 25 and 500 feet. Soil slipping is often common, and the steep slopes have a succession of short vertical exposures or "cat steps." Runoff is high and geologic erosion is active.

Rough mountainous land refers to mountainous areas, dominantly stony, that include small areas of land suitable for cropping, and, in places, considerable land suitable for grazing. *Rough mountainous land* is essentially a complex of *Rough broken and stony land*, shallow phases of unidentified soils, and small areas of unidentified soils suitable for crops or pastures. Local relief is generally more than 500 feet. This unit is included in mapping legends only in reconnaissance surveys.

Rubble land includes areas with 90 percent or more of stones and boulders. It is the extreme of *Stony land*, as *Rock outcrop* is of *Rock land*. Practically no soil is exposed. If some purpose will be served, *Rubble land* may be modified by the name of the principal rocks from which the stones are derived, as *Granite rubble land*.

Scoria land consists of areas of slaglike clinkers and burned shale and fine-grained sandstone characteristic of burned-out coal beds. Although it commonly supports a sparse cover of grasses, this land is of low value for grazing and of no value for crops.

Slickens are accumulations of fine-textured materials separated in placer-mine and ore-mill operations. Slickens from ore mills consist largely of freshly ground rock that generally has undergone chemical treatment during the milling process. Such materials may be detrimental to plant growth but are usually confined in specially constructed basins.

Stony land includes areas having enough stones and boulders to submerge other soil characteristics. At the upper limit 90 percent of the exposed surface is stones; the lower limit is ordinarily 15 percent unless other features place the land in some other miscellaneous land type anyway. The word "stony" may appear in land type names if over 3 percent of the area is covered with stones, as for example, *Rough broken and stony land*. Areas having over 90 percent stones are called *Rubble*. Where significant to forestry or grazing, areas having more than 50 percent stones and boulders are called *Very stony land*. If a soil type has prominent soil features, despite more than 15 percent of stones, a very stony phase of the soil type may be defined with 15 to 50 percent of the area occupied by stones.

Stony land may be combined with other miscellaneous land types to give, for example, *Stony alluvial land*, *Stony colluvial land*, or *Rough broken and stony land*. If significant to land use, the type may be subdivided to *Stony smooth land* (A and B soil-slope classes), *Stony rolling land* (C and D soil-slope classes), and *Stony rough land* and *Stony steep land* (E and F soil-slope classes). *Stony land* may form a complex with *Rock land*, as *Stony rock land*. Significant differences can be indicated by modifying the type name to indicate the source of material, as for example, *Stony smooth land* (*Hagerstown soil material*) and *Stony rough land* (*Muskingum soil material*).

Areas of *Stony land* or *Very stony land* too small to enclose with boundaries are indicated by symbols and defined as to the area represented by one symbol. If areas of both *Stony land* and *Very stony land* are recognized in detailed surveys, a separate symbol is needed for each.

Swamp consists of naturally wooded areas, all or most of which are covered with water much of the time. *Tidal swamp* is influenced by salty tidal water, and *Fresh water swamp* is influenced by nontidal fresh water. Some *tidal swamp* has a characteristic growth of mangrove, as along the coast of southern Florida. In places it is associated with *Tidal marsh*. Occasionally it is significant to indicate the dominant kind of trees, as *Tidal swamp (mangrove)* or *Fresh water swamp (cypress)*. *Swamp* is not suitable for agriculture without extensive reclamation by drainage and dikes. (These designations are used sparingly. Most swamps and marshes have some kind of soil.)

Terrace escarpments include sloping or steep relatively even fronts of terraces. Where the terrace face is broken by numerous intermittent drainage channels and the differences in elevation exceed 25 feet, the areas should be classified as *Rough broken land* or *Badland,* rather than *Terrace escarpments.* Where gullying has been active, the areas should be classified as *Gullied land.* Where the terrace escarpments are especially stony they may be named *Terrace escarpments (stony).* Of course, many terrace escarpments have well-developed soil types on them that should be mapped as such.

Tidal flats include essentially barren, nearly flat areas of mud, periodically covered by tidal water. The lower parts of these areas are covered by water daily; the higher parts may be covered only at unusually high tides. The flats consist of silty and clayey material that in places contains considerable very fine sand. Normally the material has an excess of soluble salts. When the surface dries, it cracks and may become hard enough to support a man.

Urban land is land so altered or obscured by urban works and structures that identification of soils is not feasible. Soil boundaries should be extended into urban areas wherever it is possible to do so with reasonable accuracy, and the use of this miscellaneous land type is restricted to the closely built-up parts of cities.

Very stony land includes areas having from 50 to 90 percent of the surface covered with stones and boulders. The same qualifying adjectives apply as to *Stony land.*

Volcanic-ash land consists of areas of nearly unmodified deposits of volcanic ash. This land type should be reserved for those few deposits of volcanic ash that are so recent as to have little or no evidence of soil development and little or no vegetation.

THE SOIL MAPPING LEGEND

After the soils have been examined, identified, and described, a mapping legend is prepared. Every soil survey needs two legends, usually developed together: (1) The identification legend and (2) the descriptive legend. Although serving different and overlapping purposes, both legends are essential and must be kept up to date by frequent revision for good results.

The task of developing and maintaining proper legends is, perhaps, the most important duty of the soil survey party chief. The quality of these legends, especially of the descriptive legend, reflects the completeness and accuracy of his study and understanding of his mapping units. If he is alert to his technical and administrative responsibilities, the legends are clear and up to date. Lack of clarity in the legend indicates poor classification and is bound to be reflected in inconsistent mapping. The larger the soil survey party the greater the hazard. The legends need to be clear to each mapper so that all draw the boundaries accurately in comparable places and so that the mapping units are consistent throughout the map.

The soil correlator or other supervisory scientist should give special attention to the survey legend. He should help the party chief to correct any inadequacies or ambiguities. A minor error, simple to correct in the early stages of the work, can grow into a major problem in requiring extensive field revision or greatly increased cost in map compilation. Administrative arrangements should provide first priority for typing soil survey legends and revised legends for use by the field party.

No mapping should be done by any member of the party until he has been furnished a legend of *all soil symbols as complete as it is possible to make*. Rarely, however, can the legend be made fully complete at the start. As each mapper finds a new soil or feature not provided for in the legend, or if he is uncertain about the application of any symbol, a note should be made on the map and the matter drawn to the attention of the party chief immediately. Any additions or corrections should be given to all mappers so that all legends within the party are alike.

Complete standardization of mapping symbols on a national or regional basis is impracticable. If enough symbols and combinations of symbols are developed to take care of every need on the most detailed surveys, symbols are bound to be far too long and unwieldy for clarity on the field sheets.

CONVENTIONAL SYMBOLS

The standard symbols for natural and cultural features are illustrated in plates 1 to 5. Nearly all of these are standard for all accurate maps. In the United States, the topographic map of

313

the United States Geologic Survey sets the standards for the general symbolization of base data on maps of the scale used in soil cartography. Yet some alternatives are provided, and some additional symbols are needed on soil maps. Thus, even within the general system of notation, differences are made for different areas, depending upon the scale of the maps, the nature of the country, and the objectives of the survey. Trails are shown when they offer the only means of entry into an undeveloped region, but not in well-settled country. For some objectives, roads are classified in more detail than for others. In areas where recreation is very important to local land use, cottages ought to be clearly set off from permanent residences.

A proper legend for any soil survey includes all mapping symbols of every kind that go on the map, as selected from the standards given. No area will require all of them; and in some areas one or more special symbols may have to be added to show a locally important feature not provided for among the standards.

The special symbols (pls. 6 and 7) for sinkholes, gullies, wet spots, eroded phases, stony phases, and the like fall between the general conventional symbols and the symbols used to identify soil areas. They are used for small areas, too small to enclose within a boundary, yet significant to soil use and management. In the soil survey legend for any area, these need to be defined specifically for that area in terms of both *area* and *quality*, depending upon the scale and significance.

A stone symbol, for example, may be used for small areas of a stony phase not isolated by a boundary. Depending upon the detail required, the symbol may be defined in area as (1) $\frac{1}{4}$ to $\frac{1}{2}$ acre, (2) $\frac{1}{2}$ to $1\frac{3}{4}$ acres, or (3) 1 to $3\frac{1}{2}$ acres. The same applies to all similar symbols. Small spots of eroded phases of soil types, too small to enclose with boundaries, may be defined similarly with different symbols, say S and SS, for moderate and severe sheet erosion, respectively.

Such symbols for phases or miscellaneous land types that contrast sharply with the adjacent soils are especially useful if the total acreage is very small or if the separate areas are too small to enclose in boundaries without exaggeration. But *none* should be used without accurate definition. On the finished map each symbol should tell the reader the nature of the land represented by the symbol and its area.

THE IDENTIFICATION SOIL LEGEND

Each mapping unit—type, phase, variant, complex, association, or miscellaneous land type—has a symbol that is placed in areas on the map to identify it. Although letters are commonly used on published soil maps, the basic symbols for field sheets are mostly numbers with letters for phases.

The identification legend is a list of all these symbols and their names, arranged alphabetically and numerically so that one may see the symbol for each kind of soil and the kind of soil for each symbol.

Each permissible symbol—*each combination of figures and letters*—used to identify areas on the soil map needs to be listed and named. If extra subdivisions, say of phases, are made for a special use of photographic copies of the field sheets but are not for inclusion on the final compiled soil map, they may be listed under one name, provided the differences between the symbols are clear from specific notations or from a general one that applies to several soils. For example, 14A and 14A$_2$ may both indicate Huntington silt loam with slope class A, the first *level*, with slopes of 0 to 1 percent, and the second *nearly level*, with slopes of 1 to 2 percent.

Commonly figures are used for soil types, with letters for soil-slope phases and either letters or figures for eroded phases added to the symbol for the soil type. A standard local convention can be very helpful to those who must remember the symbols accurately. Some use a convention in the soil-type number symbol so that the last digit indicates the textural class as follows: (1) Clay, (2) clay loam, (3) silty clay loam, (4) silt loam, (5) loam, (6) fine sandy loam, (7) sandy loam, (8) loamy fine sand, (9) loamy sand, and (10) sand. This scheme will not work in many areas, because more than ten textural class names need to be recognized. Further, its use may result in the mapping of insignificant differences in soil texture. The biggest difficulty with this kind of scheme is the need for three figures in the soil-map symbol. If all mapping units can be conveniently symbolized between figure 1 and figure 99, significantly less space is required on the map for the symbols.

Where needed, the soil-slope symbol—A, B, C, D, E, or F—directly follows the soil-type number or is the first letter in the denominator of a fractional symbol. If photographic copies of the field sheets are to be used by laymen, it may be helpful to add the soil-slope symbols to all soil-type symbols, including those falling wholly within one slope class. This makes it possible to read soil slope approximately without consulting a legend for the numbers. But if the field sheets are not to be used directly, the soil-slope symbol may be omitted from any symbol if all the areas of a soil type fall within one slope class.

The symbol for an eroded phase, if needed, usually follows the soil-slope symbol in the numerator, or is put as the second symbol in the denominator of a fractional symbol. Either letters or numbers may be used, whichever are more convenient. Thus, Dexter silt loam, eroded sloping phase, could be shown as 24Cn, $\dfrac{24C}{3}$, or $\dfrac{24}{C-3}$. The first of the three is easiest to place and takes the least space.

Symbols for stony phases may be added to the above as needed, say 24CnS, or $\dfrac{24S}{C-3}$, although stony phases and eroded phases are not usually needed within the same soil type. Commonly, however, stony phases are indicated with a separate numeral for this phase of the soil type.

Less common phases, like drained phases and depth phases, can often be handled most conveniently by a separate number, such as 84 Brookston clay loam and 814 Brookston clay loam, drained phase.

Where land use must be mapped, the symbols should be used separately, not as a part of the soil legend. Generally, it is better to map land use on a separate photograph or overlay, especially in detailed work. It can be mapped on the same photograph if colored ink is used both for symbols and boundaries or if dotted lines are used for the boundaries; yet with much detail such maps become exceedingly difficult to read accurately and very costly to compile for publication.

To the field mapper it is most helpful if the legend is arranged alphabetically by soil names, or first by major groups according to physiographic position or on some other broad basis, and then alphabetically within each group. To the map user, it is most convenient to have the legend arranged, progressively, by symbols, from the smallest figure to the largest, with subdivisions by soil slope classes and eroded phases or other phases under these numbered symbols. A small section from such a list reads as follows:

40Cp	Tippah silty clay loam, severely eroded rolling phase
41Dl	Susquehanna very fine sandy loam
41Dp	Susquehanna clay, severely eroded phase
42Bl	Dulac silt loam
42Bm	Dulac silt loam, slightly eroded phase
42Bn	Dulac silt loam, eroded phase
42Cl	Dulac silt loam, rolling phase
42Cm	Dulac silt loam, slightly eroded rolling phase
42Cn	Dulac silt loam, eroded rolling phase
42Cp	Dulac silty clay loam, severely eroded rolling phase
42Al	Dulac silt loam, level phase
42Am	Dulac silt loam, slightly eroded level phase
43Dl	Cuthbert fine sandy loam
43Dn	Cuthbert clay loam, eroded phase

The conventions used in the soil legend should be worked out individually for each area, bearing in mind the following principles:

1. The primary purpose of the identification soil legend is to key the kinds of soil areas to the names in the legend. The symbols should be as brief as possible and still be legible to the user after photography. Long involved fractional symbols should be avoided since they are difficult to place properly without being made too small for legibility. The more symbols that must be placed outside of small areas and keyed into them with an arrow, the greater the chances for confusion and error and for obscuring other symbols. Recent experience has shown that agricultural advisers and farmers have great difficulty in reading accurately photographic copies of field sheets with symbols placed outside of the areas to which they apply and keyed into them with a short arrow. Since so many soil features are relevant, if one tries to

go far beyond the main purpose of identification in order to develop connotative symbols, his legend may fail in its primary function. No connotative symbol can be more than an oversimplification at best and its small value can be many times offset by decreased legibility of the map.

2. The symbols should all be defined and named in the legend. Wherever the party chief and soil correlator are doubtful of the name, a local name (not already used in correlation) should be given the soil. Separations or subdivisions of major soil types, phases, or other units *need names.* Symbols should not be left dangling by themselves, especially complicated ones that only the members of the immediate soil survey party can read with understanding. This is highly important if photographs of the field sheets are to be used by agricultural advisers or other technicians in farm planning.

3. The legend needs to be revised from time to time and retyped so that all additions are arranged in their proper places. It is equally important to drop out any symbol for kinds of areas that were expected but that were not found, or for subdivisions, further study of which has revealed to be insignificant. If any symbols have been used, they need to be retained in the complete legend but marked "discontinue" to avoid the possibility of having unnamed symbols on the field sheet. (As an extreme example, one tentative legend provided for over 100 separate symbols each meaning exactly the same thing—*Rough gullied land from limestone material!*)

UNCONTROLLED SOIL LEGENDS

The most costly experiments in soil mapping have been with the uncontrolled soil legend. The errors have been so large, avoidable delays in publication so long, and the resulting avoidable extra cost so great, that this kind of legend deserves special emphasis.

The uncontrolled legend is really a means for avoiding the problem of classification. It postpones the problem but does not solve it. If a useful report and map are to result, a classification will be needed. Any generally useful soil map must have clearly defined, named, and classified units. The time to make the classification is before and during mapping, not afterward.

By an uncontrolled legend is meant a scheme of symbolization in which classes of certain selected soil features, or combinations of selected features, are set up independently of one another and used in any combination. Such a scheme might provide for 25 to 100 "soil types," let us say, defined *only* in terms of profile (or some arbitrary combinations of soil features and qualities), 6 classes of slope, 3, 4, or 5 classes of erosion, perhaps subdivided for gully and sheet erosion, and other classes as needed for stoniness, effects of soil blowing, and the like.

If the soil mapper is free to map any combination of these, many hundreds, even thousands, of mapping units may result, and errors and inconsistencies are inevitable. As pointed out repeatedly in this *Manual,* the significance of soil slope, effects of erosion, stoniness, and the like, depend upon the other factors involved in the combination. A difference in slope that is critically important on one soil type may not be so on another. Differences in stoniness critical to otherwise potentially arable soils have no significance on nonarable soils. Thus, with such a scheme, the mapper may use several symbols for areas that should be shown with one symbol and given one name. Then too, he is bound to get some of the boundaries in the wrong places; the divisions between soil-slope phases among different soil types, for example, may come at different percentages of slope.

Besides that, mappers, especially the less experienced ones, are likely to map erroneous combinations—combinations that cannot exist—either through error in writing the symbol or from ignorance of the relationships among the factors. Suppose, for example, that through failure to observe properly or to remember the correct symbol, the mapper uses the symbol for Brookston silt loam—a nearly level poorly drained soil—but adds the symbol for class C soil slope and the one for moderate erosion. A skilled map reader will, of course, recognize this as an impossible situation. With so many kinds of symbols on the map—perhaps thousands of them—the chief of party may not find such errors. If all combinations are checked and listed, many hundreds of them may be found to apply to only a few acres each, primarily because of such errors as the example above.

The greatest source of error with the uncontrolled legend, however, is excessive categorical detail—the separation of all soils on the basis of small differences in one or more features—differences that are really significant in only a very few soils.

Only a soil scientist familiar with the particular area can tell from a complicated symbol what the conditions really are—can, in other words, evaluate the combination into an integrated soil unit. The compilation of a soil map from such field sheets is an enormous undertaking, since a vast group of symbols need to be combined and arranged into classificational units. A draftsman, untrained in soil science, simply cannot do it consistently. A soil scientist familiar with the area needs to go over the whole mass of field sheets and to prepare a new manuscript map for use in compiling the published map. Even with all of this extra work, time, and expense, the results are bound to be poor, since many of the boundaries will not have been drawn in the appropriate places. Yet, the field party will have drawn more lines with such a legend than with a proper soil legend. As the number of lines and symbols per square mile increases, the chances for error greatly increase. The aim should be to place only the really significant lines on the map and to place them accurately.

Obviously, uncontrolled legends greatly increase the problem of accurate soil correlation, since the units may not be properly synthesized soil units in the first place. The elimination of insignificant units *en masse,* by a rule for the map draftsman to follow, is rarely satisfactory. Where such generalization is needed, it can only be done satisfactorily in the field before the field survey is completed.

All legends for soil surveys need to be controlled. Every symbol —every combination of letters and figures used to identify areas— needs to stand for a specific, named (or nameable) unit in the classification. It is the *combination* of letters and figures that is the mapping symbol, not the individual parts of it. Any new combination of letters and figures must be regarded by the mapper and the party chief as an entirely new symbol—just as much a new symbol as if a different letter or figure had been introduced into the legend. Any new symbols proposed by field mappers in the party should be considered immediately by the party chief. Any added to the legend need to be described in relation to the other units, and all legends appropriately revised. Where the proposed new symbol is not needed, the party chief should explain how the area is to be classified and why.

THE DESCRIPTIVE SOIL LEGEND

Besides the identification soil legend, the party chief needs to prepare a descriptive soil legend. The *first duty* of the soil correlator or other supervisory scientist is to help the party chief with the first draft of this legend and help him keep it revised from time to time as the work progresses.

A descriptive legend serves as:

1. A guide to each soil mapper in the party for all symbols and for descriptions of all mapping units in ways that show their relationships to each other, how they are differentiated from one another, their relationships to physiography, geology, and vegetation, and a tentative assessment of their use capabilities and management requirements.

2. A current summary of the research and mapping work that can be made available to cooperators, agricultural advisers, farm planning technicians, and others needing to use the field work that has already been completed.

3. A guide and record of research that can be turned over to a new party chief, if necessary, so that he may go ahead with the work without interruption.

4. The skeleton of the soil survey report under which field notes, photographs, literature reviews, and other materials may be sought and collected as the field work progresses.

It would not be possible to overemphasize the importance of the descriptive soil legend. Through it the soil correlator and other scientists can give the maximum help to the party chief. It gives the other members of the party a uniform guide and, at the same time, an excellent medium for making suggestions and additions of great value to the total effort. Around it and its revision, staff conferences of the party can be organized. The quality of final soil maps and reports bears an amazingly close correlation with the quality and up-to-dateness of the descriptive soil legend. A good descriptive legend is, perhaps, the most important evidence of an efficient party chief. Failures to develop and keep up to date a proper legend have led to great additional cost and delay, especially where party chiefs have changed during the progress of the survey.

The form of the legend can vary, although the major items of the soil survey report outline should be provided for, especially in drafts following completion of about one-half of the field mapping. The following items should be included:

1. The identification soil legend—a list of all soil mapping symbols and their names—preferably in order of numbers so one can find quickly the proper soil name to go with any symbol identified on the map.
2. Brief local definitions of slope classes, by groups of soils, erosion classes, and the like.
3. Descriptions of all soil series, either alphabetically, or alphabetically under broad soil or physiographic groups. The series descriptions do not necessarily need to be so complete as the official series descriptions used in correlation, *except for new ones*. Yet the description of each soil series should set it off clearly from any other soil series. Under each soil series, the *names* and symbols of each type, phase, or variant should be included with whatever descriptions are necessary to distinguish them from one another. Complexes and miscellaneous land types should be included in the proper place alphabetically, or at the end after the soil series descriptions.
4. A genetic key to the soil series.
5. A schematic soil association map, which can be very useful to the mappers in areas of contrasting soil regions.
6. Summaries of geology, relief, vegetation, and the like, as required in a soil survey report; these should be prepared as it becomes possible to do so.

Besides these main points, the party chief may add references to books and papers of special significance to an understanding of the nature and use of the soils in the area being surveyed.

PLOTTING SOIL BOUNDARIES IN THE FIELD

After a suitable base map has been selected, the soil mapping units identified, and the legends prepared, soil mapping can begin. In those few areas where the field party needs to prepare its own base map, it is best to lay out the primary traverse or grid in advance of soil mapping. The plotting of detailed base features and the soil mapping can be done together afterward.

Most of the important operations and requirements of soil mapping have already been discussed under specific topics. Here we are concerned with only a few general principles.

Soil mapping is a technical art. Men lacking sound training in soil science should not be expected to do well, especially those unfamiliar with the principles of the earth sciences. Yet some well-trained men, even men well above the average in competence in soil classification, lack the ability to plot soil boundaries accurately. Some can learn slowly, whereas others are unable to develop good skills. A competent soil mapper is able to abstract the essentials of the pattern of soil landscapes before him and sketch this pattern on the map; then, in reverse, from the lines and symbols on the map, he visualizes the soil pattern they collectively represent. His lines and symbols are drawn carefully. They are clear and neat.

Above all, the successful soil mapper is accurate. He maintains uniform standards of accuracy in his work, in open country and through the bush. He realizes that soil maps without accurate boundaries—guessed at rather than determined—are poor soil maps, regardless of the classification. No man of questionable honesty in research should ever be retained in a soil survey party. It is too difficult to check his results in the critical places; and the damage from using a poor soil map may be very serious.

LOCATION OF BOUNDARIES

Soil boundaries are located on the mapper's route or line of traverse and are sketched accurately on the base. Foot traverses need to be near enough together for accurate plotting between locations. In detailed basic soil surveys, the minimum distance between routes or traverse lines is about $\frac{1}{8}$ to $\frac{1}{4}$ mile, say about 800 to 1,600 feet, depending upon the scale of the map and the complexity of the soil pattern. Even with traverses at around 800 to 1,000 feet, some side traverses are needed to locate boundaries and to identify soils. Although soil boundaries are not actually traversed, *they must be plotted from observations made throughout their course* in detailed soil mapping.

Once identified, the boundaries between most soil types, phases, and other mapping units, coincide with observable features on the surface, such as the foot of a slope, the crest of a ridge, the margin of a swamp forest, a change in color of surface soil, and so on. Such correlations between surface features and soil boundaries require continual testing.

The experienced soil mapper lays out his traverses in order to cross as many soil boundaries as possible. Commonly, he walks roughly at right angles to the drainage. As he proceeds, he plots *tentatively* the soil boundaries apparent from surface features a short distance ahead of himself. As he crosses these boundaries he verifies them. Not until then does he plot them in final form and place the symbol in the area that he has crossed. Good mappers commonly turn and reappraise the landscape they have just crossed before plotting the boundaries finally.

Not all soil boundaries are correlated with external features. Many have to be "dug for." For example, unlike soils varying widely in use capabilities may be developed from interbedded lacustrine or alluvial deposits and have no reliable external features to guide the sketching of boundaries. They need to be located with the spade and auger. In desert and semidesert areas especially, many soil boundaries must be sketched primarily from excavations or borings. Characteristics of the lower horizons and layers of little significance to the native vegetation are often very important to potentialities for irrigation and to hazards of waterlogging and salinity under irrigation. Yet even in the desert, the skilled mapper, able to recognize land forms and plant species accurately, uses external features a great deal, although he continually checks the soil boundaries with test holes.

Some soil boundaries are sharply defined; others are midway lines in transition zones within which one soil gradually merges with another. The establishment of transitional units between the original mapping units often worsens the problem by requiring two boundaries in place of one, each of which is even more difficult to sketch satisfactorily.

On detailed soil maps to be published at about 2 inches to the mile (1:31,680), boundaries should be accurate within at least 100 feet. Even more important is the relative positional accuracy of boundaries in relation to roads, streams, and other local reference points. Even though a soil boundary were in error by only 50 feet, if it were placed on the wrong side of a stream or road, the error would be so conspicuous that map users would lose confidence in the work. Soil maps are commonly read by reference to base features. A farmer, for example, is concerned with the soils in his fields, say in one between a stream or gully and the road, in another between the stream and a steep hill, and so on. The engineer may be vitally interested in the soil just where a road crosses a railroad. Correct relative position is more important to the accuracy of a soil map for most of its uses than absolute or geodetic accuracy.

Only the most experienced mappers can estimate distances accurately beyond one-eighth mile or 660 feet, even under the best conditions. Most mappers need checks on estimates beyond 300 feet in detailed mapping. Variations in land form introduce many illusions of distance that mislead the beginner. Equal distances, for example, when viewed over water, cleared land, or brush land or through trees, do not appear equal to the beginner. The distance across a smooth valley appears to be less than a similar distance across a valley with low hills in it.

In reconnaissance soil mapping, the boundaries are not necessarily observed throughout their course. They are plotted where the lines of traverse cross them; but between these points of observation, many boundaries are sketched from the appearance of patterns on aerial photographs and the general appearance of the landscape. Exceptional skill is required in the interpretation of external features.

In soil mapping it is recognized that some soil boundaries are more important than others. Boundaries between highly contrasting soils need emphasis, like those, for example, that separate wet soil from dry soil, very clayey soil from very sandy soil, level soil from hilly soil, and stony soil from nonstony soil. The boundaries that carry a color distinction on the published map are especially critical because they commonly separate soils of different, broad use potentialities as well as those of different management requirements.

The sketching of soil boundaries is a continual check on the soil classification. Theoretically, it may be possible to develop a good system of soil classification without mapping; yet few, if any, such systems have been developed. Soils are areas, and in this sense the boundaries are a part of their definitions. If boundaries cannot be clearly and similarly identified by competent men, the classification obviously needs revision. If the mapper needs many supplemental symbols and notes to describe the mapped areas, beyond those provided for in the mapping legend, the classification is inadequate or the units are inadequately described in the descriptive legend. Without the test of drawing soil boundaries, classifiers may set up mapping units that are really points, not areas. Poor mapping units may be established on the basis of characteristics in the lower part of the solum that cannot be regularly observed or that vary erratically. Then too, the early drafts of a mapping legend may suggest the use of taxonomic units as mapping units but later experience shows the taxonomic units should be recognized as parts of defined complexes.

Perhaps the ability to conceive the soil pattern, in contrast to a group of individual mapping units, is the most difficult skill for a beginning soil mapper to acquire. No skill is more important. Put simply, he must learn that all the soil must be "called something." It is far easier to pick out well-established and easily identified areas, enclose them with boundaries, and ignore the rest. But in making a soil map, one is not simply mapping out individual units; rather, he is sketching a pattern of units. The boundary of one soil unit is also that of another or parts of several others. In legends and instructions, party chiefs and supervisory scientists always need to emphasize relationships among the units—not simply individual, detached descriptions of each unit. To do this job effectively, the mapper must learn what kinds of units go together in geographic patterns.

SIZE OF AREAS AND DETAIL

Attention has already been drawn to the difference between categorical and cartographic detail. Here we are concerned with the latter. The problem is most frequently posed in terms of the minimum size of areas of one mapping unit to separate from another. The party chief should study this problem and issue instructions that will insure uniformity throughout the map.

As a general rule, all areas need to be shown that are significant to differential predictions of soil use and management requirements. If a separate field boundary is required by the farmer for effective and economical use of the soil area, certainly the boundary needs to be shown. In regions of very intensive soil use, areas of as little as ½, 1, or 2 acres may need to be shown. In areas of extensive soil use for crops, areas smaller than 5 acres may be ignored unless they are strongly contrasting.

Spots of wet soil, steep soil, rocky soil, or of other soil unsuited for crops should be indicated on the map if they occur within areas otherwise potentially useful for crops. Depending on the mapping scale, they may be enclosed by boundaries or indicated by symbols shown in the standard legends and defined as to the kind of area represented and its size. Thus, the more important the boundary, the smaller is the minimum size of area to be enclosed by it. Yet the size of such small areas should not be exaggerated on the map. For the really small ones, defined symbols should be used.

Where the pattern of small areas becomes too complex for accurate mapping and symbolization, the soil mapping legend needs to be reexamined with a view of using soil complexes as mapping units.

The following rule should be a strict guide: *No boundaries should be placed on the detailed soil map unless they can be sketched accurately.* Between soils that gradually grade from one to another, the soil boundary may be placed within a broad transitional belt. Such occasional soil boundaries are not precise; they cannot be; but they are placed after detailed examination of the soils and their associated features.

SECONDARY SHEETS

Secondary sheets are used for secondary traverses or side routes where it is impractical to carry the master map, as in heavily wooded areas. The data from the secondary sheets are transferred to the master field sheet as soon as convenient. These sheets should be filed as a part of the original manuscript material.

Secondary sheets are also used for the entire area, or some part of it, to show data or fine distinctions beyond those included on the master map. Their use should be limited to clearly established needs, because they increase the time and cost of the survey. Data not intended for the final published map, such as land cover or subphases of soil slope, stoniness, or eroded soil, may be mapped on secondary sheets for some special objective. The extra time and cost of handling the secondary sheets are less than in the assembly of a soil map from highly detailed field sheets, from which the boundaries and symbols to be published have to be sorted out from many that are not to be published. Transparent, oil-treated paper is preferable for such use.

Field notes to accompany the soil map should be made for any special conditions not adequately expressed by the map itself. These are especially helpful during the early stages of a survey, before the legend has been worked into final form. Any suggested departures from the legend should be noted by the mapper on the spot and brought to the attention of the party chief immediately. The party chief should help beginners learn to keep such notes of their mapping, as a part of their essential training and in order to assist him in checking their work, both in the office and in the field. Still it must be recalled that greater accuracy and uniformity can be had by the use of well-defined standard symbols than by written notes. When copious field notes are necessary to explain the boundaries and departures from the symbols, it is evident that the legend is not correct or that it is improperly understood by the mappers.

CHECKING FIELD SHEETS

Every field sheet needs to be checked with all adjoining sheets to be sure that boundaries and other lines properly join and that symbols are alike. The separate sheets should also be examined for any open boundaries, areas without symbols, and other omissions. Each mapper should check his own sheets; and besides, they should be rechecked by some other worker to be sure that each part of the map is complete and clearly legible. The chief of party should check the sheets of each mapper in several places in the field. The field sheets of beginners will need much field checking. The party chief can assign the work in such a way that he gets daily comparisons among men at the borders of their sheets. The soil correlator or supervisory soil scientist responsible for the technical standards should check boundaries and symbols on several sheets selected at random.

Finally all the field sheets are given a careful final checking, including checks for corrections and remapping required by the soil correlator, by the chief of party just before they are sent forward to the correlator for review. Omissions on the map or in the legend, or inconsistencies between them, greatly increase the costs of map construction and delay publication.

COLLECTION AND EXAMINATION OF SOIL SAMPLES

Besides the soil characteristics observed and measured in the field, other measurements need to be made in the laboratory. A complete soil, of course, cannot be moved into a laboratory; only parts of it. Items of great importance to soil classification and behavior, such as temperature and living organisms, cannot be preserved in samples, nor can slope, stoniness, or the thickness and arrangement of horizons in the profile.

The value of laboratory work depends upon care in sampling and upon a synthesis of the results with field morphology in making interpretations. No matter how carefully laboratory work is done, firm predictions cannot be expected from such data alone.

The selection of sample areas has been discussed in the section on Examination and Description of Soils in the Field. Each soil sample needs to be a fair sample of a specific genetic horizon or other layer of a kind of soil worth sampling. Samples collected by arbitrary depths, unrelated to the genetic horizons, are generally useless—even worse than useless and downright misleading if they contain unknown mixtures of two or more contrasting horizons. It is wasteful to use laboratory facilities and time on poorly collected soil samples or those without adequate descriptions and names.

Then too, the purpose of the samples needs to be clearly in the mind of those collecting them. For measurements of constituents present in only tiny amounts, for example, unusual care to prevent contamination is required. Also it needs to be recalled that soil samples must be fumigated when passing through some quarantine stations. This can be done without injuring them for all ordinary uses, at least, and is a necessary precaution against the spread of harmful insects and diseases.

COLLECTION OF SAMPLES

Depending on how well the soils in a survey area are known, soil samples may be required at the start, during the course of the survey, and after the field mapping is completed. In areas having new or doubtful taxonomic units, analyses may be needed to establish the appropriate limits or ranges to be allowed. Many decisions on soil correlation cannot be made accurately without considerable mapping, but the more that can be made at the start of the survey the better. After the map is well along it makes extra work in the cartographic office to combine several units into one. In entirely new areas, samples of many tentative soil units are needed at the very start, before the legend for a detailed survey is well established.

Samples are collected from soil survey areas for laboratory measurements for (1) determining the fundamental properties of soils in relation to their classification as specific types, series, families, and great soil groups; (2) suggesting their genesis and relationships to their environment; (3) checking field measurements and observations of textural class, pH, soluble salts, carbonates, permeability, and the like; (4) help in suggesting their responses to management practices; and (5) help in assessing their physical properties that influence trafficability, highway and airport design, and similar engineering uses. Although some measurements are common to two or more of these objectives, different sets are needed. Besides these uses in the laboratory, samples are taken for comparing the color and structure of soils and for exhibits used as visual aids in soil recognition.

FRAGMENTAL SAMPLES

As Cline[1] has emphasized, soil volumes, not areas, are sampled. Each sample needs to represent a homogeneous volume insofar as that can be determined by field observations. Where possible, samples should be collected to represent the volume and appraise its parameter. By statistical tests, the range in variability and accuracy of results may be determined. Nevertheless, the use of statistical methods in no way reduces the need for careful selection in the field.

It is not possible to make separate determinations on a large number of representative samples of the same horizons, except in a few selected and important soils. The cost is usually too great. For precise studies of soil genesis, however, several samples of each representative horizon lead to more accurate results than single samples.

Selection of sampling site.—Since one, two, or three sites within a mapping unit ordinarily can be sampled in detailed soil surveys, these are located to represent the unit. (Even where many samples can be taken the sites should be randomized only *within* a narrowly defined taxonomic unit.) Within the soil type or phase the scientist should be careful to avoid bias. The sites chosen should represent the taxonomic unit as it occurs. In view of the large amount of time needed to handle the samples, and their importance for correlation and analyses, adequate time needs to be allowed for the location of representative sites. The soil scientist should be ever mindful that much time and expense on the part of other workers in the laboratory, in the greenhouse, and on the field experimental plot may be nullified if he neglects to collect representative samples from well-described profiles.

Where conveniently available, virgin soils are sampled for correlation and analyses unless the samples are specifically taken for a study of cultivated soils. In selecting sites for virgin soils those showing evidence of disturbance, even of the very upper part, are avoided.

---

[1] For an excellent discussion of sampling, see Cline, M. G. PRINCIPLES OF SOIL SAMPLING. Soil Sci. 58: 275–288. 1944. For a shorter discussion, with special reference to sampling for chemical analysis, see Cline, M. G. METHODS OF COLLECTING AND PREPARING SOIL SAMPLES. Soil Sci. 59: 3–5. 1945.

Abbreviations of the names of the States and Territories (and full names for those not abbreviated) used in the standard soil sample labels are as follows:

State	Abbreviation	State	Abbreviation
Alabama	Ala.	New Mexico	N. Mex.
Arizona	Ariz.	New York	N. Y.
Arkansas	Ark.	North Carolina	N. C.
California	Calif.	North Dakota	N. Dak.
Colorado	Colo.	Ohio	Ohio
Connecticut	Conn.	Oklahoma	Okla.
Delaware	Del.	Oregon	Oreg.
Florida	Fla.	Pennsylvania	Pa.
Georgia	Ga.	Rhode Island	R. I.
Idaho	Idaho	South Carolina	S. C.
Illinois	Ill.	South Dakota	S. Dak.
Indiana	Ind.	Tennessee	Tenn.
Iowa	Iowa	Texas	Tex.
Kansas	Kans.	Utah	Utah
Kentucky	Ky.	Vermont	Vt.
Louisiana	La.	Virginia	Va.
Maine	Maine	Washington	Wash.
Maryland	Md.	West Virginia	W. Va.
Massachusetts	Mass.	Wisconsin	Wis.
Michigan	Mich.	Wyoming	Wyo.
Minnesota	Minn.		
Mississippi	Miss.	*Other areas*	*Abbreviation*
Missouri	Mo.	Alaska	Alaska
Montana	Mont.	Canal Zone	C. Z.
Nebraska	Nebr.	Hawaiian Islands	T. H.
Nevada	Nev.	Panama	Panama
New Hampshire	N. H.	Puerto Rico	P. R.
New Jersey	N. J.	Virgin Islands	V. I.

For other countries use full name or standard abbreviation if it does not conflict with the others in this list.

Drying and storage of samples.—The soil samples should be dried[2] in a place where there are no gases or dust that might contaminate them. Depending on circumstances, the samples may be removed from their containers and spread out on papers. Large lumps are crushed. Small or relatively dry samples may dry well enough in the opened container. On arrival at headquarters, samples are transferred to labeled glass jars for storage. Usually small subsamples of about 100 grams are filed in glass vials for ready reference. Each horizon sample is placed in a separately labeled glass vial. The several samples of a profile may be viewed together and compared with other samples of the same and related soil types. The vial samples are useful mainly for comparisons of texture and color.

Samples placed in the large glass jars may be used for laboratory analyses. Representative portions are removed and sieved through a 2 millimeter screen. That passing through the screen is then made ready for analyses.

SOIL MONOLITHS

Monoliths of soil profiles are taken as visual aids in soil study and identification. The collection of complete undisturbed mono-

---

[2] Except, of course, samples that change irreversibly upon drying.

liths takes much time and is not commonly done in the research work itself. Monoliths are useful, however, for display and classroom work.

Both thick and thin monoliths have been used. The thick monoliths are collected by placing a box around an undisturbed section, and the soil is thereafter preserved in this open-faced box. Generally, the section is about 6 or 8 inches wide, 4 inches deep, and long enough to include a part of the C horizon. The collection is made from an excavation. The exposed wall is cut so that a vertical section of the soil just fits into a wooden or metal box. The box is placed over the monolith and held in place while the back side of the monolith is loosened from the wall. A cover is placed on the exposed side. This cover is removed when the monolith is exhibited. The disadvantages of these thick-boxed monoliths are the great care necessary in collection, the great weight of the resulting monolith, and the hazard of damage in handling. They have been collected only a little in the United States.

A better method of collecting monoliths depends on the use of an adhesive that holds a section an inch or less thick to a stiff board. In one process, the wall of the excavation is smoothed and cellulose acetate is sprayed or painted directly on the soil material. When dry the soil adheres to this tough film. The somewhat flexible monolith is cut from the bank and glued to a board. Any excess soil is removed. The monolith is treated with a vinylite resin to harden the soil material and to preserve it from damage. Details of this method of collection are given by Smith and Moodie.[3]

Another process to achieve the same kind of thin monolith has been described by Berger and Muckenhirn.[4] A thin section of soil is removed from the wall of the excavation by use of a metal form and is then treated directly with vinylite resin to preserve it.

These thin monoliths have been used a good deal in the past 5 years. They are light in weight, resistant to damage, easy to store, and exhibit soil structures and colors satisfactorily. They are hard to take in stony soils.

SOIL MICROMONOLITHS

Micromonoliths are being used increasingly in soil correlation work. Small thin sections of each horizon are taken with a metal cutter that is fitted with a wooden plunger (fig. 52). These sections are glued to a stiff narrow piece of cardboard, one above the other in natural sequence. This gives the effect of a small-scale monolith. Such a monolith can be taken in 10 to 15 minutes and is easy to file. These micromonoliths have advantages over the vial samples. They can be taken more quickly and they allow better comparisons between samples. But the vial samples are needed for comparisons of texture.

[3] SMITH, H. W., and MOODIE, C. D. COLLECTION AND PRESERVATION OF SOIL PROFILES. Soil Sci. 64: 61–69, illus. 1947.
[4] BERGER, K. C., and MUCKENHIRN, R. J. SOIL PROFILES OF NATURAL APPEARANCE MOUNTED WITH VINYLITE RESIN. Soil Sci. Soc. Amer. Proc. 10: 368–370, illus. 1946.

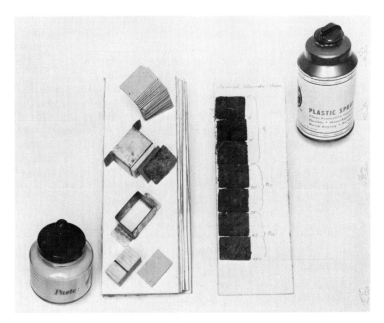

FIGURE 52.—Equipment for mounting micromonoliths, and a mounted one.

Bushnell has described the method of collection and mounting these micromonoliths.[5]

After selection of a site, the soil profile is exposed. The plunger is inserted in the cutter. A small backing card of blotting paper, about 1 inch by 1⅜ inches, is fitted over the plunger and within the cutter. This is coated with liquid paste or "waterglass." The cutter is forced into the soil, either directly on the wall of the cut or into a large lump. The cutter, with an excess of soil on its face, is cut away. The excess soil on the face is carefully removed to preserve the natural structure of the sample. By pushing the plunger, the sample is pushed out; then it is pasted in its proper place on a 10- by 2-inch mounting strip of heavy blotting paper.[6] If each individual microsection is tight against the next, they will help support one another.

After all horizon samples are fixed on the mounting, the assembled strip is marked with depth figures and horizon designations. Dried specimens may be strengthened by immersing the trimmed monolith in a 10-percent solution of vinylite or by applying it as a spray or with a soft brush.

These fixed strips may be pasted onto a stiff mounting card, say 4 or 6 inches by 10 inches, on which depth figures, horizon designations, and data about the soil may be lettered.

[5] BUSHNELL, T. M. SOIL PROFILE SAMPLING MADE EASY. Purdue Univ. Agr. Expt. Sta. Spec. Cir. 2, 8 pp., illus. Lafayette, Ind. 1949.
[6] Many prefer to mount the samples directly on the stiff mounting card and omit the intermediate mounting on strips of blotting paper, partly to complete the whole job, notes and all, on the spot.

The individual small sections are most often made in a standard size of 1 by 1½ inches and then glued to cards 3 or 4 inches wide and 10 inches long.

The use of individual sections of the same size, regardless of horizon thickness, distorts the micromonolith in relation to the actual profile. Some avoid such distortion by using an adjustable cutter so that the widths of the micro-samples are made proportional to the thicknesses of the horizons. One long side of the cutter is movable with a thumb screw. An assortment of small backing cards of various widths may be carried. The resulting micromonoliths then reflect the true scale of the soil profile. The extra work is scarcely justified in taking micromonoliths for use by soil scientists in soil correlation, since they are not misled by the apparent distortion. Properly scaled micromonoliths are much preferred for exhibits or for use in the classroom.

USEFUL LABORATORY DATA

Generally, it may be said that all accurate physical, chemical, and mineralogical measurements on representative samples of soil horizons from well-described soils are helpful. Yet certainly not all are equally useful. Measurements that are exceedingly helpful in one soil area, or even in understanding relationships among one group of soils within an area, may not be especially revealing with another group of soils. Above all, the value of the laboratory data depends upon the associated morphological data: The two sets of data must be interpreted together. Chemical data obtained on soil samples collected with augers, unaccompanied by good profile descriptions, are usually not worth the expense, except possibly in broad exploratory surveys of totally unknown areas.

Plans for laboratory work should be laid in advance of the soil survey, with provisions made for additional studies should the need arise. These plans should be developed jointly between the field scientists and the laboratory scientists, and the results should be interpreted jointly, especially where the problems are complex. Judgment is needed in selecting the determinations to be made with the facilities available. It is easy to load a laboratory with routine measurements of such low significance that it loses its effectiveness in the research program.

Laboratory determinations made as a part of the soil survey may be roughly classed into five main groups according to their purpose.

1. Those to establish the characteristics of genetic soil types, elucidate their origin, and set each off from related soil types. Here are included mechanical analyses, pH, organic carbon, exchangeable cations, carbonates, nitrogen, bulk density, permeability, mineralogical composition, sometimes total chemical analyses, and perhaps others depending upon the problem involved.
2. Those to check identification of ₜestablished soil types and field determinations. These include mechanical analyses, pH, carbonates, sometimes organic carbon, and sometimes others.

3. Those used as an aid in suggesting management practices, including determinations of permeability, available or soluble plant nutrients, exchangeable cations, pH, and the like.
4. Those needed for predicting the effects of irrigation, the drainage and management practices required if soil is placed under irrigation, and the requirements for rehabilitation of soil that has become salty through the effects of irrigation. The field methods are explained briefly in the section on Estimation and Mapping of Salts and Alkali in the Soil.
5. The determinations required for predictions of highway design, airport location and design, trafficability, and other problems in soil engineering. The results of such determinations may be used directly in a particular project and also to characterize soil types, provided that the samples are collected by defined soil horizons and types.

A full treatment of the laboratory methods and work to be done to accompany soil classification and interpretation lies beyond the scope of this *Manual*. Only a few principles need to be dealt with here.

First of all, field scientists and laboratory scientists, to work effectively, need considerable knowledge of one another's skills and problems. Only a few men can or should attempt to be highly proficient in actually doing both kinds of work. The laboratory scientist needs to have an appreciation of the problems of soil classification, soil mapping, and soil management, and of the range of variability in the universe that a soil sample represents. Often time is wasted to achieve an accuracy within the laboratory between duplicates from the same sample that is out of proportion to the error of field sampling. The field scientist must learn a good deal about the methods used in laboratories and the value and limitations of laboratory data. Field men often ask for laboratory work without realizing fully the time and cost involved or how the results may be useful to them.

Both kinds of specialists need to work together. Especially in analyzing the field problems and collecting soil samples for extensive work in fundamental soil characterization and soil genesis, the scientist responsible for the laboratory work should take part in enough of the field work to have a clear picture of the problem. Only then can the final decisions be made concerning the set of laboratory determinations most likely to be helpful. For many problems a geologist should also be a member of such study parties.

Standard methods need emphasis so that widely separated soils may be compared. New and better methods need to be adopted as they are developed, but only when clearly superior. Often it is necessary to make determinations by both old and new methods for some time so that the results of the one can be interpreted by comparison with those of the other.

Work plans for survey areas should provide for laboratory service more adequately than has generally been the practice in the past. Too often all the laboratory work follows the completion of the field work, after the soil separations have been made. Where laboratory data are needed for deciding clearly between soil units, these should be obtained in the very beginning of the survey. Once the differences are established, study of soil morphology will usually disclose accessory characteristics that may serve as criteria for identification in the field.

In developing data for use in making predictions about fertilizers, lime, and other amendments, the aim is to establish the *responsiveness* of the soil type to the various treatments. For the purpose of making predictions of management practices, the soil survey party chief should interpret the data in cooperation with specialists in soil fertility and management. Specific recommendations depend upon the previous use of amendments and the cropping history as well as upon soil type. Determinations of available plant nutrients will give different results, of course, on different areas of the same soil type that have had different treatments. Among highly responsive soils these differences may be simply enormous. In the soil descriptions and management predictions, the responsiveness of the soil, or the level of yields under a given management system, is the thing fixed in the soil type, not the specific treatment required from year to year. Cooperation with advisory soil scientists can be mutually useful. Soil classification is an essential tool in advisory work with fertilizers, since most of the "quick-test" results, used by farm advisers, have a different interpretation on different soil types.

ESTIMATION AND MAPPING OF SALTS AND
ALKALI IN THE SOIL

Strongly alkaline soils and those containing harmful amounts of salts need to be separated from other soils in soil mapping. Those having sufficient quantities of soluble salts or such a high degree of alkalinity as to interfere with the growth of crop plants are largely confined to arid and semiarid regions, although they also occur in humid regions in coastal strips affected by tides and in local areas affected by seepage of salty waters. Such soils require special management practices and measures for reclamation. The amount and kind of salts in the soil, now and in the past, are commonly reflected in the morphology of the soil profile, but not with sufficient specificity to suggest the actual quantities or specific crop adaptabilities. This is especially true of young or recent soils on alluvial deposits. Many salty soils are useful for crops if the salts are removed and are not allowed to accumulate again, provided the other soil characteristics are favorable.

A considerable part of the irrigated soils in the West contain sufficient salts or are alkaline enough to depress crop yields. On some, crop production is curtailed or even prevented. Many acres of irrigated land have had to be abandoned because of salts that were originally present in the soil or especially because of salts that accumulated during irrigation.

One of the principal purposes of detailed soil surveys in such areas is to identify soils that cannot be irrigated practicably and to suggest the probable problems and methods of reclamation and use for those that can be used for crops. The amount of soluble salts in a soil or its degree of alkalinity, and the many other soil conditions that affect salt accumulation or movement, even to great depths, are observed and evaluated in the classification and its interpretation.

THE NATURE AND ORIGIN OF SALINE AND ALKALI SOILS

A *saline soil* contains enough salts so distributed in the profile that they interfere with the growth of most crop plants.

An *alkali soil* has either so high a degree of alkalinity—pH 8.5 or higher—or so high a percentage of exchangeable sodium—15 percent or higher—or both, that the growth of most crop plants is reduced. Thus, alkali soils, as a group, have a wide range of exchangeable sodium and of pH. Some soils with more than 15 percent exchangeable sodium, for example, have pH values less than 8.5 if the other exchangeable cations are mainly hydrogen.

A *saline-alkali soil* has a combination of harmful quantities of salts and either a high alkalinity or high exchangeable sodium, or both, so distributed in the profile that the growth of most crop plants is reduced.

Locally, the terms "alkali" and "alkali soil" have been used for all these conditions. Some have used "alkali soil" as the general term, "white alkali" as roughly equivalent to saline soils as now defined, and "black alkali" as roughly equivalent to alkali soils. The term "black" was suggested by the dark color caused by the dispersion of the organic matter at a high pH. These older terms should not be used in soil descriptions or reports, except in quotes with a footnote explanation of local usage where it exists.

The soluble salts in soils may come from the deposits left by decomposition of primary minerals in rocks, from sedimentary rocks, from invasion of the sea, or from the salt carried in winds off the sea ("cyclic" salt). Salts are readily carried by water and accumulate within the soil or at the surface when the water evaporates. Thus, salty soils commonly occur in low areas and many have periodically or permanently high water tables. Generally speaking, salty soils are formed in arid or semiarid regions in low places or on seepy slopes that would be occupied by swamps in humid regions. A high water table, or a perched water table, may exist naturally above underlying impervious strata, or a water table may be caused or elevated by excessive irrigation or by seepage from streams or water-distribution systems. Large quantities of salt may be added to the soil in salty irrigation water. Some sedimentary rocks contain large quantities of gypsum and other salts that contribute to the salt content of the soils developed from them. Water seeping through such rocks carries the salts to soils at lower elevations. Where rainfall is so light and evaporation so high that little leaching takes place, the salts released from the minerals in the soil remain in it; yet rarely do enough salts accumulate in this way alone to make a soil too salty for crops.

Many combinations of different salts occur in saline soils. The presence of normally neutral, or nearly neutral, salts, like the chlorides and sulfates of sodium, calcium, and magnesium, does not make the soil strongly alkaline; but the alkaline salts, like sodium carbonate and bicarbonate, do cause a strongly alkaline reaction.

The exchangeable cations in a soil greatly influence its properties. In pure water, acid clays are fairly easily dispersed;[1] calcium-clays are mildly to moderately alkaline and usually less easily dispersed; while sodium-clays are strongly to very strongly alkaline and are most easily dispersed. While a high salt concentration is maintained in the soil, the colloids are flocculated; but

---

[1] The degree of dispersion and other properties of clays depend also on the type of clay mineral. Even acid clays of well-developed Latosols are not easily dispersed. Flocculation and granulation in natural soils also depend upon the kinds and amounts of organic matter, root growth, and the microflora and fauna. For these reasons, some acid clays are as well aggregated as calcium-clays. The flocculation of clays by excess salts is not necessarily like the granulation developed through the effects of living organisms. Then too, simple replacement of the sodium by calcium may not be enough to induce granulation without alternate wetting-and-drying, incorporation of organic matter, or other treatments.

as drainage improves and excess salts are removed, the sodium-clays become strongly or very strongly alkaline and easily dispersed in water, and sticky when wet and hard when dry.

The proportion of the several cations absorbed by the soil colloids depends upon the soluble salts present. In the presence of a large proportion of sodium salts, sodium becomes dominant on the exchange complex. Such soils may not have a high pH (above 8.5) so long as excess neutral salts are present. With the removal of the excess salts by leaching, hydrolysis of the sodium-clay produces sodium hydroxide and a strongly alkaline reaction. The carbon dioxide of the soil air combines with the sodium hydroxide to form sodium carbonate. Thus the sodium carbonate in alkali soil originates within the soil itself, except where the leachate from an alkali soil collects in another soil at a lower elevation. More than 15 percent exchangeable sodium in the exchange complex is ordinarily harmful to the growth of crop plants.[2]

The alkalinity of alkali soils is expressed by pH, percentage of exchangeable sodium (or sodium plus potassium), or by a combination of the two. Strictly, any soil above pH 7.0 is alkaline, whether salty or not. (See section of Soil Reaction.) Soils made alkaline by calcium carbonate alone are called *calcareous* and rarely have pH values above 8.5. Soils above pH 8.5 usually contain a high percentage of exchangeable sodium and are called alkali soils, along with some with as much as 15 percent exchangeable sodium that have pH values below 8.5.

Morphological differences occur among saline and alkali soils. Saline soils are usually friable; but soils with well defined structure, for example, a typical Chestnut soil, may become saline naturally or through irrigation practices. Strongly saline soils often have salt crusts, or efflorescences, on the surface and streaks, layers, or spots ("eyes") of salts within the profile. The structure of many saline soils is favorable to the movement of water and air. Saline-alkali soils are morphologically similar to saline soils as long as excess salts are present and the clays do not swell or become dispersed. As salt concentrations are reduced, the clays may disperse as in alkali soils. In time, many natural alkali soils develop characteristic prismatic or columnar B horizons. A man-made alkali soil, developed incident to irrigation as a result of the leaching of a saline soil high in exchangeable sodium, becomes massive, hard when dry, and slowly permeable, without a distinctive structural profile other than a puddled surface soil that shrinks and cracks with drying.

Saline and alkali soils are extremely variable, both vertically and horizontally. Salts may be localized in the surface soil or in a lower horizon, or they may be more or less uniformly distributed throughout the soil profile. Slight differences in texture may result in unequal movements of salty water and large differences

[2] The following was drawn on considerably for this section: DIAGNOSIS AND IMPROVEMENT OF SALINE AND ALKALI SOILS. United States Regional Salinity Laboratory. L. A. Richards, Ed. 157 pp., illus., 1947. [Processed.]

in salt accumulation. Some growing shrubs take in large amounts of salts and "pump" them from the lower soil to the surface; others do not. Thus, salt content and pH, or both, may vary widely within a few feet, depending on differences in vegetation [3] as well as differences in relief and stratigraphy. Within a small area, soils of widely different characteristics may be found, and at any one spot the salt content may fluctuate with the seasons, weather conditions, and irrigation management.

Genetic groups.—In addition to the terms already given for saline and alkali soils, the soil scientist finds others used in the literature, defined primarily on the basis of morphology and genesis. Although the two sets of terms are not entirely consistent, a brief explanation of the genetic types may be helpful. If soils in this general group—saline and alkali soils— are defined primarily in chemical terms, one gets some strange morphological bedfellows; and if they are defined primarily according to morphology, one gets some strange chemical bedfellows. Then too, some nonsaline soils may appear to have profiles suggestive of Solonetz or solodized-Solonetz.

The light-colored, flocculated, salty soils are sometimes called "structureless" soils. They are not really structureless, but are softly and finely granular. Characteristically, they lack either prismatic or blocky structure. Soils dominantly of these characteristics are called *Solonchak* in genetic soil classification. If a salt crust exists at the surface, the soil is sometimes called an "external" Solonchak, or a "puff" Solonchak if the crust is immediately underlain by a fluffy layer. Where the salts have moved up part way into the solum in capillary water and are concentrated at some level beneath the surface, the soil may be called an "internal" Solonchak. Since the salts often enter the soil from beneath, Solonchaks are commonly variable and occur in intricate patterns with zonal and other soils of the region. Yet, "flooded" Solonchaks, which occupy old ponded basins, may be relatively uniform, even though exceedingly salty.

The term "Solonchak" is also modified by the name of the dominant salt present. One having dominantly calcium salts is called a calcium-Solonchak. With improved drainage and removal of the salts, it gradually changes to a normal soil. With leaching and removal of the excess salts, following improved drainage under natural conditions, the sodium-Solonchak may change to a Solonetz or solodized-Solonetz, and perhaps finally to a Soloth, before the processes responsible for the development of a zonal soil become dominant.

The development of the morphology required of the Solonchak is not always coincident with the definition of a saline soil. A saline soil may be produced simply by the addition of salts to a nonsaline soil, a process called "salinization." Thus there are many intergrades between Solonchak and other soils, as Solonchak-Chernozem, Solonchak-Sierozem, and so on. In detailed soil surveys the local soil types and phases are separated on the basis of salt conditions significant to crop growth and to reclamation and management practices. Later they may be placed in the appropriate genetic groups.

While excess salts are present, Solonchak soils with different kinds of salt look much alike; but when drainage improves during the ages and the excess salts leach out, enormous differences may develop. The calcium-clays remain flocculated, granulated; whereas the sodium-clays become easily dispersed and puddled, or "run together." The soil becomes highly alkaline— so much so that part of the organic matter is dissolved and may form a dark coating around the soil grains or aggregates. Some sodium ions of the colloid are disassociated to form sodium hydroxide and finally sodium carbonate. Since the colloids are easily dispersed, some of them start to move downward, out of the surface layers, and accumulate beneath. The puddled soil cracks on drying. The next rain causes more dispersion, and fine material moves down. After long periods, this results in an accumulation

[3] ROBERTS, R. C. CHEMICAL EFFECTS OF THE SALT-TOLERANT SHRUBS ON SOILS. 4th Internatl. Cong. Soil Sci. Trans. 1: 404–406. Amsterdam. 1950.

of fine material in the B horizon, with the silt and sand left in the A. Besides, continued weathering of minerals within the B horizon contributes to its high content of clay.

The B horizon has a characteristic columnar structure; the soil exists in hard vertical prisms with rounded caps. This process of change is sometimes called "solonization," and the resulting soil is called a Solonetz. Thus in contrast to Solonchak, the Solonetz has a striking structural profile.

If the leaching continues actively for a long time, the soil may finally become acid in the surface, with a deep gray layer over an acid blocky B horizon. Such soils are called Soloth, and the process of change of Solonetz to Soloth is called "solodization." Fully developed Soloth soils are relatively uncommon in the United States, and in the world for that matter. In morphological characteristics they merge with the Planosols. Far more common are the intergrades—the solodized-Solonetz soils—soils with well-developed structure and texture profiles having the leached A horizons of the Soloth and the nonacid columnar B horizon of the Solonetz.

A great many soils are transitional between Solonchak, Solonetz, and Soloth. Some have characteristics of all three. In fact, Solonetz with neither excess salts in the solum nor suggestion of solodization in the A horizon is rare. The solodized-Solonetz is especially common. These soils may have acid A horizons and very slightly acid to strongly alkaline B horizons with well-developed columnar structure. Since the formation of Solonetz usually takes place during a very gradual lowering of the water table, the upper layers change to Solonetz and the surface horizons become strongly leached, though the lower solum is still salty. Thus a soil may go from a sodium-Solonchak to a solodized-Solonetz without ever being in position of a Solonetz. Then too, after a well-developed solodized-Solonetz morphology has developed, calcium and magnesium may be released from the soil minerals by further weathering in place to be brought up by the native vegetation, and replace most of the sodium. Advanced weathering of the clays releases magnesium especially. Thus soils with the striking morphology of the solodized-Solonetz may have lost most of their exchangeable sodium. Soils developed from stratified materials—sand over clay—may develop a structural profile quite like that of solodized-Solonetz, even though the clay has little exchangeable sodium.

Frequently, the leached surface layer of the solodized-Solonetz is blown away during periods of great drought, exposing the hard clay of the B horizon in the bottoms of shallow pits. Such soils are called truncated solodized-Solonetz. Locally, the shallow pits are called "slick-spots" or "scabby-spots." Enormous areas containing many small spots of these soils exist in the Chestnut and Brown soil regions of the northern Great Plains. After truncation, the solodized-Solonetz may go through another stage of being a solodized-Solonetz. But gradually with improved drainage and the invasion of the normal native vegetation, the soil again becomes saturated mainly with calcium and calcium or calcium and magnesium and changes to the zonal soil of the region, for example, Chestnut or Brown.

Well-developed solodized-Solonetz soils are formed only after considerable time. They are not found on young alluvial flood plains. They are more common in temperate or cool-temperate regions than in warm ones, although they do exist in warm areas, even near the Equator.

Commonly all these soils, and especially the solodized-Solonetz, occur irregularly. The solodized-Solonetz nearly always occurs in intricate complexes, like "smallpox on the face of the steppe." After frequent tillage, the spots may not be easily identified. Where irrigation is being considered, the soils need to be examined with great care, since irrigation of them raises serious hazards.

THE ELECTROLYTIC BRIDGE FOR FIELD USE

Determinations of the approximate salt content or degree of salinity of soil samples are made in the field by use of a Wheatstone bridge specially designed for this purpose (fig. 53).

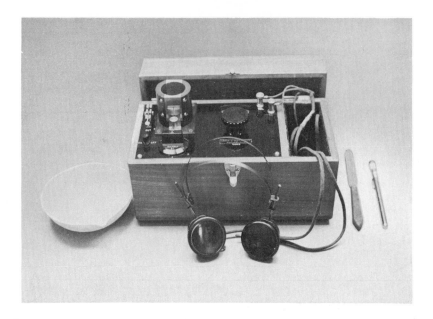

FIGURE 53.—Portable Wheatstone bridge, especially designed for field use, with "Bureau of Soils" cup in place.

The electrical conductivity of the soluble salts is determined by measuring the electrical resistance of a prepared sample of the soil in a special cup, called "Bureau of Soils" cup, inserted in the bridge circuit. The results of the resistance determinations may be expressed in terms of percentage of total salts in the air-dry soil or in terms of conductivity in millimhos of the saturation extract.

Electrical resistance is affected by the degree of dissociation of the salts, moisture content, kind of exchangeable cations, and temperature, as well as by salt concentration. In field operations, corrections for temperature and compensation for moisture content are made. The approximate salt content or degree of salinity is determined from curves or from tables compiled on the assumption of average conditions in chemical character and relative proportions of different kinds of salts.

Soil samples for salt determination are carefully selected from representative locations. Some should be chosen to represent the salt content in places of maximum concentration and others to represent the lower and intermediate degrees of accumulation. To obtain data for phase distinctions or for compiling a special map showing the distribution of salts and alkali, samples should represent average conditions and ranges of salt accumulation over areas of such extent and uniformity of character that they may be shown clearly on the map. Samples of maximum salt accumulation on the immediate surface, including crusts and efflorescence, or localized in any horizon of the soil profile may be taken for special study.

As a basis for defining mapping units, soil profile samples are obtained for the determination of the approximate salt content. Samples are taken by horizons from soils that show distinct morphological differences. Soils with weakly developed profiles are sampled at arbitrary depths, depending upon the character of the salt accumulation, stratification, and the presence of a water table or of layers of rock or gravel. Samples are preferably taken with a spade, but the lower part of the soil may be sampled with an auger where the use of a spade is impracticable. Care is needed to avoid contamination, especially where the auger is used.

Determinations of salt content may be made in the field at the time the samples are taken or later in a laboratory or other convenient place where water is available for washing equipment. For field tests, it is necessary to carry distilled water for saturating the soil and a large can of water for washing equipment. The soil samples may be mixed on small squares of oilcloth.

Frequently field testing is preferable, for the salt content of the soil can be correlated immediately on the spot with vegetation, drainage, relief, surface appearance of the soil, and other related factors. In this way the field scientist can quickly form a sound basis for estimating the salt content of soil types and can draw fairly accurate boundaries of salt-affected areas. Determination in the field is often desirable when the soil conditions in the area are not well known, as at the beginning of a survey. Where general correlations are known, however, it may be preferable to take samples and make the tests at some more convenient place and time. It often saves time not to interrupt the field mapping and to make a number of salt determinations at once. If tests are made at headquarters, the scientist may find it necessary to return to the field for checking after the results are available. Boundaries showing salt or alkali conditions can then be drawn or revised partly on the basis of the test results.

In preparing the soil sample for determination of the approximate salt content, pebbles, root fragments, and other foreign materials are removed. A portion of the sample is placed in a convenient mixing cup and distilled water is added slowly while the soil is stirred with a spatula and mixed until saturation is reached. This saturated soil is called a soil paste. Since dry samples of plastic clays adsorb water slowly, it may be necessary to crush the sample and pass it through a 2-millimeter sieve before attempting to saturate it with distilled water. The hard rubber cup, or conductivity cell, is filled with the saturated soil. The cell should be tapped gently to release air bubbles. The top of the soil is struck off with the spatula, leaving the surface smooth and the cell evenly filled. The cell is placed between the electrical contacts, the circuit closed, and the bridge pointer turned back and forth around the scale, placing the 10-, 100-, or 1,000-ohm coils into the circuit as needed, until the null point is found, as is indicated when the buzzing in the earphone is reduced

TABLE 8.—*Reduction of the electrical resistance of soils to a uniform temperature at 60° F.*

Degrees, Fahrenheit	Resistance when indicated resistance is—								
	1,000	2,000	3,000	4,000	5,000	6,000	7,000	8,000	9,000
	Ohms	*Ohms*	*Ohms*	*Ohms*	*Ohms*	*Ohms*	*Ohms*	*Ohms*	*Ohms*
32	625	1,250	1,875	2,500	3,125	3,750	4,375	5,000	5,625
32.5	632	1,264	1,896	2,528	3,150	3,792	4,424	5,056	5,688
33	639	1,278	1,917	2,556	3,195	3,834	4,473	5,112	5,751
33.5	646	1,292	1,938	2,584	3,230	3,876	4,522	5,168	5,814
34	653	1,306	1,959	2,612	3,265	3,918	4,571	5,224	5,877
34.5	660	1,320	1,980	2,640	3,300	3,960	4,620	5,280	5,940
35	667	1,334	2,001	2,668	3,335	4,002	4,669	5,336	6,003
35.5	674	1,348	2,022	2,696	3,370	4,044	4,718	5,392	6,066
36	681	1,362	2,043	2,724	3,405	4,086	4,767	5,448	6,129
36.5	688	1,376	2,064	2,752	3,440	4,128	4,816	5,504	6,192
37	695	1,390	2,085	2,780	3,475	4,170	4,865	5,560	6,255
37.5	702	1,404	2,106	2,808	3,510	4,212	4,914	5,616	6,318
38	709	1,418	2,127	2,836	3,545	4,254	4,963	5,672	6,381
38.5	716	1,432	2,148	2,864	3,580	4,296	5,012	5,728	6,444
39	722	1,444	2,166	2,888	3,610	4,332	5,054	5,776	6,498
39.5	729	1,458	2,187	2,916	3,645	4,374	5,103	5,832	6,561
40	736	1,472	2,208	2,944	3,680	4,416	5,152	5,888	6,634
40.5	743	1,486	2,229	2,972	3,715	4,458	5,201	5,944	6,687
41	750	1,500	2,250	3,000	3,750	4,500	5,250	6,000	6,750
41.5	757	1,514	2,271	3,028	3,785	4,542	5,299	6,056	6,813
42	763	1,526	2,289	3,052	3,815	4,578	5,341	6,104	6,867
42.5	770	1,540	2,310	3,080	3,850	4,620	5,390	6,160	6,930
43	776	1,552	2,328	3,104	3,880	4,656	5,432	6,208	6,984
43.5	782	1,564	2,346	3,128	3,910	4,692	5,474	6,256	7,038
44	788	1,576	2,361	3,152	3,940	4,728	5,516	6,304	7,092
44.5	794	1,588	2,382	3,176	3,970	4,764	5,558	6,352	7,146
45	800	1,600	2,400	3,200	4,000	4,800	5,600	6,400	7,200
45.5	807	1,614	2,421	3,228	4,035	4,842	5,649	6,456	7,263
46	814	1,628	2,442	3,256	4,070	4,884	5,698	6,512	7,326
46.5	821	1,642	2,463	3,284	4,105	4,926	5,747	6,568	7,389
47	828	1,656	2,484	3,312	4,140	4,968	5,796	6,624	7,452
47.5	835	1,670	2,505	3,340	4,175	5,010	5,845	6,680	7,515
48	842	1,684	2,526	3,368	4,210	5,052	5,884	6,736	7,578
48.5	849	1,698	2,547	3,396	4,245	5,094	5,933	6,792	7,641
49	856	1,712	2,568	3,424	4,280	5,136	5,992	6,848	7,704
49.5	862	1,724	2,586	3,448	4,310	5,172	6,034	6,896	7,758
50	868	1,736	2,604	3,472	4,340	5,208	6,076	6,944	7,812
50.5	875	1,750	2,625	3,500	4,375	5,250	6,125	7,000	7,875
51	881	1,762	2,643	3,524	4,405	5,286	6,167	7,048	7,929
51.5	887	1,774	2,661	3,548	4,435	5,322	6,209	7,096	7,983
52	893	1,786	2,679	3,572	4,465	5,358	6,251	7,144	8,037
52.5	900	1,800	2,700	3,600	4,500	5,400	6,300	7,200	8,100
53	906	1,812	2,718	3,624	4,530	5,436	6,342	7,248	8,154
53.5	912	1,824	2,736	3,648	4,560	5,472	6,384	7,296	8,208
54	919	1,838	2,757	3,676	4,595	5,514	6,433	7,352	8,271
54.5	926	1,852	2,778	3,704	4,630	5,556	6,482	7,408	8,334
55	933	1,866	2,799	3,732	4,665	5,598	6,531	7,464	8,397
55.5	940	1,880	2,820	3,760	4,700	5,640	6,580	7,520	8,460
56	947	1,894	2,841	3,780	4,735	5,682	6,629	7,576	8,523
56.5	954	1,908	2,862	3,816	4,770	5,724	6,678	7,632	8,586
57	961	1,922	2,883	3,844	4,805	5,766	6,727	7,688	8,649
57.5	968	1,936	2,904	3,872	4,839	5,807	6,775	7,743	8,711
58	974	1,948	2,922	3,896	4,870	5,844	6,818	7,792	8,766
58.5	981	1,962	2,943	3,924	4,905	5,886	6,867	7,848	8,829
59	987	1,974	2,962	3,949	4,936	5,923	6,910	7,898	8,885
59.5	994	1,988	2,982	3,976	4,971	5,965	6,959	7,953	8,947
60	1,000	2,000	3,000	4,000	5,000	6,000	7,000	8,000	9,000
60.5	1,006	2,012	3,018	4,024	5,030	6,036	7,042	8,048	9,054
61	1,013	2,026	3,039	4,052	5,065	6,078	7,091	8,104	9,117
61.5	1,020	2,040	3,060	4,080	5,100	6,120	7,140	8,160	9,180
62	1,027	2,054	3,081	4,108	5,135	6,162	7,189	8,216	9,243
62.5	1,033	2,066	3,099	4,132	5,165	6,198	7,231	8,264	9,297
63	1,040	2,080	3,120	4,160	5,200	6,240	7,280	8,320	9,360
63.5	1,047	2,094	3,141	4,188	5,235	6,282	7,329	8,376	9,423
64	1,054	2,108	3,162	4,216	5,270	6,324	7,378	8,432	9,486
64.5	1,061	2,122	3,183	4,244	5,305	6,366	7,427	8,488	9,549
65	1,068	2,136	3,204	4,272	5,340	6,408	7,476	8,544	9,612
65.5	1,075	2,150	3,225	4,300	5,375	6,450	7,525	8,600	9,675
66	1,082	2,164	3,246	4,328	5,410	6,492	7,574	8,656	9,738
66.5	1,089	2,178	3,267	4,356	5,445	6,534	7,623	8,712	9,801
67	1,096	2,192	3,288	4,384	5,480	6,576	7,672	8,768	9,864
67.5	1,103	2,206	3,309	4,412	5,515	6,618	7,721	8,824	9,927
68	1,110	2,220	3,330	4,440	5,550	6,660	7,770	8,880	9,990

TABLE 8.—*Reduction of the electrical resistance of soils to a uniform temperature at 60° F.—Continued*

Degrees, Fahrenheit	Resistance when indicated resistance is—								
	1,000	2,000	3,000	4,000	5,000	6,000	7,000	8,000	9,000
	Ohms	*Ohms*	*Ohms*	*Ohms*	*Ohms*	*Ohms*	*Ohms*	*Ohms*	*Ohms*
68.5	1,117	2,234	3,351	4,468	5,585	6,702	7,819	8,936	10,053
69	1,125	2,250	3,375	4,500	5,625	6,750	7,875	9,000	10,125
69.5	1,133	2,266	3,399	4,532	5,665	6,798	7,931	9,064	10,197
70	1,140	2,280	3,420	4,560	5,700	6,840	7,980	9,120	10,260
70.5	1,147	2,294	3,441	4,588	5,735	6,882	8,029	9,176	10,323
71	1,155	2,310	3,465	4,620	5,775	6,930	8,085	9,240	10,395
71.5	1,162	2,324	3,486	4,648	5,810	6,972	8,134	9,296	10,458
72	1,170	2,340	3,510	4,680	5,850	7,028	8,190	9,360	10,530
72.5	1,177	2,354	3,531	4,708	5,885	7,062	8,239	9,416	10,593
73	1,185	2,370	3,555	4,740	5,925	7,110	8,295	9,480	10,665
73.5	1,193	2,386	3,579	4,772	5,965	7,158	8,351	9,544	10,737
74	1,201	2,402	3,603	4,804	6,005	7,206	8,407	9,608	10,809
74.5	1,208	2,416	3,624	4,832	6,040	7,248	8,456	9,664	10,872
75	1,215	2,430	3,645	4,860	6,075	7,290	8,505	9,720	10,935
75.5	1,222	2,444	3,666	4,888	6,110	7,332	8,554	9,776	10,998
76	1,230	2,460	3,690	4,920	6,150	7,380	8,610	9,840	11,070
76.5	1,238	2,476	3,714	4,952	6,190	7,428	8,666	9,904	11,142
77	1,246	2,492	3,738	4,984	6,230	7,476	8,722	9,968	11,214
77.5	1,254	2,508	3,762	5,016	6,270	7,524	8,778	10,032	11,286
78	1,262	2,524	3,786	5,048	6,310	7,572	8,834	10,096	11,358
78.5	1,270	2,540	3,810	5,080	6,350	7,620	8,890	10,160	11,430
79	1,278	2,556	3,834	5,112	6,390	7,668	8,916	10,224	11,502
79.5	1,286	2,572	3,858	5,144	6,430	7,716	9,002	10,288	11,574
80	1,294	2,588	3,882	5,176	6,470	7,754	9,058	10,352	11,646
80.5	1,302	2,604	3,906	5,208	6,510	7,812	9,114	10,416	11,718
81	1,310	2,620	3,930	5,240	6,550	7,860	9,170	10,480	11,790
81.5	1,318	2,636	3,954	5,272	6,590	7,908	9,226	10,544	11,862
82	1,327	2,654	3,981	5,308	6,635	7,962	9,289	10,616	11,943
82.5	1,335	2,670	4,005	5,340	6,675	8,010	9,345	10,680	12,015
83	1,343	2,686	4,029	5,372	6,715	8,058	9,401	10,744	12,087
83.5	1,351	2,702	4,053	5,404	6,755	8,106	9,457	10,808	12,159
84	1,359	2,718	4,077	5,436	6,795	8,154	9,513	10,872	12,231
84.5	1,367	2,734	4,101	5,468	6,835	8,202	9,569	10,936	12,303
85	1,376	2,752	4,128	5,504	6,880	8,256	9,632	11,008	12,384
85.5	1,385	2,770	4,155	5,540	6,925	8,310	9,695	11,080	12,465
86	1,393	2,786	4,179	5,572	6,965	8,358	9,751	11,144	12,537
86.5	1,401	2,802	4,203	5,604	7,005	8,406	9,807	11,208	12,609
87	1,409	2,818	4,227	5,636	7,015	8,454	9,863	11,272	12,681
87.5	1,418	2,836	4,254	5,672	7,090	8,508	9,931	11,344	12,762
88	1,427	2,854	4,281	5,708	7,135	8,562	9,989	11,416	12,843
88.5	1,435	2,870	4,305	5,740	7,175	8,610	10,040	11,480	12,915
89	1,443	2,886	4,329	5,772	7,215	8,658	10,091	11,544	12,987
89.5	1,451	2,902	4,353	5,804	7,255	8,706	10,157	11,608	13,059
90	1,460	2,920	4,380	5,840	7,300	8,760	10,220	11,680	13,140
90.5	1,468	2,936	4,404	5,872	7,340	8,808	10,276	11,744	13,212
91	1,477	2,954	4,431	5,908	7,385	8,862	10,339	11,816	13,293
91.5	1,486	2,972	4,458	5,944	7,430	8,916	10,402	11,888	13,374
92	1,495	2,990	4,485	5,980	7,475	8,970	10,465	11,960	13,455
92.5	1,504	3,008	4,512	6,016	7,520	9,024	10,528	12,032	13,536
93	1,513	3,026	4,539	6,052	7,565	9,078	10,591	12,104	13,617
93.5	1,522	3,044	4,566	6,088	7,610	9,132	10,654	12,176	13,698
94	1,531	3,062	4,593	6,124	7,655	9,186	10,717	12,248	13,779
94.5	1,540	3,080	4,620	6,160	7,700	9,240	10,780	12,320	13,860
95	1,549	3,098	4,647	6,196	7,745	9,294	10,843	12,392	13,941
95.5	1,559	3,118	4,677	6,236	7,795	9,354	10,913	12,472	14,031
96	1,569	3,138	4,707	6,276	7,815	9,414	10,983	12,552	14,121
96.5	1,579	3,158	4,737	6,316	7,895	9,474	11,053	12,632	14,211
97	1,589	3,178	4,767	6,356	7,945	9,534	11,123	12,712	14,301
97.5	1,599	3,198	4,797	6,396	7,995	9,594	11,193	12,792	14,391
98	1,609	3,218	4,827	6,436	8,045	9,654	11,263	12,872	14,481
98.5	1,619	3,238	4,857	6,476	8,095	9,714	11,333	12,952	14,571
99	1,629	3,258	4,887	6,516	8,145	9,774	11,403	13,032	14,661

to a minimum. The product of the coil resistance and the scale reading is the bridge reading, or the resistance of the soil uncorrected for temperature. For example, if the 100-ohm coil is used and the scale reading is 1.25, the resistance of the soil is 125. If the null point is found to occur near the end of the scale, it is advisable to place the extra 100-ohm test coil in the circuit; then 100 ohms is subtracted from the product of the soil resistance and the scale reading to obtain the bridge reading. The temperature of the saturated soil in the cell is recorded immediately after the resistance is measured, and the reading corrected to a uniform basis. Electrical resistance of irrigation, drainage, or other waters may be determined by substituting the water sample for the saturated soil in the cell.

Temperature correction of bridge readings.—The soil resistance is corrected to a uniform temperature of 60° F. This may be done by using the values in table 8, taken from Bureau of Soils Bulletin 61,[4] or by the use of a nomogram.

In other types of Wheatstone bridges that may be used in the laboratory and which operate from batteries or from 110-volt alternating current, the null point may be determined by an electric eye rather than the earphone. A cell that corrects for temperature can be used with this type of bridge.

Interpretation of bridge readings or soil resistance.—Two methods are presented for interpreting the bridge readings. The older and more common interpretation of soil resistance readings has been in terms of the approximate salt content of the soil sample expressed in percentage on the basis of dry weight of soil. As an example; suppose the resistance at 78° F. to be 1,439 ohms: A resistance of 1,000 ohms at 78° is shown in table 8 as having a value at 60° of 1,262 ohms, one of 400 ohms (one-tenth of 4,000 ohms) an equivalent value of 505 ohms, one of 30 ohms (one one-hundredth of 3,000 ohms) a value of 38 ohms, and one of 9 ohms is equivalent to 11 ohms. The sum of these corrected values is 1,816 ohms, which is the corrected value for 60° as shown below.

Resistance at 78° F.	*Resistance at 60° F.*
1,000	1,262
400	505
30	38
9	11
1,439	1,816

The conversion of the soil resistance readings into approximate salt content of the soil sample is made by use of the standard values given in table 9, adapted from Bureau of Soils Bulletin 61, or by use of a standardization curve prepared for the particular area. Where unusual local conditions are suspected, samples should be sent to the laboratory for analysis. Since variations in soil texture affect the quantity of water required for saturation of the soil sample, soil class must be taken into consideration in making the conversion. Table 9 may be used for estimating the approximate content of salts. The figures represent parts per

[4] DAVIS, R. O. E., and BRYAN, H. THE ELECTRICAL BRIDGE FOR THE DETERMINATION OF SOLUBLE SALTS IN SOILS. U. S. Dept. Agr., Bur. Soils Bul. 61, 36 pp., illus. 1910.

TABLE 11.—*Electrical conductivity of natural waters (in millimhos per centimeter) at 25° C.,*[1] *with a cell constant of 0.25*[2]

[k × f$_t$ to be divided by bridge resistance to obtain conductivity]

°C.	°F.	k × f$_t$	°C.	°F.	k × f$_t$	°C.	°F.	k × f$_t$
3.0	37.4	432	17.0	62.6	299	31.0	87.8	222
4.0	39.2	420	18.0	64.4	292	32.0	89.6	218
5.0	41.0	408	19.0	66.2	286	33.0	91.4	214
6.0	42.8	396	20.0	68.0	280	34.0	93.2	210
7.0	44.6	385	21.0	69.8	273	35.0	95.0	207
8.0	46.4	375	22.0	71.6	267	36.0	96.8	203
9.0	48.2	365	23.0	73.4	261	37.0	98.6	200
10.0	50.0	355	24.0	75.2	255	38.0	100.2	196
11.0	51.8	346	25.0	77.0	250	39.0	102.2	193
12.0	53.6	338	26.0	78.8	245	40.0	104.0	190
13.0	55.4	329	27.0	80.6	240	41.0	105.8	187
14.0	57.2	321	28.0	82.4	235	42.0	107.6	184
15.0	59.0	314	29.0	84.2	230	43.0	109.4	181
16.0	60.8	306	30.0	86.0	226	44.0	111.2	179

[1] Millimhos per centimeter at 25° C. multiplied by 600 gives approximate parts per million of salt in natural waters.
[2] With cell constant (k) at 0.25, f$_t$ is temperature correction.

a copy of any one of the following nomograms may be had (1) for relating resistance in ohms, temperature, and electrical conductivity in millimhos per centimeter at 25° C. of solutions in natural waters as measured in a "Bureau of Soils" cup, assuming a cell constant of 0.25; (2) for reducing soil-paste resistance in ohms at a particular temperature, as measured in the "Bureau of Soils" cup, to resistance at 60° F., assuming a cell constant of 0.25; or (3) for changing soil-paste resistance readings from "Bureau of Soils" cup to percentage salt, based upon the old methods.

Care of the electrolytic bridge.—The electrolytic bridge is a delicate instrument easily broken by unusual shock or jar. It may be carried safely in the field if placed in a container with good cushions or packing. The electrodes of the hard-rubber cell need to be bright and free from grease, and the cell and bridge parts should not be allowed to become encrusted with mud. Contacts should be kept clean. Major adjustments of the bridge and repairs should not be attempted in the field. When shipping or transporting the bridge long distances, the heavy electric battery in the lower compartment should be removed, as it might become loosened and cause serious damage.

OTHER METHODS OF DETERMINING SOIL SALINITY

The Wheatstone bridge has for many years been useful in determining the approximate salt content of soils. The salt content is measured by soil resistance, but results are only approximate. The electric current carried by a saturated soil may vary considerably with salts of different composition, even though

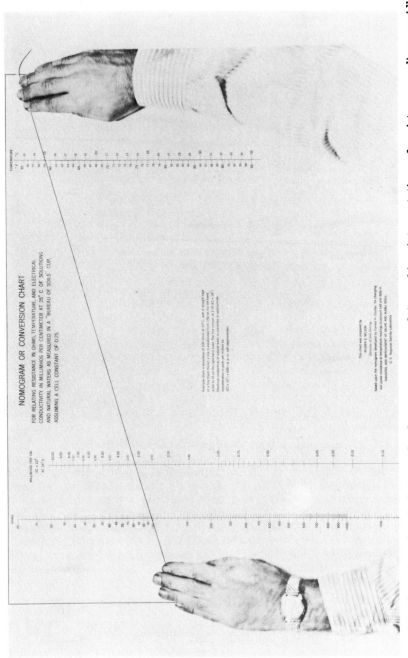

FIGURE 54.—A much reduced photograph of a nomogram used in making interpretations of resistance readings rapidly.

the total salt content is the same. A chemical analysis[7] that determines the composition of the soluble salts offers a more accurate method of determining the salt content of a soil and the concentration of salt in a soil solution. Such chemical analyses are not readily adapted to field needs and can be justified only for special studies or as checks. Variations in the conductivity of soil minerals and variations in moisture content of the soil paste are other sources of error if salt content is determined by measuring the resistance of the saturated soil.[8]

Direct conductivity measurements of a soil solution or soil extract may be used for estimating soil salinity or for appraising its relation to plant growth. Conductivity measurements of soil extracts are more precise than interpretations of paste resistances, but are less so than chemical analyses. More apparatus is required for conductivity measurements of soil extracts, and the method is slower than measurements of the resistance of saturated soil. The extract method may be adapted for field use by setting up the equipment in a convenient location within the survey area. A complete laboratory is not necessary.

The use of conductivity measurements for appraising the salinity of soil samples is explained in the manual *Diagnosis and Improvement of Saline and Alkali Soils* prepared by the United States Regional Salinity Laboratory. The use of the extract from the saturated soil—called the saturation extract—is recommended for conductivity measurements. This is the lowest feasible soil-moisture content for extracting the soil solution for routine testing. With medium-textured soils, the moisture percentage at saturation is approximately twice the field capacity. Thus measurements made on the saturation extract are related to the soil solution at field capacity; and the salt dilution effect in clay soils, due to their higher moisture-retaining capacity, is automatically taken into account. The conductivity of the saturation extract can be used directly for correlating salinity with plant growth, without conversion or reference to any other scale.

The saturation extract is obtained from the saturated soil, prepared as described for use of the electrolytic bridge, by using a suction or pressure filter. Electrical conductance is the reciprocal of resistance and is expressed in terms of mhos or reciprocal ohms. The standard unit for conductivity is mhos per centimeter at 25° C. For use with extracts from saline soils, the millimhos per centimeter (1,000 millimhos equals one mho) is a convenient conductivity unit. After the saturation extract is obtained from the saturated soil sample, its conductivity is measured by means of a suitable conductivity bridge and cell. From correlating measurements of electrical conductivity of the saturation extract

---

[7] MAGISTAD, O. C., REITEMEIER, R. F., and WILCOX, L. V. DETERMINATION OF SOLUBLE SALTS IN SOILS. Soil Sci. 59: 65–75. 1945.

[8] REITEMEIER, R. F., and WILCOX, L. V. A CRITIQUE OF ESTIMATING SOIL SOLUTION CONCENTRATION FROM THE ELECTRICAL CONDUCTIVITY OF SATURATED SOILS. Soil Sci. 61: 281–293, illus. 1946.

with plant growth, soil samples with conductivities greater than 4 millimhos per centimeter are now considered to be saline.

Measurements for electrical conductivity of extracts of greater dilution than the saturated soil, such as 1:1 or 1:5 soil-water suspensions, have also been used for salinity appraisal. Since the extract can be obtained by filtering without suction or pressure, such extracts are convenient for rapid determinations. The reliability of conductivity measurements made on these extracts depends upon the kinds of salts present. If only chloride salts are present, the results are little affected by the moisture content, but if calcium sulfate is present in significant quantities, the quantity brought into solution depends upon the soil-water ratio. Calcium carbonate has a much smaller effect, significant only at very low values. In evaluating the accuracy of methods, one must remember the unavoidable errors of soil sampling. Extra expense and time for accuracy of measurement, beyond the accuracy with which the samples represent the soil in the field, are not warranted.

THE MAPPING OF SOILS TO INDICATE SALT AND ALKALI

The field scientist has many problems to consider in mapping soils to indicate the salt and alkali in them, as these qualities relate to other soil characteristics and to predictions about use and management. Many of these conditions can be described adequately on the basis of the soil type. Usually, however, special phases and symbols or special maps must be used to show defined classes of salt and alkali in sufficient detail for the predictions needed. Different kinds of salts and combinations of salts have varied effects on crops. In many soils salts are transitory, whereas in others they are comparitively stationary. Alkalinity may or may not be combined with excess salts. In setting up mapping units to indicate the conditions in saline or alkali soils, account must be taken of the crops most likely to be grown.

In dry-farming areas where the removal of salts or the correction of alkali conditions is ordinarily impractical, the mapping problem differs from that in irrigated areas or areas of potential irrigation. Salts are usually fairly stable in dry-farming areas; and where they exist only in the deep subsoil or substratum, shallow-rooted crops may be grown. In dry-farming areas, soils do not ordinarily need to be sampled for salinity below the depth of moisture penetration. By studying the soils and the depth of root penetration, the field scientist can judge the depths to which he needs to take samples.

In irrigated areas, or where irrigation is anticipated, the problems are more difficult. Deep strata that are not significant in the natural environment become so with the addition of water. If a saline water table occurs within a depth of 6 feet, salt may rapidly accumulate in the solum, especially if the surface is barren and capillary rise is moderate to high.

The vegetation, especially the native cover, aids in recognizing saline or alkali soils and their boundaries. Using the land form, vegetation, and other features as guides, salt and alkali tests are made to correlate the different concentrations of salt or degrees of alkalinity with the observable features. The different concentrations can then be used in drawing boundaries on the map. Plants vary in their tolerance of salt according to species, variety, and even age, and somewhat with other growing conditions. Some plants are not good indicators, because they grow well with either fair amounts of salt in the soil or in the absence of salinity or alkalinity.

Soil morphology may also be correlated with the salinity and alkalinity as determined by the testing of soil samples. Such correlations are of primary importance among mature soils, but are less dependable among those of young flood plains.

Soil samples used in the appraisal of salinity and alkalinity should be taken with specific regard to the existing problems. In dry-farming areas, where the movement of salts in the soil is usually very slow, the samples should be taken to determine the specific portions of the soil in which salts occur or which have a high degree of alkalinity. In irrigated areas, especially those in which subirrigation is used or in which ground-water levels are high, sometimes most of the salts occur on the surface or in the uppermost few inches of the surface soil. In most irrigated Alluvial soils it is suggested that salt content be determined on composite samples of the topmost 6 inches and on composite samples taken at 6 to 18 inches, 18 to 36 inches, and 36 to 72 inches. If the soil is markedly stratified, however, the specific strata should be sampled separately. Soils with developed profiles are sampled according to horizons. If the germination of seed is of prime importance, it may be necessary to test the topmost 2 or 3 inches of soil separately. In fields with furrow irrigation, salt may accumulate rapidly on the top of the ridges. If any reason exists to suspect salt or alkali problems, sufficient samples should be tested to appraise the general condition.

SALINE AND ALKALI CLASSES

Soils with harmful quantities of soluble salts and those with a high degree of alkalinity are shown separately on detailed soil maps from nonsaline or nonalkali soils. Each subdivision of a soil type according to salinity or alkalinity needs to be defined and predictions for its use developed, together with recommendations for its treatment. The definition of mapping units varies with the character and condition of salt accumulations, the physical character of the soil, the possible utilization of the soil, and the objectives of the survey. In areas where salinity is widespread and the salt concentrations vary from one part of the area to another or where the degrees of alkalinity are varied, soils may be grouped in terms of the agronomic significance of salt and alkali, as follows:

Class 0: Soils free of excess salt or alkali. Practically no crops are inhibited by or show evidence of injury from excess of salts or alkali.

Class 1: Soils slightly affected by salt or alkali. The growth of sensitive crops is inhibited but that of salt-tolerant crops may not be.

Class 2: Soils moderatey affected by salt or alkali. Crop growth is inhibited and no crop does well.

Class 3: Soils strongly affected by salt or alkali. Only a few kinds of plants survive.

The first group (Class 0) includes those soils in which the average concentration of salts, or the degree of alkalinity to a depth of 5 or 6 feet, is such that crop plants are not affected and there is no localization of harmful salts in any one horizon within the rooting zone of plants. Mapping units are rarely, if ever, entirely homogeneous in respect to the limits of just one of these classes. If the salt or alkali pattern is especially uneven, with only spots of affected soils, a defined complex is mapped.

Boundaries separating soils free of excess salts or alkali from these slightly, moderately, or strongly affected, are usually drawn on the map after the sample locations are plotted and the analytical data are available. The boundaries are drawn by evaluating the recorded data, the apparent effects of the salt or alkali on the soil, crops, and native vegetation, and the other features of the landscape. Boundaries can be made generally reliable so that few crop plants on the soils mapped as "free" will be noticeably damaged by salt or alkali. This does not mean that the concentration of soluble salts will everywhere fall within the range set up for the typical soil of the mapping unit. Small areas having stronger concentrations or small areas of salt-free soils may be included in the area. It is not economically practicable to map out every small body that differs in salt concentration.

If saline and alkaline conditions are not common among the soils, or if it is not necessary to establish a complete range of classes, two conditions—(1) salt-free and (2) salt- or alkali-affected—may be enough. If salt accumulations are infrequent they need not be indicated by soil boundaries; the conditions may be shown satisfactorily by symbols, defined according to area and the results of field tests. Ordinarily, however, if the accumulation of salts presents a definite problem, some boundaries drawn according to differing degrees of salinity or alkali will be necessary within soil types.

Excess salts, and especially alkali, are often characteristic of individual soil types, so that field boundaries drawn between classes according to salt or alkali coincide with soil-type boundaries.

Symbols to indicate salt- and alkali-affected areas and boundaries among classes are shown on the completed map in red or blue[9] (pl. 7). They are published on the master soil map unless the boundaries and symbols are so numerous as to obscure the other symbols. Where very intricate, a separate salt or alkali map is prepared on the same scale as the soil map. If the symbols are numerous and the pattern intricate, the field mapping is done

---

[9] In blue rather than red, if there is no other reason to make a red plate.

on an overlay of acetate rather than on the aerial photograph or the soil map.

The data on individual samples are placed in a special table in the soil survey report. The site of each profile sampled can be indicated on the published map by a red dot with a reference number keyed to the data in the table. Such a table should include the depth of each horizon or layer, the percentage of soluble salts, the pH value, and where relevant, the depth of the water table.[10]

Determination of salinity classes.—The significance of the average salt content in the soil profile in determining the classes to be recognized in defining mapping units and in predicting the capabilities of the soil for use are, of course, modified by a concentration of salts in the surface soil or any other horizon in the rooting zone and by soil texture. Generally, the salt concentration of the surface soil or the average concentration of the profile, whichever is the higher, is used in determining the salinity class of the soil.

Two sets of values are presented for the limits among salinity classes: (1) The older method of using values for the percentage of salts and (2) the more recent and better method of using measurements of the conductivity of the saturation extract.

In the older method based on percentage of salt, the dividing percentage between saline and nonsaline soils, below which most crop plants are not affected, is set at 0.15 percent. At one time, this percentage had been placed at 0.2; but surface concentrations exceeding 0.15 percent may be sufficient to limit or prohibit crop production, even though the average salt content to a depth of 6 feet may fall under this percentage. Sometimes, but not always, the soil needs to be classed as at least "slightly affected" if any horizon in the profile has a salt content greater than 0.15 percent, although most crop plants are not harmed with 0.15 percent in the lower soil.

Slightly affected soils contain from 0.15 to 0.35 percent of salt, so distributed in the profile as to injure crops or decrease yields. Moderately affected soils have concentrations of 0.35 to 0.65 percent of salt, which cause serious decreases in yields and in the capabilities of soil for agricultural use. Strongly affected soils contain salts in excess of 0.65 percent. High concentrations are usually associated with barrenness and crusts. Such soils cannot be used for crops.[11] These limits are suggested guides that may

---

[10] A former method for recording salt concentrations of individual profiles tested with the conductivity bridge was to print a fraction on the map in which the numerator indicated the quantity of soluble salts in the surface soil or surface foot, and the denominator the average quantity of soluble salts of the profile to a depth of 6 feet, or to the depth of the sampling up to 6 feet. Sodium carbonate or a high pH value was indicated by the letters C or B after the fraction.

[11] The percentages of salts just suggested are usually valid where chloride salts or sodium sulfate predominate. If calcium sulfate (gypsum) is present in appreciable quantities, each limit may be raised by 0.05 or 0.1 percent, since the gypsum, even though it is not highly soluble, affects the reading obtained with the electrolytic bridge.

need to be varied somewhat locally to develop the most meaningful classes and mapping units. The precise limits for a specific soil, for example, vary with soil texture and water-holding capacity. With further research and experience, refined standards may be developed for broadly defined kinds of soil profiles.

More nearly adequate standards for converting measurements for conductivity of the saturation extract into salinity classes have been established by the United States Regional Salinity Laboratory. The interpretation is in terms of millimhos per centimeter as shown in table 12.

TABLE 12.—*Approximate limits of salinity classes*

Class	Percentage of salt[1]	Conductivity of extract in millimhos per centimeter[2]
Class 0: Free	0–0.15............	0–4.
Class 1: Slightly affected	0.15–.35...........	4–8.
Class 2: Moderately affected	0.35–.65...........	8–15.
Class 3: Strongly affected	Above .65	Above 15.

[1] See text for qualification.
[2] Suggested values based on recent research.

By comparison with table 10 it will be noted that the two sets of values are approximately the same for soils with 50 percent moisture at saturation, normally clay loams.

Determination of alkali classes.—Soils may be both saline and strongly alkaline. Many are. Yet some Solonetz soils are strongly alkaline but not saline.

With saline soils of high alkalinity, salinity classes should be supplemented with values for pH, or percentage exchangeable sodium, or both. Besides these, determinations of permeability, swelling, and clay minerals may be helpful. Samples for pH tests may be collected from the same layers or horizons as those used for determining salts. It may also be necessary to sample a thin surface crust or coating in order to detect the detrimental alkali conditions. Surface crusts or specific horizons of dispersed soils should be tested.

The approximate pH of the soil may be determined in the field with indicators. Useful indicator solutions and their effective ranges are: Bromthymol blue, pH 6.0 to 7.6; phenol red, pH 7.0 to 8.6; cresol red, pH 7.2 to 8.8; thymol blue, pH 8.0 to 9.6; and phenolphthalein, above pH 8.3. The color of phenolphthalein should be strongly pink or red to indicate strong alkalinity. Color charts are available for the other indicators. Thymol blue and cresol red give a generally satisfactory range for strongly alkaline soils. Determinations made with these indicators in the field, using similar soil-water ratios, agree fairly well with glass-electrode measurements. Phenolphthalein is useful but does not give definite pH values.

Tests of pH with the indicator solutions are made in spot plates. The color readings are most nearly accurate with soil-water dilutions between 1 to 4 and 1 to 10. Some skill is required to arrive at the proper amount of soil and solution to make the test. One may count the number of drops required to fill a depression in the spot plate. Then the depression may be filled with soil and divided into as many portions as there were drops. Five drops of indicator solution added to one portion of the soil would then give a dilution of about 1 to 5.

Readings near the upper or lower limit of the indicator range are less reliable than those more nearly midway on the color chart. Those near the limits of the range can be checked with another indicator. The indicator solution itself must have the correct pH; its color should match that of the color chip midway in its range. If the indicator fails to match the proper color chip, it may be corrected by use of dilute solutions of acid or base. Concentrations of indicator solutions of about 0.01 percent have been satisfactory. This dilution avoids too much indicator color, which may give an erroneous value.

The glass electrode is generally regarded as a more reliable means of measuring the pH of a soil. In areas where alkalinity is a major problem, it may be helpful to have a pH meter of this type in the field.

Although pH alone is not a positive diagnosis for all alkali soils, most soils that have pH values above 8.5 have significant quantities of exchangeable sodium. A very few may also contain abundant exchangeable potassium. Generally, pH values of a paste between 8.5 and 9.0 indicate soils with alkalinity problems; and values above 9.0 indicate serious alkalinity problems. Some soils with significantly harmful quantities of exchangeable sodium have pH values below 8.5. An alkali soil may contain small quantities of soluble salts, sufficient to depress hydrolysis, with the result that the soil may not have a pH above 8.5 when the soil paste is tested. Since pH values and values for exchangeable sodium are not always correlative, a strongly alkaline soil, as defined in terms of exchangeable sodium, may not have a pH above 8.5. Yet a soil paste having a value of 8.5 may have a pH above 8.5, even as high as 10.5, on dilution to 1:5, 1:10, or more.

In predicting the feasibility of irrigating a saline soil, it is important to know the pH that will develop after the soil has been leached of excess salts. This is suggested by determining soil pH at dilutions of 1:5 or greater and comparing these results with the pH of the soil paste.[12] Most soils having a pH above 9.0 with a dilution of 1:5 are high in exchangeable sodium and are apt to swell and puddle when the excess salts are leached out.

---

[12] The methods for determining pH, including indicators and dilution used, should be recorded in the field notes. It is not satisfactory to measure pH by using ordinary indicator solutions on a soil paste placed in spot plates. Indicator solutions are generally used at a soil-water dilution of 1:5, but they can be used with greater dilutions. The Hellige Triplex indicator and the soil reaction powder for the Truog soil reaction test can be used to an upper limit of pH 8.5 in the field for determining the pH of a paste sample.

Some soils having a pH between 8.5 and 9.0 contain sufficient gypsum so that after dilution the pH will be reduced below what it would be if gypsum were not present. Such soils may or may not have clearly visible crystals of gypsum.

The percentage of exchangeable sodium is required in defining alkali soils that do not have high pH values. The dividing point between alkali and nonalkali soils, on the basis of exchangeable sodium, has been set, tentatively, at about 15 percent exchangeable sodium in the exchange complex. Determinations of exchangeable sodium are made in the laboratory. A quick test has been described for determining the total soluble sodium. From a knowledge of the salt concentration and the percentage of soluble sodium, exchangeable sodium may be estimated with the Gapon equation.[13] The adequacy of the method is yet to be determined by correlation with field experience.

Like salinity, the pH of soils varies within the profile and within very short horizontal distances. Some areas have many spots of alkali soils where the pH ranges from 8.5 to about 8.8. In others, the pH of the alkali-affected spots ranges from 9.0 to 10.0. If the spots in two such areas were about equally distributed and the growth of most crop plants is prevented in the spots, both areas should be classed similarly, as far as alkalinity is concerned. (Of course, the soils might have other mappable differences.) In a discussion of the soils it should be brought out that the spots with the lower pH probably could be reclaimed more easily or with less expense than those of higher pH.

If spots of alkali soils with pH values of 8.5 or above are intermingled with alkali-free soils, the mapping units for (1) *slightly affected,* (2) *moderately affected,* and (3) *strongly affected* areas are defined by the percentage of the area occupied by the alkali soils. If the spots are comparatively few, they may be shown by defined symbols.

The following values are intended to serve as guides for mapping units:

(0) *Alkali free:* Excepting those conveniently shown by defined symbols, spots of alkali are too few to be significant.
(1) *Slightly affected:* From very little to 5 percent of the area has alkali soil unsuited to most crops.
(2) *Moderately affected:* From 5 to 35 percent of the area has alkali soil unsuited to most crops.
(3) *Strongly affected:* More than 35 percent of the area has alkali soil unsuited to most crops. Such areas are unproductive.

For some survey areas mapping units defined in terms of combinations of salinity and alkalinity classes are needed. These classes may become mapping units within one or more soil types, or parts of defined complexes that include other taxonomic units.

[13] See footnote, p. 341. See also, RICHARDS, L. A. CHEMICAL AND PHYSICAL CHARACTERISTICS OF SALINE AND ALKALI SOILS OF WESTERN UNITED STATES. 4th Internatl. Cong. Soil Sci. Trans. 1: 378–383. 1950.

As with slope, stoniness, and similar features, the classes according to salinity and alkalinity need to be evaluated in relation to the other characteristics of the soil in defining mapping units. If for some other reason, a soil is not suitable for crops or pasture, no useful purpose will be served by making fine distinctions in salinity.

Perhaps a final warning is needed. Field scientists must guard against such exclusive attention to the salt concentration and alkalinity of saline and alkali soils that they neglect their many other important characteristics. No one can either classify or map these soils properly on the basis of values for salt content, pH, and exchangeable sodium alone. Such data on soil samples are exceedingly valuable, but only when properly synthesized with all the other characteristics that combine to make a soil area of a certain kind.

ŕinds of soil progresses, we shall be able to go much further than we can now. The prediction tables being made today are vastly improved over the beginning tables of some 20 years ago. As yet, data and techniques for analyzing them do not permit us to distinguish the yield differences that might result from every small difference between sets of management practices, even though significant differences can be seen on some farms where records are kept. Further, the management of a farm involves a very large number of practices that influence yield. Even with the best record books, only a few of the major practices are noted. These major practices are defined, but we cannot conclude that the yields obtained resulted from these recorded practices alone. A farmer who follows several good practices is likely to do the other things necessary for good results, and on time. It is the whole collection of practices that gives the yield.

At least for the present, in soil survey interpretation only fairly broad definitions of management can be dealt with, broader in some survey areas than in others. As much specificity and sub-division of management classes should be made as the available data will permit and as will be useful, but no more.

Management classes are commonly defined in terms of levels and sets.

Levels of management.—Under comparable conditions, the farm operators in a county, say, ordinarily group themselves into a small "poor" class, a large "average," or modal, class, and a small "superior" class, according to the efficiency of their production, or yields in relation to inputs of materials and labor. The management practices followed by such groups are sometimes called "levels" of management.[1]

In the early work with yield estimates and soil productivity ratings, the "average," or modal, level was chosen for definition in physical terms. Perhaps "most common" practice is a better expression, since the yields are usually above the county average.

---

[1] Farms may be also stratified according to types or systems of farming. Such stratification is not essential to the development of the classes of management used in yield predictions. In areas, however, with strongly contrasting types of farming, it may be helpful to block out areas according to general systems of farming within which the classes of management are chosen.

These differences among farming systems arise partly out of management decisions, partly out of the capabilities of the soil pattern on the farm, and partly out of size and location. The potentialities for various systems of farming are related more appropriately to soil associations than to the individual mapping units of a detailed soil map. Yet areas of the same kind of soil may be found as important parts of a grain farm, a dairy farm, a beef-cattle farm, a mixed, or general, farm, and a fruit farm. Even though one may return more income than another, no one system can necessarily be judged "best" without considering the varying skills, labor force, and desires of the operator and his family. The crops grown on the soil and the practices to produce them may be different in the different systems. On one farm, for example, a sloping soil may be used for permanent pasture, while on another it may be terraced and used for a rotation with corn and small grains.

A few estimates have also been made for the low or "poor" level, but ordinarily these are less useful. Few who go to the trouble to read and use the soil survey, or to seek advice based upon it, are interested in estimates at the low level.

Far more important are the yields and management practices at the superior level (not counting "play" farms or other uneconomic units). Generally, these are practices that other farmers can follow under comparable conditions.

Yields and practices can occasionally be estimated at a still higher or "ceiling" level, above superior, where the best combination of all known practices is followed. Where established and functioning, such are the sets of management practices finally developed on a pilot-research farm.

Summarizing, definitions of management practices may be sought at three primary levels—always at one, usually at one and two, and occasionally at all three—as listed below. Since the actual sets of practices may vary within any one level, most importance must be attached to their definition.

Level 1.—The most common combinations of management practices followed by the majority of successful farmers using the soil being dealt with.

Level 2.—The superior combinations of management practices followed by the leading farmers using the soil, perhaps 1 percent or perhaps over 10 percent.

Level 3.—The optimum combinations of management practices developed on pilot-research farms, if any, or on other farms that represent the best (or "ceiling") that can be done in the present state of the agricultural arts.

As progress is made in the development of methods for making yield predictions, this admittedly loose concept of levels of management according to poor, average, and superior managers is being replaced by defined sets of management practices at different levels of intensity (inputs).

Sets of management practices.—Sets of management practices are the combinations of tillage practices, crop rotations, fertilizer practices, and so on that are combined to produce the crop or a group of crops. The table of predicted yields should include one or more sets near the minimum intensity, and possible intermediate ones. Sets of management practices that should have separate predictions may vary by only a single factor, such as continuous wheat and alternate wheat and fallow, for example, on a Chestnut soil. Other sets of management practices selected for the table may vary by several factors, such as the rotation, the tillage practices, and the fertilizers used. Since farmers use sets of practices, the predictions are valid even though it may not be possible to isolate the individual effect of any one practice on yield.

Ideally, it would be useful to have yield predictions for each significantly different set of management practices, physically defined, under three levels of intensity. These levels might be further stratified by important systems of farming. Usually such refinements of distinction are beyond the available data and resources for the soil survey project. How far the soil survey party can and should go in making distinctions among sets of management practices depends a great deal upon the research and interest of the other agriculturists at the cooperating experiment stations.

Classes of management.—The important sets of management practices selected from among those that represent each important level of management and used in the table of yield predictions are often referred to as classes of management. These need to be described in considerable detail and as definitely as possible. It is not enough to indicate merely the level. It is only when the sets of management practices are physically defined in terms of crop rotations, kinds and amounts of fertilizer and lime, drainage, irrigation, contour cultivation, and so on, that the estimates can be used in predicting the farm returns for existing or reorganized farms by the ordinary process of budgeting.

For many survey areas, the same management classes at each level are not appropriate for all soils, especially where the soils vary widely in major use capabilities—crops, pasture, and forestry, in adapted crops, or in responses to management. In footnotes to the tables, in an accompanying explanatory legend, or in the text, each management class should be clearly explained and keyed to the soils to which it applies.

Bench marks.—If the number of separate figures for yields in a single season under each class of management, however developed, are plotted for each soil in the usual frequency distribution curves, some curves are flatter than others. Let us say that 40 bushels of corn, for example, is the average yield. It may represent a median between 35 and 45 for 90 percent of the values, or for 80 percent of them, or even for only 50 percent. Individual yields reported from a soil in a given management class may depart widely from the average over a period of years. With the average yield of corn at 40 bushels, for one soil one-half the yields may fall between 30 and 50 bushels, while for another soil perhaps only one-third may fall within that range.

Several factors cause departures from the average yield figure: (1) Certain hidden factors of management are not included even in a detailed description of the principal items that define the management class. (2) Crops are subject to many variations in weather and to destruction by animals, insects, and diseases. (3) Even with unusual care in soil classification and mapping, no soil mapping unit is entirely homogeneous; and some fields are near one extreme of the definition and others near the other extreme. (4) Depending upon the responsiveness of the soil to fertilizers, lime, and similar management practices that change its fertility or tilth, past management is reflected in current crop yield in ways often difficult to allow for accurately. (5) Yields taken from fields often reflect some inclusions of other soils shown on the map. (6) Since seasonal variations in weather produce good years and poor years, yield records collected over a short term of years may not provide reliable predictions of average expectancy.

The length of time in years required to represent the normal climatic variation is not the same for all soil regions. Among the podzolic soils generally, for example, about 10 years can be expected to give a fair sample of seasons; while among Chestnut soils, 10 years is too short a period.

Bench-mark average yields, in tons, bushels, or pounds, predicted for the principal soils, and used as a basis for giving expected yield values for all soils in an array from highest to lowest, should have added to them, where possible, an indication of expected variations. For example, both a Gray-Brown Podzolic soil in Maryland and a Chestnut soil in western North Dakota may have valid yield expectancies for wheat of 20 bushels per acre. Varieties and class of management practices are, of course, different. The expected variation in yield from year to year is also different. Over a 20-year period, it may turn out to be 20 $\pm$ 20 in North Dakota and 20 $\pm$ 7 in Maryland, for say 90 percent of the values.

Party chiefs are not required to give such ranges in variability everywhere, only where sound data are available for doing so. The aim should be to give the best yield estimates possible with the data at hand, using such statistical analyses as may be helpful. Both the setting of impossibly high standards for yield estimates in areas having few data and the failure to make full use of the available data in areas having a great many need to be avoided.

Reliability of yield predictions.—After the task is completed, the party chief and supervisory scientists should explain the sources of data and suggest the general reliability of the table of yield expectancies and management classes by one of the following notations:

1. *Fair:* Developed mainly from estimates based upon observations and interviews supplemented by a few records and experimental data.

2. *Fairly good:* Developed from estimates based upon observations, interviews, farm records, and experimental data

3. *Good:* Developed from farm records and experimental data, supplemented by observations and interviews.

In addition, it is helpful to underscore the "bench mark" values included in the table.

Information on the productivity of soils and their responses to management has its origin in measurements or estimates of crop yields. Some estimates can be had in terms of tons, bushels, and pounds; others can be had only in relative terms—one soil higher than another and a third one lower. Such values are related to the combinations of soil characteristics that define soils as mapping units and the management practices applied to them.

Field observations.—Observations of crop growth on different soils and under different sets of management practices made during the course of the survey are an important source of information. Such observations are not precise yield estimates, of course, but can be of aid in arraying the soils from highest to lowest in productivity for a crop. Valuable observations of relative crop growth can be made on two or more soils within the same field. This kind of information is very useful in making an array of the soils. Most soil scientists make many such observations every day. Their usefulness increases with their number and with orderly notation and assembly.

Of course, if two or more soils that normally respond to quite different management practices occur in one field, all of which is managed in the same way, an evaluation of yields from these different soils cannot lead to valid comparisons of their productivity. One soil may produce low yields simply because the management practiced in the field is poor for it, whereas those practices may be near optimum for another soil in the field.

Experimental results.—Data on crop yields from experimental plots have an accessory value for yield predictions, besides the primary objectives of the experiments, provided the plots are fair representatives of the mapping units. Where experimental stations, substations, farms, or fields are on any of the soils mapped in the county, arrangements should be made for study of data on crop yields. If a proper soil map has not already been made, one may be needed of the plots. The experimental sites need not necessarily be within the survey area so long as the soils and other growing conditions are similar.

Many experimental stations arrange with farmers for trials of new crop varieties or of new practices. Sometimes accurate yields

[2] On this subject, as well as on other phases of the problem of developing yield predictions, see the following:

ABLEITER, J. K. PRODUCTIVITY RATINGS OF SOIL TYPES. *In* The Classification of Land. Mo. Agr. Expt. Sta. Bul. 421, pp. 13–24. 1940.

ODELL, R. T. MEASUREMENT OF THE PRODUCTIVITY OF SOILS UNDER VARIOUS ENVIRONMENTAL CONDITIONS. Jour. Amer. Soc. Agron. 42 (6): 282–292, illus. 1950.

——— and SMITH, GUY D. A STUDY OF CROP YIELD RECORDS BY SOIL TYPES. Soil Sci. Soc. Amer. Proc. 5: 316–321, illus. 1940.

———. A STUDY OF SAMPLING METHODS USED IN DETERMINING THE PRODUCTIVITY OF ILLINOIS SOILS. Jour. Amer. Soc. Agron. 42 (7): 328–335. 1950.

SIMONSON, R. W., and ENGLEHORN, A. J. METHODS OF ESTIMATING THE PRODUCTIVE CAPACITIES OF SOILS. Soil Sci. Soc. Amer. Proc. 3: 247–252. 1938.

SMITH, GUY D., and SMITH, R. S. A STUDY OF CROP-YIELD RECORDS BY SOIL TYPES AND SOIL RATINGS. Soil Sci. Soc. Amer. Proc. 4: 375–377. 1939.

are reported from such trials. Either the county agricultural agent or workers in the State experiment station may be expected to have records of the results.

Yields obtained in experiments or field trials may be recorded on Form No. 1 (pp. 375 and 376). Since the production practices used in experimental work are usually recorded, the set of practices for each yield value should be entered on Form No. 1.

Yield measurements on experimental plots are more accurate as a rule than those obtained from other sources. The management conditions, however, are not generally similar to those on most farms. Experiments usually include a considerable range of soil management practices. The data from plot experiments can be very useful, nevertheless, especially in estimating the effects of different soil management practices on yields and on long-time soil productivity, even though the yields are apt to be higher than yields on farms.

At the same time the experimental data are being analyzed for yield estimates, they should also be analyzed for use in making predictions in the report on such soil management practices as liming, use of fertilizers, terracing, crop rotations, tillage practices, varieties of adapted crops, weed control, irrigation practices, pasture management, time of seeding, rates of seeding, and information of this kind.

Data from experimental plots need to be used cautiously in the establishment of bench marks to be sure that the management practices used represent management classes for which predictions are to be made. The party chief can generally use the analyses and summaries of the experiments already made by experiment station workers. It is his responsibility, however, to be sure that the soils are comparable.

Data from pilot-research farms are also useful but there are not yet many of these. The large and growing number of unit-test demonstration farms on which records are kept are very useful. Data from these are obtained chiefly from farm record books.

Field samples.—Useful data may be obtained where sample areas of the crops have been harvested from different soils within the same field. Such data are especially useful in arranging the soils relative to one another and can be used to establish bench-mark yields. The method also makes possible more efficient use of farm records where fields lack homogeneity of soil types and phases. Unfortunately, not many data are yet available from the use of this method.

Farm experience.—The experience of farmers managing different soils under the different management practices is potentially, by far, the most important source of data on soil productivity. Unfortunately, however, only a few farmers keep accurate records of their yields and practices by individual fields that can be related to soil types or soil associations.

Even those who record their receipts and expenditures often do not record crop yields and management practices. These farmers can only furnish their experience out of their memories

Form No. 1—Sheet 1

CROP YIELD RECORD SHEET

County_____ Farm operator_____

Legal description of farm_____

Year_____

Field No.	Crop	Acres	Production	Name of variety (or hybrid)	Soil mapping units

In using this form to record data from farm record books, circle the number of fields where the soil pattern is too complex to be used in relating yields to soils. The proportion of different soils making up such fields need not be estimated.

Data from: Farm account books_____

Experiments_____

Farmer's memory_____

Other source[1]_____

Other source_____

[1] Indicate source.

Form No. 1—Sheet 2

Field No.	Lime		Fertilizer		Manure (tons)	Cover crop plowed under (kind)	Other treatment (specify)	Is this field—			Management class[a]
	Kind	Quantity	Kind (formula)	Quantity				Planted on contour	Drained	Terraced	

[a] The management class will be entered after the crop history and treatment of the field previous to the year of record have been studied and after the management classes for the soils of the county have been determined.

Farm record books.—Well-kept farm record books that include an annual record of yields and management practices by fields are perhaps the best source of data. Although shorter records are of value and should by all means be explored, records long enough to represent the normal cycle of weather adequately are best. A 10-year record is satisfactory in most humid areas, but longer records are better in semiarid regions with marked fluctuations in weather.

The party chief should explore all possibilities for record books. Even if only two or three usable records are found, the data from them may be very useful in establishing bench marks and giving quantitative values for the soils arrayed relatively on the basis of other observations and estimates. Those farmers who have kept some records, even though not by fields, are more likely to recapture their past experience out of their memories than farmers who have kept no records at all. Therefore, when selecting farmers for questioning, those having record books should be given priority, provided that the locations of the farms and their soil patterns give promise of fields uniform enough to warrant getting yield data from them. A single visit with such a farmer may suffice to examine his record books, to appraise their usefulness, and to leave with him a questionnaire on yields and practices. In selecting the farmers, one must recall that the selection of those with record books may introduce some bias that needs to be taken into account. That is, farmers keeping record books are apt to follow a higher level of management practices than those who do not. They may follow practices not listed in the record books or may use more skill in following the listed practices, especially in timing them.

The usefulness of records, especially those not broken down by fields, depends a lot on the soil pattern. If the entire farm consists of one kind of soil, total production figures and soil management information are nearly as useful as field data. Rarely, however, are farms that simple. Where yield estimates are made for individual soils, the presence of only one soil in a field is desired. Even this situation does not exist generally, and judgment will need to be exercised about which fields to use and which to reject. It must also be kept in mind that yields from one soil in a field may be influenced by the presence of other soils in the same field, if they delay the timing of operations. Where yields depend on timely planting, for example, the presence of a soil that dries out slowly may delay planting beyond the ideal time for other soils. Yields may sometimes need to be measured or estimated by soil associations.

The most satisfactory farm record book contains a diagram of the farm showing the individual fields and giving annual records of management and production. Where such records are promising, even outside the survey area, a soil map can be made. Even though only one field has uniform soil, the yield and treatment record should be summarized by fields for the whole farm. Comparison of the soil map with the farm map will permit sorting out the fields that can be used. Ordinarily, this can be done more conveniently in the office after the records are taken than at the farm. Fields may need to be rejected if 10 percent or more of the soil is markedly different from the predominant soil. Yields from associations of two soils occurring in a field may be valuable, however, if this is a common association on many fields.

A form similar to the one illustrated as Form No. 1 may be used to record yields and practices by fields as well as to record yield figures and estimates from other sources. Where data are obtained from a farm record book, a tracing of the farm map showing the boundaries and identification numbers of the fields for which yields are recorded on Form No. 1 should be saved and clipped to the form. The date needs to be written on the tracing so that it can be placed with the form for that year. If the field layout remains unchanged for two or more years, the tracings can be so dated.

If field boundaries change a great deal, it may be better to make, as a basis for later tabulation on Form No. 1, an outline sketch of the farm for each year and to show directly on these sketches the crops grown, the management practices, and the yields.

Some farmers have kept records as a part of the soil productivity research program of the cooperating experiment station. These records should be treated in a way similar to those from experimental plots. The party chief can usually work with the analyses and summaries already developed.

The first step in analyzing the data of farm records is to study the soils of the individual farm, including the soil pattern in relation to the field pattern. Having classified the fields by soil mapping units and chosen the ones to use, the next step is to define the soil management classes for which yield predictions will be made and to classify the important sets of practices that may be permitted in each class. Perhaps this grouping is the most difficult part of the procedure. The analyst must decide on a relatively small number of management classes that can be handled practicably and that will permit a display of the significant variations. It may be helpful to array the yields of key crops in tabular form, giving individual yields and associated descriptions of soil management. From the study of such a summary of all available records, whether from record books or questionnaires, appropriate classes of soil management practices may be established and defined.

Questionnaires.—Since the actual yield records that can be related to kinds of soil and to classes of management are so few in most survey areas, yield experience drawn from the memories of farmers will usually need to be used. Representative fields of the important soils can be selected and the operators asked to cooperate in the work by estimating the production from one or more fields along with crop varieties and practices used. Ordinarily this information may be expected to go back only 2 or 3 years, although some may have notes that will allow them to go back farther than that.

The most reliable estimates usually can be had by visiting the farm, explaining what is wanted and why, and asking the farmer to report his estimates on a questionnaire left for him to fill out later and to mail. He may not do a good job if he is asked to recall yields and practices on the spur of the moment, especially if he is busy at the time of the visit. It is helpful to select in advance fields that seem from the soil map to be ones that would be useful. The field or fields can be identified to the farmer at the time of the visit and also in the questionnaire left with him. There follows a sample questionnaire of a type that has been used, together with a covering letter explaining its purpose to the farmer.

Covering letter for suggested field questionnaire

Office of the County Agent

. . . .

Mr. . . . .

. . . .

. . . .

Dear Sir:

For the past few months the . . . . State Agricultural Experiment Station and the United States Department of Agriculture have been conducting a detailed study of the soils of . . . . County. The purpose of this research and survey is to make a detailed basic soil map and gather as much information as possible about the soils of your county.

You are one of the ten farmers in your township asked to cooperate with us in obtaining this information. Your help will be greatly appreciated.

We are trying to classify the soils on their physical and chemical properties and how and from what they are formed or developed. We need information concerning the best adapted crop rotation, methods of handling the soils for the different crops, and average crop yields under the different management practices. All of this information we will use in making recommendations for rotations and farm and soil management practices for the different soils, which we will incorporate in the report accompanying the soil map. We realize the farmer can furnish part of this information out of his experience and are taking this method to obtain it. The more aid you can give us in determining these matters, the more reliable the report will be.

The questions asked apply to your own farm. We have tried to prepare the questions so that they will require only a little time to answer. Most of the questions can be answered with one word or figures; others require short statements, as brief as possible. It is realized that it is not always possible to give exact yields; and where exact yields are not known, your best estimate will be sufficiently accurate.

The questions refer to one particular field on your farm. It is identified in the first paragraph and on the attached farm outline. This particular field has been selected because specific information about the cropping and farm management practices on the soil in that field is needed.

Your answers will be treated confidentially and will not be quoted individually, but will be used in assembling facts for use in the soil survey report of . . . . County, ...

Your cooperation is sincerely desired and will be appreciated.

Sincerely,

. . . .

(County Agricultural Agent)

Suggested Field Questionnaire[3]

.... Farm

Section .... Township .... County, ...

All questions in this form refer to the particular field of your farm consisting of approximately .... acres in the .... Section .... Township ...., and lying ....
of your farm buildings. Also see attached outline map for location of field.

1. What crop rotation have you found best adapted to this field? (Give one complete rotation, as, for example, wheat 2 years, corn 1 year, alfalfa 2 years.)

....
....
....

2. Give yield for each crop in the above rotation and year it was obtained. (For example, wheat yield in 1942 .... bushels, and 1943 .... bushels; corn yield 1944 .... bushels; alfalfa yield 1945 .... tons, and 1946 .... tons.)

....
....
....

3. If you do not use a fixed crop rotation for this field, list the crops grown, year grown, and yield per acre, for the last 5 years the field was in crop.

Crop	Year	Bushels or tons per acre
....	19	....
....	19	....
....	19	....
....	19	....
....	19	....

4. Have you used commercial fertilizers: Yes ...... No ......; barnyard manure: Yes ...... No ......; or green manure: Yes ...... No ...... on this field? (Check yes or no following type of fertilizer used, if any.)

5. If fertilizers were used, please fill out the following table. (If the use of fertilizer gave no increased yield, be sure to put a check mark in column under "No increase observed." It is as important to find out if no increased yields were obtained as it is to find out if there were increases. In the last column, if check strips were used to estimate increases, write "yes;" if not, write "no.")

Kind and analysis of fertilizer used	On what crop	Year used	Amount per acre (lb.)	No. of applications	How was fertilizer used	Approximate date of seeding	Estimated increase due to fertilizer	No increase observed	Check strips (yes or no)

6. If your rotation does not contain a legume, what year did you last grow a legume on this field? ....

[3] An actual questionnaire of this kind needs to be approved by the Budget Bureau Committee on Statistical Standards before it can be used by workers in the U. S. Department of Agriculture.

7. Have you noticed any parts of this field that consistently yield differently than the rest of the field? . . . . If so, what parts, and how did they differ in yield? Roughly sketch areas with different yield on enclosed map.

. . . .
. . . .
. . . .
. . . .

8. Have you had difficulty in getting certain crops to grow in this field? . . . . If so, what crops and how did they act? . . . .

. . . .
. . . .

9. Have you noticed any crops or varieties that seem particularly well adapted to this field? . . . . . . If so, what crops or varieties? . . . .

. . . .

10. Do you have engineering structures such as terraces or artificial drainage systems on this field? . . . . . . If so, are they successful? . . . . . .

11. Do you till this field on the contour? . . . . . .

12. List other crops not already mentioned that you have grown in the field and state whether you feel they are well adapted or not well adapted to it. Give the yield you obtained. . . . .

. . . .
. . . .

13. How many years has this field been in cultivation? . . . .

14. How many years have you farmed your present farm? . . . .

In the particular survey area where this sample questionnaire would be appropriate, lime and fertilizers would not be generally used. In areas where they are generally used, additional questions need to be added to bring out the amounts and kinds used. In other areas, questions will be needed on drainage and irrigation methods. Questions on crop varieties are frequently needed. Sometimes more reliable estimates of yields can be had if the farmer is asked to estimate the total production from a field of known size rather than if he is asked for yields per acre; others are accustomed to think more in terms of acre yields.

Farmers should not be asked to estimate their normal, or average, yields from a field until they have estimated the yields for individual years. Different farmers are apt to have different concepts of such terms as "normal" or "average." The tendency is widespread to think of normal, or average, yields as those obtained in the relatively good years, neglecting to include the poor years in the averaging process. Years of crop failure are sometimes omitted; yet predicted yields should be on the basis of planted acres, not simply harvested acres. It is better, therefore, to help the operator estimate the yields year by year, beginning with the latest crop year, then going back to the year before that, and so on as far as reliable estimates can be recalled.

The date should be given for each specific crop year. This makes it possible to use weather data as a check to detect cases in which a serious error might have been made. If years of severe drought, for example, are not reflected in a farmer's estimated yield, his yield figures may need to be rejected if the evidence indicates that he is confused regarding the years in which particular yields were obtained. Especially in regions of fluctuating weather, the omission of 1 year of near crop failure from a series of 3 to 5 years can result in a serious error for the average figure.

Interviews.—Members of the soil survey party encounter farmers regularly during their work. Conversations with them are a normal part of the daily work, since farmers are interested in what the soil mapper is doing and why. In these conversations, the soil mapper can get a farmer's general observations on crops and soils. He can also estimate the possible value of the records and estimates the farmer gives. Besides that, he may get some useful points for supplementing his own observations on soil response.

Usually, however, not a great deal of value for making yield estimates comes from these more or less casual conversations. Farmers cannot quickly recall out of their memories sufficiently accurate estimates. It is much better to give them some sort of questionnaire of the type already illustrated so that they may have more time to think about the matter.

Other yield estimates.—Adjacent to many soil survey areas are other areas covered by soil survey reports made at an earlier date. Tables of yield predictions in these older reports may be helpful, but the party chief must be careful that they do not prejudice him. It is best that he withhold analysis of them until he has made the first draft of his own tables of estimates. These old estimates may vary from his because of differences in agricultural practices. Ordinarily he may expect to have additional data because of the rapidly growing interest in this research. There may be slight differences in the homogeneity of the mapping units between the two areas. Small but significant differences in climate may be reflected in yields. Yet after the completion of his own work, the party chief may find them a useful check.

Other sources.—Various public agencies have obtained estimated yields of crops on individual farms. All such sources should be investigated.

Census data.[4]—The United States Census Bureau provides estimates of acres and yields for the principal crops on a county basis every 5 years. These reports give some general suggestions of management, for the acres of different crops grown, the number of livestock, and the amount of lime and fertilizer used are included. These data are of limited use because they cover only every fifth year, are compiled on a county basis, and generalize management practices too broadly.

In addition, some States have an annual farm census made every year by the local assessors. This census gives data on acres of crops and yields by counties and sometimes by townships. This

---

[4] For a good discussion of the use and limitations of census data see BLACK, JOHN D. THE RURAL ECONOMY OF NEW ENGLAND. 796 pp., illus. Cambridge. 1950.

information is of considerable value, as it discloses something of the important fluctuations in climate. Where the township is the reporting unit, the data help in estimating the farming systems and their productivity in relationship to soil associations.

Other county offices of agricultural agencies.—As a part of the agricultural conservation program, 10-year average yields of wheat are kept for many individual farms in some States. The county office of the Production and Marketing Administration should be visited for records of this sort. In States where the land is sectionized, the yield records are associated with the regular description of the land so that the farm can be located on the soil map. In most other places farms can also be located from the records. Farms having soil patterns uniform enough to enable the arraying of yields by soil mapping units can be sorted out and the yields tabulated. Records of this kind, however, rarely give an adequate statement of the management practices, including rotations, use of lime and fertilizer, tillage, contour cultivation, use of winter cover crops, and the like. Before they can be used it may be necessary to visit some of the farms to obtain additional information on management practices. After information on management practices has been obtained, sorting can begin. For sorting, it is usually helpful to have a separate sheet for tabulating the yields of each crop on each soil as provided for in Form No. 2 (pp. 384 and 385). That is, one would have a single sheet for corn on Tama silt loam, rolling phase, another for corn on Tama silt loam, undulating phase, and so on. The data may be arranged in vertical columns under the two, three, or more classes of management set up for each soil mapping unit in Form No. 2. These classes are established after a study of the data from all sources. The analyst needs to exercise judgment in defining a few major classes in order to display the important relationships. In arriving at this judgment, it is often helpful to discuss the classes and their definitions with other agriculturists in the county or in the cooperating experiment station.

Having sorted the yield data from various sources according to the several management classes for each soil, the average yield and the variation among the yields reported for each management class may be shown somewhat as indicated on Form No. 2.

The variation should be shown by arraying the individual yield figures; that is, by placing them in descending or ascending order of magnitude, as 31, 29, 25, 19 bushels. If a given yield occurs in more than one case, the number of times it occurs can be put in parentheses directly after the yield figure, thus: 51 (4), 49 (3). Where the number of cases is so large that they cannot conveniently to be arrayed on Form No. 2, an additional sheet can be attached to Form No. 2 to show the array or frequency distribution of the yields for each management class. Giving merely the range between the high and low yields, say 20 to 55 bushels, is not enough, since this would give no indication of how many times yields occur high or low in the range.

Form No. 2

SOIL ....

CROP ....

	Management class:		
	I (Define)	II (Define)	III (Define)
For yields reported by years: No. of cases[1]			
Array of cases[2]			
Average yield[3]			
No. of years for which yield record was obtained[4]			
For yields reported as average over a period of years: Average yield			

[1] Each yield reported for 1 year on a field constitutes a case.

[2] Arrange cases of yield in descending order of magnitude, e.g., 85, 83, 80(2), 79(3), 75, 70, 66, 63 bu. Figures in parentheses following a yield figure indicate number of cases of that yield, where it is more than 1. Letter "(e)" following a yield figure indicates a yield from an experiment.

[3] Mean of all cases.

[4] For example, if yield records on this soil under management class I were obtained in 1941, 1943, and 1945, the number of years would be 3.

Supplement to Form No. 2
ARRAY OF CORN YIELDS UNDER MANAGEMENT CLASS II
Tama silt loam, undulating phase

75	70(4)	66	62
73	69(3)	65(2)	61
72(2)	68(5)	64(2)	60
71(4)	67(4)	63	58

Because of the possibility that changes in the management classes might be made after discussion of them with other agriculturists, computation of average yields and recording of yield arrays or frequency distributions should be delayed until the management classes to be used have been finally determined.

Cases of average yields reported from farms should be tabulated on a separate copy of Form No. 2 from that used to report cases of yields for individual years. The mean of these averages can be checked against the mean of the yields from individual years to help gain an estimate of the reliability of the figures.

The Bureau of Reclamation has collected crop-yield data from irrigated farms on many of its projects. Such data may also be related to soil mapping units on some of the fields. These data are treated like those from other sources.

ESTIMATES OF YIELD EXPECTANCY

From studies and comparisons of the yield data from several sources, tentative estimates of average expected yields are set up for each soil mapping unit under each defined class of management. If the observations for a given soil and management class are limited to a short period, say 3 or 4 years, averages of these observations alone may not represent the yields that could be expected over a longer period, because of the great effect on the average value of just 1 year of unusual weather. To avoid errors through use of data from short periods, it may be necessary to study the weather data for the years covered by the observations. Comparison of weather data for the short period covered with those of a longer period may help in making yield adjustments. If average county-yield figures are available for the period covered by the observations, these may be compared with long-time yield averages to discover any effects of weather. In making such comparisons, however, the effects that better varieties, improved management practices, and major shifts in total acreage have on yield trends need to be kept in mind so that differences in yield due to these factors are separated from those due to differences in weather.

Because of unmeasured variations in management, several observations in any one year are needed to give reliable yield estimates. The proper evaluation of the data from the many sources is important. On the one hand the analyst needs to guard against subjective selection that may lead to unconscious bias, and on the other, against statistical averages of uncomparable data. Rough statistical tests sometimes can be devised to determine which estimates from different sources can usefully be combined.

SAMPLE PRODUCTIVITY TABLE No. 1

[From table 5, page 71, in the Soil Survey of Tama County, Iowa, by A. R. Aandahl *et al.* Data for many of the soils and estimates of probable erosion hazard omitted to save space; hence, headings and numbering of footnotes in this sample table do not conform exactly with those of the original table.]

Estimated average yields per acre of important crops on each soil of Tama County, Iowa, under different systems of soil management

Soil (type, phase, or land type)	Symbol	Crop rotation[2]	Lime[3]	Fertilizer[4] (Pounds)	Manure[5] (Tons)	Other practices[6]	Corn (Bushels)	Soybeans[7] (Bushels)	Oats (Bushels)	Clover and timothy (Tons)	Alfalfa (Tons)	Pasture[8] (Cow-acre days)
Bremer silt loam	A	CCO	No	0	0	Tile drained if necessary	55	24	40	(9)	(10)	150
	B	CCOM	No	0	4	do	60	26	45	1.4	(10)	190
	C	CCOM	Yes	0	8	do	70	28	50	2.0	(11)3.8	---
Bremer silty clay loam	A	CCO	No	0	0	do	40	18	30	(9)	(10)	140
	B	CCOM	No	0	4	do	50	20	35	.8	(10)	170
	C	CCOM	Yes	0	8	do	60	22	40	1.2	(11)2.0	---
Buckner sandy loam	A	CCO	No	0	0	None	10	4	15	.2	(10)	20
	B	CCOM	No	0	4	do	15	8	20	.4	(10)	40
	C	COMM	Yes	200	8	do	30	14	35	.6	.8	---
Carrington loam	A	CCO	No	0	0	do	30	10	27	(9)	(10)	100
	B	CCOM	No	0	4	do	45	14	40	1.2	(10)	170
	C	CCOMM	Yes	200	8	Contour cultivation	55	22	52	2.0	3.4	---
Eroded gently rolling phase	A	CCO	No	0	0	None	25	4	17	(9)	(10)	70
	B	CCOM	No	0	4	do	35	8	27	1.0	(10)	140
	C	COMM	Yes	200	8	Contour strip cropping	50	16	40	1.7	3.0	---
Carrington silt loam	A	CCO	No	0	0	None	35	12	30	(9)	(10)	105
	B	CCOM	No	0	4	do	45	16	40	1.4	(10)	180
	C	CCOMM	Yes	200	8	Contour cultivation	55	24	52	2.0	3.6	---
Eroded gently rolling phase	A	CCO	No	0	0	None	25	6	20	(9)	(10)	80
	B	CCOM	No	0	4	do	35	10	30	1.2	(10)	150
	C	COMM	Yes	200	8	Contour strip cropping	50	18	45	1.8	3.2	---

Eroded rolling phase	A	CCO	No	0	0	None	20	2	15	(9).8	60
	B	COM	No	0	4	do	30	6	25	(12)1.6	110
	C	COMMM	Yes	200	8	Contour strip cropping	45	12	40	2.8	
Chariton silt loam	A	CCO	No	0	0	Drained if necessary	30	18	30	(10)1.0	140
	B	CCOM	No	0	4	do	40	20	35	1.4	180
	C	CCOM	Yes	200	8	do	50	24	40	(11)2.2	

[1] 3 systems of soil management defined for most of the soils and indicated by the letters A, B, and C are used as the basis for estimating the average acre yields of most of the crops. Pasture management is defined separately.

[2] Crops included in the rotations are indicated by the following letters: C, O, and M. The letter "C" means corn, with one exception. When the average acre yield of soybeans is substituted for 1 crop of corn in the rotation, except for continuous corn when it is considered that soybeans are raised every third year. The letter "O" indicates oats. Meadow, "M", is meant to include a mixture of timothy with red, white, and alsike clovers, except when the yield of alfalfa is estimated or when there are 3 or more years of meadow in the rotation. For these two exceptions, meadow is meant to be alfalfa.

[3] When lime applications are included in the management system, they are made once during the rotation in quantities sufficient to neutralize the soil acidity. It is applied prior to the planting of the legumes.

[4] The fertilizer application is 20-percent superphosphate (P_2O_5), and it is applied on the oat crop. This application is not to be considered the recommended one.

[5] The manure applications are made once during the rotation on the first or second corn crop.

[6] Grassed waterways are included with contour cultivation and contour strip cropping.

[7] Soybeans are a relatively new crop in Tama County, and data on yields and soil adaptations are limited; consequently, the estimated average yields per acre are less accurate than for other crops.

[8] Only 2 systems of pasture management are defined for estimating the productivity of the soils for pasture:

System A:
(1) No application of lime or fertilizer is made.
(2) Vegetation consists principally of grasses, although no effort is made to improve the species or to add legumes.
(3) Weeds are not eradicated.
(4) Pastures are not overgrazed.

System B:
(1) Enough lime is applied every 6 to 10 years to maintain neutrality of the soil.
(2) A good stand of grasses and legumes is maintained.
(3) Phosphate fertilizer (400 pounds of 20-percent superphosphate) is applied at the time of seeding the legumes and every 5 years thereafter.
(4) Weeds are eradicated.
(5) Pastures are not overgrazed.

The term "cow-acre days," used to express the carrying capacity of pasture land, is the product of the number of animal units carried per acre multiplied by number of days the animals can be grazed without injury to the pasture; for example, a soil that supports 1 animal unit per acre for 360 days rates 360; a soil supporting 1 animal unit on 2 acres for 180 days rates 90; and a soil supporting 1 animal unit on 4 acres for 100 days rates 25.

[9] System of management does not include this crop in the rotation.
[10] Because alfalfa is very sensitive to acid conditions, no estimate of yield is given unless an application of lime is included.
[11] Rotation is COMMM for estimating the average acre yield of alfalfa.
[12] Rotation is COMM for estimating the average acre yield of clover and timothy.

In some areas it may be best to start with the bench-mark yields for the important soils by management classes established under the levels used. Ideally, these bench marks should be developed for soils of high and low productivity and for all of those between for which good data can be had. At this stage, reviews by other agriculturists may be helpful. Following this, the other soils may be arrayed between the bench marks in accordance with estimates of their relative productivity.

In other areas it may be best to start by making arrays of the soils by crops under each class of management according to productivity for individual crops, and then translate these into absolute values in terms of pounds, bushels, and tons from the bench-mark figures that can be had.

Yield estimates for a crop are given only for those soils to which the crop is well enough adapted that farmers use them for it. No yield estimates are given in the tables for many of the miscellaneous land types and some of the other mapping units not used for crops or pasture. Where needed for clarity, figures for a yield estimate may be replaced with the word "unsuited." Some mapping units are given estimates for pasture and hay, but not for other crops if they are unsuited.

The tentative yield estimates set up after an analysis of all the recorded data and estimates should be discussed with other well-informed agriculturists. Depending upon interest and competence, these should include the county agricultural agent, the staff members of the agronomy, soils, and farm economics departments at the cooperating State agricultural experiment station, and perhaps also PMA committeemen, local farm loan supervisors, soil conservation technicians, and crop reporters. Especially useful will be those soil scientists, agronomists, and horticulturists familiar with the performance of improved varieties.

Final yield estimates prepared for the soil survey report should be reasonable when viewed in the light of the available data and the judgment of informed agricultural scientists and advisers familiar with the crops and soils in the survey area.

Methods of presentation.—Forms of yield tables can be seen in most of the recent soil survey reports published by the United States Department of Agriculture. Two sample tables from this source are included here. The one for Tama County, Iowa, has the advantage of showing the principal features of the management classes directly in the table. Variations in this county are not so great as in many other counties. Usually it is necessary to describe the management classes for which predicted yields are estimated more fully than is possible within the table. This is done by describing the management classes for each of the soil mapping units under the subhead *Use and management* in the soil survey report or in one of the tables. The general features of the management classes can be used as a basis for grouping soils having common management requirements, as discussed in the section The Soil Survey Report.

The table for Calloway County, Ky., is less readily used because it depends entirely on the accompanying text to explain the management classes under which the yields are estimated. These descriptions in the text are difficult to associate with particular estimates.

SOIL PRODUCTIVITY RATINGS

The most useful expression of soil productivity is average crop yield under defined management classes. For making comparisons among soils, it is convenient, although less precise, to have a productivity rating or index under defined management classes in terms of National standards. This is calculated as follows:

$$\text{Productivity rating index} = \frac{\text{Expected yield per acre}}{\text{Standard yield per acre}} \times 100.$$

Such productivity ratings allow rough comparisons among soils, especially by people who do not have in mind the standard yields of various crops. That is, a person unacquainted with the production of sweetpotatoes might not know whether a yield of 100 bushels per acre is high or low. They also permit some broad comparisons of the productivity of soils that are normally used for widely different crops.

The table of yield estimates is directly translatable into productivity ratings from standard yields of the individual crops. Examples of such standard yields for a few crops are given in table 13. These are by no means the highest yields. Under superior or ceiling management, many soils have ratings greater than 100. If included in the soil survey report, the productivity rating table can be prepared by clerical assistants from the yield estimates and standard yields.

In addition to productivity ratings for individual crops, there is some usefulness for a general productivity rating, considering all the adapted crops. No entirely satisfactory method has yet been developed for giving statistically satisfactory summaries. Where such general ratings are developed, full account is taken of the ratings for individual crops and the relative importance of those in the farming system. But no satisfactory formula has been developed for doing it mathematically. For example, soils that may be highly productive for crops like rye and buckwheat are often not used at all for those crops because of their more economic use for some more intensive crops, as sugar beets, for example. On the other hand, a soil that has low productivity for most crops grown on it may have a very high productivity for one particular crop, such as flue-cured tobacco, or, to take more extreme examples, blueberries or cranberries.

This general rating can serve to sum up the combined effects of all the soil qualities, including fertility, frequency with which a high-value crop can be grown, ease of tillage, moisture relationships, erosion hazard, and flood hazard, as they may be expected to influence the ratio of inputs to outputs. These general ratings are made relatively within large regions rather than for the United States as a whole. Party chiefs should make them relatively within their areas. Where presented, the soils may be arrayed by groups in 5, 10, or some other number of classes according to general productivity.

TABLE 13.—*Standard yields of selected crops used in calculating productivity ratings from predicted yields*

Crop	Yield per acre	Crop	Yield per acre
Alfalfa seed . . . . . bushels. .	10	Timothy and	
Apples . . . . do. . . .	200	clover . . . . ton. .	2
Barley . . . . do. . . .	40	Velvet bean . . . . . do. . . .	1
Beans, navy . . . . do. . . .	25	Lespedeza seed. . .pounds. .	450
Broomcorn . . . . . . .pounds. .	600	Oats . . . . bushels. .	50
Buckwheat . . . . . . bushels. .	25	Peaches . . . . do. . . .	200
Clover, red, seed. . . . .do. . . .	7	Peanuts . . . . pounds. .	1,200
Cabbage . . . . ton. .	12	Peas . . . . bushels. .	25
Corn . . . . bushels. .	50	Permanent	
Corn silage . . . . ton. .	12	pasture . . . . .cow days. .	100
Cotton, lint . . . . . . pounds. .	400	Potatoes . . . . bushels. .	200
Flax . . . . bushels. .	15	Sorghum:	
Green beans (truck) .do. . . .	120	Forage . . . . ton. .	4
Hay:		Grain . . . . . bushels. .	40
Alfalfa . . . . ton. .	4	Sorghum (sorgo)	
Alsike clover . . . .do. . . .	2	syrup . . . . .gallons. .	100
Cowpea . . . . .do. . . .	1	Strawberries . . . .quarts. .	2,000
Lespedeza . . . . .do. . . .	1½	Sugar beets . . . . .ton. .	12
Millet . . . . .do. . . .	3½	Sweetpotatoes . . .bushels. .	150
Native . . . . .do. . . .	1	Tobacco:	
Oat . . . . .do. . . .	2	Bright leaf . .pounds. .	1,000
Red clover . . . . .do. . . .	2	Burley . . . . .do. . . .	1,500
Soybean . . . . . . .do. . . .	2½	Western	
Sweetclover . . . .do. . . .	2	fire-cured . . .do. . . .	1,000
Timothy . . . . . . .do. . . .	2	Wheat . . . . .bushels. .	25

SOIL USES AND MANAGEMENT PRACTICES

A soil survey report should give adequate and reliable information on suitable uses and management practices for each soil. The more complete and specific this information, the more valuable the soil map to farmers and farm advisers. These interpretations can never be substituted for full descriptions of the soils. In fact, the more specific the interpretations, the more quickly they become out of date.

For the convenience of readers, much of the information should be explained in easy-to-read tables and outlines. A large part of the basic stuff for such tables and outlines has already been developed in making the yield estimates. Without a sound table of yield estimates by management classes, it is not possible to make good interpretive groupings.

It is very important that the report contain clear statements of the major uses for which the soils are capable, such as crops requiring tillage, permanent pasture, and forestry. Usually, some soils are marginal and hard to place. Under some economic conditions or in some farms, they should be used in one way; whereas, under other economic conditions or in other farms, they should be used in another way. Thus, the soil scientist should avoid categorical recommendations on the one hand, and lack of clarity and specificity of the results of alternative sets of practices on the other.

In an earlier section on Purpose of Soil Maps and Reports, the requirements for farm planning have been broadly outlined. The party chief should go as far as possible in assembling facts to serve that purpose. The following items are especially important for each soil potentially suitable for crops:

1. Suitable crop rotations, including cover crops.
2. Suitable crop varieties, where these are reasonably well fixed and different for different soils in the survey area. Specific varieties of some of the common field crops are almost too subject to change to emphasize by name in so permanent a document as the soil survey report. But principles of choice may be discussed, broad groups suggested, and specific varieties that are reasonably stable, like those of tree fruits, mentioned. The soil type preference of varieties of field crops are more appropriately emphasized in special leaflets and notices to farmers.
3. Lime requirements.
4. Fertilizer requirements.
5. Suitable tillage practices, including time of tillage, where important.
6. Suitable special practices for runoff and erosion control where needed, including terraces, contour cultivation, and strip cropping.
7. Suitable drainage systems and practices, if required.
8. Suitable irrigation practices, including methods of salinity control, if important.
9. Special practices for the establishment and maintenance of improved pastures.
10. Special practices for controlling soil blowing, if important.

For soils unsuited to crops but suited to permanent pasture, the practices to use are to be explained. Where forestry is important and differences in management are related to soil types, these practices should be discussed, if authentic information can be found about them.

To insure that each item is covered for each soil to which it applies, the party chief will find it helpful to provide himself with blank forms listing each item. This complete record for each mapping unit helps him to avoid missing any item and helps him throughout the preparation of his report in the development of statements on use and management and summary tables.

The sources of information on suitable uses and practices are about the same as those already outlined in detail for developing yield estimates. Reports and summaries of experimental results are especially useful. Most State agricultural experiment stations attempt to keep their summaries of experimental data, revelant to different purposes, up to date. In areas with well-developed unit-test demonstration farms, useful data can be had from the summaries of the county agricultural agent, other extension specialists, and through interviews. As with yield estimates, the most valuable data are those from good farm record books.

SOIL GROUPINGS

Much of the material needed to characterize the soils in terms of use and practice can be presented in various sorts of tables and groupings. These need to vary widely because of the differences in conditions and problems in different areas. After the table of predicted yields itself, of first importance are groupings of the soils according to their broad use capabilities or use suitabilities and groupings according to management classes or management requirements for optimum production. Various kinds of useful groupings are mentioned elsewhere in the *Manual*. Many can be seen in recent soil survey reports published by the United States Department of Agriculture. A special bibliography of reports is included near the end of this *Manual*. A few important examples may be summarized briefly as follows:

Soil-use capability.—In areas where the soil mapping units vary widely in their broad use capabilities, it is necessary to group them under three main headings according to their suitability for (1) crops requiring tillage, (2) permanent pasture or grazing, and (3) forestry. Besides these, a few mapping units may be essentially wasteland. As a first major grouping, it is usually helpful to divide the first group—the soils suitable for crops requiring tillage—into three subgroups that may be called (1) excellent for crops and pasture, (2) good for crops and pasture, and (3) fair for crops and pasture. For many uses to which soil maps are put, this broad grouping into five major classes is exceedingly helpful; but, of course, the major problems and the necessary management practices for the individual soils within the same group vary widely. In some soil survey areas, this grouping is less useful than in others because only a few of the major groups are represented. If all the soils are at least reasonably well suited to crops, for example, the important distinctions to be made are within the first major group. Nevertheless such a simple grouping is so easily grasped by many people wanting some sort of general "land inventory" and unlikely to study the detailed classes and ratings that it should be made in most, if not all, surveys.

Management requirements.—The most important grouping is the one by management requirements. The management groups are subclasses of the major use groups. These management groups are related as nearly as possible to the classes of management used in developing the yield estimates, although it may be useful to have more management requirement groups than management classes for yield estimates.

The number of management groups required depends upon the range of soil conditions within the area, intensity of use, and adequacy of detailed information. The broader the groups, the less specific can be their definitions and the descriptions of management requirements. *It cannot be expected that all mapping units within a group have identical management requirements.* The specific variations within the groups need to be dealt with under individual names of the soil mapping units. This is very important to the use of the soil survey. The benefit from management groupings can be wholly offset by ignoring the specific requirements of individual soil types, phases, and complexes, on the one hand, or by making a very large number of separate groupings, varying only slightly from one another, on the other. On some very complex areas the number of groups required to provide homogeneity that will permit specific statements about management is so great that little is gained by the grouping. In such areas tables which list management needs of individual mapping units should be used.

Fertilizer and lime requirements.—In some areas the requirements for lime and fertilizer can be described adequately under the management groups, although sometimes they can be handled properly only by individual kinds of soil or by a slightly different grouping. These needs can be made clear by supplemental groups indicating requirements for lime, phosphatic fertilizers, potash fertilizers, nitrogen fertilizers, and perhaps others, individually. Even though most farmers in an area now use mixed fertilizers mainly because of habit or trade practices, the "straight goods" may be more economical. Many farmers forfeit income by using low-analysis fertilizers.

Actual recommendations for lime and fertilizer applications to a specific field depend upon the cropping system and previous use, including any former additions of these materials. The soil survey report needs to make this clear. In areas where good recommendations can be made through a proper soil-testing service, this should be made clear. At the same time, the needs for fertilizers should be indicated as specifically as possible.

Irrigation.—In areas proposed for irrigation, the soils can usefully be grouped in about five classes according to arability under irrigation. Under some situations, fewer classes may be required; and under others, more. The individual mapping units may be grouped under five headings as follows:

1. Soils very well suited to irrigation.
2. Soils moderately well suited to irrigation.
3. Soils poorly suited to irrigation.
4. Soils very poorly suited to irrigation.
5. Soils unsuited to irrigation.

The irrigation practices suited to the soils should be explained, usually by subgroups under the main classes. Such practices include length of runs, rate of application of water and amounts of water applied, dimensions of borders, relations between slope gradients and ditch layout, and the like.

Drainage.—In survey areas where drainage works are under consideration, the soils may be grouped into five classes according to their suitability for use with drainage, as suggested for irrigation. Usually, however, they may be grouped in three classes according to (1) drainage necessary, (2) drainage helpful, and (3) drainage not needed. In some areas the first group needs to be subdivided according to type of drainage—tile, ditches, or bedding.

Individual crops.—Usually it is not necessary to make separate groupings of soils according to their suitability for individual crops. Yet there are places where such groupings are highly useful. Where the agriculture of an area is largely built around a single crop, as is often the case with corn, wheat, cotton, or fruit, suitability for the major crop largely determines land values. For people concerned with land values, a suitability grouping for the major crop, with ten classes, might be more valuable than the general productivity rating. While it might appear that suitability can be readily interpreted from the table of yield estimates under management classes, this is not always so.

If the management requirements of the soils vary widely, two soils with about the same predicted yield for a crop might vary in their suitability for the crop. In the Middle West, for example, the Humic-Gley soils (Wiesenboden) are commonly planted to corn 2 years out of 3 or 4, while associated Gray-Brown Podzolic soils are planted to corn only 1 year out of 3 or 4. Yet yields per acre may be similar.

Even though farmers generally in an area are concentrating on one main crop, it does not necessarily mean that other more economic alternative systems should not be used. Where they are known, such alternatives need emphasis in the report.

For clarity and ease of reading of the report, it is often helpful to make groupings of soils by individual crops, especially for pasture and specialty crops. Usually four classes are adequate, as (1) excellent, (2) good, (3) fair, and (4) poor; sometimes finer distinctions are possible and helpful.

Erosion hazard.—The erosion hazard is normally dealt with adequately in the discussion of groups according to management requirements. Yet, if the erosion hazard is especially important, it may be useful to group the mapping units into three classes, as (1) slight to none, (2) moderate, and (3) high. In a few instances, it may be helpful to use five classes, as (1) none, (2) slight, (3) moderate, (4) high, and (5) very high. For such classes to be meaningful, the soil management assumptions must be stated.

These distinctions in erosion hazard are usually most conveniently displayed in the table of the report setting forth the characteristics and behavior of the individual soils.

General productivity.—The groupings according to general productivity, as discussed under soil productivity ratings, follow from the table of soil productivity ratings if one is prepared. Ordinarily, ten classes are used from the highest to the lowest. Of course, within any such class, soil management requirements may vary widely. That is, two soils may be highly productive, in class 1 or 2, and still have great differences in adapted crops and in the practices required to reach a high ratio of output to input. If a productivity rating table is not included, these general ratings may be included as a separate column in the table of yield predictions.

Although groupings according to general productivity are not especially helpful in presenting material needed in farm planning, they are useful for purposes of land appraisal for tax assessment and the like.

SINGLE-FACTOR GROUPINGS

Soils may also be grouped according to single soil factors, like slope, depth, color of one horizon, and so on, and maps showing these groupings may be prepared. These are not generally useful, however, because it is rarely possible to make dependable interpretations from any single factor. If other characteristics vary only within narrow limits and the general setting is known, single-value maps have some practical uses. The soil scientist must recall, however, that his primary task in making the soil map and classification useful is one of synthesis rather than analysis. Even though single-factor groupings and maps are relatively easy to prepare, usually they do not help the reader, since the guidance he seeks from a soil survey requires the syntheses of many factors, no one of which has a simple direct relationship to the combined result.

SOIL CORRELATION AND INSPECTION

The ultimate usefulness of soil classification and soil mapping depends upon accurate soil correlation. This process involves (1) comparing local classificational units—soil types and phases—with those already defined and named in the general system of classification; (2) recognizing, establishing, and naming new units consistent with the system; (3) grouping taxonomic units into series, families, great soil groups, suborders, and orders; (4) grouping geographic units into named and defined soil associations; and (5) arranging the units into keys or groups, as needed to bring out principles and relationships, according to observed characteristics, inferred qualities, genetic factors, or combinations of these.

It is the responsibility of the chief of the party, with the guidance of the supervisory soil scientist or soil correlator, to define the units in his survey so that their appropriate correlation and nomenclature will be facilitated. At the same time he should avoid any possible warping of the definitions of local units in anticipation of particular correlations. The party chief's first responsibility is to see to it that the classification in his area is internally consistent and adequate. Correlation of these units with those of other regions follows.

Names of established units should not be given the local units until the party chief and supervisory scientists are reasonably certain that correlation will hold in the subsequent review; else workers in the party may get a name associated with a wrong set of soil characteristics.

INSPECTION AND CORRELATION REPORTS

Since the same supervisory scientist—the soil correlator—is usually charged with inspection of the classification, mapping, and report writing for adequacy and accuracy, as well as with correlation, the inspection and correlation reports are often combined in one document. A report of inspection is made by the supervisory soil scientist or soil correlator in charge after each visit to a survey area and is designated as *first, progress,* or *final,* as appropriate. Reports on the progress of the soil survey are made on standard forms, with attachments, providing for the following:

Report of....................... inspection
(First, progress, or final)

Date submitted:.....................
Name and number of area (including county and State):.................
....
....

Organizations (a) initiating and (b) cooperating in survey:.............
....
....

Size of area:................ Date survey started:.....................
Sq. miles (or) Acres

Type of survey:...
(Detailed, reconnaissance, detailed-reconnaissance, or other)

....
Other (Explain)

Status of field work:..
....

Survey party (Indicate party chief and organization of each member):
....
....
....

Transportation: Cost arranged by.................................
Is it ample?.............. Is character of service severe?...........
....
....

Base map (including aerial photographs): Kind....................
Scale.............. Is scale adequate?............... Are control data
available? ....
....
Are alterations or revisions being shown properly and accurately?......
Where used, are aerial photographs mounted on plane table when necessary
for accurate orientation?.....................................

Legibility of maps: Boundaries clearly defined?............ Symbols in all
areas?.......... Symbols oriented?.......... Streams named?..........
Bench marks and section corners marked?.........................
Individual sheets—Do they show: Date of survey?...................
Name of area?.......... Name of surveyor?.......... Scale?........
Magnetic north?.......... On the margin of sheet, a list of soil symbols
used?.. Are they joined?........
(Further remarks) ....

Legend: Submit list showing all mapping units as soil types, phases, complexes, or miscellaneous land types, classes for soil slope, erosion, stoniness,
and excess salts where established, and classes (if any) for land use or
other special features. (Include complete description of all new soil series
or other classificational units and any variations in existing units as a
part of the inspection report.)....................................
....
....

Indicate if complete descriptive legend, showing all mapping symbols and
permissible combinations of symbols and soil separations, including types,
phases, and complexes, has been given each member of field party........
.... (If answer is "No," explain provisions for getting
it done.)
....
....
....

Does each party member report new symbols or new combinations of symbols
used each day?...

Field notes (how kept, by whom, and if full enough for a soil survey report):
....
....

Soil samples: Have they been collected?........ Does party chief understand
collection of soil samples and their importance?...................
....

What provision is being made for an extra copy of the map for cooperating
agencies? ....
....

Give the name and address of the county agricultural agent, and mention any local organizations especially interested in the survey and results:

....
....
....

What provisions are being made to obtain relevant agronomic data and other data regarding the responsiveness to management of individual soil types (and phases) from farmers, extension agents, planning technicians, and experiment stations?..

....
....

What progress is being made toward developing a table of expected average yields of the adapted crops for each soil type (and phase) under alternative, physically defined classes of management?.....................

....
....
....

What provisions are being made for soil groupings according to adaptability for specific crops, general productivity, erosion hazard, management requirements, or other?...

....
....
....

Report: Who is to prepare?............................... Expected date of completion?........................ What progress has been made?

....

Remarks (recommendations given to field men, changes and departures from preliminary field working agreements, etc.):.............................

....
....
....
....
....

....
                            Signature of Soil Correlator

Date reached area........................... Time............
Date left area.............................. Time............

Date	Approved by	Agency
....	....	....
....	....	....
....	....	....
....	....	....

The field legend is prepared jointly by the party chief and the soil correlator, often with the help of representatives of cooperating agencies, at the time of the first visit of the soil correlator and is attached to the first inspection report. It is made as nearly complete as practicable and includes a list of all soil types, phases, and other soil mapping units and related features to be mapped in the survey, together with the map symbols. Provision must be made for the inclusion of additional soil types, phases, and other features not recognized during this first inspection visit. Great care needs to be taken with the first inspection report, since it serves as the mapping guide to the field party. As soon as it is finished the party chief should proceed with preparation of the descriptive legend.

Progress inspections are made during the course of the work in order to check the adequacy and accuracy of the mapping, to review the descriptive field legend with the chief of the party, and to help him plan the supplemental studies for yield estimates, soil groupings, and the soil survey report. Besides actual visits to the field, the supervisory scientist needs to make frequent checks by letter and especially through the descriptive legend. The completeness and adequacy of this legend is the best single evidence of how well the party chief is doing his job, his competence, and his potential suitability for increased responsibility.

The final inspection is made at the close of the survey work in an area. Field mapping is thoroughly checked for adequacy and accuracy and discussed in the field with the chief of party and with representatives of cooperating agencies. The soil correlator also checks the suitability of the field maps for cartographic compilation and drafting for publication, the detailed outline and progress of the survey report, and the collection of soil samples. During this same visit a field correlation memorandum is prepared and attached to the final inspection report. It includes a list of all mapping units and symbols shown on the map, together with recommendations for nomenclature.

PURPOSE OF SOIL CORRELATION

The immediate purpose of soil correlation is to assign names to the mapping units to be shown on the published maps that are consistent with the general system of classification and nomenclature. In correlation, decisions are reached to identify the soils in the new survey with similar soils already established and named and to name new soils that need to be recognized by new names. Each mapping unit is properly designated as a soil type, phase, variant, complex, undifferentiated unit, miscellaneous land type, or soil association.

The results of soil and other agricultural research and of farm experience are related to specific kinds of soil through the use of the standard soil names. Purely descriptive names like "permeable brown loam" or "gray sandy soils with hardpans" are wholly inadequate for detailed predictions. Such a large number of characteristics are combined to make a soil of a certain kind that any adequate descriptive name would be unwieldy beyond words, just as would be such names for individual plants, animals, or people. Many broad interpretative groupings of soils may usefully employ descriptive names.

Good soil correlation is essential to the usefulness of the soil map and to the many interpretative groupings and land classifications derived from it.

PROCEDURE

Field.—Even though the preparation of the inspection and correlation report is the responsibility of the soil correlator, it is desirable that representatives of cooperating agencies accompany him on his visits to the area and review the work with him and with the party chief. This is most important for the initial visit when the legend is being established and for the final inspection and field correlation. Copies of the report are signed by the soil correlator and representatives of cooperating agencies, forwarded to the principal soil correlator for his review, and finally sent to the chief soil correlator.

The field correlation memorandum includes the recommended nomenclature of all units shown on the map, descriptions of all new soil series, and suggested modifications of established series. In its preparation full recognition is given to the established classification, nomenclature, and definition of both taxonomic and mapping units (great soil groups, families, series, types, phases, associations, and complexes) ; to any local peculiarities of the soil units in the soil survey area; and to available data on the soils from field and laboratory study. This memorandum is prepared by the soil correlator working with the party chief and representatives of cooperating agencies. If practicable, it is prepared along with the inspection report and attached to it; but if considerable time is necessary for additional study to prepare it, the inspection report should be forwarded at once and a date set for the later submission of the field correlation memorandum.

Regional.—After receiving the field correlation memorandum from the soil correlator, the soil samples, map, relevant laboratory data, and soil survey report or descriptive field legend, the principal soil correlator reviews the field correlation memorandum carefully and thoroughly. The proposed definitions and suggested nomenclature of all mapping units are carefully checked against the standard definitions. He or his delegated representative may set a date for a correlation conference to which all interested representatives of cooperating agencies are invited. Such a conference needs be scheduled only if important differences in judgment seem to exist between soil correlators or between the soil correlator and the representatives of cooperating agencies. Additional laboratory work or joint field studies may be required to resolve such differences. Only differences of interpretation of data may be reconciled in the office.

After acceptance or modification of the individual recommendations in the field correlation, copies of a suggested correlation memorandum are forwarded for comment to the chief of the soil survey party and representatives of the cooperating agencies, including those who may have failed to attend the correlation meeting. After considering all the evidence and suggestions, the principal soil correlator sends his approved regional correlation memorandum to the chief correlator, who is responsible for nomenclature throughout the country, together with copies of the field correlation memorandum, statements of approval or objections from all cooperating agencies, and reasons for any differences between the field and regional correlation memoranda. Descriptions of any new soil series and suggestions for modifications of existing definitions of any soil units are forwarded, along with samples of all new or redefined soil series.

Final.—The chief soil correlator reviews the regional correlation memorandum in relation to the whole system of soil classification for the country. He approves it or makes such changes as are necessary to maintain uniformity of standards in the system. Copies of the approved correlation memorandum are sent to the principal soil correlator for his use and for transmittal to representatives of the cooperating agencies. Even after a final correlation memorandum has been approved, amendments may be proposed to the principal soil correlator or to the chief soil correlator, on the basis of new evidence. These are handled like an original correlation.

Throughout the progress of the soil survey, up to the time of the release of the manuscript map and report for publication, the laboratory data may be requested on selected soil samples. Since these data are expensive to get, they should be requested only as needed for proper definition, nomenclature, classification, or interpretation. Blanket requests for "chemical, physical, and mineralogical data on the soils of the area" should not be approved. But when an important decision depends upon particular determinations, the request should be made promptly. If these data are to be useful to the field party, the proper samples should be taken immediately when the problem is recognized and given high priority in the laboratory, so the results may be sent back to the field party as soon as possible. Where the chief of the party and the soil correlator are faced with a serious problem requiring extensive morphological and laboratory study, special research projects need to be established cooperatively with the laboratory for joint study and joint interpretation of the results.

SOIL GROUPING ON THE MAP

Since 75 to 200 different kinds of soil—types, phases, complexes, and variants—may need to be recognized in a modern detailed soil map of an area to show the significantly different conditions, the soils need to be grouped in various ways to bring out their similarities, different potentialities for use, and management requirements.

Soil groupings are made for many purposes. Those relating to soil use and management are discussed in the section on Yield Predictions and Soil Management Practices, and examples of the groupings are included in the section on The Soil Survey Report. Taxonomic units are discussed in the section on Units of Soil Classification and Mapping. It would not be practicable to describe in this *Manual* the host of useful soil groupings used in the many scientific, educational, and service programs.

In this section we are concerned primarily with color groupings for the soil map. By using color groupings, one is able to establish two orders of soil boundaries—(1) a line alone and (2) a line marking a color change—and to present a map with major color patterns as well as with all the details of boundary lines and symbols. Further, it would be unwise to show, or attempt to show, each mapping unit in a different color, because of the mechanical problems and the enormous costs.

Not all soil maps are printed with color, partly because of the cost. With clear lines and symbols in black, of course, all the information can be read from the map. Color helps in map reading, in differentiating one soil area from another, and especially in reading the map broadly—in seeing the patterns of the major groups of soils in relationship to other physical and cultural features. Uncolored soil maps can be colored by the map users rather easily, according to the grouping on the map legend, or in other ways that are most useful to them. In fact, so many useful groupings can be made that many users of soil maps find it convenient to have several soil maps of the same area colored in different ways, in order to bring out different sets of relationships and interpretations. In printing soil maps, some copies are obtained without color for this purpose.

Soil groupings according to color on the map are designed, first of all, to give the maximum help to the map reader. In reaching that objective their forms vary from area to area.

A soil grouping based upon those soil characteristics that determine management requirements is commonly the most useful one. In surveys where more than 15 of these groups are necessary, some broader grouping, consistent with that used in the text of the soil survey report, may be necessary. Ordinarily, 10 to 15 individual colors or color patterns may be used on a soil map. Even more can be printed at additional cost if the value of the soil map will be greatly increased.

In some soil surveys, color groupings based upon characteristics determining management requirements may also carry interpretations of soil-use capability or suitability, with subgroups that can be interpreted in terms of soil management. The advantages of such groupings, however, are partly offset by the likelihood that they may become outdated in the future. Individual crops and cropping systems vary widely in their adaptability to a soil type or soil phase. That is, there are great contrasts even among the kinds of soil placed in one class called "highly productive" or "class 1." For these reasons color groupings should be based on the more or less fixed features. Yet if color groups based upon soil characteristics are quite unlike the interpretative groupings put forward in the report, the map loses some in readability for the layman.

Many relationships among soils need to be developed. In some areas other color groups based on soil characteristics may give maximum readability of the map even though they are not directly interpretable in terms of soil-use capability or soil management requirements. In some of these areas, the grouping of soils by management requirements, and especially by soil-use capabilities, might give misleading results.

Since many agricultural advisers and farmers use the soil maps, color groups that can be given reliable interpretations in terms of soil management are preferred so long as there is no undue risk of the groupings misleading the reader either when the map is published, or shortly thereafter. Since conditions vary so widely, no hard-and-fast rule can be laid down beyond the basic one of helping people to read and understand the map as clearly as possible.

As a general guide, it may be said that soils similar in common characteristics that influence their use in management should be placed in one group that is shown on the published map in a single color. Where practicable, the grouping of soils under a single color on the map should be avoided if differences in their characteristics are likely to make them (1) suitable for different major uses—forest, pasture, or crops requiring tillage; (2) suitable for very different crops; or (3) require very different management practices. For example, poorly drained soils should generally not be shown with the same color as well-drained soils, or steeply sloping soils in the same color as gently sloping soils, or shallow soils in the same color as deep soils. Exceptions should be made, however, for a group of soils having some one or more characteristics so extremely unfavorable to agriculture as to make them essentially nonarable. Several miscellaneous land types, for example, may be combined and shown with one color on the map. Each unit, of course, will have its individual symbol for specific identification.

A useful grouping can be made by placing the soils into five broad soil-use capability classes, such as first-, second-, and third-class land for crops requiring tillage, fourth-class land for pasture, and fifth-class land for forest. These may then be subdivided into groups according to the characteristics that determine their management requirements. It must be recalled that no groupings can be established that are homogeneous in respect to all the factors of importance to soil use and management. Only the individual soil type or phase can carry all the available information. Coloring the map according to such groupings has two distinct disadvantages. (1) Some users are inclined to accept the color groups as a homogeneous unit and ignore the important differences among the soils shown in the same color; and (2) any grouping, though making it easy to see the relationships for which it is designed, commonly makes it difficult to see other relationships that may be equally important.

The groupings used on the soil map need to be consistent with but not necessarily identical to the groupings used in the soil survey report. Often several groupings need to be used in the report, many of which are more detailed than can be handled in the map legend. For this reason, among others, it is important that the soil survey report be outlined in considerable detail at the close of field work and before soil correlation and the preparation of the soil map. The use and management groups in the report should be so devised that they do not straddle or overlap two or more of the color groups shown on the map. That is, where color groups by management classes are shown on the map, each should consist of one or more whole management groups and not parts of several.

Each group of soils shown with one color on the soil map should be given a *local* descriptive name, which will explain to the map user the basis on which several soils were grouped under one color. Names of groups, for example, might be, "Deep, well-drained, gently sloping, medium-textured soils from limy till" or "Deep, loose sands." It is not practicable to attempt standardization of such connotative names for a large region or State. Attempts to do so lead to long unwieldy names, to serious oversimplification, or to an incorrect use of soil terms. Within an area, suitable names can usually be developed, since the number of soils to be dealt with is relatively small and the characteristics that they have in common can be omitted from names while bringing out the local contrasts.

The names of the groups should show what distinguishes each group from the others, but do not necessarily need to show all the important characteristics of each group. No connotative name could. In a local area, for example, a group of "Steeply sloping soils" may be distinguished from all other groups by the steep slopes. If so, it is not necessary to name this group, say, "Steep, medium-textured, well to excessively drained, shallow to moderately deep soils from sandstone or shale materials."

It is important that the name should indicate mutual exclusiveness of the soils in the different groups. For example, two groups named "Poorly to imperfectly drained soils with slowly permeable subsoils" and "Dark-colored poorly drained soils with slowly permeable subsoils" are not mutually exclusive. Either could contain poorly drained soils with slowly permeable subsoils. Further, all soils having the characteristics expressed in the name of a group should be included in that group. For example, if a group is named "Dark-colored poorly drained soils with slowly permeable subsoils," no soil having the characteristics indicated in the name of this group should be placed in some other group.

Having the full descriptions of each mapping unit in outline form on an individual card or sheet facilitates the development of the groupings. Several alternative schemes may easily be tested. It is important above all that a consistent basis be used, so that each soil can fall easily into some one group. "Sandy soils," "Poorly drained soils," and "Nearly level soils" could not be used as major headings, for these would leave no clear group for a level poorly drained sandy soil.[1]

Three sample outlines for placing the mapping units into color groups for the map follow:

Soil Survey of Roane County, Tennessee:
First-class soils:
Uplands.
Bottom lands.
Second-class soils:
Uplands.
Terraces.
Colluvial slopes.
Bottom lands.
Third-class soils:
Uplands (on sandstone and shale).
Uplands (on limestone).
Colluvial slopes.
Bottom lands.
Terraces.
Fourth-class soils:
Terraces.
Uplands.
Bottom lands.
Fifth-class soils:
Uplands (on limestone)
Uplands (on sandstone and shale).

Soil Survey of Grainger County, Tennessee:
Soils of the undulating and rolling uplands derived from relatively pure limestone.
Soils of the undulating and rolling uplands derived from cherty or siliceous limestone.
Soils of the undulating and rolling uplands derived from highly argillaceous limestone.
Soils of the undulating and rolling uplands derived from interbedded limestone and shale.
Soils of the undulating and rolling uplands derived from acid shale.
Soils of the hilly uplands derived from cherty limestone.
Soils of the hilly uplands derived from relatively pure limestone.
Soils of the hilly, steep, and very steep uplands derived from interbedded limestone and shale.

---

[1] The late Dr. C. F. Marbut often referred to all such inconsistent groupings with an example for the grouping of houses: "Little houses, red houses, and brick houses."

Soils of the hilly and steep uplands derived from acid shale.
Soils of the hilly and steep uplands derived from interbedded sandstone and shale.
Soils of the steep uplands derived from cherty limestone.
Soils of the relatively gently sloping colluvial slopes.
Soils of the steeper colluvial slopes.
Undulating to sloping soils of the terraces.
Sloping and strongly sloping soils of the terraces.
Well-drained soils of the first bottoms or depressions.
Imperfectly drained soils of the first bottoms or depressions.
Poorly drained soils of the first bottoms, depressions, or terraces.
Stony, rough or gullied land types.

Soil Survey of the Casa Grande Area, Arizona:
Soils well suited to irrigation:
Heavy but friable; no lime accumulation.
Heavy but friable; no lime accumulation (over tough subsoil).
Medium to light texture; no lime accumulation.
Soils moderately well suited to irrigation:
Slight lime accumulation.
Moderate lime accumulation.
Tough nodular lime layer of fragmental hardpan.
Soils requiring special management under irrigation:
Heavy, tight, more or less salty.
Heavy texture, compact limy subsoil.
Fragmental lime hardpan.
Sandy and porous.
Loose and sandy.
Frequently overflowed.
Lime hardpan.
Solonetzlike (alkali).
Solonetzlike with lime hardpan.
Soils definitely unsuited to irrigation:
Severely eroded.
Miscellaneous land types.
Concentrations of salts and alkali.

THE SOIL SURVEY REPORT

A complete soil survey includes a soil map and a report or text that describes the kinds of soils shown on the map and summarizes what is known about them. The report interprets the results of agricultural research in terms of kinds of soil. In a sense, it links the laboratory, the experimental plot, and the research farm to the individual tracts of land in the survey area.

The characteristics, responses to management, and capabilities for use of each mapping unit are given to enable farmers, farm advisers, and other users to make full use of the soil map. At best, it is not possible to include more than a very tiny fraction of the relevant information with the map legend.

Most soil survey reports are designed primarily for agricultural users of the map. With a basic scientific soil classification, many other useful interpretations can also be made; but nonagricultural interpretations can usually be handled better in another special report than in the one intended for agricultural users.

The principal purposes of the report are (1) to make all the specific information about each kind of soil that is significant to its use and behavior available to those who must decide how to manage it and (2) to provide such descriptions of the mapping units that the survey can be interpreted for those purposes requiring the fundamental facts about the soil. This first purpose can be accomplished most adequately by presenting predictions of expected yields for each kind of soil under specific sets of management practices, together with predictions of adapted crops and management requirements for optimum sustained production. It must be recalled that the descriptions of the mapping units need to be in objective terms so that the survey may be interpreted for a number of purposes, some of which may be unforeseen by the writers at the time the survey is completed. In addition, the relevant facts about climate, physiography, geology, land use, agriculture, and public facilities need to be included to the extent that they influence soil use and management. Discussions of land use, agricultural systems, forestry, grazing, erosion control, drainage, irrigation, salinity control, fertilization, and the like, should bring out specific relationships to individual soils or special groups of soils. General discussions of such subjects, however, unrelated to the units shown on the map, are out of place. Since the basic soil survey serves many purposes, those of importance in any specific survey area need to be reviewed in advance of preparing the report so they may be given proper emphasis.

Three basic sets of values are needed for each mapping unit: (1) The observable characteristics of the soil as a natural body; (2) the inferred qualities—productivity, fertility, erodibility, drainage, and so on; and (3) yield predictions of adapted crops under alternative defined sets of management practices.

The data necessary to develop these sets of values come from three main sources: (1) Observations of soils in the field and of samples in the laboratory in relation to vegetation, relief, geological formations, and present use; (2) synthesis of the data obtained in other soil and plant research on the same or similar soils, including adaptability of various crops and varieties of crops, responses to lime and fertilizer, the amount of runoff and erosion under different treatments, response to drainage and irrigation, and the like; and (3) analysis of farm experience to find out what yields practical operators have received under different systems of management and the effects that these systems have had on soil productivity.

Many of the data and predictions should be assembled in tables for convenience of the rapid reader and to bring out relationships and contrasts among the soils. Such tables are best completed before the final descriptions of the individual soils for the report are written, since they serve as a helpful check list to avoid omissions from the text of important things to be said about the individual soils. It is a good practice to systematize the preparation of soil descriptions and tables by using a set of cards, one card for each soil, on which all the standard items are listed. These cards can be sorted into groups according to soil management requirements, use capability, response to lime, or to any one of many bases that may be useful. From them, it is easy to abstract general descriptions of the groups.

The text should be prepared for the convenience of the readers, most of whom are not soil specialists. The writing ought to be direct and simple. Concrete terms are better than abstractions, and positive statements usually better than negative ones. Where clarity of statement requires the use of technical terms, these should be defined.

Some otherwise excellent soil surveys have lost effectiveness because of clumsy writing.[1] The writer needs to have his material clearly in mind and then write it as simply as possible. Long,

---

[1] Nearly all writers need some writing aids, including a dictionary and one or more handbooks of grammar, punctuation, and composition. The authors hesitate to make specific recommendations, since the needs of individuals vary widely. The following are suggestive of ones that may be useful to many soil scientists:

GOWERS, ERNEST. PLAIN WORDS: A GUIDE TO THE USE OF ENGLISH. 94 pp. London. 1948.

HALL, MILTON. GETTING YOUR IDEAS ACROSS THROUGH WRITING. U. S. Fed. Sec. Agency Training Manual No. 7. 44 pp. Washington. 1950.

ROBERTS, C. W., HARRIS, J. W., and JOHNSON, W. G. A HANDBOOK OF ENGLISH. 292 pp. New York. 1944.

UNIVERSITY OF CHICAGO PRESS. A MANUAL OF STYLE. Ed. 11, 497 pp., illus. 1949.

WOOD, G. W. SUGGESTIONS TO AUTHORS OF PAPERS SUBMITTED FOR PUBLICATION BY THE UNITED STATES GEOLOGICAL SURVEY, WITH DIRECTIONS TO TYPISTS. U. S. Dept. Int. Ed. 4. (Rev. by B. H. Lane), 126 pp. Washington. 1935.

WOOLLEY, E. C., SCOTT, F. W., and BERDAHL, E. T. COLLEGE HANDBOOK OF COMPOSITION. Ed. 4, 452 pp. Boston. 1944.

b. Systems of tenure.
    (1) Percentage of farms rented for cash; for share of crops (census).
    (2) Briefly but clearly state prevailing systems of renting farms where other than for cash.
    (3) Any relation to soils?

8. *Farm buildings and farm home conveniences* (third-grade head). Show relation to soils if possible.

Descriptions of the individual soil mapping units shown on the map.—The description of the individual soil units shown on the map is a basic feature of any report. The legend on the map itself can include little besides an identification symbol or "tag" for the various kinds of soil. Depending partly on the classes of users for whom the report is intended, narrative descriptions, block descriptions, tables, schematic drawings, and photographs are used, or some combination of these devices.

In many reports this section begins with an explanation of how the soils differ and a general description of the soils and their occurrences. It helps if the report is keyed to the map by using the symbol for each unit with the name of the unit in tables and description headings.

In the organization of the report a part of the material on management problems is often combined with the description of the mapping unit. This arrangement minimizes the amount of searching necessary to find information on any particular soil, and facilitates the use of the report by those interested only in a very few of the soils on the map. The following suggests how these descriptions may be introduced:

The soils of Blank County, their use and management (major head):

Three tables are normally inserted at the beginning of this section. The first shows acreages of the soils in the county [Sample table not given in this *Manual*]; the second, some important characteristics of soils [See Sample Table A, p. 416.]; and the third, position, parent material, and profile characteristics [See Sample Table B, p. 417]. One or more illustrations, as block diagrams showing the relation of soils to parent material and topography, are added as further aids to seeing the relationships among the principal kinds of soils (fig. 55).

Following this introductory material, the individual soils mapped in the county are described in alphabetic order by *series* name. In the text, the most extensive or important *type* in the series may be described first, followed by less important types in turn. The first type or the first phase of a type should be described in detail, but the less important types and phases may not need to be described fully by themselves if their nature is made clear by cross reference to the others. Miscellaneous land types should be described in alphabetic sequence along with the series and types. For example, Rough broken land will fall among the series beginning with "R."

Sample Table A

TABLE [Insert No.].—*Blank County soils: Some important characteristics*

Map symbol	Soil	Dominant slope range	Drainage through the soil[1]	Occurrence of high water table[2]	Moisture supplying capacity[3]	Layer limiting root penetration (if any)[4]	Depth above layer limiting root penetration[5]	Erosion hazard[6]	Natural fertility[7]	Special soil management problems[8]
[To be entered by editor.]	Lakeland sand.	*Percent* 3-8	Rapid	None	Low	None		Slight	Low	Fertility maintenance.

[1] In absence of high water table, report as: none, very slow, slow, medium, rapid, or very rapid.

[2] Report in appropriate terms as: none, intermittent, in winter, etc.

[3] Refers to relative capacity of the soil to *take in* and *hold supply* of moisture in amounts favorable to most crop plants.   It reflects slope, infiltration capacity, moisture retentiveness, and depth of the soil.   Report as very high, high, good, fair, low, or very low.

[4] Layer that hinders penetration of roots of many crop plants, even if free of high water table, or if kept moist, as by irrigation.   Report as: bedrock, hardpan, gravel, caliche, etc.

[5] Report as: very shallow, shallow, moderately deep, deep, or very deep, with depth figures in inches as appropriate (see p. 285).

[6] Report as: none, slight, moderate, high, or very high; or none to slight, moderate, or high.

[7] Report as: low, moderately low, moderate, moderately high, high.

[8] Includes presence of salts or alkali, flood hazard, need for artificial drainage, maintenance of good tilth, etc.

Sample Table B

TABLE [Insert No.].—*Physiographic position, parent material, and profile characteristics of the soil series of Blank County*

Physiographic position	Series	Map symbol[1]	Parent material	Relief	Internal drainage	Surface soil			Subsoil			
						Color	Consistence	Approximate thickness	Color	Consistence	Texture	Approximate thickness
SOILS OF THE UPLANDS								*Inches*				*Inches*
Highland Rim plateau.	Dickson		Material residual from cherty limestone.	Undulating	Slow	Brownish gray	Friable	6–8	Brownish yellow	Friable	Silty clay loam.	12–18
Ridge tops of Highland Rim escarpment.	Baxter	do	Rolling	Medium	Brown to light brown	do	5–8	Brownish red	Firm, friable.	Cherty clay loam to cherty silty clay loam.	20–30	
	Frankstown	do	do	do	Dark gray	do	8–12	Brownish yellow	do	Cherty silty clay loam.	18–36	
SOILS OF THE COLLUVIAL LANDS												
Foot slopes	Greendale	Mimosa and Dellrose soils, mainly.	Gently sloping.	Medium	Grayish brown to dark brown.	Friable	12–18	Yellowish brown	Firm, friable.	Silty clay loam.	10–20	
	Burgin	Soils developed from limestone residuum.	Nearly level to gently sloping.	Very slow	Dark gray to black.	do	8–12	Medium gray mottled with yellow and brown.	Tough, plastic.	Silty clay	12–24	
SOILS OF THE TERRACES												
Low terraces or second bottoms.	Etowah	Alluvial, chiefly from soils developed from limestone residuum.	Gently sloping to sloping.	Medium	Grayish brown to brown.	Friable	8–12	Yellowish brown to reddish brown.	Firm, friable.	Clay loam to silty clay loam.	18–40
	Wolftever	do	Nearly level to gently sloping.	Slow	Light grayish brown.	do	6–12	Yellowish brown	Compact	Silty clay loam.	12–18	
	Taft	do	do	do	Brownish gray	do	6–10	Brownish yellow	Firm, friable.	do	10–24	
	Robertsville	do	Nearly level.	Very slow	Gray or light brownish gray.	do	6–10	Mottled yellow and gray.	Compact	Silty clay	12–20	

[1] Map symbols to be entered by editor.

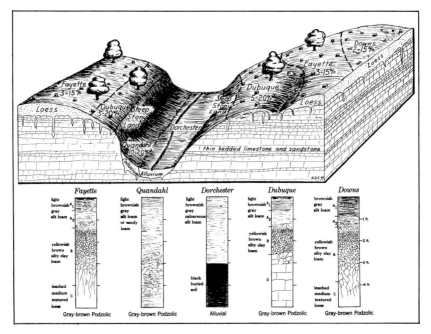

FIGURE 55.—A block-diagram sketch showing the relationships among local soil types and phases within a soil association. (Fayette-Dubuque stony land in the northeastern part of Iowa.) Such diagrams are helpful to the reader in visualizing the relationships between kinds of soil areas and such factors as relief, parent material, and vegetation.

Soil phases are commonly subdivisions of a soil type. A soil type, therefore, includes all its phases. When a soil type is divided into phases on the basis of slope, each of the subdivisions should bear its slope class designation. For example, Tama silt loam, as found in Tama County, Iowa, is divided into the following phases, which may be described in the order of increasing gradient (percent):

Tama silt loam, 1–3 percent slopes.
Tama silt loam, 3–8 percent slopes.
Tama silt loam, 3–8 percent slopes, eroded.
Tama silt loam, 8–12 percent slopes.
Tama silt loam, 8–12 percent slopes, eroded.

Note that the soil type, Tama silt loam, consists of a total of its five phases. This is a departure from a former practice of designating one of the phases of a type as the type itself and only the others as phases. When a soil type is not divided into phases on the basis of slope, but *is* divided into phases on the basis of some other characteristic, such as stoniness, the phase or phases that are characterized by the condition of stoniness should be designated; for example, stony or very stony; and the phase that is not characterized by the condition, if such a phase is mapped, should be designated by the name of the type alone without phase designation and may then be referred to in the text as the typical phase of the type. This convention keeps the names of the individual units as short as possible and avoids the use of terms like "noneroded" and "nonstony" in the names. Commonly two or more features used to differentiate phases are coexistent and appear in the name of the mapping unit, as in Hayter stony loam, eroded steep phase, for example. Many soil types, of course, are not divided into phases.

An outline for soil descriptions follows:[4]

1. **Name of mapping unit** (boldface side head):
   a. Use one or two sentences to point out the *outstanding features or important facts* about the soil, that will help the reader to identify it.
      (1) Relief and physiographic position, association with other soils, and the kind of landscape in which it exists. These may include one or more of the following:
      (2) Parent material.
      (3) Drainage.
      (4) Native vegetation.
      (5) General location in the county and extent. Highly detailed descriptions of the location of areas of the soil, such as "2 miles northwest of St. Andrews Church and south of Blackhawk School," should not be given. The great majority of users do not need to know where all the bodies of a particular soil are located. Those who do can find them from a study of the map.
   b. Profile description (without head):
      Either block or running description of the soil profile may be used, but the block description is usually best. It should cover only the main horizons, rather than all the subdivisions that need to be dealt with in a genetic study of the profile.
      The following characteristics of each main horizon should be kept in mind and satisfactorily covered in the profile descriptions:
      (1) Color.
      (2) Texture.
      (3) Structure.
      (4) Consistence.
      (5) Thickness.
      (6) Reaction and content of lime.
      (7) Organic matter.
      (8) Permeability to roots, moisture, and air.
      (9) Salts or alkali.
      (10) Stone, gravel, or chert.
      (11) Water-holding capacity.
      (12) Known deficiencies in plant nutrients.
      The description should be simple, concise, and nontechnical. Following is a description of Muscatine silt loam, taken from Soil Report No. 71 of the Illinois Agricultural Experiment Station, that meets this requirement:

      Soil Profile.—The surface is a brown or dark-brown heavy silt loam 8 to 10 inches thick and only weakly granular. The subsurface layer is a silt loam varying from a yellowish brown to brown. The subsoil begins at a depth of 16 to 20 inches. It is a grayish-yellow silty clay loam or silty clay with brown coatings. The entire profile absorbs water readily. Carbonates (free lime) usually occur below 40 to 50 inches. In some small areas which are entirely surrounded by Hartsburg silty clay (244) the free lime begins at 20 to 35 inches and the soil is somewhat lighter colored throughout.

---

[4] An alternative arrangement for soil descriptions of soil types not divided into phases is given later.

This description is perhaps not so complete as might be desirable, for some soils at least. It does not mention consistence, for example, nor the usual reaction of the surface layer. It is, however, clear and concise.

It is not necessary or desirable to describe soil profiles in this section of the report in all the detail that might be needed by soil scientists for accurate definition of a soil series. More detailed descriptions of profiles of important representative soils can be given in the section How the Soils of Blank County Were Formed and How They Are Classified. For other soils, the very detailed descriptions are needed only in the correlation work.

In a separate paragraph mention principal inclusions in the mapping unit of soils other than the one named.

c. Soil qualities (without head):

Follow the objective description with a paragraph dealing with significant inferred qualities such as fertility, productivity, erodibility, and the like, as important. Although helpful, such statements are more subject to change with further research than the basic soil descriptions.

d. Use and management (italic side head):

(1) Present use. Include estimated proportion cleared; estimated percentage in crops, pasture, forest, and idle; and mention the more important crops. Indicate differences in use among different parts of the area, if significant.

(2) Prevailing systems of management. This should define the sets of management practices for the appropriate column in the table of predicted yields. If other sets of management practices are important, each should be described. Yields reported or predicted should be tied to the appropriate set of management practices. If the prevailing practices are closely similar on two or more soils, a complete description can be given for one of these, and reference made to this one when the other soils are described. Mention for each set of management practices:

  (a) Rotations.
  (b) Fertilization of crops in the rotation, kind, and frequency; also use of lime and manure.
  (c) Engineering methods of water control, including those for control of runoff and erosion and for drainage and irrigation.
  (d) Methods of preventing salt accumulation or removing excess salts or alkali (where applicable).
  (e) Tillage practices, kind, and timing.
  (f) Pasture management.

(3) Suitable uses and management practices. This discussion should be developed in cooperation with the State agricultural experiment station and have its approval. Some management practices apply generally to a good many of the soils. This might be true of the choice of varieties of some of the crops. To avoid continually repeating descriptions of the same management practices, those that apply to many soils may be given in the subsection Use and Management of Important Groups of Soils for a whole group of soils. The discussion here could then be used primarily to emphasize those practices that are especially appropriate on this soil in view of its characteristics. Also, where two or more soils receive very similar discussions of suitable uses and management practices, a complete discussion can be given for one and reference made to this one when the second soil is described. Mention:

  (a) Suitable crops and crop varieties; other uses.
  (b) Good management practices. This discussion should include the definition of management for the appropriate column in the table of expectable yields. It should cover the items listed above under (2).

(c) In the management discussion, emphasis needs to be given to the influence of acidity, claypans, or other features so that the reader may be able to estimate the responses of the soil to other sets of practices besides those described in detail—sets of practices that may become practicable in the future after the report is published, due to advancements in the agricultural arts.

An alternative arrangement for the description of soil types, when these are not divided into phases, is as follows:

Tama silt loam (boldface side head):
   Outstanding features (of type as a whole).
   Profile description (of type as a whole).
      1–3 percent slopes (italic side head).
      Use and management.
      3–8 percent slopes (italic side head).
      Use and management.
      3–8 percent slopes, eroded (italic side head).
      Difference in profile from the rest of the type.
      Use and management.

An alternative arrangement for describing the soil mapping units is illustrated by the following, adapted from the manuscript of the soil survey report of Cherokee County, Tex.:

Caddo fine sandy loam, level (0–1 percent slopes) (side head).—This is a light-gray poorly drained soil that occurs in nearly level streamhead positions in association with higher lying better drained soils, mainly of the Bowie, Lakeland, and Ruston series. It stays wet during the cool season, is of very low natural fertility, and is unsuitable for crop use unless artificially drained.

   A. Representative profile: (Virgin area, 2½ miles southeast of Alto along State Highway 21.)
      1. 0 to 4 inches. Gray fine sandy loam; very friable; strongly acid.
      2. 4 to 15 inches. Light-gray very fine sandy loam slightly mottled with yellowish brown; very friable; hard when dry; contains a few rounded concretions of iron oxide; grades to horizon below; strongly acid.
      3. 15 to 40 inches. Mottled yellow and light-gray sandy clay loam; massive; porous; friable; strongly acid.
      4. 40 to 60 inches or more. Light-gray strongly acid sandy clay loam, mottled with yellow and containing a few spots of reddish yellow or strong brown.
   B. Variations: In disturbed areas, the surface layer is light gray or white; texture of horizons 1 and 2 ranges from loamy sand to fine sandy loam.
   C. Parent material: Light-gray or mottled light-gray and yellow acid sandy loam and clay loam, more or less thin-bedded and stratified.
   D. Relief: Nearly level to very gently sloping surfaces with gradients dominantly less than 1 percent, but ranging up to 3 in small areas.
   E. Drainage: Surface runoff is very slow; internal drainage is slow, mainly because a high water table is at or near the surface during the cool season.
   F. Erosion hazard: Not susceptible to erosion.
   G. Native vegetation: Forest, mainly of water oak, gum, and shortleaf pine with thick ground cover of shrubs, brambles, and sedges.
   H. Location and extent: Small areas scattered throughout the county; total extent is 5,800 acres.
   I. Utilization: Mainly forest; small areas cleared and used for pasture; 5,360 acres, or 92 percent, are under a cut-over forest cover, and 170 acres, or 3 percent, are cleared and used for pasture.

    J. Suitability for agriculture: Unsuitable for cropland unless drained; best use is for forest or, if cleared, for pasture. Good pastures of lespedeza and Dallis, carpet, and Bermuda grasses can be developed.

    K. Management for pasture: Phosphate disked in; weed control by mowing; regulated grazing; shallow ditching and diversion terraces.

    L. Management for forest: Selective cutting and thinning; removal of undesirable species; plantings in bare areas; controlled burning.

Predictions of crop yields under different sets of management practices.—The importance of the yield predictions and the requirements for useful predictions have been outlined in the section on Yield Predictions and Soil Management Practices. This information is ordinarily presented in a table, but in some reports the yield prediction could be expressed as a part of a narrative discussion of the management of each soil, accompanying the description of that soil. The table covering yield predictions for all the soils in the county has the great advantage that the different soils can be more easily compared. In the narrative presentation, the system of management associated with each yield prediction can be more completely described.

    In some reports more than one table should be used. For example, if separate tables for rotation cropland, for permanent pasture, for orchards, and for forests are used, each is fairly simple as compared to a combined table for all of them.

    The details of the yield tables and the way in which the classes of soil management are defined probably vary more among reports than any other section. In the design and preparation of these tables it should be kept in mind that many of the users of the report are interested in increasing crop yields. Therefore, the predictions should include yields at optimum levels of management as indicated by recent research on the soils of the area or on similar soils in nearby areas. The sets of management practices must be defined specifically enough that the reader will be able to get an idea of the procedures and costs that are involved in obtaining higher yields through changing the management. A sample table of this kind (Sample Table C) is shown on page 424; another—the one from the Soil Survey of Tama County, Iowa— is shown in the section on Yield Predictions and Soil Management Practices.

    In some areas the detail necessary for defining management classes may be too great to include in a table. If so, the management classes may be designated by letter or number in the table and defined for each soil or each group of soils in the text of the report. The requirement that the management classes be specific is not relaxed where this type of arrangement is followed.

    A brief discussion of the bases for the yield table should be included, indicating the sources of information and the relative accuracy of the different values.

The management problems of each soil.—In this section the relationship between soil characteristics and management problems, and the ways in which specific practices are fitted to soil characteristics, are explained.

This information can be presented in a number of ways. In some reports the entire discussion of management appears with the descriptions of the individual mapping units. In other reports the soils are grouped according to management requirements, and discussed by groups. Tables are also useful for this purpose. For brevity, it is sometimes best to write a general discussion of the principles of good soil management as they apply to all the soils, followed by more detailed explanations of how these principles can be fitted to each soil or group of soils.

In these discussions reference should be made to the locations of important research centers where information useful in solving soil management problems in the area is being obtained, even though these centers are not within the survey area. It is sometimes helpful to call attention to similar soils outside the survey area so that users of the map may relate farm experience in other areas to problems within the survey area.

It should be emphasized that predictions rather than recommendations are given in this section on soil management. The ways in which management practices interact with soil characteristics should be the central theme. Comparisons of the effects of different management practices have more value than a "sales talk" for any one system.

Sample Table C on p. 424 shows how tables may be used to simplify presentation of information on soil management.

Practically every soil survey report contains material besides the topics already listed. Some of these additional features are as follows:

Introduction.—The best form of introduction is a brief statement of the potentialities and problems in the area, which answers the general question briefly: "What was found out about the soils in terms of their future use and development?" Unrealized potentialities of the soils should be high-lighted. Soil management problems requiring special emphasis, such as crop adjustment, needs for lime or fertilizer, runoff control, drainage, irrigation, and erosion prevention, can be high-lighted. Promising new crops or systems of farming can be mentioned. Other related problems of soil use in forestry, grazing, or combined resource development should be brought out. No one statement should deal with all of these things—only those of outstanding and general significance.

Interpretive groups for special purposes.—This feature of the report is essentially a subdivision of the section on management. The use of interpretive groupings varies even more from one area to another than the other parts of the soil management discussion.

Wherever a particular crop is of special importance to the agriculture of an area, a rating or grouping of the soils according to their suitability for that crop is useful. Corn suitability ratings have been used in some areas, for example, and suitability for tung orchards in others. Since the suitability of a soil for any crop is also dependent on soil management, the set of man-

Sample Table C

TABLE [Insert No.].—*Predicted crop and pasture yields under different systems of soil management*[1]

SOILS SUITED TO PRODUCTION OF INTERTILLED CROPS

Map Symbol	Soil	Rotation[2]	Manure, fertilizer and lime[3]	Other practices	Yields				
					Corn	Soybeans	Oats	Hay	Rotation pasture
XL	Xyz loam...	60 percent intertilled, and 20 percent meadow.	None	None	*Bu.* 40	*Bu.* 18	*Bu.* 35	*Tons* 2: Red clover and timothy.	*Cow-days per acre*[4] 105: Red clover and timothy.
		30–40 percent intertilled and 30–40 percent meadow.	Lime and phosphate on new seedings; complete starter fertilizer on corn; 8 tons manure or 40-60 lb. N on second-year corn.	Tile drainage; thick planting of corn.	65	20	50	3: Alfalfa	140: Alfalfa-brome.

SOILS SUITED TO PERMANENT PASTURE

Map Symbol	Soil	Kind of pasture	Fertility practices[3]	Other management practices	Cow-days per acre[4]
VL	Vuw loam ..	Bluegrass-lespedeza	None	Deferred grazing in spring; mowing for weed control.	100
		Orchard grass-Ladino clover...	Lime plus 60 lb. P₂O₅ and 30 lb. K₂O when seeded; annual top dressing with 0-2-1 ratio as needed.	Rotation grazing; mowing for weed control.	150

[1] In all yield predictions the use of adapted crop varieties and methods for insect, disease, and weed control is assumed.
[2] Intertilled crops refer to corn and soybeans; meadow refers to grass-legume mixtures grown in rotations and used for hay or pasture.
[3] The amounts and kind of fertilizer used should be based on test of samples submitted to the county agent at Blankville. Additional information on the fertility problems of each soil is found in the section "Soils of Blank County".
[4] Cow-days per acre refers to the number of days one acre will carry one animal unit without supplemental feed. See the pasture calendar for seasonal distribution of this grazing.

agement practices under which the rating or grouping is devised should be specified.

Other groupings according to erosion hazard, need for drainage, suitability for irrigation, and the like are necessary in certain areas. In any specific area, the users may benefit from special interpretive soil groupings according to local potentialities and problems in the area. Basically, the interpretive grouping should be regarded as a device for facilitating the use of the survey for a particular purpose. Since the purposes of such groupings vary from area to area, and even from time to time for the same area, their use in a soil survey report is based upon local needs at the time the report is written.

Interpretative soil grouping may take such forms as:

Soils well suited to alfalfa	*Soils not well suited to alfalfa*
Dunkirk silt loam.	Carlisle muck.
Honeoye loam.	Colwood loam.
Honeoye silt loam.	Eel silt loam.
Ontario loam, undulating phase.	Fulton silt loam.
Ontario loam, rolling phase.	Toledo silt loam.
Palmyra gravelly loam.	Poygan silty clay loam.

It is not desirable that groupings of this sort should be made for all crops or all kinds of practices, because of the space that would be required, and also because the suitability of the soils to most crops will have been brought out in the table of predicted yields, and the need for particular practices will have been shown in the table giving suitable soil management practices. Special groupings of this kind can be used to advantage, however, for (a) potentially valuable crops in the survey area with which resident farmers have had little experience; (b) crops for which quality so offsets yield that yield does not afford an adequate measure of productivity, such as most types of tobacco, for example; or (c) practices already demonstrated to be valuable on similar soils in other counties or on experiment stations, but which are not yet widely adopted by resident farmers.

It may be explained that by using the soil map in connection with soil groups or lists of this kind, special interpretive maps showing groups of soils suitable for an individual crop or practice may be prepared on uncolored copies of the soil map. Besides, it may be pointed out that single-factor maps showing groups of soils with a particular characteristic in common, such as steep slopes or slowly permeable subsoils, may be prepared from the soil map. Many users of such single-factor maps need to be cautioned against using them for purposes in which the other soil characteristics influence the interpretation of the one emphasized.

In addition to groupings for agricultural purposes, special groupings of soils for engineering purposes, especially road and airstrip construction, can be given where essential information is available. Preparation of engineering groupings require consultation with competent highway engineers who know the soil engineering problems of the survey area.

See other discussions of soil grouping, pages 391 to 395 and pages 403 to 407.

Special practices.—In some areas it may be advisable to emphasize certain groups of practices by discussing them in a separate section of the report. Practices for runoff and erosion control, drainage, irrigation, salinity control, and weed control are examples. Like the interpretive groupings, however, such material is fundamentally a subdivision of the discussion on soil management. If a separate section is used for high lighting a group of practices, such as water control, the manner in which soil characteristics influence the performance of terraces, contouring, strip cropping, drainage systems, and irrigation and water distribution systems, can be explained, with alternative solutions of the particular water-control problems indicated. In most reports it is better to handle all the practices together rather than to separate part of them for a special section. Unless the writing is carefully coordinated, the reader may get an unbalanced and incorrect impression of the whole management problem for each of the mapping units.

In forested areas, a special section on land-clearing methods may be helpful.

The morphology and genesis of the soils.—How the soils of the area were formed and how they are related to the soils of other areas are explained in this section. Ordinarily this can be done conveniently by starting with the parent materials and physiography and explaining how the soils were formed from these materials under the various soil-forming processes with time. It is important to fit this discussion to the area, rather than "forcing" the soils of the area into a predetermined pattern taken from textbooks or other survey reports. Inasmuch as soil classification is a relatively young branch of science, the criteria that are used in classifying the soils, especially into higher categories, should be explained. Other soil scientists, for example, will want to know why a soil is designated as a Chernozem or a Podzol.

Wherever possible, the mechanism by which the significant soil characteristics were formed should be explained. For example, has a claypan been formed by movement of clay, by weathering in place, or as an inheritance from stratified parent material? If such points are reasonably well established, they should be included in the report. Any laboratory data relevant to the genesis and classification of the soils may be included in this section.

Information on soil morphology and genesis is most difficult to present in a way useful to laymen. Where the report is intended primarily for other users, and the material on morphology and genesis is necessarily technical it should be placed in an appendix.

For preparing the material on morphology and genesis of the soils, the chapter on this subject in the soil survey report of Tama County, Iowa, (published 1950) presents one helpful example. The following outline is also suggested as an aid in the organization of this material.

How the soils of Blank County were formed and how they are classified (major head):

    A. Introductory paragraph (without head) enumerating the forces in soil development. This will include statements concerning the influences on soil formation of parent material, climate, relief, biologic forces, and time.

    B. *Factors of soil formation as related to Blank County* (second-grade head):

        This subsection will tell how the environmental factors have operated to make the soils of Blank County.

    C. *Classification of soils* (second-grade head):

        Brief discussion of the classification of the soil series of the county into families, great soil groups, suborders, and orders, as appropriate, including mention of some of the catenary relations. Include a table showing the classification of the soil series into families, great soil groups, suborders, and orders. The table might also show for each series the environmental factors of parent material, relief, and vegetation.

    D. *Morphology of soils by great soil groups and families* (second-grade head):

        1. (Great soil group name) Description.

           a. (Soil family name) Description.

           (1) Series (a detailed description is needed for one soil series in each family and for each series correlated for the first time in this county).

               (a) Setting.

               (b) Block profile description. If the genetic horizons are known, designate them consecutively from the top by letters (A, B, C, and so on), adding the appropriate numerals for subhorizons; if not known, use numbers (1, 2, 3, and so on) for the layers.

               (c) Physical and chemical data and their interpretations.

           b. (Soil family name) Description.

           (1)

               (a)

               (b)

        2. (Great soil group name) Description.

           a. (Soil family name) Description.

           (1)

               (a)

               (b)

        Treat each great soil group, with its families and series, in the manner suggested above. In describing and comparing the great soil groups, families, and series, point out, as far as is known, the causal relations between the factors of soil formation and the morphology of the group.

Literature cited.—Proper credit by means of a literature citation should be given to each source of material definitely cited in the report.

At the end of the text under the major head Literature Cited arrange literature cited in the alphabetical order of authors' names. It is important that authors of soil survey reports carefully verify citations to literature, for many publications are not available to the editors at headquarters. Be sure citation is complete with name(s) of author(s), date, title of publication, publisher, number of pages, whether illustrated, and place of publication, in this order. When in doubt about abbreviations, spell out. Previously, mimeographed material and unpublished references were cited in footnotes, whereas they are now all included in Literature Cited. Indicate references to Literature Cited thus: (*12*). A footnote should be indicated thus: [6]; and footnotes are numbered consecutively from the beginning to the end of the report.

Other materials to be prepared for a soil survey report.— Wherever publication of a colored map is planned, color designations for the various soils should be submitted with the map and the manuscript. Ordinarily the number of different colors shown on the map should not exceed 15. This restriction is imposed by cost factors in color printing processes. Since practically all surveys include more than 15 separations, a grouping of soils for coloring is necessary. In the preparation of this grouping the main objective should be that of making the map easier to use.

There are two procedures that should be considered in selecting the type of color grouping. The first one is to attempt to have the greatest possible contrast in the color of adjacent soil areas. This type of grouping is of greatest value to the user interested only in a small segment of the map. It may be expected to work out well in an area where markedly different soils occur in an intricate pattern.

The second type of color grouping attempts to group similar soils under one color. This type of grouping is most useful to those interested in the entire map, since it brings out relationships between large areas at first glance. Soil characteristics that are important in determining management requirements provide the most logical basis for this type of grouping. In many reports the soils are grouped for the discussion of management practices. These groups can then become the basis of the color scheme, provided a number of important characteristics are common to all members of any group. Where dissimilar soils may happen to have the same management requirements, for example in a county where the Lithosols and Solonetz should be used only for limited grazing, they should still not be shown in the same color on the map. (See section on Soil Grouping on the Map.)

THE OUTLINE OF THE REPORT

Two suggested outlines for reports are offered to help writers include all the useful information they have about soils, to call their attention to gaps in their notes, and to help them organize the materials for the convenience of readers. It is not intended that the outlines will be followed precisely. In some areas, certain parts of the outlines require special emphasis.

The specific outline for the report should be developed by the party chief after the field work is well under way. In a real sense, the descriptive soil legend is the first tentative report. First drafts, at least, of tables, soil cards, and descriptions should be finished with the completion of field mapping. By beginning the work early, the observations and suggestions of other members of the party can be fully used. Plans can be laid for filling in gaps and for assembling data from other research groups, including especially the State agricultural experiment stations.

It is entirely possible that a good report could be prepared in which the description of the mapping unit and a discussion of its management problems and yield predictions under various defined systems of management would appear under a single major heading for each map unit. Headings for the general description of the area, plus headings for each of the mapping units, could constitute the outline of such a report. For an area with a large number of mapping units, such a report would probably be very long and repetitious. On the other extreme, if each soil characteristic and each soil management practice for all soils were discussed under a separate heading, the user would be placed to great inconvenience in locating the information about any particular mapping unit. The best outlines fall somewhere between these two extremes.

The following outlines are suggested as examples:

Outline No. I

Main topic headings:
    I. Table of contents.
    II. Introduction.
    III. How to know the soils. (How to use the map and report.)
    IV. Principles of good soil management.
    V. Use and management of important soil groups. (Yield predictions are included in this section.)
    VI. The soils of Blank County, their use and management. (Description and brief management discussion for each mapping unit.)
    VII. Special soil groups and interpretive maps.
    VIII. Geography and agriculture of Blank County.
    IX. How the soils of Blank County were formed and how they are classified.
    X. Literature cited.
Attachments:
    1. Color grouping for map legend.
    2. Table of characteristics for map supplement.

Outline No. II

    I. Table of contents.
    II. Introduction.
    III. The soil survey report and how to use it.
    IV. General character of the area.
        A. Physiography, relief, and drainage.
        B. Climate.
        C. Water supply.
        D. Vegetation.
        E. Agriculture.
    V. The soils of Blank County, description and classification.
        A. Soil series and their relations.
        B. Classification of soil series into higher categories and factors that have contributed to differences in soil morphology.
        C. Soil types, phases, and miscellaneous land types (arranged alphabetically).
            1. (Soil series name) followed by description and brief discussion of management for each mapping unit.
            2. (Soil series name), etc.
    VI. The soils of Blank County, interpretation and use.
        A. Use and management of soils (include basis for grouping).
            1. Soils of group 1. (This section includes a discussion of the management problems of the group, a table

of yield predictions, and the definition of the set of management practices for each predicted yield.
2. Soils of group 2, etc.
B. Special interpretive groupings (such as use-suitability groups).
C. Soil associations.
VII. Soil survey methods and definitions.
VIII. Literature cited.
Attachments:
1. Color grouping for map legend.
2. Table of characteristics for map supplement.

SUGGESTED ORDER OF PREPARING SECTIONS OF THE REPORT

1. Prepare a card for each soil mapping unit giving the information needed in the description of the unit, the management tables, yield predictions, and tables on characteristics and classification. The use of such cards greatly simplifies and speeds up the compilation and writing, besides helping to avoid omissions and contradictions.

2. Prepare the following tables:
   a. Table—.—Average yields to be expected over a period of years.
   b. Table—.—General uses and management practices recommended for the soils in the area.
   c. Table—.—Some important characteristics of the soils in the area.
   d. Table—.—Position, parent material, and profile characteristics of the soil series in the area.
   (Some of these may be split as suggested elsewhere, and others may be added.)

3. Write the soil unit descriptions. The material in items 1 and 2 above will serve as sources of information and, having been arranged before, will also provide the check needed to insure completeness.

4. Prepare other sections in the outline. It may be advantageous to write outline items II and III (see p. 429) last, since by that time the pattern will be clear and examples will be in mind.

5. Prepare suggested grouping of soils for the map color legend.

6. Select illustrations, prepare titles, and enter references in the text.

7. Check references to Literature Cited closely. Accuracy is important. It is better to give too much information than not enough. The editor can then trim it down.

ILLUSTRATIONS

The value of a soil survey report can be greatly increased with good illustrations, including illustrative maps, diagrams, charts, and photographs of soil profiles, typical soil areas, and farming methods.

Work on the soil survey report, including the illustrative material to go with it, should begin as soon as the field work is well under way. Draft sketch maps and diagrams can be made and photographs obtained as the field work goes forward. These need to be planned in relation to the form of final publication, including size, proportion, and amount of reduction.

Preliminary plans or drafts of maps and diagrams should be submitted to the central office before the detailed work of preparation, so that matters of scale, size, and form may be decided upon in advance. In nearly all instances, it is most economical for the author to submit accurate drafts in pencil for final drafting by draftsmen. Few authors have the skill or facilities for preparing drawings suitable for direct reproduction. Any time spent beyond that required for an accurate draft to be followed by a skilled draftsman is wasted if the sketch must be redrawn anyway.

Yet there are instances where the author can do some drawings better than a draftsman, say pen-and-ink sketches of soil profiles for example. Then too, cooperating agencies may have facilities for preparing maps and drawings that should be used. Even in such instances, the general plan should be discussed in advance with those preparing the material for the printer to insure a useful form. The minimum of printing should be included within the drawing or sketch itself, especially of soil names or other terms that are subject to change. The printing on drafts needs to be of the size that will be clear when reductions are made. Where possible, lettering should be left in pencil until just before submission of the manuscript to the printer.

Illustrations too large for a single page may, with careful planning, be split into two parts for facing pages. Still larger ones, requiring special folding and insertion, are used, but because of cost, only when they clearly make a large and substantial contribution to the use and interpretation of the soil map. Plans for these should be made and approved well in advance of any detailed work on them. The use of funds and facilities for the preparation of illustrations cannot be allowed to delay the preparation of the basic soil map itself.

Charts should be planned for showing data only when they are much superior to tables in the text.

Preparation of drawings and maps.—As already pointed out, usually the final drawing can be done better in the central office than in the field, but the author himself or a cooperating agent may have facilities for preparing illustrations in final form that could not otherwise be included. The following suggestions may be helpful:

Line drawings reproduce best if made on clean white illustration board or bond paper of high quality.

Line drawings should be in sharp black. It is often impracticable to reproduce drawings made in color.

Maps for the text should remain uncolored. If the coloring of areas will clarify details, this should be done on a duplicate copy where needed for the guidance of the draftsman. Areas on the printed sketch map are identified with symbols or with black-

and-white printed screens (such as Zip-A-Tone). These screens can be had from dealers in artist's supplies.

Printing on maps and charts for direct reproduction needs to be done in simple standard lettering with unusual care in spelling, capitalization, word-compounding, and abbreviations. The *Style Manual* of the Government Printing Office should be followed. For example, the symbol for "percent" is not used, nor can the word be split into two or hyphenated. It must be printed as a single word, *percent*. Units of measurement should be all abbreviated or all spelled.

A map or diagram needs to be free of excessive details. A single-line border is best. Coast lines, rivers, and other lines need to be smooth enough to be clear when reduced.

Symbols for soil types and phases on special maps in the text should be identical to those used on the basic soil map; so temporary symbols in pencil should be used until the basic map legend is prepared.

If hatchings are shown on a black-and-white map, the legend with the hatched blocks and spaces for words and symbols should be placed within the border if there is room. These blocks should be large enough for clear reading with reduction, and should not contain symbols or figures besides the hatching itself.

Most drafts of diagrams, charts, and maps for the text are made about 1½ to 2 times larger than the final reproduction, with lettering to correspond.

Charts and diagrams, and most maps, should be prepared without captions. These are set in type underneath.

Photographs.—Photographs need to be kept flat and clean—free of inkstains or fingerprints. Paper clips damage them. They may be seriously damaged by typing on the back, or by writing unless it is done lightly with a pen.

Glossy prints give better results than those with a dull finish. Often commercial prints are unsatisfactory, and yet good ones can be made from a good negative. It is well to forward two prints and the negative with the manuscript.

Only good clear pictures illustrating specific parts of the discussion are included, since others detract from the publication rather than enhance it.

The taking of suitable photographs is discussed in an earlier section of this *Manual* under Examination and Description of Soils in the Field.

Size of illustrations.—Sketches, maps, diagrams, and charts should be about 1½ to 2 times larger in scale than the final illustration. The reproduction of photographs is ordinarily better if the originals are large enough to permit some reduction; but very good ones can be enlarged somewhat if necessary.

The maximum size for illustrations on the printed page in soil survey reports is about 4⅜ by 7½ inches. This includes the space for the printed lines of the legend under the cut. Observing this space requirement when handling the original copy of larger illustrations makes it possible to lay them out in proper proportion for reduction to page size, with room for the type used in the legend.

Printed legends run the narrow way of the page for small cuts and also for full-page cuts with the base narrower than the height; and the long way of the page for full-page cuts with the base broader than the height. Therefore reduction to $4\frac{3}{8}$ by not more than 7 inches will usually leave space for a legend at the bottom of the page, although a long legend may make it necessary to make the cut a little less than 7 inches. Reduction to $7\frac{1}{2}$ by about 4 inches will ordinarily leave room for a legend running the long way of the page. Careful observation of these proportions saves much time and expense and makes possible effective use of the space.

Where necessary, an illustration can completely fill the page, with the legend at the foot of the facing page. This method increases the cost of printing somewhat. Since printed illustrations larger than page size need to be folded and tipped in, they are very costly. Wherever practicable, illustrations should be planned so they can be reduced to page size and still be clearly legible.

Most illustrations should come down to $4\frac{3}{8}$ by 7 inches, with the legend at the bottom of the page; 4 by $7\frac{1}{2}$ inches with the legend on the side; or $4\frac{3}{8}$ by $3\frac{1}{2}$ inches with the legend at the bottom for one-half page. Nearly all drawings may be planned with proper proportions to reduce to one of these three sizes. As guides to trimming photographs, rectangular openings of these sizes, and of proportionately larger ones, can be cut into sheets of opaque paper or cardboard. These can be laid over the print and adjusted to indicate the best part of it to use; and the margins of the print may then be trimmed away.

Labeling and assembling.—The material that goes to the printer is of two kinds: (1) The text manuscript with pages numbered 1, 2, 3, . . . and (2) the illustrations, numbered separately 1a, 2a, 3a, . . . The illustrations are numbered lightly on the back in the upper right-hand corner with a very soft pencil or crayon. The numbers are in the same order as the illustrations are mentioned in the text. The illustrations are placed in a separate large envelope, labeled with the name of the soil survey area on the outside, except for very large ones that are wrapped separately. These large ones should also be noted on the envelope.

Illustrations need to be protected and kept flat, except for large ones on paper or tracing cloth that may be rolled into mailing tubes. None should be folded.

Italic capital letters $(A, B, C, . . .)$ are used to designate separate objects in a single numbered illustration; and small italic letters $(a, b, c, . . .)$, abbreviations, or symbols are used to designate subparts of an object.

All lettering on illustrations in one publication should be as nearly the same type and size as possible *after* reduction. Under most conditions, authors will submit illustrations with all lettering in pencil.

Legend for illustrations.—A descriptive legend is needed for each illustration, including each photograph, clearly describing the pertinent features. The legend should be typed at the place in the text containing the reference to the illustration. A pasted carbon copy can be used.

Although a legend needs to be written compactly, it should be sufficiently self explanatory to carry the main point alone without reference back to the text.

Appropriate credit lines to individuals and organizations should be added to the legends for borrowed pictures and illustrations.

Legends on one line need to be centered. If there are two lines, make the first line page width and center the second; if there are more than two lines, indent the second and all subsequent lines at the left. This last is called "hanging indention." All three forms can be seen in almost any well-illustrated soil survey report.

Each letter for a subpart of an illustration should be explained in the legend, not simply in the text. Each illustration in a soil survey report needs to be referred to in at least one place in the text. Except for incidental reference, the order of these references in the text will determine the order of numbering the illustrations.

A list of all the legends, with the usual carbons, should accompany each manuscript in the envelope with the illustrations.

RECONNAISSANCE SOIL MAPPING

So far this *Manual* has dealt chiefly with the classification and mapping of soils in detailed basic soil surveys. The basic principles of soil description, classification, and identification are similar regardless of the scale of mapping. In broad reconnaissance mapping, the classificational units need to be grouped into soil associations. Larger inclusions of other soils are permitted within each mapping unit than in detailed surveys.

In comparatively well-known areas, the classification units that compose the associations are defined as types and phases as they are in detailed mapping. The number and kind of phases recognized depend upon the purpose for which the map is made. In new and relatively unexplored areas, the associations are defined in terms of categories higher in the classification than soil types. In many areas, these units are great soil groups or families, subdivided according to parent material, and with phases for relief and sometimes for stoniness, effects of erosion, and other features.

The mapping methods in reconnaissance surveys are somewhat different from those used in detailed surveys. In this section the major points of difference are discussed.

The kinds of soil maps have already been defined in the section on Character of Soil Maps and Reports. In this *Manual* we are concerned primarily with original field surveys rather than with generalized maps. A generalized soil map is one produced from original surveys through orderly abstraction of classificational and mapping units. Both soil boundaries and soil identification are developed in reconnaissance soil surveys by original research in the field, although parts of published reconnaissance soil maps may be generalized from detailed maps.

Any original soil survey in which only a part of the soil boundaries are actually seen by the field scientist is a reconnaissance survey, in contrast to a detailed survey in which boundaries are sketched from observations of their entire occurrence on the ground. Thus, reconnaissance surveys may be only a little less detailed than the standard detailed soil survey. These are often called semidetailed soil surveys or "detailed reconnaissance." The term "detailed reconnaissance" is objectionable, however, since it is apt to be confused with detailed-reconnaissance (with the hyphen) used for soil maps that are partly detailed and partly reconnaissance.

Beyond reconnaissance soil surveys, and even less detailed, are exploratory soil surveys, in which the boundaries are obtained mainly through compilation from existing sources as in a schematic soil map but in which the soil associations are identified mainly through original field research. The methods used in exploratory soil mapping vary so widely with objectives and conditions that they are not treated specifically in this *Manual*. Many of the same principles followed in reconnaissance soil mapping apply to exploratory soil surveys.

OBJECTIVES

Perhaps reconnaissance soil surveys may be grouped more usefully by objectives than by the physical characteristics of the maps themselves, as follows:

1. Surveys of the principal soils and soil associations in developed areas suited only to extensive uses, especially grazing and forestry: Such soil surveys are critically needed for large regions of the western part of the United States as a basis for grazing and forest management, and for estimating water intake and water yield under different conditions.

2. Surveys in developed areas to locate soils suitable for more intensive use: The soil associations of such reconnaissance surveys can be defined in terms of the same kinds of taxonomic units as those recognized in detailed soil mapping. A characteristic purpose is to locate, within regions now used for extensive cropping and grazing, areas promising for effective reclamation through irrigation or drainage. After the location of such areas, detailed soil surveys are made of them to guide the planning of the project and soil management practices. It is wasteful to make the highly detailed soil surveys needed for planning irrigation or drainage structures unless there is reasonable prospect that they will be used for that purpose. Detailed soil surveys with less categorical detail will serve fully the needs of "dry-land" farming and grazing.

3. Surveys in partially developed areas of scattered settlement or scattered villages, partly to locate new soil for expansion and development with small colonies or infiltration settlement, and partly as a basis for guiding agricultural advisory programs among existing farmers: Such surveys are usually partly generalized from sample detailed surveys in which the classification is developed and the associations defined and interpreted.[1]

4. Surveys in new or undeveloped areas to locate soils suitable for agricultural development, especially for crops, but also for grazing and forestry: The soil associations in reconnaissance and exploratory surveys of little known areas cannot be defined in terms of the narrowly defined units used in detailed soil surveys, at least not at first. Associations can be defined in terms of soil families or other subdivisions of great soil groups that differ in parent material, with phases for relief and stoniness, and perhaps for other features.

The making of such reconnaissance (or exploratory) surveys should be preceded by compiling the best possible schematic map from the available evidence on soil, relief, geology, vegeta-

---

[1] Several excellent soil surveys of this type have been made in Canada. See, for example: MITCHELL J., MOSS, H. C., and CLAYTON, J. S. SOIL SURVEY OF SOUTHERN SASKATCHEWAN (FROM TOWNSHIP 1 TO 48 INCLUSIVE). Soil Survey Report No. 12, 259 pp., illus. (maps in box). Univ. of Saskatchewan. Saskatoon. 1944.

tion, and climate. Representative sample areas are then chosen for detailed soil survey within each broad association on the schematic map. From these, taxonomic units at the family, series, or possibly type level, with appropriate phases, may be established. Then using reconnaissance methods, the boundaries of the schematic map may be redrawn from original field research.

SCALES AND BASE MATERIAL

The scales of published reconnaissance soil surveys vary widely from around 62,500 to about 1:500,000. Around 2 inches to 1 mile (1:31,680) is a common field scale. Field scales of 1:1,000,000 can be used for very broad exploratory surveys but that scale is too small for sketching boundaries from field observations. The field scale depends upon the objectives of the survey, the roads available for entrance, and the base maps available for use. In sectionized areas, with established land lines around each square mile, one may use a grid or a combined grid and road map. Areas without roads can be cruised on foot with the compass, using such a map and grid.

Perhaps the best base for reconnaissance survey is the aerial mosaic at about 2 inches to the mile (1:31,680). Controlled mosaics are usually out of the question, since they are rarely made for the kinds of areas needing a reconnaissance soil map, and they are too expensive for the usual budget allowed for reconnaissance soil surveys. Photo indexes at the same scale are nearly as good. Most photo indexes have a scale of 1 inch to the mile (1:63,360), which is too small for easy reading of the patterns. But these may be enlarged for field use. Photographs at larger scales, say up to 1:20,000, give sheets of an awkward size to use or give too many to use in most reconnaissance surveys.

Where aerial photographs, vertical or oblique, are available as single pictures, they can be used to advantage as supplemental aids in sketching, even though the field mapping is done on a planimetric base of smaller scale. With the boundaries located along the lines of traverse, such pictures are a great help in sketching the course of the boundaries between located points, *provided that the scientist has an opportunity to study the soil in sample locations of each pattern that shows up in the photographs.* Without such sample studies on the ground, pictures in a new kind of country can be very misleading indeed, even to the experienced scientist.

Besides a thorough search for all available base maps and aerial photographs, and a determination of their accuracy and limitations, the scientist needs to locate any geological maps, cover maps, and the like that may be useful in sketching boundaries and in planning his work. Organization of these materials into a tentative schematic soil map in advance of field work can be most helpful.

Assuming good training in soil science, ability to visualize soil and landscape patterns, ability to recognize and interpret land forms and plant associations, and ability to travel under rough conditions without serious discomfort, perhaps the most important characteristic of a good soil mapper in reconnaissance and exploratory surveys is resourcefulness—the ability to find and use all sorts of maps and evidence that bear on his problem. Excellent soil scientists for some kinds of research, including detailed soil surveys, fail utterly in reconnaissance soil mapping. They may be unable to visualize large and complex patterns or become mentally harassed by indecision in the face of vague and apparently conflicting evidence.

SOIL CLASSIFICATION

One can scarcely be specific about soil classification for reconnaissance soil surveys in general, except to say that the principal mapping units should be defined soil associations. On this point the old reconnaissance surveys in the United States cannot be used as models. Many of these maps were valuable indeed, and still are with proper interpretation.[2] The maps did show associations, of course, but unconsciously on the part of the classifiers. For the most part each mapping unit was named according to the principal soil type in it, which was allowed to have many inclusions and many undefined phases. More appropriate boundary lines can be drawn by defining the mapping units as soil associations in the first place. Then by detailed mapping of samples in each one, the proportions of the various units can be set down with reasonable accuracy. The user of the map can then be told what units to expect in an area shown on a map, how to recognize them one from another on the ground, and their capabilities for various uses and their management requirements. In fact, the text report of reconnaissance surveys in well-developed areas should contain yield estimates and other predictions in the same form as in the detailed soil surveys for the *taxonomic units*. Naturally, for soils in areas for which only reconnaissance surveys are made, data from experimental plots and from farm or ranch experience are less abundant than for most soils in areas of detailed soil surveys. Therefore, the predictions made are less precise and depend mainly upon judgment based on known principles of relationship between soil characteristics and soil management practices and on experience with similar soils elsewhere.

In places the catenary soil association is a convenient mapping unit. The boundaries among such associations are drawn mainly on the basis of differences in land form and parent material, and the constituent units vary in characteristics related to differences in relief and drainage. But rarely can catenary associations be used conveniently throughout the whole survey area without introducing excessive detail—the very thing that must be avoided in a reconnaissance soil survey. That is, in many regions the complexity of pattern is primarily one of contrasting

---

[2] Except for the naming of several mapping units as soil series and types, rather than as soil associations, the following is a good example of a reconnaissance soil survey: CARTER, W. T., and others. SOIL SURVEY (RECONNAISSANCE) OF THE TRANS-PECOS AREA, TEXAS. U. S. Dept. Agr. Soil Survey. Series 1928. No. 35, 66 pp., illus. (maps). 1928.

parent materials—say, steep hills and alluvial valleys, contrasting interbedded sediments, or folded interbedded hills. The classifier needs to consider these complexities and not hold strictly to catenary associations.

Interpretive groups should not be used as mapping units in reconnaissance soil mapping for reasons already emphasized. Any interpretive grouping depends upon the present state of the agricultural arts and of economic conditions. As a result, any map of such groups alone soon becomes outdated and cannot be reinterpreted. By using mapping units defined on the basis of fundamental taxonomic units, many interpretations can be made for different purposes and under different conditions. Some time ago, for example, a reconnaissance soil survey was made in terms of productivity of the soils for wheat. Shortly after its completion, new varieties were introduced and new soil management practices were developed. The maps became essentially useless as a basis for prediction very soon after publication.

Nor can soils be grouped according to single factors such as slope, texture, permeability, drainage, and so on, or by some arbitrary combination of them, partly for the same reason—the combinations chosen are an interpretation based on past use experience—and partly because the significance of any one factor depends upon the others. Each individual taxonomic unit must be considered as a whole; that is why we have a soil classification in the first place. By using the names and definitions in the standard system of soil classification, an enormous number of data, collected and synthesized by these units and their close relatives, can be used for interpretation both when the survey is made and later.

In well-known areas, such as most parts of the United States, the legends for reconnaissance soil surveys can be made up of perhaps some individual soil types and phases as mapping units and of soil associations defined in terms of soil types and phases. Even here, soil families and phases of soil families, when more adequately defined, will appear as components of the soil associations and as mapping units.

In little-known areas, that is, little known in terms of soil classification, which includes large parts of the world outside of the temperate regions, it will be impossible to use taxonomic units as narrowly defined as the soil series, types, and phases of the standard system used in the United States, at least at first. The legends are made up of associations consisting of subdivisions of the great soil groups made according to parent material, with phases according to relief and stoniness and perhaps other characteristics. For many areas, the uncertainty of great soil group names and definitions, and of their adequacy, raises a serious problem of nomenclature. Thus local names are essential. The classifier should develop the definitions as nearly as he can at some one specific categorical level—great soil group, family, or series—so they may be correlated in an orderly way with one another and in a general system of soil classification.

MAPPING METHODS

The sharp distinction between detailed and reconnaissance soil surveys is in the matter of sketching boundaries. In detailed soil surveys boundaries are seen throughout their course, whereas in reconnaissance soil surveys they are sketched from estimation and secondary evidence between points of observation. Under the best conditions, roads are traversed with a car and the soils are examined to characterize specific *local* types or conditions, as is done in a detailed soil survey. That is, the classifier does not examine the profiles of an association, complex, family, or even series; rather he examines the profiles of soil types within such broader taxonomic groups or geographic associations. The classifier, then, has more definitions to remember as he interprets the results of his examinations in terms of mapping units than in a detailed soil survey. He must not be misled into the exaggeration of variants and miscellaneous land types as components of his mapping units simply because they may be more obvious as compared to the commonplace.

The examinations of soil profiles and of soil slope and other external soil features are used to recognize the components of the association. Then the mapper must decide how these fit into the defined pattern of the association around which he draws his boundary lines. Aerial pictures are useful. He observes the major changes in plants, or plant associations, the courses of streams, ridges, and escarpments, that tell him how the "country runs," and the pattern of relief and drainage, related, of course, to geological strata and land form.

In districts with few roads, it is best to traverse the roads first, with full equipment for soil examinations and mapping materials. Areas between are filled in by foot traverses, planned according to previous estimates of the conditions to be dealt with. Long trips may be made partly by boat and pack animal, with hikes from major control stations.

Along the traverses, abundant notes can be taken of value in defining the soil associations. Some of these notes can be put directly on the map and left in pencil. The degree of cartographic detail on the map should be uniform, except as clearly indicated on the map itself or in an accompanying sketch showing relative reliability.

In areas covered by reconnaissance soil maps, accessibility to the country may vary widely. Some parts may be covered in considerable detail and others only at wide intervals. These differences may be indicated on a diagram, printed beneath the legend on the published map. Certain areas may appropriately be left blank as "unexplored." The usefulness of the reconnaissance soil map having two widely different degrees of detail may be increased by using solid colors for areas mapped in the "standard detail" and by using proportional bars of color, according to the estimated proportion of each association, in large areas less completely examined.

INTERPRETATIONS

In the reconnaissance soil survey two levels or kinds of interpretations are required (1) of the soil associations as units and (2) of the individual taxonomic units that are components of the associations. For both, detailed soil maps of sample areas are exceedingly helpful.

Where possible, the same sets of predictions about yields and management practices should be given for each of the detailed taxonomic units and phases as are made in a detailed soil survey. Many uses of the reconnaissance map are concerned with small areas—fields and farms too small to show individually on the map. The reader can be given clues, especially by the use of soil keys within each association, that permit him to distinguish the local soil types within the association as he sees them on the ground. Then he can select the appropriate recommendations and interpretations for the local soil type and phases from the accompanying tables in the text.

For many uses of the reconnaissance soil survey, it is necessary to suggest potentialities of broad areas for settlement or reclamation. Problems and recommendations for flood reduction, forest potentialities, and the like, need to be explained in terms of the results disclosed by the survey. Perhaps even more than in a detailed soil survey, the soil scientist interpreting reconnaissance soil maps and classifications needs to integrate his data and judgments with those of other specialists according to the nature of the problem which the survey is to help solve.

DEVELOPMENT OF A SOIL SURVEY PROGRAM
FOR UNDEVELOPED AREAS

The results of soil classification in many undeveloped areas are desperately needed as soon as possible—long before there is time for the necessary research to establish all the taxonomic units that will be needed eventually. In such areas the following procedure, or a practical variation of it according to local conditions and problems, can be followed.

1. A schematic soil association map is compiled for the area on the basis of available data on soils, geology, relief, vegetation, and climate. The scale of such a map varies from 1:100,000 to 1:500,000, accommodated to local sources of information and soil conditions.

2. One or more representative sample areas are selected in each important soil association for detailed classification and mapping as already explained in this *Manual* for a detailed basic soil survey.[3] It is better to locate compact representative areas than to use long narrow strips chosen at random. These samples must be large enough to be representative and to disclose the pattern of the unit in the association.

As a part of the soil survey procedure, an adequate laboratory is needed for basic physical and chemical determinations on

---

[3] Soil associations made up wholly of Lithosols or other soils unsuited for use may not require detailed samples for adequate definitions.

samples of the soil horizons and for comparing any arable soils now used with virgin soils and with one another. Where possible, research plots to test crop adaptability, fertilizer needs, tillage practices, and the like, should be established in the principal contrasting taxonomic soil units.

3. For each sample area, a key to the soils *within the association* is developed for use in the assembly of all units in a system of classification for the whole area and to train agricultural advisers in local soil identification by name.

4. The best possible set of predictions and interpretations for each local soil unit is developed in terms of suitability for crops, pasture, and forestry, adapted species and varieties of crops, estimated yields, management requirements, and effects of sets of soil management practices on sustained productivity.

5. Field conferences for local agricultural advisers and other agricultural technicians can be held in each area where these people may be shown how to use the soil key, how to recognize the local soil types and phases, and how to use the tables of predictions or recommendations.

6. The map for the region is revised by reconnaissance survey methods, and an improved legend of soil associations, based upon the research in the sample area, is supplied.

7. The completed reconnaissance soil map is published with its report, which contains an assembly of the sample maps and a key to the soils of the whole region, together with predictions and interpretations for application, by local soil types and phases, to local fields and farms as well as for soil associations as a whole.

Following such a reconnaissance soil survey, detailed soil surveys can be made in the parts of the region having the greatest potentialities, considering the complementary relationships among all the resources available—soils, forests, water, and minerals—and the timing of the establishment of other services—hospitals, transport, trading centers, and the like.

GENERAL BIBLIOGRAPHY

This bibliography suggests books and papers for the basic reference shelf in a permanent soil survey office. To these should be added the books and bulletins dealing with the soils of the region being studied, as well as with the flora, climate, geology, geography, and agriculture. Many of the references noted in the footnotes to discussions of specific topics in this *Manual* may also be helpful. Then, too, the reference shelf should have the current scientific journals dealing with soil science, including Soils and Fertilizers, published by the Commonwealth Bureau of Soil Science, Harpenden, England, which includes abstracts of important books, bulletins, and papers that need to be added to the library. Each soil survey office should make a special effort to establish publication exchanges with other offices in the world having similar soils.

BEAMAN, W. M.
    1928. TOPOGRAPHIC MAPPING. U. S. Geol. Survey Bul. 788: 161–378, illus.
BEAR, FIRMAN E., ed.
    1945. METHODS IN CHEMICAL ANALYSES OF SOILS. Soil Sci. 59 (1): 109.

    1949. SOIL CLASSIFICATION. Soil Sci. 67: 77–191.
BLACK, J. D., CLAWSON, M., SAYRE, C. R., and WILCOX, W. W.
    1947. FARM MANAGEMENT. 1073 pp., illus. New York.
CLARKE, F. W.
    1924. THE DATA OF GEOCHEMISTRY. Ed. 5, U. S. Geol. Survey Bul. 770, 841 pp.
COHEN, M. R., and NAGEL, E.
    1939. AN INTRODUCTION TO LOGIC AND SCIENTIFIC METHOD. 467 pp. New York.
COTTON, C. A.
    1942. CLIMATIC ACCIDENTS IN LANDSCAPE-MAKING. 354 pp., illus. London, and Christchurch, New Zealand.

    1948. LANDSCAPE AS DEVELOPED BY THE PROCESSES OF NORMAL EROSION. Ed. 2, 509 pp., illus. Christchurch and New York.
FENNEMAN, N. M.
    1931. PHYSIOGRAPHY OF WESTERN UNITED STATES. 534 pp., illus. New York.

    1938. PHYSIOGRAPHY OF EASTERN UNITED STATES. 714 pp., illus. New York.
FLINT, R. F.
    1947. GLACIAL GEOLOGY AND THE PLEISTOCENE EPOCH. 589 pp., illus. New York.
GLINKA, K. D.
    1927. THE GREAT SOIL GROUPS OF THE WORLD AND THEIR DEVELOPMENT. [Transl. by C. F. Marbut.] 235 pp. Ann Arbor, Mich.
HITCHCOCK, A. S.
    1951. MANUAL OF THE GRASSES OF THE UNITED STATES. U. S. Dept. Agr. Misc. Pub. 200, Ed. 2. 1051 pp., illus. [Rev. by Agnes Chase.]

IGNATIEFF, V., ed.
    1949. EFFICIENT USE OF FERTILIZERS. Food and Agr. Organ of U. N.
        Agr. Studies No. 9, 182 pp., illus. Washington.
INTERNATIONAL CONGRESS OF SOIL SCIENCE.
    1928. PROCEEDINGS AND PAPERS. 4 v., 1st Internatl. Cong. Wash-
        ington.

——— 1933. PROCEEDINGS AND PAPERS. 6 v., 2d Internatl. Cong. Moscow.

——— 1935. PROCEEDINGS. 3 v., 3d Internatl. Cong. London.

——— 1950. PROCEEDINGS. 3 v., 4th Internatl. Cong. Amsterdam.
JENNY, H.
    1941. FACTORS OF SOIL FORMATION. 281 pp., illus. New York.
KEMP, J. F.
    1923. A HANDBOOK OF ROCKS FOR USE WITHOUT THE MICROSCOPE.
        Ed. 5, 282 pp., illus. New York.
KILMER, V. J., and ALEXANDER, L. T.
    1949. METHODS OF MAKING MECHANICAL ANALYSES OF SOILS. Soil
        Sci. 68: 15–24.
LOBECK, A. K.
    1939. GEOMORPHOLOGY. 731 pp., illus. New York.
LONGWELL, C. R., KNOPF, A., FLINT, R. F., SCHUCHERT, C., and DUNBAR, C. O.
    1941. OUTLINES OF GEOLOGY. Ed. 2, 381 + 291 pp., illus. New York.
LUTZ, H. F., and CHANDLER, R. F., JR.
    1946. FOREST SOILS. 514 pp., illus. New York.
MARBUT, C. F.
    1935. SOILS OF THE UNITED STATES. In U. S. Dept. Agr. Atlas of
        American Agriculture, pt. 3, Advance Sheets No. 8, 98 pp.,
        illus.
MICHIGAN STATE HIGHWAY DEPARTMENT.
    1946. FIELD MANUAL OF SOIL ENGINEERING. Rev. ed. 304 pp., illus.
        Lansing.
MILLER, E. C.
    1938. PLANT PHYSIOLOGY, WITH REFERENCE TO THE GREEN PLANT.
        Ed. 2, 1201 pp., illus. New York and London.
NEUSTRUEV, S. S.
    1927. GENESIS OF SOILS. Russ. Pedol. Invest. 3, Acad. Sci., 98 pp.
        Leningrad.
OLMSTEAD, F. R., HICKS, L. D., and BODMAN, G. B.
    1949. ENGINEERING USE OF AGRICULTURAL SOIL MAPS. Highway Res.
        Bd. Bul. 22, 128 pp., illus.
PEECH, M., and others.
    1947. METHODS OF SOIL ANALYSIS FOR SOIL FERTILITY INVESTIGATIONS.
        U. S. Dept. Agr. Cir. 757, 25 pp.
ROBINSON, G. W.
    1950. SOILS, THEIR ORIGIN, CONSTITUTION, AND CLASSIFICATION; AN
        INTRODUCTION TO PEDOLOGY. Ed. 3, 573 pp., illus. London.
RUSSELL, SIR E. J.
    1950. SOIL CONDITIONS AND PLANT GROWTH. Ed. 8, 635 pp., illus.
        London and New York. [Rev. by E. W. Russell.]
SMITH, GUY D.
    1942. ILLINOIS LOESS—VARIATIONS IN ITS PROPERTIES AND DISTRIBU-
        TION: A PEDOLOGIC INTERPRETATION. Ill. Agr. Expt. Sta.
        Bul. 490: 137–184, illus.
SMITH, H. T. U.
    1943. AERIAL PHOTOGRAPHS AND THEIR APPLICATIONS. 372 pp., illus.
        New York.
SNEDECOR, G. W.
    1946. STATISTICAL METHODS APPLIED TO EXPERIMENTS IN AGRICULTURE
        AND BIOLOGY. 485 pp., illus. Ames, Iowa.
SOIL SCIENCE SOCIETY OF AMERICA.
    1942. LIFE AND WORK OF C. F. MARBUT. 271 pp., illus. Columbia, Mo.

UNITED STATES DEPARTMENT OF AGRICULTURE.
    1938. SOILS AND MEN. U. S. Dept. Agr. Yearbook. 1232 pp., illus.

    1941. CLIMATE AND MAN. U. S. Dept. Agr. Yearbook, 1248 pp., illus.

    1948. GRASS. U. S. Dept. Agr. Yearbook, 892 pp., illus.
UNITED STATES REGIONAL SALINITY LABORATORY.
    1947. DIAGNOSIS AND IMPROVEMENT OF SALINE AND ALKALI SOILS.
        Ed. by L. A. Richards. 157 pp., illus. [Processed.]
VON ENGELN, O. D.
    1942. GEOMORPHOLOGY. 655 pp., illus. New York.
WALLACE, T.
    1951. THE DIAGNOSIS OF MINERAL DEFICIENCIES IN PLANTS BY VISUAL
        SYMPTOMS. Ed. 2, 107 pp. + 312 pls. London.

SPECIAL BIBLIOGRAPHY OF SOIL SURVEYS

In this section is presented a bibliography of soil surveys developed in the National Cooperative Soil Survey program and published by the United States Department of Agriculture. Selections have been made to illustrate surveys, published or to be published very soon, in contrasting soil regions and various features of maps or reports. The selections are not necessarily the "best" reports and maps. In some regions, several very good reports might have been selected; in others, the one chosen may still have some serious deficiencies by present-day standards.

Progress in soil classification, mapping, and interpretation has been so rapid in recent years, since the earlier edition of this *Manual*, that few surveys made before 1940 would be made in exactly the same way today. Thus, the student will find inconsistencies between the methods used in many of the recently published surveys, including the ones listed, and those outlined in the *Manual*. This should be expected in an actively growing field of research. Many methods had to be tried out, tested in actual surveys, before a judicious selection could be made.

Some 100 or more additional soil surveys of excellent quality are under way in the field, are being prepared for publication, or are in the process of being printed. This list is offered as a general guide to reading that may be helpful to both professors and students of soil survey. Besides these surveys, many good examples can be had from other countries, as well as some special soil surveys published by State agricultural experiment stations in the United States.

Soil Survey of the Casa Grande Area, Arizona. Poulson, E. N., Wildermuth, Robert, and Harper, W. G. U. S. Dept. Agr. Soil Survey Ser. 1936, No. 7, 94 pp., illus. 1941.

The Casa Grande Area lies in the Red Desert soil region of south-central Arizona. The principal irrigated crops are cotton and alfalfa.

The map is published on a scale 1:62,500. The 129 mapping units are placed in 17 color groups based on the physical characteristics of the soil, and the legend is arranged according to the relative suitability of the soils for agriculture under irrigation. Special red boundaries and symbols on the map show the relative concentration of soluble salts and alkali.

For description in the report, the soils are grouped according to the quantity of accumulated lime and the physical character of their subsoils, but in the section on Land Uses and Management recommendations of soil management are given for each soil unit and for the groups shown on the map.

Although recent reports, like the one for Tama County, Iowa, for example, are perhaps better; at the time of its preparation this one marked a definite forward step in specifying use and management practices for individual soils.

Soil Survey of Lee County, Alabama. Wonser, C. H., Striker, M. M., Brackeen, L. G., McIntyre, C. L., and Sherard, Hoyt. U. S. Dept. Agr. Soil Survey Ser. 1938, No. 23, 80 pp., illus. 1950.

This map and report deal with Red-Yellow Podzolic soils that occur in both the Piedmont and Coastal Plain physiographic provinces in the southeastern part of the United States. The map is published on a scale of 1:48,000, and the 66 soil-mapping units are placed in 22 color groups on the basis of their principal physical characteristics, such as texture, consistence, slope, and drainage. A table giving the important physical characteristics of each mapping unit is carried as a supplement to the map.

The soil descriptions in the report are presented briefly in block form, which helps to set them apart. Estimated yields and productivity ratings under current practices and under improved practices of management are given for each mapping unit. The soils are placed in eight groups, according to management requirements and responses. The photographs illustrate the shift from cotton to hay and pasture crops that is occurring in parts of the Southeast.

Although not outstanding in the treatment of any particular item, this report carries information on a considerable number of soil types common to the Piedmont and Coastal Plain.

Soil Survey of the Coalinga Area, California. Harradine, F. F., and party. U. S. Dept. Agr. Soil Survey Ser. 1944. [In press.]

The Coalinga Area lies on the western side of the San Joaquin Valley. Barley, flax, and cotton are the principal irrigated crops. The zonal soils are similar to Brown and Reddish Brown soils, but their precise identification as great soil groups is still uncertain. The map is being published at a scale of 1:63,360.

The report is good but not unusual. The descriptions of the soil units are good, and there are special sections on Alkali, Water Supply and Irrigation, and Erosion. The 86 soil-mapping units are rated according to their general productivity; tables show the relative suitability of the soils for intensive agriculture and specific crops; and the ranges in yields of the individual crops are given by the suitability classes. Sketches show the geographic distribution of the soil series according to the physiographic divisions across the valley.

Soil Survey of the Akron Area, Colorado. Knobel, E. W., and party. U. S. Dept. Agr. Soil Survey Ser. 1938, No. 14, 80 pp., illus. 1947.

The Akron Area is in a region of Brown soils and includes parts of the High Plains and Colorado Piedmont sections. The soils are used with and without irrigation.

The map is published on a scale of 1:63,360. The 61 mapping units are placed in 23 color groups, based on their physical characteristics and their physiographic position. The individual soil descriptions are good.

The discussion of cropping practices for the individual crops, based partly on research work at the Dry Land Field Station at Akron, is a strong feature of this report. Tables of estimated yields and productivity indexes are included for two levels of rainfall.

Soil Survey of the Grand Junction Area, Colorado. Knobel, E. W., Dansdill, R. K., and Richardson, M. L. U. S. Dept. Agr. Soil Survey Ser. 1940. [In press.]

The Grand Junction Area in western Colorado is an important irrigated fruit-producing area. The soils belong mainly in the Gray Desert and Alluvial great soil groups. The map is being published at 1:48,000.

This report has good discussions of the crops of the area and the crop and soil management practices. The descriptions of the individual soil series and 74 mapping units are also well done. A table of estimated yields includes only one level of management. In a special chapter, investigations on the saline soils of the area, in which the United States Regional Salinity Laboratory and the Colorado State Agricultural Experiment Station actively cooperated, are reported.

Soil Survey of the Idaho Falls Area, Idaho. Mogen, C. A., Poulson, E. N., Poulson, A. E., Van Slyke, E. J., and Colwell, W. E. U. S. Dept. Agr. Soil Survey Ser. 1939, No. 8, 69 pp., illus. 1950.

The Idaho Falls Area lies in southeastern Idaho and forms a part of the irrigated Snake River plain. The soils belong in the Brown and Sierozem great soil groups.

The map is published on a scale of 1:31,680. The 50 soil-mapping units are shown in 22 color groupings, based on physical soil characteristics and physiographic position.

This survey is representative of those dealing with irrigated soils in the Brown and Sierozem soil region. The report is not outstanding but contains the usual photographs, figures, soil descriptions, table of predicted yields at two levels of management, and discussions of soil management. The section on morphology and genesis of the soils is good.

Soil Survey of St. Joseph County, Indiana. Ulrich, H. P., and party. U. S. Dept. Agr. Soil Survey Ser. 1938, No. 27, illus. 1950.

St. Joseph County, in northern Indiana, is an area of Gray-Brown Podzolic, Prairie, and Wiesenboden (Humic-Gley) soils used in diversified agriculture.

The map is published on a scale of 1:31,680. The 112 soil-mapping units are shown in color as groups based on slope, drainage, parent materials, and physiographic position.

The generally good all-around report includes adequate descriptions of the soil units, with profile descriptions in the block form, good photographs, a good discussion of crops, a key to the soil series, a table of predicted yields at two levels of management, a discussion of soil management groups, and a good section on soil morphology and genesis. Besides, interpretive maps are included that show lime requirements and drainage, and single-factor maps of soil slope and of soil colors. This last map suggests contents of organic matter and nitrogen.

Soil Survey of Tama County, Iowa. Aandahl, A. R., and party. U. S. Dept. Agr. Soil Survey Ser. 1938, No. 22, 109 pp., illus. 1950.

Tama County, of east-central Iowa, lies in the region of Prairie soils. Some Gray-Brown Podzolic soils also exist there. Farms produce much corn and livestock.

The map is published on a scale of 1:63,360. On it, 50 kinds of soil are placed in 13 color groupings on the basis of their management requirements.

The report has excellent photographs and drawings, including diagrams of individual texture profiles. The relationships among soil series are shown in their relative position in a table that itemizes detailed soil management practices and gives predicted yields at three levels of management. An additional table outlines the management practices for the management groups shown in color on the map. Practices that control erosion and maintain soil fertility are emphasized. A glossary is added. This report is probably one of the best.

Soil Survey of Taylor County, Iowa. Leighty, Ralph G., and party.[1] U. S. Dept. Agr. Soil Survey Ser. 1947. [in press.]

Taylor County, of southwestern Iowa, is in the Prairie soil region. Corn and livestock are produced. The map is being published on a scale of 1:31,680.

A special effort has been made to point this report directly toward a farmer audience. Emphasis has been placed on simple soil descriptions and the presentation of specific combinations of management practices, for which yield predictions are given at two levels of management. Photographs and other illustrations, including block diagrams to show the relationships among soil series and the features of the landscape, are used to replace, in part, text descriptions. Although an excellent discussion of soil morphology and genesis is included, several sections appearing in other reports dealing with general agriculture are missing.

Soil Survey of Iron County, Michigan. Foster, Z. C., Veatch, J. O., and Schoenmann, L. R. U. S. Dept. Agr. Soil Survey Ser. 1930, No. 46, 29 pp., illus. 1937.

Iron County lies in the western part of the Upper Peninsula of Michigan. The soils are principally Podzols, Half Bogs, and Bogs, formerly forested but now cut over. Only a small part is suited to cultivated crops.

The map is published on a scale of 1:63,360. The 34 mapping units are shown by separate colors. Today the map would be regarded as reconnaissance rather than detailed. Any parts mapped in detail would need a larger scale for publication.

An insert map shows nine "natural land divisions" described in terms of relief, soil texture, amount of available moisture, natural fertility, and original forest growth. The discussions of soil morphology and genesis are

---

[1] Report prepared by W. H. Scholtes, F. F. Riecken, and Guy D. Smith.

good. Soil use is discussed generally, but the management of the individual mapping units is treated less adequately than in modern detailed soil surveys.

Soil Survey (Reconnaissance) of the Red River Valley Area, Minnesota. Nikiforoff, C. C., and party. U. S. Dept. Agr. Soil Survey Ser. 1933, No. 25, 98 pp., illus. 1939.

This report and series of maps present a broad picture of the morphology and genesis of soils developed on the lacustrine deposits of glacial Lake Agassiz in an area of transition from forest to prairie vegetation in the North Temperate region. Eight maps, printed on a scale of 1:125,000, show the schematic soil pattern of nearly 5½ million acres in eight counties. The map legend illustrates the incorrect practice of old reconnaissance maps of using the names of the dominant soil types for what are really soil associations. Thus the legend suggests far greater uniformity of soil conditions than actually exists. The report contains numerous good photographs and black-and-white sketches of soil profiles classified as Podzols,[2] Chernozems, Wiesenboden, Solonetz, and intergrades among them.

Soil Survey of Jasper County, Missouri. Shrader, W. D., Springer, M. E., Hamby, Robert, Pettijohn, W. J., and Miller, J. T. U. S. Dept. Agr. Soil Survey Ser. 1942. [In press.]

Jasper County of southwestern Missouri lies in a transitional area between the Ozark Plateau to the east and the grasslands to the west. Prairie, Planosol, and Red-Yellow Podzolic soils are represented. They are used in mixed farming. The map is being published on a scale of 1:63,360.

This survey is included mainly because of the interesting complexity of this transitional area between forest to the east and grassland to the west and between the Red-Yellow Podzolic soils to the south and the Gray-Brown Podzolic soils to the northeast. Although written concisely, with emphasis on soil management practices for the individual soil units, the report is not exceptional.

Soil Survey of Strafford County, New Hampshire. Shearin, A. E., Williams, B. H., Gladwin, F. J., Howard, Montague, Jr., and Coates, W. H. U. S. Dept. Agr. Soil Survey Ser. 1940, No. 5, 141 pp., illus. 1949.

The soils of Strafford County belong in the Brown Podzolic and Podzol great soil groups. The county lies across two physiographic provinces of New England—the Seaboard Lowland and the New England Upland. Dairy farming predominates.

The map is published in two sheets on a scale of 1:31,680; 116 mapping units are shown in 18 color groupings, based on their physical characteristics and physiographic positions. A large table enclosed with the map shows the principal characteristics of each mapping unit.

Besides detailed descriptions of the individual soil units, the report includes a list of trees, shrubs, and other plants; a key to the soil series; a generalized soil association map; and tables of predicted crop yields and productivity ratings for two levels of management. The low level of soil fertility is emphasized as the main reason for the low carrying capacity of many pastures.

Soil Survey of Jackson County, North Carolina. Goldston, E. F., Davis, W. A., and Croom, C. W.[3] U. S. Dept. Agr. Soil Survey Ser. 1938, No. 19, 87 pp., illus. 1948.

Jackson County includes a part of the Blue Ridge Mountains in western North Carolina. The normal soils belong to the Red-Yellow Podzolic and Gray-Brown Podzolic great soil groups. Somewhat less than one-half of the total area is in farms. Most are small mixed farms with a high degree of self subsistence. The rest of the county is forested.

The map is published on a scale of 1:48,000 and carries 20 color groupings

[2] Part of these, at least, have been identified as equivalent to the Gray-Wooded soils of Canada.

[3] Report revised by M. G. Cline, R. C. Jurney, and M. J. Edwards.

based on physical characteristics of the 78 mapping units. A descriptive legend accompanies the map.

The report gives specific recommendations of soil management practices by management groups. The soils are first grouped into five classes according to their relative suitability for use. These major groups have a total of 13 management subgroups. Crop adaptations, rotations, fertilizer and lime requirements, and practices for runoff and erosion control are given for each management group. Predicted crop yields are given for each mapping unit in another table.

The report also contains a glossary of common terms used in soil science. Soil profile descriptions are set out in block form.

Soil Survey of Morton County, North Dakota. Edwards, M. J., and party, U. S. Dept. Agr. Soil Survey Ser. 1936, No. 28, 145 pp., illus. 1951.

Morton County lies in the Chestnut soil region of the northern Great Plains. Agriculture consists of extensive grain farming, ranching, dairying, or some combination of these. Dissection and glaciation have combined to produce a detailed pattern of soils, especially of soil phases for slope, stoniness, and solonization. Unfortunately, the map is published on a scale of 1:63,360. Because of the detailed soil pattern it should have been on a larger scale.

In addition to detailed descriptions of each of the 87 mapping units, the report carries a number of useful features, including a tabular key to the soil series; a list of the grasses, shrubs, and trees; a table of productivity ratings; maps of soil associations at two levels of generalization; several photographs; and a discussion of the evolution of Solonchak, Solonetz, and solodized-Solonetz. From the field sheets of this survey, the rural lands were classified in detail for tax assessment.

Soil Survey of the Deschutes Area, Oregon. Torgerson, E. F., and party.[4] U. S. Dept. Agr. Soil Survey Ser. 1945. [In press.]

The Deschutes Area is in west-central Oregon, just east of the Cascades, and is mainly in the Brown soil region. The soils are used for livestock grazing, wheat growing, and irrigation farming. The map is being published on a scale of 1:24,000. The color groups on the map are based on soil characteristics and their use, management, and irrigation recommendations.

An outstanding feature of the report is the tabular information on soil use and management and on such irrigation practices as length of run, head of water, and frequency of watering. The text is supplemented with helpful photographs and sketches.

Soil Survey of Union County, Pennsylvania. Bacon, S. R., Taylor, David, Boileau, Alfred, and Yoder, Gerald. U. S. Dept. Agr. Soil Survey Ser. 1940, No. 2, 115 pp., illus. 1946.

Union County, of east-central Pennsylvania, lies in the Gray-Brown Podzolic soil region and within the Appalachian Valley and Ridge Section. Dairying and general farming predominate.

The map is published on a scale of 1:48,000. On it 116 soil-mapping units are placed in 18 color groupings based on drainage, parent materials, and physiographic position. The selection of colors sharply differentiate the soils of the Susquehanna Lowland from those of the mountains.

The principal characteristics of the soil series are shown in tabular form, but the report is weak on details of soil management practices for the individual soil units.

Soil Survey of Bedford County, Tennessee. Strickland, L. J., and party.[5] U. S. Dept. Agr. Soil Survey Ser. 1938, No. 12, 120 pp., illus. 1947.

Bedford County, Tennessee, in the region of Red-Yellow Podzolic soils, lies across a part of the Nashville Basin and Highland Rim escarpment. The agriculture is based largely on livestock farming, but some cotton is grown as a cash crop.

[4] Report prepared by W. J. Leighty.
[5] The report was revised by M. G. Cline and R. C. Jurney.

The map is published in one sheet on a scale of 1:48,000. On it, 57 soil-mapping units are placed in 8 major color groupings on the basis of physiographic or topographic position and in 18 subgroups according to drainage and steepness of slope. The color pattern gives an interesting picture of the county as a whole.

The report carries the usual features of those of this period. It includes photographs, a sketch map of the physiographic subdivisions, a tabular summary of the principal characteristics of the soil series, a description of the individual series, detailed descriptions of the individual mapping units, tables of predicted yields and productivity ratings under three levels of management, a grouping of the soils into five physical land classes based on use suitability, and a grouping of the soils according to their management requirements.

The report is generally good and is outstanding for a table showing the common use and present management of the individual soil units; a table listing the soils in management groups and giving the relative ease by which plant nutrients, soil material, and good tilth are conserved in each; a map and discussion of associations of the physical land classes; and the section on soil morphology and genesis.

Soil Survey of Benton County, Tennessee. Odom, L. E., and party. U. S. Dept. Agr. Soil Survey Ser. 1941. [In press.]

Benton County, Tennessee, is in the region of Red-Yellow Podzolic soils on the East Gulf Coastal Plain and the Highland Rim section of the Interior Low Plateaus. The map has a scale of 1:24,000. Its legend is in two parts: (1) An alphabetical list of the 95 soil units and (2) a good group legend based on physical characteristics of the soil.

The report is generally good. It has excellent photographic illustrations. The individual soil descriptions are very good, with profile descriptions set out in block form. The report has a good table of predicted yields at each level of management. Specific management requirements are well handled by soil groups. Good sections on interpretive maps and on soil morphology and genesis are included, as well as special ones on water control on the land.

This survey and the ones for Grainger, Jackson, and Bedford Counties are examples of those made as a part of the program for agricultural development in the Tennessee Valley. Many new developments of general application grew out of this intensive research, supported in part by the Tennessee Valley Authority. In the most recent surveys in progress, for example, the color groups on the soil map are based on soil management requirements.

Soil Survey of Grainger County, Tennessee. Hubbard, E. H., Matzek, B. L., and Jenkins, Clifton. U. S. Dept. Agr. Soil Survey Ser. 1940, No. 4, 203 pp., illus. 1948.

The Grainger survey covers an area, largely of Red-Yellow Podzolic soils, in the Appalachian Ridge and Valley section of northeastern Tennessee. The map is published in two sheets on a scale of 1:24,000, and the color pattern brings out the ridge-and-valley aspect of the landscape very effectively.[6] The 128 soil-mapping units are shown in 19 color groupings on the basis of broad use capability, relief, drainage, parent material, and topographic position.

The descriptions of the principal soils are given in box form, which appears to improve the readability of the text. The report includes a number of effective photographs, as well as tables of predicted crop yields, soil productivity ratings, land classes, characteristics of soil series, and acreages of land classes by the soil units. The soils are placed in 13 groups and discussed according to their use capability and management requirements. Unfortunately, the soil association map is printed at too small a scale.

---

[6] The large soil maps of Grainger County are somewhat cumbersome. Claiborne County, Tenn., has a similar map in 10 smaller and more convenient sheets. Although very good, the Claiborne County report is not quite so outstanding, perhaps, as that of Grainger County.

Soil Survey of Brown County, Texas. Templin, E. H., Mowery, I. C., Watkins, W. I., Glassey, T. W., and Beck, M. W. U. S. Dept. Agr. Soil Survey Ser. 1939, No. 4, 87 pp., illus. 1948.

Brown County lies in central Texas and includes parts of the Grand Prairie, the West Cross Timbers, and the Rolling Plains. Soils belonging in the Red-Yellow Podzolic, Reddish Prairie, Reddish Chestnut, and Rendzina great soil groups are present. Farming is varied, with ranching, cash-crop farming, and general farming as major types. Irrigation was being introduced at the time of the survey.

The map is published on a scale of 1:63,360. On it 57 soil-mapping units are grouped into 23 color patterns according to their principal physical characteristics.

The report has good photographs, a key to the soil series patterned after botanical keys, and a soil association map. The profile descriptions are set out in block form. Predicted yields and productivity ratings are given only for the most common level of management. The section on soil morphology and genesis is interesting. The report suffers from a lack of emphasis on improved soil management practices and livestock management.

Soil Survey of McLennan County, Texas. Templin, E. H., and party. U. S. Dept. Agr. Soil Survey Ser. 1942. [In press.]

McLennan County, Texas, is in the Blackland and Grand Prairies. The soils belong in the Rendzina, Reddish Prairie, and Red-Yellow Podzolic great soil groups. The map is being published on a scale of 1:48,000. Its legend is in two parts: (1) An alphabetical list of individual mapping units and (2) 14 color groups based on physical characteristics of the soils.

The discussion of the soils is very good. Soil series descriptions are integrated with the descriptions of mapping units, which have block descriptions of profiles. Soil management is discussed by soil groups, with a special section on runoff and erosion control, and a summary table. A table gives predicted yields under two levels of management. A good section on soil morphology and genesis includes a key to the mapping units.

The general descriptions of agriculture suffer from a lack of information on livestock and livestock products, farm expenses, and farm investments.

Soil Survey of the Salt Lake Area, Utah. Jennings, D. S., Youngs, F. O., and party. U. S. Dept. Agr. Soil Survey Ser. 1936, No. 22, 83 pp., illus. 1946.

The Salt Lake Area, Utah, lies at the western foot of the Wasatch Range and occupies a part of prehistoric Lake Bonneville. Probably the area belongs in the region of Brown soils. Solonchak and Solonetz soils occur extensively. A diversified irrigation agriculture is practiced.

The map is published on a scale of 1:63,360. On its 81 soil-mapping units are shown in 5 major color groupings, based on physiographic position and drainage, and in 24 subgroups according to such additional physical factors as texture, color, permeability, and parent materials. A supplemental map, based on an intensive examination of the soils in the field and numerous readings with the Wheatstone electrolytic bridge, is used to show the distribution of the soils according to their relative content of soluble salts.

The report carries a table of predicted crop yields and a grouping of the soils according to their suitability for crop production, as based on productivity, ease of management, and water-holding capacity. A key to the soils appears in an appendix. Some of the soil series are defined somewhat more broadly than in more recent surveys; and some variants appear as phases.

Soil Survey [Detailed-Reconnaissance] of Kittitas County, Washington. Smith, L. H., Dwyer, C. H., and Schafer, George. U. S. Dept. Agr. Soil Survey Ser. 1937, No. 13, 69 pp., illus. 1945.

Kittitas County lies between the crest of the Cascades and the Columbia River to the east. Since it covers a very wide range of climatic and physiographic conditions, there are many kinds of plants and soils and types of farming.

The reconnaissance map is published on a scale of 1:125,000, and the detailed soil map at 1:63,360 as a separate sheet.

The survey was selected partly as an example of a detailed-reconnaissance survey and partly as an example of an exceedingly complex area, since it includes Podzol, Brown Podzolic, Brown, Gray Desert, Bog, and Solonchak soils. Photographs illustrate some of these conditions.

Soil Survey of Hawaii. Cline, M. G., and party. U. S. Dept. Agr. Soil Survey Ser. 1939 [In press.]

The soils are predominantly Latosols from old and recent volcanic rocks. Since rainfall, slope, elevation, and soil age vary widely, some 405 mapping units are recognized. These are placed in 45 color patterns on the map.

In the report the soils are grouped into families and great soil groups. This is the first large survey in which the family grouping has been used.

The report contains a wealth of interesting material besides descriptions of the soils. Many laboratory data are included. There are discussions of soil morphology and genesis and of the relation of the soils to climate, vegetation, and other factors of the environment.

Part of the soils are used for sugarcane and pineapples under very intensive management, including heavy fertilization, machine methods, and irrigation in places. Special chapters deal with soil management and productivity for these crops as well as for fruits, vegetables, forestry, and pasture.

Soil Survey of Puerto Rico. Roberts, R. C., and party. U. S. Dept. Agr. Soil Survey. Ser. 1936, No. 8, 503 pp., illus. 1942. [Summary in Spanish.]

Puerto Rico has a complex pattern of soils including Latosols, Red-Yellow Podzolic, Chernozem, Red Desert, Solonchak, and many others. In fact, it is an outdoor soil museum. A wide variety of crops are grown on farms varying from tiny subsistence gardens to great sugar plantations.

The soil map is published at 1:50,000. On it some 358 mapping units are placed in 46 color groups according to physical characteristics, relief, physiographic position, parent material, and climate.

The report includes excellent descriptions of the principal crops and their culture, good soil descriptions, a table of soil productivity ratings, and an interesting discussion of soil morphology and genesis.

If the survey were being made today, the mapping would be done in more detail and some mapping units would be subdivided.

APPENDIX I. MAP PREPARATION WITH THE PLANE TABLE

The use of aerial photographs in soil mapping began about 1926. Their use steadily increased until they nearly replaced other media as a base for mapping soils in the field between 1935 and 1940. Yet some soil mapping may still need to be done where aerial photographs or suitable planimetric maps are not available. In the earlier edition of this *Manual* the use of the plane table is explained in detail. Enough of that discussion is repeated here to guide the field scientist in its use where it offers the best way to proceed with the necessary soil mapping that cannot await aerial photographs.

Making of the plane-table traverse consists of plotting on paper the direction and distance of certain features of the landscape in such a way that all the objects shown occur on the map in the same relative positions that they occupy on the land. Although the system used is simple and the operation easily performed, neatness and care are required for the production of an accurate base map.

Plane table and accessories.—In soil mapping a rather simple plane table or traverse board is used (fig. 56). A tripod supports a drawing board, usually 15 by 15 inches, which is oriented by means of a compass placed in a notch at one side.[1] To the bottom of the board is screwed a brass plate by which the board is fastened to the tripod with a spring and thumbscrew. Except when in actual use, the board, together with the map on it, is kept in a leather case. The board is placed in the case with the compass at the top, and always in the same way so that the leather will not be discolored by the metallic plate, except on one side.

A high quality of special drawing paper mounted on cloth is used for the map. Such paper is cut into squares slightly smaller than the plane-table board and held in place by the four thumbscrews in the four corners. Best results are obtained by using flat paper. It should fit on the board tightly. Because the paper must be kept tight at all times, the thumbscrews should not be turned in the full distance when mounting paper during dry weather. The paper will be inclined to buckle during moist periods and then it can be tightened by turning the thumbscrews all the way down. The plane-table sheet is protected by a dull-brown cover paper, in order to confine exposure only to the parts that are actually being worked upon.

When set up for use, the plane table is made approximately level by adjusting the position of the tripod (fig. 57). The board is then oriented by the compass. Steel culverts, railroad tracks, power lines, or other sources of magnetic attraction must be avoided. Even pocket knives and similar objects must not be brought near the needle. Only brass tacks and fittings can be used in the board itself. The compass needle should be released only when in actual use in orienting the board.

For sighting, drawing lines, and measuring, a simple alidade made from flat boxwood is used. It has two beveled white celluloid edges and is fitted with folding sights and usually graduated into fiftieths of an inch (fig. 58). Of course, alidades may be made for whatever scale is most convenient.

Measurements on the ground may be made with a chain, by pacing, or with a special speedometer, called an odometer, fitted to an ordinary automobile. Such an odometer must operate directly from the front wheel and not from the drive shaft as does the speedometer on ordinary automobiles.[2]

---

[1] In areas with magnetic attraction the plane table cannot be oriented in the usual way by the magnetic compass, and the Baldwin Solar chart may be used. (See Beaman, W. M., as cited in General Bibliography.)

[2] For detailed shop suggestions for installing gears over a front-wheel brake drum, see the earlier edition of this Manual. (KELLOGG, CHARLES E. SOIL SURVEY MANUAL. U. S. Dept. of Agr. Misc. Pub. 274, 136 pp., illus. 1937.)

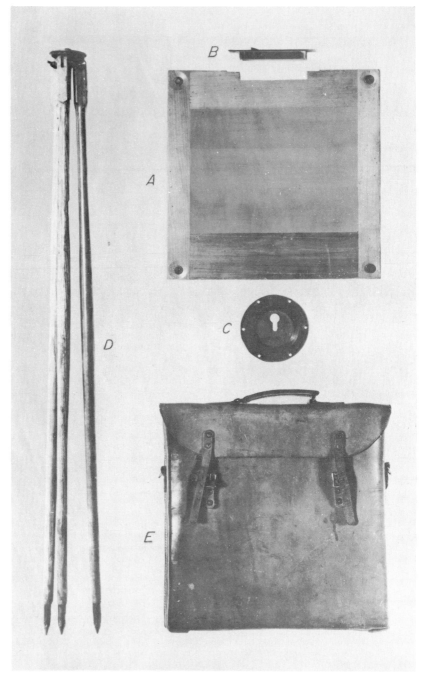

FIGURE 56.—Plane table, unassembled: *A*, Board; *B*, compass; *C*, head; *D*, tripod; and *E*, case.

FIGURE 57.—Plane table assembled for use.

The odometer can be adjusted roughly by the proper choice of gears. Final adjustment is made by varying the tire pressure. Along some road convenient to the survey headquarters an exact mile is laid off with a surveyor's steel tape. The tire pressure is then adjusted until the odometer gives an exact reading. It will need to be checked from time to time, since the required pressure changes with the age of the tire and with the load in the car. It also changes with temperature during the day. For example, if one is working on earth roads during the cool of the morning and later in the day drives onto a hot pavement, the tire pressure will need to be adjusted.

Where these odometers are used regularly a full set of parts should be kept on hand, for the cables and fiber gears are subject to considerable wear. By simply tilting the fiber gear, the odometer may be disengaged so that the equipment does not operate except when needed for measurements.

Measurements by use of such an odometer, even under the best conditions, are not so precise as the more time-consuming methods. Yet with care, this instrument is entirely satisfactory for surveying in all ordinary terrains that are not too hilly or where the roads are not extremely winding or crooked, especially if control points can be located accurately on the field sheets. Measurements with the odometer cannot be depended upon when roads are very slippery.

Traversing.—With the plane table set up, leveled, and oriented with the compass, a sharp-pointed needle is pressed into the paper in the exact position[3] which the plane table occupies in the area to be shown on the field sheet. To draw a line on the map between the plane table and some distant point, the margin of the alidade is placed against the needle and

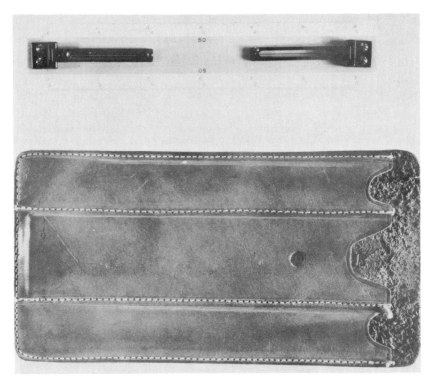

FIGURE 58.—Alidade with case.

rotated until its two sights are directly in line with the distant point. With the alidade held firmly in place, a fine line is drawn on the paper. The distance between the plane table and the distant point along the road is measured with the odometer or by some other means. In the same way, additional lines or "shots" may be drawn toward other prominent features of the landscape.

When the work at the initial station is completed, the compass needle is lifted from its pivot, and the surveyor proceeds in the direction of his shot. The surveyor continues along the road until it bends, until he has reached the distance on the ground somewhat less than one-half the length of the compass needle on the map,[4] or until he reaches a road intersection or some other place where a station must be made.

The surveyor may or may not need to set up the plane table at the end of his sight. If the distance from the first station is relatively short and if he does not need to make side "shots," he may merely record his distance measurement and regard the point as a "turning point." Such a turning point is the end of his last forward sight and will be the end of the backward sight at his next station.

Let us assume that he used the end of his first sight as a turning point. He proceeds to another bend in the road or prominent intersection as before, noting his measurements. The plane table is set up and oriented by the compass at the new station. The distance from the first station to the end of the first sight—turning point—is laid out with the scale on the margin

---

[3] Approximate position when starting a new sheet.
[4] With such an instrument, orientation is not sufficiently accurate to proceed far on a single sight.

of the alidade and the needle pressed into the paper at that point. By placing the alidade against the needle and sighting back upon this last point, a line can be drawn to the present station. The distance from the turning point to the present station is laid out with the scale and the needle pressed into the paper at the new position of the plane table, after which a new forward sight is taken on the road and any other necessary sights are made along intersecting roads or to other features. With a mapping scale of 2 inches equals 1 mile (1:31,680) measurements can be plotted within about 15 feet.

In this system the plane table is set up at every other station, or at every other bend in the road if intermediate stations are unnecessary. This is called the system of "turning points." If errors from magnetic interference are suspected, the plane table should be set up at the intermediate point and the previous forward shot checked by a back sight. If magnetic attraction cannot be avoided, traverses can be made for a short distance by orienting the plane table by back sights rather than with the compass. This requires setting up the plane table at every station. The alidade is placed firmly on the paper parallel to the last forward shot and the board turned until the previous station is sighted. The map is then oriented, and, after determining the present position of the plane table on the map by plotting the distance, a new forward sight can be taken. The equipment described here is not sufficiently precise for use without a compass, except for short distances. When the plane table is oriented by the compass, the error is compensating; but when oriented by back sights it is accumulative.

When the plane table is set up for making sights along the primary line of traverse, houses and other features near the road may be plotted from the measured distances and by sighting with the alidade. Frequent stops to examine soils and to make side traverses should be avoided while a primary traverse is in progress. Houses and other features distant from the road may be located with reasonable accuracy by the intersection of sights made from two or three stations. The distance between these stations must be sufficiently great that the inside angle is about 90°. This technique is called "graphic triangulation." It is much simpler than the triangulation carried on with more precise instruments. Trees along a stream in open country may be located temporarily in this way and serve as guides to sketching the stream channel. Other features may be located as aids in sketching soil boundaries. It is also helpful to locate trees and other distant landmarks by intersection as aids for checking subsequent foot traverses through areas distant from the primary traverse.

All traverse work on a single sheet should be based on one starting point, preferably near the center. Ordinarily, more accurate traverses are made by starting each sheet from a separate point near the center than by traversing to the edge of one sheet and continuing from the margin of that toward the interior of another. Some distinct feature near the edge of the sheet, such as a cross road or a tree, should be selected as an end point for the traverse. This point may be located on the traverse from the center of the next sheet. It is helpful to have common roads located on each sheet by individual traverses in order to help in their final joining and adjustment.

With the completion of the primary traverse, secondary traverses are made between the primary ones for completing the base map and for plotting soils. Except in heavily wooded or brushy country, the plane table can be used conveniently. The technique is similar to that used for the primary traverse except that much of the measuring must be done by pacing. Foot traverses should be tied to control points or other points located by the primary traverse at frequent intervals. Locations on foot traverses can be checked by sights on two or more previously located points. The plane table is set up, oriented with the compass, and sights taken at the two other locations. The new station is located at the intersection of the lines drawn from these sights. In very rough country it is commonly necessary to place special flags in conspicuous places for use as control stations. In sectionized areas it is possible to identify section corners, which may be located on the map by construction from the grid of the primary traverse, supplemented by data from accurate plats, and use these points for checking secondary traverses or as control stations when locating new stations by graphic triangulation.

If it is necessary to occupy a point where the plane table cannot be oriented by the compass because of magnetic attraction, and to which measurement cannot be made, the location can be determined as follows: A forward sight is taken from a known point toward the new position. The plane table is then set up at the new station and oriented by sighting back at the previous station. A second sight is taken at some other known station, and the intersection of the two lines gives the location of the new station.

Traverse notes should be preserved until the map is finished. Measurements of distances between traverse points, turning points, streams, cross roads, houses, and soil boundaries, should be recorded in a notebook. A convenient method of recording readings is to begin at the bottom of the notebook page and proceed upwards as the work progresses. By the side of the odometer reading, the exact distance can be set down. Frequent checks of the total distance along the traverse, as shown by the odometer, with the sum of the plotted distances, serve to call attention to any possible error in plotting before a large amount of work needs to be corrected.

A line showing magnetic north is recorded on each plane-table sheet. If the magnetic declination is great, the compass may be set at an appropriate angle to the board, by means of a brass plate, so that the mapping is oriented approximately with the cardinal directions.

Control and accuracy.—When completed, the field sheets are joined and adjusted to control points by cartographers so that the completed map is geographically correct. Thus it is important that the plane-table traverse be tied to all known accurate control stations. These should be prominently marked on the field sheets. It is also helpful to locate section lines, railway stations, mileposts, and similar features that help in adjusting the traverses. The direction of the principal traverses should be shown with small arrows in red ink. The closure error—overlaps or gaps of plotted lines at the point of closure—are indicated by looped lines in red ink.

The date of survey is shown on each map, and the accuracy of the cultural features is considered as of that date.

Errors may arise in several ways. They may be caused by incorrect measurements or inaccurate plotting of the distances, by incorrect measurement of angles, or by mistakes in field computations. An error in sketching may result from the misinterpretation of the shape of a distant or otherwise veiled feature seen in perspective. Sometimes one error is followed by another error in the opposite direction. Such errors are called "compensating," since one tends to offset the other. If compensating errors are nearly equal, results under some conditions may give the false appearance of accuracy, since the traverse will close, and yet the traverse may be in error in two or more places. Small compensating errors may be disregarded, but large errors must be found and corrected.

In order to guard against errors, traverse lines should be run in circuits closing on themselves, or run from one located point to another located point, insofar as possible. Even if no mistakes are made, a traverse rarely closes exactly, because of the normal error due to the instruments. These "closure errors" should not be adjusted in the field but should be left for adjustment by cartographers. If the closure error is greater than the allowable error for the survey, however, and the error is not revealed by replotting the field data, the traverse should be run again.

Mounting partial maps on the plane table.—Topographic maps, planimetric maps, or aerial photographs may be placed on the board and held with brass thumbtacks. The plane-table is oriented by the compass in some known position shown on the map from which a distant known point, also shown on the map, is clearly visible. A faint line is drawn between the two points and the alidade kept carefully parallel with this line. The map to be mounted is placed in approximate position and lightly fastened by one tack and then rotated until the alidade is sighted directly on the distant object. The map or photograph can then be fastened firmly by additional thumbtacks.

APPENDIX II. MAP PREPARATION WITH COMPASS TRAVERSE

In heavily wooded country the compass may be preferable to the plane table, especially for secondary traverses. Since it is less convenient and less accurate than the plane table, it should not be substituted for it unless there is already an adequate planimetric base or grid of land lines that can be followed. Traverse with an ordinary compass requires more time than one with the plane table, since each reading must be plotted on the map with a protractor.

Under ordinary circumstances in wooded country it is best to follow a straight line with the compass and avoid the need for plotting frequent changes in direction. In sectionized country it is best to follow the land lines, since the mapper has an opportunity to locate section corners for control. If the going gets especially difficult, time may be saved by plotting the traverse on a path or foot trail, but ordinarily these trails are so crooked that their ease of travel does not compensate for the time required in plotting their meanderings. As with the plane table, a record of the compass readings and of the distances measured by paces or chain should be preserved for any necessary recalculations to locate errors. Compass readings are noted as so many degrees east or west of true north or of true south, whichever is more convenient.

The most convenient compass for traversing under these conditions is the forester's or geologist's compass shown in figure 59,A. For short secondary traverses this compass is held in the hand, but for more accurate work a Jacob's staff is used as a support. This is a staff about 4 or 5 feet long, fitted with a steel point at the lower end for thrusting into the soil and with an adjustable universal joint at the upper end for fastening onto the compass.

The forester's compass should be adjusted for the magnetic declinations, so that readings can be taken directly in respect to true north, thus avoiding the need for making individual corrections with each reading. Compasses brought into a new area are frequently out of adjustment. The sliding weight on the needle must be moved if the needle is so out of balance that one end touches the glass cover of the box when leveled.

In areas with magnetic attraction a sundial compass must be used. One is shown in figure 59,B that is similar to the forester's compass, except that a string extends from the top of the rear sight to the opposite side of the box and a sundial is marked on the margin. This compass cannot be used in the hand but must be well supported by a Jacob's staff. The compass is fitted with a needle similar to that of the ordinary forester's compass, so that it can be used like any ordinary compass in nonmagnetic areas.

Each sundial compass must be individually standardized for the particular area where it is to be used and from time to time within that area. First, a true north-and-south line is established. If the attraction is only local, this can be done with a magnetic compass in a nonmagnetic part of the survey area. Generally a line of known direction can be found even in a magnetic country. After the compass has been oriented in a true north-and-south line, beginning early in the morning and continuing throughout the day, readings are taken on the sundial at intervals of 5 minutes as determined with an unusually accurate watch. A watch varying more than a few seconds within 24 hours is unsatisfactory. After the readings have been obtained, they are plotted on regular coordinate paper, using the time by the watch as one axis and that of the sundial as the other. A curve showing the relationship between the two is then drawn by connecting the points. Curves are individual for each compass and have small but irregular and significant variations from a true straight line of 45°. This curve is carried by the mapper in the field.

To establish direction in the field with a sundial compass, the instrument

FIGURE 59.—A, Forester's or geologist's compass; B, sundial compass.

is first set up firmly with a Jacob's staff and leveled. A point on the curve about 1 minute in advance of the time by the watch is chosen, and the equivalent time on the sundial noted from the curve. The compass is moved so that the instant the chosen time on the watch is reached, the equivalent time is indicated on the sundial. The compass is now oriented in a true north-and-south line. By releasing the needle and noting the variation, the direction of lines in respect to true north can be obtained. Orientation by this method is more dependable in the middle of the day than in early morning or late afternoon when the shadows move more rapidly.

No compass less precise than the ordinary geologist's or forester's compass should be used for traverse work. The common pocket, or box, compass, although convenient for picking one's way, is not suitable in survey work. With a good instrument and experience in the woods, a mapper can run satisfactory lines for considerable distances; yet, where measurements are made by pacing, frequent checks on section corners or other control points established by a primary traverse are essential.

Pacing.—Many short distances plotted on soil maps are measured by pacing. Each surveyor's pace, like the Roman pace, consists of two full steps, and the paces are counted by counting alternate steps. Where much pacing is necessary, a surveyor should use a tally register and not attempt to carry the count in his mind. Each individual needs to determine the length of his natural stride. Then he will need to train himself to keep this natural stride, regardless of the slope, ground cover or fatigue. His paces must be exactly the same on the open highway as they are in the brush or in the field. An individual can standardize his pacing against a known distance and prepare a table showing the number of paces for each division on the mapping scale. Many men have about 1,000 paces for a mile.

Although an experienced man becomes very skilled at pacing, he may make errors because of fatigue or minor illnesses of which he is unaware. Either plane table or compass traverses, where measurements are made by pacing, need to have frequent control even with good terrain. Experience has shown that about 3 miles between control points is the extreme outside limit for pacing by the most experienced men.

Saddle horses need to be used in extremely rough and broken country where walking is too difficult and too slow. Occasionally saddle horses may be found that pace with some uniformity; but ordinarily locations must be established by graphic triangulation, intersection from section corners, or by following some base map, land grid, or air photo.

APPENDIX III. NOTES ON MAP COMPILATION AND REPRODUCTION

Soil maps can be constructed or compiled by several different methods. Techniques and methods depend mainly on the material used as a base for the soil survey. With some techniques, highly accurate maps are made at low cost. Other techniques, made necessary because of the type of base material used, lead to far less accurate maps, increased cost, or both.

Each job should be planned prior to commencing the field work. Before starting the map compilation careful study and analysis should be made of the field material, existing control, other map data, and lithographic requirements in order to select the most economical methods for producing a satisfactory map.

Such work is handled by cartographers familiar with mapping and surveying and able to judge the control needed for various methods of base construction and the degree of accuracy that may be expected. Understanding of the various types of aerial photographs and skill in photogrammetric methods are especially needed by those compiling modern soil maps. Besides methods in cartographic assembly, lithographic processing must be understood in order to prepare the kind of copy necessary for economical and accurate reproduction.

One of three major methods of preparation are usually used with soil maps, although some techniques are common to two or more methods: (1) The construction of base maps and soil surveys from aerial photographs; (2) the assembly of base maps from existing published maps on which the soil data are plotted; and (3) the assembly of bases and soil surveys from original plane-table surveys. Although some are more adaptable than others, any one of these methods generally can be adapted to permit reasonable standardization of techniques and procedures. Combinations of two or more of the methods increase the difficulties of map construction.

METHODS OF MAP CONSTRUCTION FROM AERIAL PHOTOGRAPHS

Methods of map construction from aerial photographs are varied. So are the instruments used and the kinds of maps produced. The largest producer of topographic maps in the United States, the United States Geological Survey, has found through many years of research that such stereoscopic plotting instruments as the Multiplex, Aerocartograph, Twinplex Plotter, and Kelsh Plotter are necessary in their photogrammetric work if their published maps are to meet the modern requirements of standard map accuracy. Several other mapping agencies use either these or similar types of stereoscopic plotting instruments. The United States Army Engineers maintain an experimental station where all types of plotting instruments are tested and evaluated.

Planimetric maps of a uniformly high degree of accuracy may be made from aerial photographs without the use of the stereoscopic plotting instruments. In areas with considerable relief however, the work can be performed more accurately and economically with a plotting instrument.

For the proper orientation and location of planimetric detail from aerial photographs the Cartographic Section of the Division of Soil Survey uses the "slotted-templet" method.[1] This method is adapted to the needs of the Soil Survey because it provides reasonable accuracy of radial triangulation, or establishment of secondary control points, with a minimum of labor and material. It enables the cartographer to utilize widely spaced ground-control points. This is especially important since few soil survey parties can be equipped and staffed to establish control.

---

[1] For details of the method, see KELSH, H. T. THE SLOTTED-TEMPLET METHOD FOR CONTROLLING MAPS MADE FROM AERIAL PHOTOGRAPHS. U. S. Dept. Agr. Misc. Pub. 404, 30 pp., illus. 1940.

Briefly, the slotted-templet method is based on the principle that lines radiating from the center of each aerial photograph, and drawn through common points identified in the overlap of the photographs, will intersect and give the proper location of each point when correctly assembled. First the ground-control points are pricked on the photograph. Besides these, nine points are normally identified and pricked on each photograph. A point very near the geometric center of the photograph is selected and is transferred stereoscopically to the overlap portion of the photographs above and below it in line of flight. Then three points are pricked parallel with the center points, one in each corner and one in the middle, on both sides of the photograph and in the common sidelap with photographs in the adjoining flights.

After these radial points have been identified and pricked on all photographs to be used in the assembly (the ground-control points having been previously pricked) the photographs are placed over bristolboard that has been cut to the size of the photographs, and all points are pricked through the photographs and into the bristolboard, which becomes the templet. The templets are then facsimiles of the photographs in the sense that all radial and ground-control points maintain their same geometric relations to one another. The center point of the templet is punched out, leaving a small hole. The templet is then placed on the slot cutter, and elongated slots of the same width as the diameter of the center hole are cut, radially, from the center through all other points pricked through from the photograph to the templet. These slots are centered on the radial points. The center of each overlapping photograph is replaced with a slot, and the other six points, three on each side, are replaced with slots. Occasionally, where considerable differences of relief exist in an area, additional points are pricked and slotted to afford the compiler less adjustment when the photographic detail is being transferred to the map base. Basic map assemblies may be made at scales other than that of the photographs by simply reducing or lengthening the distance of the center of the slots from the central point of the templet in ratio to the known scale of the photographs and the desired map scale.

The templets are then ready for assembling on a projection, usually polyconic, which is constructed at the desired scale of the map base and at the same scale as the templets (fig. 60). The projection used for the templet assembly is constructed on rigidly mounted masonite sheets, on the surface of which has been painted two or more coats of enamel. This surface is buffed, and the projection constructed and inked on with fine lines. All ground-control points that have been identified and pricked on the photographs and slotted on the templets are then plotted carefully on the projection by their geographic positions. A round flat-base metal stud, with a shaft pierced for insertion of a needle, is fastened securely and precisely over each plotted ground-control point. The templets are then assembled by flights, with the slots of the ground-control stations fitting with very close tolerance over the control-station studs. Additional studs are placed in all radial-point slots and center holes. These latter studs are placed beneath the bottom templet so that their base is against the projection and they are free to move longitudinally along the slot. In this manner the center of each stud finds its true position mechanically when the slots of all overlapping templets are placed over the stud and force it into position. The hole in each stud now represents the original photographic centers and radial points identified and pricked on the photographs; but now the points are located in their true positions on the projections as they were on the surface of the ground.

When the templet assembly has been completed a needle is inserted through the hole in each radial-point stud and a small point pricked on the projection base. The templets are removed, the pricked points recovered, and a small inked circle inscribed around each. This completes the work of the slot-templet assembly.

The projection, ground-control points, and radial points are then transferred to sheets of vinylite transparent plastic used as a compilation base for the map. The photographs are placed in overhead projectors, adjusted

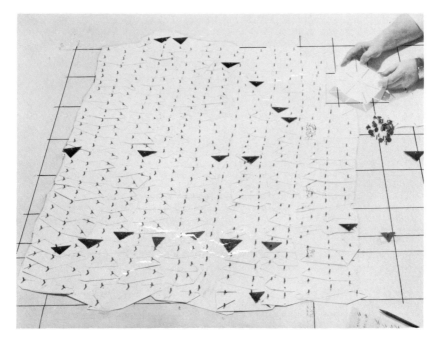

FIGURE 60.—View showing templets being assembled on an enameled board, with projection lines inked.

by enlargement or reduction to fit the scale of the compilation bases, and all basic map features are traced on the vinylite in pencil. The radial triangulation points here play their important part by enabling the compiler to adjust the reflected image of the photograph and compilation base to the same relative scale between the radial points, which are visible on each. Additional adjustments are necessary within the areas bounded by three or four radial points, and these are accomplished visually by the compiler with the slight scale differences of the points as arguments. After all needed features have been delineated on the bases from the photographs they are inked by the compiler. This serves as a manuscript map for the additional phases of map preparation.

No expensive stereoscopic plotting instruments are required in the slotted-templet assembly work. Actually the only major instruments needed are stereoscopes, accurate scales, center-point and slot cutters, projectors, and light tables. The photographs and bristolboard are the only items expended. The other instruments are small and usually found in every well-equipped mapping office. Even the photographs used are of the least expensive type—unrectified contact prints.

Dependable soil maps are constructed with extreme care, patience, and accuracy. The photogrammetric construction requires people well trained in surveying, photogrammetry, and photo interpretation and with some appreciation of soil patterns and their relation to the other physical features.

METHODS OF MAP ASSEMBLY FROM EXISTING MAPS

Soil maps can also be compiled on published base maps of high quality, if ones of recent issue are available. Techniques vary with the kind of map, the form of the field sheets, and other factors.

One such method employs the negatives from the color separation plates of the original map. From the negatives, black-line impressions of the culture and drainage are reproduced on a dimensionally stable plastic. A nonphotographic composite of the base map is also reproduced for transfer, adjustment, and correlation of the soil data. After the soil data have been adjusted to the nonphotographic composite they are transferred, through photographic processes, to the black-line impression of the culture plate. This method of compilation produces copy suitable for reproduction by lithography without the need for reinking the culture and drainage of the original map. It does, however, require the normal finishing techniques for the soil data, the necessary changes in cultural and drainage features, and the addition or shifting of place names and marginal data.

In other methods of compilation the existing published maps are used simply as manuscripts. A set of the base maps bearing the soil data are assembled and adjusted to fit a master grid for the sheet sizes desired. The assembled maps are copied and reproduced in nonphotographic images on dimensionally stable materials. The nonphotographic images are then used as a manuscript for finishing the various color separations for the lithographic copy.

The assembly of soil maps from plane-table sheets employs techniques similar to those used in compiling the map from published quadrangles. The adjustment of the plane-table sheets is usually more complicated and frequently requires the optical projection of the data in order to assemble the manuscript. Once the manuscript map is completed the finishing of the color separations follows the same techniques as used in other methods.

MAP FINISHING

Map finishing requires the preparation of color separations suitable for direct copy for lithography. This operation involves the finishing of the line work to prescribed standards, the blocking of soil areas for the tint screens, the layouts for placement of lettering, and the arrangement of place names, marginal notes, borders, and legends.

To reproduce the soil map in color it is necessary to prepare a separate plate for each group of various features to be reproduced in one color or tint. One plate is used for all features to be printed in black, another for those in blue, and another for each of the separate tints of the three primary colors, blue, red, and yellow, used for the soil areas. Screen rulings used with the latter three colors make possible a total of 63 tints on the published map. With two color plates and screen rulings, 15 color tints can be had. While a much greater number of tints can be obtained by additional plates, the cost is greatly increased, because of the extra press runs and the cost of the additional separation negatives. Since the use of many colors on the map is costly, their number should be held to a minimum.

To obtain these color plates the manuscript map is reproduced in a nonphotographic image on metal-mounted map paper or glass. A separate plate is made for each proposed color or tint. The symbols and areas to be reproduced in a given color are then inked on one specific plate.

It is standard practice in map finishing to ink on paper mounted on aluminum sheets, so that a minimum amount of dimensional change takes place. The manuscript map is reproduced in nonphotographic blue on a set of these plates. The culture, soil symbols and boundaries, and lettering are finished in black, using the nonphotographic image of the manuscript as a guide. The drainage is inked in black on another set of plates. Since these inked plates are for direct reproduction, the ink work must meet rigid specifications for symboling, spacing, and density of line work. The color plates are made by making the areas to be tinted opaque on an acetate overlay placed over the soil plate or on an additional set of the blue-line plates.

In another common method of finishing maps, the manuscript map is reproduced on glass plates, which have been coated with an opaque solution and sensitized. Drafting is done on this glass, which serves either as a negative for a press plate or for reproducing a black-line plastic print, which may be used as copy by the lithographer. The plastic print is necessary if the final map scale is to be different from the compilation scale. Color tints are prepared from blue-line plastic prints.

The glass-drafting technique may be used when the soil mapping is done on aerial mosaics and the map is to be reproduced with a photographic background. The mosaics bearing the soil data are reproduced with a half-tone screen and printed on a coated glass plate. The survey data are then drafted on a separate glass plate, which serves as a negative, drafting one for each color. The press plates are made from the half-tone negative and from the separate glass negatives for culture, drainage, and soils. The engraving needs to be done to highly precise standards, with special drafting tools for cutting roads, drainage, houses, soil boundaries, and other features.

All lettering used on soil maps is prepared by letter-press printing with standard types and sizes. The type is set and printed on thin transparent acetate sheets. Small sheets with the appropriate lettering are coated with a wax adhesive and applied to the finished map.

MAP EDITING AND PROOFING

Normally a thorough edit is given the manuscript map. Control, projections, culture, drainage, soil boundaries, soil symbols, and other items affecting the accuracy of the map are carefully reviewed and inspected. As the manuscript map is not in finished form, the final appearance of the map and its quality for reproduction cannot be checked at this stage. By thoroughly checking all items affecting the accuracy of the map, however, most corrections can be made before the map is prepared in finished form.

After the color separations have been inked or drafted on glass the plates are reviewed for appearance and quality of line work. Symbols used, spacing and weight of lines, density of ink work, placement and spelling of lettering, arrangement of legend, marginal notes, and other items affecting the final appearance of the map are checked.

Upon completion of this edit it is necessary to proof the various color separations for register. A composite copy of the different color separations is reproduced in color. Various photographic and direct printing processes are used to make the color copy. The colored print is then reviewed to insure that all tints for the soils appear in the proper areas, are of the proper screen patterns, and that the combinations of the various tints produce the required patterns. Registration of the separate features is checked and careful inspection given to the legibility of the map as a whole.

MAP REPRODUCTION AND LITHOGRAPHY

Adequate facilities for map reproduction are essential throughout the preparation of a soil map. First, field workers are supplied with contact prints or enlargements of aerial photographs, copies of various forms of base maps, or controlled mosaics. As the preparation of the map is undertaken, field sheets are copied and reproduced; manuscript maps are reproduced on metal-mounted papers and glass; prints of the various color separation plates are reproduced for lettering layouts and editing work; black-and-white composites are made for area determination and editing; and color proofs are used for final checking. Special maps, line drawings, and the like are used in the soil survey report. Workers with a wide range of skills are required.

All final soil map reproduction of the Division of Soil Survey is done by commercial lithographers under contract. The Cartographic Section prepares the specifications for the lithography, estimates costs, and inspects and checks the work prior to acceptance.

Lithographers prepare lithographic plates from the finished color separations supplied. These are done either by photographic copy or direct printing, depending on the material supplied and whether scale changes are necessary. The lithographic plates are attached to the press-plate holder, the rollers inked, and the map sheets fed through the press to obtain an impression of one color. The plate for the next color is then put on the press, rollers inked, and the second color run on the same map sheets. This process is continued until all colors have been run and the final composite-colored map is produced.

During the process the lithographer supplies lithographic proofs. The first proof shows the culture, drainage, and soil boundaries, and the second one shows the color tints. The last combined proof is usually sent to the chief of the party and to others who may have cooperated in the survey. Since the field sheets are retained in the Cartographic Section, this proof is checked only for titles, credit lines, and similar items. Where practicable, the party chief is given an opportunity to inspect the map after the edit of the color separations and before it goes to the lithographer. Necessary corrections can be made at this stage at minimum cost. Corrections made after receipt of the final lithographic proof are very expensive and should be avoided unless absolutely necessary. Proof copies requiring no changes need only to be acknowledged by letter as correct.

brown when dry; loose; weak medium or fine crumb structure; strongly acid. 1 to 4 inches thick.

B$_{21}$ 2 to 6 inches, yellowish-brown or brown loam when moist; coherent in place; very friable when removed; weak very fine crumb structure; strongly acid. 3 to 5 inches thick.

B$_{22}$ 6 to 15 inches, like the above except light yellowish brown to yellowish brown in color. 6 to 10 inches thick.

B$_{23}$ 15 to 24 inches, light yellowish-brown loam when moist; firm in place, friable when removed; weak very fine crumb structure; strongly acid. 10 to 12 inches thick.

B$_3$ 24 to 30 inches, olive or light yellowish-brown loam when moist; firm in place, friable when removed; weak very fine crumb structure that may grade into weak medium platy in the lower part; strongly acid. 6 to 12 inches thick.

C   30 inches +, olive loam when moist; both crushed and uncrushed aggregates have the same color, very seldom with any surface skin on the aggregates; compact in place, friable when removed; medium platy; strongly acid. (Water seldom runs horizontally above this horizon as it does in the Paxton and Woodbridge soils.)

Range in characteristics.—These soils are stony both internally and externally, but not so much so as the Gloucester soils. The thickness of solum is about 30 to 36 inches in southern New England and about 24 to 30 inches in northern New England. At the boundary of the Podzol region these soils grade into the Berkshire soils—their Podzol analogs—and a nearly arbitrary line of demarcation needs to be established in detailed surveys.

Relief.—The soils are on nearly level to steep uplands including drumloidal hills. Soil slopes vary from 5 to 20 percent.

Drainage.—Well drained; runoff is rapid, and internal drainage is medium.

Vegetation.—Red and white oaks, sugar and red maples, gray birch, white pine. Pastures contain sweetfern, sumac, blueberry, and hardhack.

Use.—Approximately 50 to 60 percent of the soil is cleared and used for hay, mainly timothy and clover. Other crops are silage corn, oats, rye, potatoes, and apples. Yields are good with adequate fertilization. The unimproved stony areas are in forest and pasture.

Distribution.—Central Connecticut, central Massachusetts, southeastern Vermont, southern New Hampshire, southern Maine, and eastern New York. Series established: Worcester County, Massachusetts, 1922.

Type location: Worcester County, Massachusetts.

Source of name: Charlton Township, Worcester County, Massachusetts.

Remarks.—The Charlton soils as now defined were previously classified with the Gloucester soils. The Charlton soils included both loose and moderately compact till up until about 1940, when the soils on the loose till were recognized separately as Grafton series. The soils of Providence County, Rhode Island, correlated as Charlton, appear to be developed on this loose till. Considerable experimental work has been done on the Charlton soils. Experimental pasture plots have been established on this soil at Storrs by the Connecticut Agricultural Experiment Station and at Highmoor Farm in eastern Maine by the Maine Agricultural Experiment Station. Bulletin 139 (1926), Connecticut Agricultural Experiment Station, compares farm management on Charlton and Gloucester soils.

Cookeville series

The Cookeville series includes Red-Yellow Podzolic soils in the transitional belt between the Red-Yellow Podzolic and Gray-Brown Podzolic regions. These soils are developed from slightly cherty moderately high grade Mississippian limestones and occur chiefly in association with Baxter, Bewleyville, Montview, and Dickson soils. They contain less chert than the Baxter soils to a depth of 4 to 6 feet. In contrast to the Bewleyville soils, B horizons of the Cookeville are red and the solum is derived chiefly from limestone residuum, whereas the solum of the Bewleyville is brownish and developed chiefly in thin loess. The Cookeville soils are fairly extensive and important agriculturally. The silt loam is the most important type.

Soil profile (Cookeville silt loam):

A$_p$ 0 to 8 inches, brown (10YR 5/3 or 4/3) to yellowish-brown (10YR 5/4) very friable silt loam with a moderate medium crumb structure. 6 to 10 inches thick.

B$_1$ 8 to 20 inches, yellowish-red (5YR 5/8) to reddish-yellow (5YR 6/6) friable moderate medium blocky silty clay loam that becomes redder, heavier, and more distinct in structure in the lower part. 10 to 14 inches thick.

B$_2$ 20 to 40 inches, dark-red (2.5YR 3/6) or red (2.5YR 5/8) firm heavy silty clay loam or silty clay with a strong medium blocky structure; the crushed material is distinctly yellow as compared with the red color of the aggregates; contains much very finely divided chert and some fine angular chert pieces. 16 to 24 inches thick.

C   40 inches +, dark-red (2.5YR 3/6) or red (2.5YR 5/8) very firm silty clay splotched and streaked with yellow, yellowish brown, and strong brown; contains much finely divided chert and some angular chert pieces; extends to bedrock, usually at depths of 6 to 10 feet or more.

Range in characteristics.—Cookeville soils are medium to strongly acid throughout the profile. The combined thickness of the A and B$_1$ horizons ranges between 16 and 30 inches. The B$_2$ horizon may be chert-free but characteristically has a considerable amount of very finely divided chert throughout. The C horizon may vary considerably in color and chert content within short distances. A thin discontinuous layer of loesslike silt is a component of the upper solum in places. Moderately eroded areas have a characteristic three-color pattern of pale brown, yellowish red, and dark red.

Relief.—Undulating to rolling (and karst).

Drainage.—Well drained; medium to rapid runoff and medium internal drainage.

Vegetation.—Originally hardwood trees consisting chiefly of red, black, post, and white oaks, with some hickory, elm, dogwood, and some maples, especially near the northern limits of its occurrence.

Use.—Practically all the soil is cleared and used for the production of general farm crops, including corn, alfalfa, lespedeza, clovers, and cotton. Strawberries and other truck crops are grown locally.

Distribution.—Mississippian Plateau of Kentucky, Tennessee, and Alabama. Type location: Central Putnam County, Tennessee.
Series established: Limestone County, Alabama, 1946.

Dalhart series

The Dalhart series includes brown to dark-brown noncalcareous well-drained Reddish Chestnut soils having brown, friable, granular, permeable B horizons. These soils occur in extreme northwestern Texas and adjacent areas, mainly on the High Plains, in association with Pullman, Richfield, and Mansker soils. Generally, the parent materials are strongly calcareous, moderately sandy aeolian mantles deposited relatively late in the Pleistocene. The Dalhart series is less reddish than Amarillo, generally is calcareous at somewhat shallower depths, occurs in the more northerly or somewhat cooler areas, and appears to be developed mainly from more recently deposited parent materials. The B horizons of Dalhart soils are more sandy than those of Pullman and Richfield and less sandy than those of Springer and Pratt.

Soil profile (Dalhart fine sandy loam):

A$_1$ 0 to 8 inches, brown (10YR 5/3; 4/2.5, moist) fine sandy loam; moderate medium granular; very friable when moist, slightly hard when dry; grades abruptly into the B horizon; neutral. 6 to 11 inches thick.

B$_2$ 8 to 21 inches, brown (10YR 5/3; 4/3, moist) sandy clay loam; mixed strong very coarse prismatic and moderate medium granular structure; friable when moist, and very hard when dry; neutral to mildly alkaline but noncalcareous. 10 to 20 inches thick.

B₃ 21 to 33 inches, light-brown (7.5YR 6/4; 5/4, moist) sandy clay loam; friable when moist, very hard when dry; weak coarse to medium granular structure; mildly alkaline. 0 to 15 inches thick.

Cca 33 to 54 inches, very pale brown (10YR 7/4) strongly calcareous sandy clay loam or sandy clay intermixed with 5 to 40 percent of soft white concretions of CaCO₃; changes gradually to less calcareous material below. 10 to 30 inches thick.

Range in characteristics.—Types range from loamy fine sand to clay loam. The color of the surface soil darkens slightly with decreasing sandiness. The color of A₁ horizon ranges from brown to dark brown and dark grayish brown and includes hues 7.5YR to 10YR, values 4 to 5.5, and chroma 2 to 3. The color of the B₂ horizon ranges from brown to grayish brown, and its texture from sandy clay loam to sandy clay or light clay. The color of the B₃ horizon ranges from grayish brown to light brown. It is calcareous or absent where the carbonate horizon occurs within 2 feet. The depth to the Cca horizon ranges from about 15 to 45 inches. In many places there are buried soils below 3 feet.

Relief.—Nearly level to gently sloping upland. May have subdued stabilized dunes several hundred feet wide and only a few feet high.

Drainage.—Good; slow to medium runoff. Naturally the substrata are permanently dry.

Vegetation.—Short grasses (mainly buffalo and gramas) on the clay loam, short grasses and mid-grasses on the sandy loams, and little bluestem and sand sage on the loamy sands.

Use.—Besides native pasture, the moderately fine textured types are used mainly for winter wheat, the sandy loam for winter wheat and sorghums, and the loamy fine sand for sorghums.

Distribution.—Panhandle of Texas and adjacent parts of Oklahoma, New Mexico, and Kansas; mostly on the High Plains north of the Canadian River; very extensive.

Type location: Dallam County, Texas.

Series established: Union County, New Mexico, 1938

Drummer series

The Drummer series includes Humic-Gley soils (Wiesenboden) of the Prairie soil region developed on water-worked glacial sediments of the uplands, or mixed loess, till, and glacial sediments of the outwash plains under poor or very poor natural drainage. The soils are coextensive with the nearly level to depressional areas and are mapped in association with the Proctor and Brenton soils of the outwash plains as well as with the soils of the Saybrook and Flanagan catenas. The solum is about neutral in reaction.

Soil profile (Drummer clay loam):

A₁₁ 0 to 10 inches, black (10YR 2/1, moist) silt loam to clay loam with moderate medium granular structure; neutral to slightly acid. 8 to 20 inches thick.

A₁₂ 10 to 17 inches, very dark-gray (10YR 3/1, moist) clay loam or silty clay loam; moderate medium granular structure; neutral to slightly acid. 6 to 8 inches thick.

Bg 17 to 27 inches, dark-gray (5Y 4/1, moist) to gray (10YR 5/1, moist) clay loam or silty clay loam with some sand; some mottling of brownish yellow and splotches of very dark gray where organic matter has come down from above; moderate medium blocky structure; neutral to slightly alkaline. 8 to 15 inches thick.

C 27 inches +, gray (10YR 5/1 to 6/1, moist) heavy loam to clay loam with brownish-yellow mottles, resting on silty, sandy, or gravelly material at 40 to 50 inches; neutral to calcareous.

Range in characteristics.—The texture of the surface soil layers ranges from silty clay loam to clay loam or silty clay. The color, texture, and mottlings of the B horizon vary. The depth to the loose sand and gravel substratum varies but is usually more than 36 inches. Small areas with sandy B horizons may be included.

Relief.—Nearly level to depressional; slopes are usually less than ½ percent.

Drainage.—Developed under high water table; natural drainage poor to very poor; runoff, very slow or none. Adapted to tile drainage.

Vegetation.—Water-loving grasses and sedges.

Use.—General farming, principally corn and soybeans.

Distribution.—Central, north-central, northeastern, and east-central parts of Illinois and adjoining States where parent materials and soil-forming forces are similar.

Type location: Iroquois County, Illinois.

Series established: Ford County, Illinois, 1929.

Source of name: Township in Ford County, Illinois.

Fargo series

The Fargo soils are Humic-Gley soils, or chernozemic Wiesenboden, of the northern Chernozem region from clayey sediments deposited in old glacial lakes and in valleys formerly blocked by till or ice. Drainage outlets have been established for most of the areas. The characteristic features of the Fargo soils are a dark, granular clayey surface soil; gray, or mottled light and dark gray, clayey subsoil; and a fairly well-defined layer of lime accumulation (C_{ca}). These soils differ from the associated Bearden series in being composed of clayey materials throughout. They resemble Parnell soils but are a little better developed, are on older sediments, and are commonly better drained.

Soil profile (Fargo clay):

A_1 0 to 16 inches, very dark-gray (N 3/, dry) to black (N 2/, moist) heavy clay, finely granular in structure. 12 to 20 inches thick.

B_g 16 to 21 inches, dark-gray (N 4/, dry) to dark olive-gray (5Y 4/2, moist) fine subangular blocky clay. 5 to 8 inches thick.

C_{ca} 21 to 33 inches, gray (N/5, dry) to dark olive-gray (5Y 4/1, moist) massive clay containing large amounts of fine lime carbonate, either uniformly disseminated or in the form of nodules and concretions. 6 to 18 inches thick.

C   33 inches +, pale-yellow (2.5Y 7/4, dry) to yellowish-brown (2.5Y 5/4, moist) calcareous lacustrine clay, showing prominent varves in some localities.

Range in characteristics.—The thickness of the dark surface horizon and the depth to free carbonates vary considerably. In a few places the soil is calcareous from the surface down. Some profiles have a C_{cs} layer. Buried soils are not uncommon.

Relief.—Level or very gently undulating.

Drainage.—Natural drainage is imperfect to poor; internal drainage is slow. The greater part of the extensive areas of Fargo soils has been improved by artificial drainage.

Vegetation.—Originally covered by a dense stand of tall prairie grasses.

Use.—Nearly all the Fargo is cultivated, especially in the Red River Valley. Wheat and other small grains are the principal crops, but alfalfa, flax, corn, and sweetclover are also grown. Uncultivated areas are used for pasture and hay.

Distribution.—North Dakota, South Dakota, and Minnesota. The largest area is in the Red River Valley.

Type location: Cass County, North Dakota.

Series established: Grand Forks area, North Dakota, 1902.

Fruita series

The Fruita soils are developed in the Gray Desert soil region from highly calcareous alluvial materials washed mainly from sandstones and sandy shales of the Cretaceous, Jurassic, and Tertiary ages. In places there is an appreciable admixture of quartzite. These zonal soils are related to the Moffat, Mesa, and Hinman series. They have weakly developed texture profiles, moderately developed horizons of lime accumulation, and substrata of fine earthy alluvium deposited, usually, over shale and sandstone bedrock. Although otherwise generally similar, their profiles are less red than those of the Moffat soils and more red than those of the Hinman. The B horizons of the Fruita soils are coarser in texture than those of the Hinman and their profiles lack the gravelly substrata of the Hinman. The Fruita soils are younger and have less segregated lime than the Mesa soils and lack their gravelly substrata. In stage of development, they resemble the Meeteetse series but appear to have developed from a more highly calcareous alluvium, to have more segregated lime, and to be less red in color.

Soil profile (Fruita very fine sandy loam):

A$_p$ 0 to 8 inches, light-brown (7.5YR 6/4) to brown (7.5YR 4/4, moist) calcareous very fine sandy loam; slightly hard and weakly cloddy. (Under virgin cover the surface ¼ to ½ inch is a soft to slightly hard vesicular crust of fine sandy loam over loose moderate very fine granular fine sandy loam to 1 or 2 inches. These horizons are very pale brown (10YR 7/3) to pink (7.5YR 8/4). Below this the light-brown very fine sandy loam to loam has a slightly hard weak coarse horizontal blocky structure. These peds readily crumble into medium granules.) 6 to 10 inches thick.

B$_{21}$ 8 to 15 inches, light-brown (7.5YR 6/4) calcareous loam; slightly hard to hard weak very coarse blocky to prismatic and weak medium and fine granular structure; when moist, the soil is brown (7.5YR 5/4) and very friable. 4 to 10 inches thick. This layer grades into:

B$_{22}$ 15 to 20 inches, very pale-brown (10YR 7/4) strongly calcareous loam; slight amount of segregated lime occurs in thin veins or in small white (10YR 8/2) mottles comprising less than 5 percent of the soil mass. Dry soil is slightly hard to hard and is weakly granular. The brown (7.5YR 5/4) moist soil is very friable. 3 to 8 inches thick.

B$_{3ca}$ 20 to 30 inches, very pale-brown (10YR 7/4) with 20- to 70-percent white (10YR 8/2) mottles, strongly and very strongly calcareous loam to light clay loam; hard weak subangular blocky structure; segregated lime occurs in seams and as lime flour in 2- to 10-inch mottlings and splotches; the moist soil is friable and brown (7.5YR 5/4), mottled with pinkish white (7.5YR 8/2). 8 to 20 inches thick. This layer grades into:

C$_{ca}$ 30 to 40 inches, very pale-brown (10YR 7/4), with mottles of white (10YR 8/2) comprising 10 to 30 percent of soil mass and decreasing in the lower part of the horizon, strongly and very strongly calcareous fine sandy loam to light clay loam; hard but friable to weak granular structure; segregated lime occurs as lime flour throughout the soil-mass and is concentrated in large and small mottles and splotches; the very friable moist soil is reddish yellow (7.5YR 6/6) mottled with pinkish white (7.5YR 8/2). 5 to 15 inches thick.

C 40 to 72 inches, very pale-brown (10YR 7/4) to pale-yellow (5Y 8/3) strongly calcareous fine sandy loam to light clay loam; massive, slightly hard to hard. The moist soil is friable. 10 to 32 inches thick.

D Bedrock of shale or sandstone at varying depths below 72 inches.

Range in characteristics.—Light brown (7.5YR 6/4) is the dominant color of the A$_p$ and B$_2$. Mapping units include soils with horizons having the browner limits of the Moffat series (i.e., light reddish brown (5YR 6/4, dry) and reddish brown (5YR 4/4, moist) as well as very pale brown (10YR 7/3). The degree of lime segregation is generally moderate but varies from slight in a horizon with 5 percent lime mottlings to strong in a horizon where 90 percent of the soil color is dominated by very strongly calcareous material. Although generally not gravelly, some mapping units include soils with varying quantities of sandstone gravel distributed throughout the profile. The depth of the alluvium over bedrock shale and sandstone is typically more than 6 feet, but a few shallower areas occur.

Relief.—Generally smooth nearly level to gently sloping alluvial fans and alluvial fan benches. Sloping and steep phases occur on deeply trenched fans.

Drainage.—Runoff is slow to medium on nearly level and gentle slopes. Internal drainage is medium. Soils are generally free of harmful concentrations of salts except where they are shallow over saline shale and are affected by seepage from irrigation.

Vegetation.—Shadscale, small sagebrush, rabbitbrush, and a few thorny desert shrubs, with 5- to 20-percent cover of galleta, black grama, bunchgrasses, and annual weeds and herbs.

Use.—These soils are productive and yields are high with good management under irrigation. They are used principally for truck crops, fruits, alfalfa, hay, and cereal grains.

Distribution.—Arid valleys in western Colorado, eastern Utah, and Wyoming.

Type location: Alluvial fan benches north of Fruita in Mesa County, Colorado. Series established: Grand Junction Area, Colorado, 1905.

Remarks.—In the soil survey of the Grand Junction Area in 1905 the Fruita series included soils occupying the low, young alluvial fans and river flood plains. The Fruita series has been redefined, and in the resurvey of the Grand Junction Area in 1947 the soils formerly called Fruita have been classified as types of the Billings, Ravola, and Green River series.

Lyons series

The Lyons series includes very poorly drained Humic-Gley (Wiesenboden) soils on calcareous glacial till from limestone with varying proportions of shale and sandstone as major constituents. Its modal profile is that of the very poorly drained member of a catena that includes the well-drained Gray-Brown Podzolic soil, Honeoye, the moderately well-drained Lima, and the poorly drained Kendaia, but its range includes the Humic-Gley associates of several Gray-Brown Podzolic and Brown Forest soils in New York developed from medium-textured materials of high to medium lime content. These include catenas of which the well-drained members are Fenner, Grenville, Nellis, Dover, and Pittsfield among Brown Forest soils; Honeoye, Ontario, and Wassaic among modal Gray-Brown Podzolic soils; and Lansing, Madrid, Lowville, and Stockbridge among intergrades between Brown Forest or Gray-Brown Podzolic soils and Brown Podzolic soils. The series is used only tentatively in some of these catenas, but in most of them the hydromorphic character of the soil overshadows differences of parent material that give rise to significant differences among zonal soils.

Soil profile (Lyons silt loam—virgin):

A₀   1 to 0 inch, forest litter, usually without a humus mat. 0 to 2 inches thick.

A₁   0 to 6 inches, very dark-gray to black (10YR 3/1-2/1) silt loam high in organic matter; moderate medium crumb structure; friable; neutral to slightly acid; filled with small roots. 5 to 8 inches thick.

G₁   6 to 12 inches, gray (10YR 5/1) silt loam with weak medium blocky structure when dry; nearly massive when wet; brown streaks along old root channels; neutral to slightly alkaline, locally, slightly acid; few small roots present; an intensely reduced horizon. 5 to 8 inches thick.

G₂   12 to 24 inches, mottled-gray (10YR 5/1) and yellowish-brown heavy silt loam with weak coarse blocky structure when dry but nearly massive when wet; firm, slightly plastic; slightly alkaline, may be calcareous; only a few large roots present. 8 to 18 inches thick.

CG   24 to 40 inches, gray calcareous silt loam from glacial till, mottled with varying shades of brown; moderately compact; firm, slightly plastic; weak coarse platy structure; mottling decreases with depth. 10 to 20 inches thick.

C   40 inches +, gray highly calcareous firm laminated glacial till with loam or silt loam texture.

Range in characteristics.—The thickness of the A₁ horizon ranges widely, especially in cultivated areas where material has been washed from adjacent fields and deposited on these low-lying areas. The degree of mottling is variable. The depth to carbonates ranges from 12 to 30 inches. Surface textures range from loam to silty clay loam.

Relief.—Nearly level; commonly in depressions, locally seepage spots on slopes.

Drainage.—Very poor; runoff, very slow; internal drainage is very slow or slow, although permeability is moderate to considerable depths.

Vegetation.—Red maple, elm, ash, willow, alder.

Use.—Forested mainly or used for pasture. When adequately drained, a productive soil for hay, pasture, corn, and vegetables.

Distribution.—Ontario Plain and Mohawk, Black River, and Hudson valleys of New York, western Massachusetts, and southwestern Vermont. Tentatively recognized in northern New York.

Type location: Wayne County, New York.

Series established: Wayne County, New York, 1919.

Source of name: Lyons, Wayne County, New York.

Mesa series

The Mesa soils are Gray Desert soils developed on old alluvial valley fillings. They occupy flat-topped mesas and piedmont plains, which are remnants of old terraces. These soils occur in many of the intermountain valleys west of the Continental Divide, where they have developed under a desert-shrub vegetation. The mean annual precipitation ranges from 7 to about 10 inches. The summers are very dry, and the winters are cold but sunny. These are mature zonal soils that have very pale-brown to light reddish-brown calcareous upper horizons over a thick, nearly white layer of accumulated lime. They are underlain by very gravelly, cobbly, or stony alluvium. Soils in the Orchard series have similar profile characteristics but have developed from alluvium of basic igneous origin. The Mesa soils are less red in color than those of the associated Bennett series; they lack the cementation of the lime horizon that occurs in the Neola soils; and they have a deeper profile over the high-lime horizon and gravel strata than the Naturita soils. The associated younger Hinman and Moffat soils have moderately developed horizons of lime accumulation. The very gravelly, cobbly, and stony alluvium occurs at much greater depths in the Hinman than in the Mesa series.

Soil profile (Mesa clay loam):

A₁₁ 0 to ¼ inch, light-brown (7.5YR 6/4) or very pale-brown (10YR 7/4) loam in a soft vesicular crust; generally calcareous. ⅛ to ¼ inch thick.

A₁₂ ¼ to 4 inches, light-brown (7.5YR 6/4) to very pale-brown (10YR 7/4) loam with soft weak platy structure that breaks to moderate fine granules; generally calcareous; structural aggregation less distinct in very friable brown (7.5YR 4/4 to 10YR 4/3) moist soil. 2 to 6 inches thick.

B₂ 4 to 15 inches, reddish-yellow (7.5YR 6/6) to light reddish-brown (5YR 6/4) calcareous clay loam containing an increasing amount of mottles of pinkish white (7.5YR 8/2) or white (10YR 8/2); large splotches of soft segregated lime, especially in the lower part; slightly hard to hard, medium to coarse blocky to prismatic structure that easily breaks down to weak medium and coarse granules. The strong-brown (7.5YR 5/8) to reddish-brown (5YR 4/4) moist soil is very friable and has a weak blocky structure. 4 to 18 inches thick.

Cₐₐ 15 to 32 inches, white (10YR 8/2) to pinkish-white (7.5YR 8/2) very strongly calcareous clay loam. Lime occurs mostly as lime flour well disseminated in the soil mass. Large irregular mottles of light brown (7.5YR 6/4) or pink (7.5YR 8/4) of less calcareous soil appear in the upper part. The dry soil is hard and massive. The pinkish-white (7.5YR 8/2) to pink (7.5YR 8/4) moist soil is friable. 10 to 40 inches thick.

D$_{ca}$ 32 to 50 inches +, white (10YR 8/2) to pink (7.5YR 7/4) very strongly calcareous very gravelly to very stony loam; hard and massive but not cemented; friable when moist.

D   50 inches +, loose porous strata of pebbles, cobbles, and stones in a matrix of sand to loam; undersides of fragments are lime-coated, especially in the upper part.

Range in characteristics.—The 8- or 10-inch plowed depth of these soils is a light-brown, pale-brown, or light reddish-brown heavy loam or light clay loam. Varying quantities of water-worn gravel occur over the soil surface and throughout the profile. The very gravelly, cobbly, or stony stratum is usually present at some depth within the 5-foot profile, although there are exceptions. The fine soil material ranges in texture from sand to light clay loam. The texture and firmness of the B$_2$ horizon varies from a slightly hard light clay loam to a hard heavy loam. The degree of mottling of segregated lime in the B$_2$ horizon is variable. The amount of segregated lime occurring in the C$_{ca}$ and D$_{ca}$ horizons is generally very great, but soils having only moderately developed horizons of lime accumulation occur in mapping units.

Relief.—Nearly level to gently sloping or undulating terraces and on mesas and piedmont plains that are remnants of old terraces and fluviatile plains.

Drainage.—These soils are well drained. Their permeable profiles and dominantly gentle slopes lead to medium runoff.

Vegetation.—Shadscale, small sagebrush, and a few thorny desert shrubs, with a 5 to 20 percent cover of galleta, black grama, and bunchgrasses, and annual weeds and herbs.

Use.—The Mesa soils are productive under irrigation. Large areas of these soils are under irrigation in western Colorado where yields of grains and root and truck crops are high because of the responsiveness of these soils to good management practices. They are used extensively and successfully for growing peaches in the Grand Junction area of Colorado. The carrying capacity of the native desert range is very low.

Distribution.—Intermountain Valleys in Colorado, Utah, and northern New Mexico.

Type location: Uncompahgre Valley Area, Colorado.

Series established: Grand Junction Area, Colorado, 1905.

Miami series

The Miami series consists of Gray-Brown Podzolic soils developed on highly calcareous glacial till of Late Wisconsin age. The Miami soils are the well-drained members of the soil catena that also includes the moderately well drained Celina, imperfectly drained Crosby, poorly drained Bethel (a Planosol), poorly drained dark-colored Brookston, and the very poorly drained very dark-colored Kokomo series. The Russell soils are distinguished from the Miami soils by the greater degree of weathering and the greater depth to calcareous till in tills of equivalent textures. The Russell soils are south of the belt of Miami and associated soils. The Miami soils have a smaller proportion of clay and dark shale fragments in the parent material and the solum than the St. Clair soils and somewhat deeper sola.

Soil profile (Miami silt loam):

A$_0$ Partly decomposed forest litter from deciduous trees. ¼ to 2 inches thick.

A$_1$ 0 to 3 inches, very dark-gray to dark grayish-brown (10YR 3/1 to 4/2, moist) silt loam; moderate fine crumb structure; friable when moist, soft when dry, and nonsticky when wet; organic content relatively high; gradual and wavy horizon boundary; slightly acid. 2 to 4 inches thick.

A$_2$ 3 to 12 inches, light yellowish-brown to brown (10YR 6/4 to 5/3, moist) silt loam; weak thin platy structure; friable when moist; slightly hard when dry, and slightly sticky when wet; gradual lower horizon boundary; slightly to medium acid. 7 to 11 inches thick.

B₁   12 to 16 inches, light yellowish-brown to yellowish-brown (10YR 6/4 to 5/4, moist) heavy silt loam to light silty clay loam; moderate fine subangular blocky structure; friable to slightly firm when moist, slightly hard when dry, and slightly sticky-when wet; medium to strongly acid; irregular lower horizon boundary. 3 to 5 inches thick.

B₂₁   16 to 24 inches, brown (7.5YR 5/4, moist) to yellowish-brown (10YR 5/4, moist) silty clay loam; strong medium to coarse subangular blocky structure; firm when moist, hard when dry, and sticky when wet; variable quantities of small partly weathered rock fragments; wavy lower horizon boundary; strongly to medium acid. 6 to 14 inches thick.

B₂₂   24 to 28 inches, dark-brown (7.5YR 3/2 to 10YR 4/3, moist) silty clay loam; strong coarse to very coarse subangular blocky structure; firm when moist, hard when dry, and sticky when wet; variable quantity of partly weathered rock fragments; wavy lower horizon boundary; neutral to slightly acid. 2 to 6 inches thick.

C   28 inches +, light yellowish-brown (2.5Y 6/4 to 10YR 6/4, moist) mixed clay loam till with coarse fragments and stones; massive to weak very coarse subangular blocky structure; varying mineralogical composition with sufficient lime to produce general effervescence with dilute acid; usually has a high percentage of limestone rock fragments.

Range in characteristics.—The color of the cultivated surface soil is grayish brown to yellowish brown when moist. The reaction of the A and B horizons in local areas is slightly acid. Silt loam, loam, sandy loam, and fine sandy loam types have been mapped. The sandier types usually have correspondingly sandier B and C horizons.

Relief.—The soil occurs on till plains or moraines; usually it occupies the high well-drained areas on an undulating terrain. Typical profiles are developed on slopes of 2 to about 7 percent, although slopes range up to 25 percent or more, especially next to low lying terraces, or drainageways.

Drainage.—Good; runoff is medium on the milder slopes, and rapid on the steeper ones; internal drainage is medium.

Vegetation.—The native vegetation included deciduous trees, principally white and red oaks, maple, ash, elm, and hickory.

Use.—Most of the Miami soils have been cleared and are used for general farming. The principal crops are corn, oats, wheat, clover, soybeans, and alfalfa, and, to a lesser extent, vegetables. Dairying is a specialty in some districts. These soils require rotations that include a considerable proportion of legumes and the liberal use of barnyard or green manures and commercial fertilizers to increase productivity. A large part of the strongly sloping phase is in permanent bluegrass pasture, and a smaller part is in forest.

Distribution.—South-central Michigan; central-western and western Ohio; central, northern, and eastern Indiana; southeastern Wisconsin; and northeastern Illinois.

Type location: SW¼ sec. 8, T. 15 N., R. 14 E. (Lewis Woods), Wayne County, Indiana.

Series established: Montgomery County, Ohio, 1900.

Source of name: Named for Miami River in western Ohio.

Ontario series

The Ontario series includes well-developed, well-drained Gray-Brown Podzolic soils on strongly calcareous firm glacial till. The till consists mainly of limestone, sandstone, and some shale, with enough reddish sandstone or shale to make the till pinkish gray when dry. The textural profile is strongly expressed. Ontario soils are commonly, but not necessarily, associated with drumlins. The Ontario series is the well-drained member of a catena that includes the imperfectly drained Hilton, the poorly drained Kendaia, and the very poorly drained Lyons soils. It differs from the Honeoye soils mainly in content of reddish materials of the parent material, which is reflected in brown or slightly reddish colors of the till and solum. Although

Honeoye soils are commonly more nearly neutral in the solum, pH as well as depth to carbonates cover approximately the same range throughout the total extent of both soils.

Soil profile (Ontario loam—virgin):

A$_{00}$ 1 to 0 inch, litter of deciduous trees, nearly all decomposed and mixed with mineral soil by midsummer. 0 to 3 inches thick.

A$_1$ 0 to 4 inches, very dark-brown (10YR 2/2) loam having moderate medium crumb structure; very friable; neutral; high in organic matter; numerous worm casts; very numerous roots. 3 to 5 inches thick.

A$_{21}$ 4 to 9 inches, light yellowish-brown (10YR 6/4) loam with weak fine crumb structure; very friable; medium acid; organic matter present in worm casts; roots are numerous. 2 to 10 inches thick.

A$_{22}$ 9 to 13 inches, pale-brown (10YR 6/3) loam with weak coarse crumb to medium subangular blocky structure; friable; medium to slightly acid; a few worm casts are present; roots are numerous. 3 to 6 inches thick.

B$_1$ 13 to 18 inches, brown (7.5YR 5/4) heavy loam with moderate medium subangular blocky structure; the aggregates coated with thin films of pale-brown silty material; friable; slightly acid; roots present. 3 to 6 inches thick.

B$_{21}$ 18 to 25 inches, brown (7.5YR 5/4) clay loam with strong medium subangular blocky structure; moderately sticky and plastic when moist; slightly acid or neutral; a few worm casts present, and large roots penetrate the horizons. 6 to 8 inches thick.

B$_{22}$ 25 to 33 inches, brown (7.5YR 5/2) clay loam with moderate coarse angular blocky structure; sticky and plastic when wet, friable when moist; neutral or mildly alkaline; a few worm casts; large roots penetrate the horizon. 7 to 8 inches thick.

B$_{23}$ 33 to 38 inches, brown (7.5YR 5/2) loam or light clay loam with weak coarse blocky structure; friable; weakly calcareous; large roots present. 4 to 6 inches thick.

C   38 inches +, brown (6YR 5/3) gravelly loam with medium to coarse platy structure; firm in place but friable; strongly calcareous; large roots extend into this horizon; pinkish gray (7.5YR 6/2) when dry.

Range in characteristics.—At the least acid extreme of the range, the entire solum is above pH 6.0 and the A$_{21}$ horizon is very weakly expressed; at the most acid extreme, the pH of the A$_{22}$ and B$_1$ horizons is near 5.5 or slightly below, and the A$_{21}$ horizon is very strongly expressed and is 8 or 10 inches thick. Organic-matter content decreases with increasing acidity. Depths to carbonates range from 30 to 42 inches. Loam is the dominant type but silt loam, gravelly loam, and fine sandy loam types are included.

Relief.—Gently sloping to hilly. Part of the soils are on drumlins.

Drainage.—Good; runoff is medium to rapid, and internal drainage is medium.

Vegetation.—Sugar maple, basswood, black cherry, ash, tulip-poplar, beech, hophornbeam, shagbark hickory.

Use.—Crops include alfalfa, timothy and clover, small grains, corn for both silage and grain, cabbage, vegetables for canning, apples, cherries, pears, small fruits, and pasture. Where gently sloping this is a very productive soil, but strong soil slope limits the use of many areas.

Distribution.—Ontario Plain to the Mohawk Valley in western and central New York.

Type location: 4 miles north of Port Byron, Cayuga County, New York.

Series established: Monroe County, New York, 1910.

Source of name: Ontario County, New York.

Remarks.—The color names are for moist soil. When first established the series included nearly all soils of central and western New York in which limestone was an important constituent of the till. In 1913 the Honeoye series was redefined to include those soils not influenced by red

INDEX

[Numbers in **bold type** indicate references to principal definitions or explanations]

Down To Now

ALSO BY PAT WATTERS

The South and the Nation
Climbing Jacob's Ladder: The Arrival of Negroes In
Southern Politics (with Reese Cleghorn)

PANTHEON BOOKS

A DIVISION OF RANDOM HOUSE, NEW YORK

Pat Watters

DOWN TO NOW
Reflections on
the Southern
Civil Rights Movement

ISBN: 0-394-47113-X

Library of Congress Catalog Card Number: 78-162562

Manufactured in the United States of America
by the Haddon Craftsman, Inc., Scranton, Pa.

9 8 7 6 5 4 3 2

FIRST EDITION

For Glenda

Foreword

I BEGAN THIS BOOK as a quest, seeking better understanding of what happened during the 1960s to the southern civil rights movement—from the bright hope of its beginnings through its great achievements to a fragmentation of it at the end of the decade. I have explored how America, in its normal functioning (as well as in aberrant behavior), opposed the deepest, best meanings of the southern movement, and how, at least in part, it did this successfully. Out of my quest, at last, I think I understand better this central proposition, understand what I really meant by "America" and "movement" and "southern" when I started the book with the belief, or really only aching feeling, that America had destroyed the southern movement. Now, with better understanding, I am able to believe something of the opposite.

All along I have struggled with confused meanings. First, about America. When I have spoken of cultural forces opposed to the movement, of the people and the society, I cannot have meant all that there is to them. This goes against everything I know, we all know, of ordinary people and the functioning of society on the most basic levels of family and community life. There is as much of good as of evil in people and society. My concern has been with the evil in society and what seems to me its growth, or—in another way of saying it—the movement's having made the dimensions of the evil more visible. This evil derives from ideas and beliefs at the core of the culture, which demand of decent people, and exalt in them, selfishness, greed, over-competiveness, violence—and stifle in them impulses to joy in life and love of one another.

This leads to the second confusion: what I have understood in my mind to be the South, southern. I seem to have been drawing the line between North and South, speaking of an American culture as though there were a differentiated southern one. I know this really not to be the case, know that southern culture has always been essentially American and that sectional differences of degree have decreased in the years since World War II, with the replacement of agriculture by industrialization and urbanization. Yet differences do remain. The easiest to understand is the position of Negro Southerners in relation to American and/or southern culture. A large difference in degree between the South and the North is that the South in slavery and then segregation expressed, in an ultimate form (so ultimate as to defy and pervert human feeling), the evil at the core of American culture. Negro Southerners escaped the worst harm of this evil because, as victims, they did not have to accept the evil, make it part of their souls—which required psycopathic adjustments on the part of whites. And though, as victims, they were excluded from the main benefits of the best of American culture, they nevertheless were far more attuned to this best part than white Southerners, with the evil in their souls, and Northerners of both races, who had to make their own adjustments to what was ongoing in the South as an expression of American culture.

The third, most crucial, confusion is easily clarified; it is a matter of definition. I have written of the southern movement with two meanings in mind, sometimes separating them, often blending them. There was the movement that was a loose coalition of organizations devoted to the same goals and methods—achievement of integration through non-violent direct action. When I talk about America's defeating the movement, about the rise and fall of the movement, I am talking about this meaning of it—the civil rights organizations and the workers in those organizations. But there was another movement, which had been here all along—that of the Negro people who fed, nourished, the organizational movement with the best of their belief, spirit and capability for human expression fuller than ordinary in America. That movement lives on, was not destroyed by America, and shows many evidences of having spread into white society far more than anyone has acknowledged. Moreover, while the organizations and civil rights workers and leaders have been fragmented, dispersed, there is reason to believe that they may come together again in stronger, more mature, more effective form.

So I have come finally at the end of this book to a guarded optimism, confidence, about the southern movement, and, by extension, what seems to me to be a national movement of people against the many problems, the terrible destruction coming out of the evil at the core of the culture. If this national movement, with the southern movement a part of it, becomes more cohesive, more effective, I have the great hope that Southerners will feed into it the qualities of spirit that gave rise to the southern movement in the first place, sustained it through the terrible stresses of the 1960s, and keep it, yet, alive. I have attempted in this book to convey, pay honor to, glorify, that life-giving spirit of the southern movement which did so much for the South and for countless people who felt it in their hearts—including myself.

I have written this book mostly from my own recollections, notes and tapes about the events as I saw them as a newspaper reporter at first and then as a writer for the Southern Regional Council. In both roles, I was an observer; this is in no way an "inside story" of the movement. I have not attempted extensive interviews of participants seeking such an inside story, or seeking what most former movement people might feel now about the history they were a part of. That would be another book, a needed one, but more appropriately done by one of those who did participate. I have done interviews to confirm some of my facts and impressions or about events that I did not see. But my purpose has been to filter through my own consciousness the events of the movement, and to find my own understanding of their meanings.

This, then, is a book about the movement by a white Southerner who did not participate in the movement—but whose life was essentially changed by it. Considering what the movement sought and what most of America never fully understood about it, this seems to me an appropriate, even vital, approach.

Acknowledgments

I AM GRATEFUL to Fred Powledge for sharing with me tapes of the Albany Movement, to Ella J. Baker, Leslie W. Dunbar and Paul Gaston for their reading and appraisals of the manuscript, to Connie Curry for her suggestions and corrections, and to Leon Hall for his suggestions and beautiful insights. I am also grateful for the encouragement and friendship of Paul Anthony, executive director of the Southern Regional Council, and for the guidance and encouragement of André Schiffrin and Verne Moberg of Pantheon Books. The hard work and patience, all the editing and typing and good cutting, the guidance and insights, and all the belief of my wife, Glenda, have made this her book as well as mine.

Finally, I gratefully acknowledge a grant from the Rockefeller Foundation's program in imaginative writing and literary scholarship which enabled me to write this book.

Contents

Back of this [repression after Reconstruction of Negro religion in the South] still broods silently the deep religious feeling of the real Negro heart, the stirring, unguided might of powerful human souls who have lost the guiding star of the past and seek in the great night a new religious ideal. Some day the Awakening will come, when the pent-up vigor of ten million souls shall sweep irresistibly toward the Goal, out of the Valley of the Shadow of Death, where all that makes life worth living—Liberty, Justice and Right—is marked "For White People Only."

—W. E. B. DuBois, *The Souls of Black Folk*, 1903

They [Negro Southerners] have prevailed in the way that Faulkner knew they would by summoning every bit of their humanity in the face of every effort to deny any of it to them. In so doing they have become more than they were, more than they themselves thought they were, and perhaps more than anyone watching them can quite put to word; bearers and makers of tradition . . . who . . .—call it existential, call it historical, call it psychological—took what they had from the past, in their minds, out of their homes, and made of *all* those possessions something else: a change in the world, and in themselves, too.

—Robert Coles, *Children of Crisis*, 1967

But it's not over yet.

—A member of the movement, 1970

Part One

A SOUTHERNER'S QUEST: THERE MUST BE A GOD SOMEWHERE

Chapter
ONE

SOMETIMES, covering events, crises in the onward sweep of the southern Negro movement during its early, greatest days, I would lie in my motel bed, half asleep, half yet with senses heightened, and hear all night the echo in my mind of the singing in the church, that incomparable music. The mass meetings and demonstrations that I saw in the early 1960s were foremost for me a deep, personal awakening, in the real sense a religious experience. Now I try to reach back through the small amount of physical time, but vast stretch of proliferated event, wide gulf of changed psychological reality, to find again in detail and exactitude all there was back then that so exalted me, and in the onrush and power of it, overwhelmed me, so that I could not distinguish then the details nor speak with any exactitude of what it meant to me. I can remember the feeling, back then, that surely everyone would soon see what only a few of us—reporters and civil rights organization "professionals," a few others attracted and caught—had been privileged to see, and feel what we had, all that sense of psychic release and of being in the presence of something different in America, something awesomely portentous and yet as full of joy and hope as childhood.

I try now to reach back to that time, the sense of it, try to recapture innocence, lost innocence—my own and the south-

ern movement's. To walk once more into the church in Albany, Georgia on a winter morning and take a seat on a back
pew to see and feel for the first time the movement in action.

It was a bleak and chilly day, and the gathering in the
church, a little group of men and women and children huddled
on the first few rows of pews, was too small to warrant turning
on lights or heat. I sat in my overcoat in the chill and looked
through the dimness to the little group of Negroes, about thirty
of them, in their coats and wraps, some of the women with
head rags tied on, some of the men in work clothes, some in
suits, one wearing a big white cook's cap. They were singing
—and it was for me the first time to hear the sweet and
swelling, eloquent church singing of the movement. It was a
tune I had never heard, an old hymn: "Over My Head I See
Trouble in the Air." They had changed the words; their music
rang out in the nearly empty church:

> Over my head
> I see freedom in the air . . .

Even now I can feel the response that went through me. Here
was something I had not known before and yet had always
known, something hinted in a lifetime of living close to the
Negro South, on intimate terms with many Negroes, something promised, unarticulated, unconsciously shared, something powerfully alive within me as well as these few brave
singers in the cold little church building:

> Over my head
> I see freedom in the air . . .
> There must be
> A God
> Somewhere.

Then a woman began to speak from the pulpit, a young
Negro matron with long wavy black hair. She wore a fashionable suit, a turquoise blouse, high and fluffy at the neck, and
gripped a microphone in white-gloved hands. She told of hav-

ing been jailed during one of the attempts of small groups of Albany Negroes to pray at the entrance to the city hall for the sins of the city fathers. "There were thirty and forty people in some of the cells designed to hold four . . . We had to stand all day long . . . The police treated us very courteously . . . We are going to raise the dead around here . . ." After each statement, during pauses in the statements, the audience responded, punctuating all that she said. (I had not heard this kind of communication before, the dialogue of audience and speaker that was the mode of all the mass meetings, a part of the tradition of the southern Negro church.)

"We're going to win *(yes)* . . . because the right *(yes?)* always wins. *(amen)* God is on our side . . . *(yes. amen)* Our children *(well?)* and relatives are in jail . . . *(oh yes)* I am so happy to see you because I know you don't mind going to jail . . . *(that's RIGHT)*"

She held the microphone in her white-gloved hands much as a priest the chalice, and in the passion of speaking wrung it in her hands, moved it back and forth with the movement of her arms and shoulders. She leaned far forward as she spoke, her tan face wrinkled, creased in the seriousness and the passion of the communication. She shook her head fervently, her black hair tossing, rippling. Finally her voice became shrill, to a breaking point of emotion:

"So, children, let us walk together . . ." And they chorused back: "Walk together. Pray together."

What then occurred was to me incredible, having come into this place out of the normality of America's everyday abnormal reality, a plane flight through sodden clouds, the glimpsing in the small Albany airport of arrival and departure, greeting and farewell, happiness and tragedy, driving the wide, flat streets of this little town where I had lived briefly—the crucial year of starting to school and learning to read—checking in at the standardized neon-glowing, pastel motel, like the motels in every locale, chatting with the selfsame reporters I had seen on hundreds of other news stories, and then driving in the chilly dampness to this little Negro-section church, like hundreds I had seen (without ever really seeing) on city and small-town corners all my life, this one red-brick and wide-gabled with three crosses on the roof, the middle one lined with neon tubing. The familiar glass-enclosed announcement board in the yard gave the name: Shiloh Baptist Church.

In that little church they began to form a line of march of those willing to confront the white police, to be arrested, to go to jail under the conditions the speaker had described. They were just ordinary Negroes up there, silently, solemnly and with such dignity undertaking this braveness I had only heard about, read about, had never felt as something real. Just ordinary Negroes—south Georgia Negroes, their faces, postures the familiar ones of all the cooks and filling station attendants I had ever seen (and had not really seen) in a lifetime in the South. They would do this incredible thing.

Fifteen of those who were in the church were willing to undertake the march, moving out of the church into the drizzling rain, hunching their backs under it as they walked toward the white part of the town. A block away stood Carver Junior High, a low, neat, spread-out, new building, one of those monuments to the South's too-little, too-late acquiescence in separate-but-equal. On the building up ahead, housing the city's radio station (one of a chain aptly calling itself "Johnny Reb"), an oversized Confederate flag drooped mournfully in the rain.

I had moved with the other reporters out of the church and into the cold drizzle behind the marchers to follow them to the Trailways Bus Terminal. It was my first experience, following the marchers, of what was soon to have the familiarity of ritual. I was still full of all the feeling that had so startlingly been present there inside the church (and, as following marches became a familiar thing, this awe on emergence from the mood, the spirit inside the churches never faded), and I was full that day in Albany of dread far out of proportion to what even then I knew to be the danger of the situation, and full, too, despite it all, of an exhilaration, a sense unstoppable of joy

entirely inappropriate to the circumstances. (These, too, remained when the movement had become ritual. One of the last
campaigns of the Southern Christian Leadership Conference
[SCLC] that I covered was in St. Augustine in 1964. I can still
feel the exhilaration, the joy that welled up in me on my first
night of following the marches there—even though I knew
about the terrible danger, the uncontrolled mob awaiting the
marchers. I walked in the familiar reporters' position alongside
the march, and the insane, soft wind of the Florida shore
poured over me as we passed the ghostly shapes of the ancient
buildings and moss-hung trees, and I threw back my head in
exultation. This is the place to be, I said; this is where I belong.
And then felt bad—the familiar sense of somehow exploiting
this great and serious thing that the Negroes were doing, and
their suffering. Now I have come to understand that my feeling
was appropriate, that instead of the shame I think a lot of
whites used to feel about their undeniable joy in the mighty
doings of the movement, we should have felt proud. For we
came as close as whites have in America to responding appropriately to the movement.)

That first time in Albany, of course, there was no time and
no room in my emotions for such introspection. The little band
of the brave walked silently to the bus station, and there awaiting their "demonstration," twenty-five state troopers in yellow
raincoats held big billy clubs, and the white paddy wagons of
the Albany police idled nearby. The demonstrators were joined
by a tall, slim black youth jauntily wearing a blue beret, and
they entered the lunch room of the bus terminal. It had been
the scene of previous arrests of "outsider" freedom riders
which precipitated the great Albany Movement, whose stirring, beginnings, I was witnessing. A waitress came hurriedly
out of the lunch room, her apron still on, her middle-aged
white face full of a consternation that might be fear, might be
rage, probably both, and she hurried across the street into a
beauty parlor. If, with her stricken, shocked face, she was the
average, well-intentioned white Southerner, casual in her ra-

cism as in adherence to other tenets of her society, caught at this time in social upheaval that was not to end until the legal system of segregation in the South had been overturned and most of the other tenets of her society called into question, then what of the other symbolic figures there in the December drizzle in Albany? In memory they are held, like a photograph: the balding, thin, middle-aged proprietor of the lunch room, in shirt sleeves and wearing his apron, his eyes excited behind rimless glasses, his broad mouth tight . . . talking with him, four Albany policemen, swollen to menacing proportion in all the militaristic paraphernalia of their uniforms and weaponry . . . the crowd of Negroes, several hundred, not of the movement, but drawn to its actions, standing warily all around the borders of the bus terminal, watching . . .

"Take 'em out," the proprietor finally said in a tight, angry voice to the police, and they moved rapidly into this place of confrontation, itself a powerful symbol, this place of heavy chipped china, grease-encrusted grill, with grits served always with the eggs and bacon, with funeral home and insurance company calendars on the wall, and, among the cluttered junk on sale at the cash register, photographs in the selfsame little plastic casings of nude women with droopingly large breasts and lurid paintings of the saints of the Catholic religion. The police made their arrests in this place of confrontation, symbolism, as southern police had been doing in such situations for more than a year. I was seeing it for the first time: the arrest of those who stood for the law by law enforcement officers who, in the act, violated the law, men with coarse faces, brutal in the very way they walked, protecting society from people with gentle faces, orderly and, by all the marks of it, good citizens. They were protesting—what? Protesting that they could not be served in this airless, dingy little place whose every aspect spoke contempt for, defeat of, life, of the very life-giving act of eating, or protesting that (surely in my excited state I only imagined it) such places should exist, demeaning all who used them, sucking the life from the gray faces of those who work in them, this with slow sweeps of the minute hand on the grease-spotted, garish advertising clock on the wall, hour by hour, day by day, year by year of death-foretelling calendars, all the thousands of such places across the nation. I was seeing it for the first time and could not contain all the feeling and meaning of it, all that sense of fearsome forces that had hovered over all the consciousness of my growing up and living in the South, finally meeting, the brooding thunder heard far-off for a lifetime suddenly built to a full storm of lightning flashes, wild wind and a pelleting rain—all about me, all that irony, that bravery, that fear and that appalled or warily watching reaction of black and white Southerners looking on there at the bus terminal, as the arrests proceeded.

So much. And that night, sitting at a portable typewriter in the motel room's air-conditioned cigarette smoke, I couldn't begin to convey it. This was not the normal frustration at newspapering's well-nigh insuperable challenge, all its limitation of space and scope and constricting conventionalities. I sensed even then I was into something more basic than the limitations of newspapering or my own incoherence, and I have since come to feel that the most important, or most useful, truth to be discovered from the experience of the southern movement has to do with a continuing difficulty of Americans to tell about or to perceive the full of what was afoot in the movement. I have tried in my mind so many times, in so many ways to grasp the whole of this most elusive truth, finally beginning this writing to seek it from many different vantages, advancing and retreating, returning again and again to probe at it, but not sure even yet if it is to be fully known, or even whether it is more than a fanciful projection merely of my own deeply personal reaction to the movement. (For how often does historical event provide the metaphor that expresses the individual's personal, inner experience, as the movement did for so many Southerners?)

What processes were at work there that day I stumbled onto the Albany experience? What out of all the South's touching worlds we know not of—mystery, voodoo, ghosts, strange happenings, the many ways in which nature in shimmering heat and insane summer nights and moist, verdant woodland wildness makes anything seem possible and nothing real, the same sense of unreality rising as often out of southern social convention as out of the nature and landscapes? What powerful forces out of the rest of America's invariable inability to know or cope with the South were at work to so resist the craftsmanship of a seasoned journalist, a Southerner, like me that day in Albany, and many other reporters who, then and since, have expressed similar frustration?

Why was it that most of America was unable to perceive and understand the real meaning of the movement? Why was it beyond my grasp that first day in Albany and through the subsequent years of the movement's greatest activity? This is the central question of my preoccupation with the movement; I return again and again to it and always find the same answer, and yet cannot fully accept or with certainty state that answer —perhaps because it is too simple, perhaps because it is too audacious. Yet nothing else encompasses and explains all that I have come to feel and know about the movement, and so I keep returning to this same answer: That what I saw and felt that first day in Albany and through the years of the movement was extra-cultural, beyond the normal limits of American culture; that my inarticulateness back then and all the failure of the media and even art to convey what was happening in the movement can be accounted for in terms of this extra-cultural quality, because the culture defines how those in it perceive reality and their repertoire of response; that the culture also makes such definitions for itself and thereby limits alternatives for the way it will continue its shaping of itself and the people who live in it; that the southern movement, in pushing beyond these limits, held forth alternatives which the culture was incapable of accepting and which, therefore, it actively resisted. The movement called this extra-cultural quality "the power of love."

I keep returning to, and at the same time rejecting, this explanation and yet returning to it again—maybe only wishfully, because American culture is so desperately in need of new alternatives. If life in America were reasonably satisfactory for most of the inhabitants of the country, if the life of the world were not threatened by aspects of American culture and its self-imposed limitations of directions of change, then maybe I would not attach so much importance to what I think I saw and felt afoot in the southern movement. I would not be so anguished because what was there is seldom expressed now, would not feel this compulsion to go back in memory and time and old, spent notebooks trying to find what was there in precise terms, coherent abstraction, trying, I guess, to find salvation. And that, after all, on the most forthright level, was what the movement offered. And America missed.

I try once more to tell what happened, what happened there in Albany, all that which resisted telling that first night in Albany, all that which was beyond what we did manage to tell. Among my Albany notebooks, one has written on the front: "Includes the night Dr. King entered the church . . ." The notes are cold now and are illegibly scrawled in places of great emotion, but it is worth the effort to try to breathe the life of what they tried to capture, to seek back to being inside that same little Shiloh Baptist Church on a clear winter's night in 1961, this time with every inch of it crowded, all the seats taken, people sitting and standing, filling the aisles and the vestibule. There had been a long time of fervent singing, praying, speaking while they awaited Dr. King, coming for the first time to Albany, having agreed to speak this one night only, to encourage the spirit of the people, as a favor to his former college classmate, Dr. W. G. Anderson, leader of the Albany Movement.

The singing was more fervent, more beautiful than I had yet heard it:

> *I'm so glad . . .*
> *Integration is on its way*
> *Singing glory hallelujah*
> *I'm so glad.*

"*I'm so glad / We're fighting to be free / Singing glory hallelujah! / I'm so glad . . .*" And then: "*Aaa-men, Aaa-men, Aaaaaaaaa-men, A-men, A-men,*" this becoming: "*Free-dom, Free-dom, Free-dom. Free-DOM. Free-DOM.*"

> *Everybody say freedom*
> *Everybody say freedom*
> *Everybody say freedom*
> *Free-DOM*
> *Free-DOM . . .*

"*Let the mayor say freedom / Let the mayor say freedom . . .*" And in the midst of it a stirring and then a great "Yea" shout from the people, and Dr. King, round-faced, dapper, smiling man, was entering the church, making his way up to the pulpit. The shout grew louder, one sustained cry of joy and welcome as, everyone on his feet, the people waved their arms to him, and he waved back. And somewhere in it, the shout became a song, a mighty resumption of "*FREE-DOM . . .*"

> *FREE-DOM*
> *FREE-DOM*
> *FREEDOM FREEDOM!*
> *Martin King says freedom*
> *Martin King says freedom*
> *Martin King says freedom.*
> *FREE-DOM! FREE-DOM!*
> *Let the white man say Freedom*
> *Let the white man say Freedom*
> *Let the white man say Freedom*
> *Free-DOM.*
> *Free-DOM.*

The sound of such music, the fervor in all that packed crowd of people in the church were like nothing I had ever known.

The faces, those black faces of solemnity and seriousness of purpose that I had been so moved the first time to see, those gentle faces were transfixed now, full of great joy, wonderful smiles, singing on, the song rolling out verse after verse of who would, who should say freedom, and then changed, with no signal given or a beat missed:

> *I woke up this morning*
> *With my mind*
> *SET on freedom*
> *Hallelu . . . Hallelu . . . Hallelu . . .*
> *There ain't no harm*
> *To have your mind*
> *Set on freedom . . .*

A stout young woman wearing an orange dress had moved up in front and was leading this outpouring. Her eyes were tightly closed, her round face radiant, her body swaying from side to side, mouth stretched wide, her powerful voice playing into the exultant singing of the crowd . . .

Then, as suddenly as it started, the music ceased, and the people began to seat themselves, the sudden quiet as full of meaning as the great cry of the song, the rustling quickly ended, hushed decorum settled over all, only a baby squawling somewhere in the crowd breaking the silence. And then the speaking began. It was in the way, now familiar, of Negro southern churches, the many preliminary speakers, attentively heard, politely received, building, building to Dr. King, the crowd serenely, patiently awaiting him, murmuring their assent, their responses to the speakers, the baby occasionally crying out again. Dr. Ralph Abernathy, round black face glistening, a luminary, too, come with Dr. King, and the penultimate speaker, leading to the waited moment, more than an hour awaited now, Dr. Abernathy crying out at one point in his talk: "I want the white man to be free . . ." And the audience, many in it, chorusing back: "I do, too."

Then at last—and the pandemonium of applause broke

forth again—Dr. King rose to speak, beginning slowly, almost
falteringly, and moving soon into the singsong cadence of his
delivery. He spoke of African independence ("Racism and
colonialism must go"), saying, "I can say nothing to you but
to continue in your determination to be free," urging the
exorcism of two myths: That only large amounts of time could
bring forth integration, and that you couldn't change the
hearts of men with legislation and decrees ("Maybe you can't
legislate morality, but you can regulate behavior. [*yes. amen.
AMEN*]"), and reaching a fervor commensurate with the
crowd's crying out: "There must be repentance for the vitriolic,
loud words of people of ill will, but also for the silence of good
people. *(yes well amen)*" He spoke of non-violence, of "mass,
direct, non-violent action." "They can put you in a dungeon
and transform you to glory; if they try to kill you, develop a
willingness to die . . ." He spoke of going to jail "without hating
the white folks," and the crowd applauded. "Say to the white
man, 'We will win you with the power of our capacity to
endure,' " and they applauded again. Then he built to the full
fervor of his speech, questioning: "How long will we have to
suffer injustices?" An older man with a very black face cried
out basso punctuation to the questions: "God Almighty . . ."
"How long will justice be crucified and truth buried? . . ."
"God Almighty . . ." And finally Dr. King listed all the evils
that would be overcome, and warned: "Before the victory is
won some must face physical death to free their children from
a life of psychological handicaps. But we shall overcome."
"Shall overcome," the crowd chorused back. His voice, full of
emotion that flowed into the crowd which poured it back to
him, almost broke, shouting: "Don't stop now. Keep moving.
Walk together, children. Don't you get weary. There's a great
camp meeting coming . . ."

Abruptly he stopped speaking, and in the silence the first
strong notes of the song "We Shall Overcome" rang out. Verse
after verse of it rolled on, kept on, the people putting more into
it even than into that first great song of welcome to him, and

the acts within its power to prevent or punish the white racist outrages. Nearly always the Justice Department (symbolic of all levels of government and of the people of the nation) did, as in the three instances in Albany, nothing at all.

Justice did attempt, predictably without success, to get a federal grand jury indictment against the sheriff in the caning incident. Attorney King recalled in 1971 that he had urged Justice Department officials not to seek the indictment, that they could proceed against the sheriff without one. Their handling of the case (including urging him not to talk or dress as he normally did when he appeared before the grand jury, in effect to be servile—which he refused to do), said Mr. King, "sullied the image of what my country had until then meant to me."

The press's ability to comprehend violence never included appreciation for its more important counterpoint—Negro nonviolence, like Mrs. King's ability to try to understand the motivation of the two whites who attacked her that day.

So very little was understood of the most important qualities of the movement, virtually nothing to appreciate them, encourage them, keep them alive.

> Over my head . . .
> I see freedom in the air . . .
> There must be . . .
> A God . . .
> Somewhere.

That was the important thing in Albany. Somehow it got lost. Lost in Albany and lost in all the little Negro churches standing on the corners in all the cities and towns and country roads across the South where the movement entered into and was fed by the spirit of the Negro people. What happened? I try to understand it in terms of my central question: Why couldn't America perceive and respond to the movement? And in so doing, I reveal myself most of all for the Southerner that I am. For, like Thomas Sutpen in Faulkner's *Absalom, Absalom!*, we in the South are forever engaged in seeking back, trying to find out, to know what the initial mistake was, what was done or undone, who or what injured, what fatal mistaken choice was made to disrupt, divert, destroy some one or another southern grand design that seemed to us so right, so logical, so sure to succeed. For once, the quest involves something truly right, deserving of success. Suddenly, once, white and Negro southern involvement in race came together in positiveness, creativeness, instead of the old destructiveness and, pushing beyond cultural limits to unknown exaltation, hope, mysticism, ecstasy, produced a shimmering vision of what life between the races might be, and more than that, what life in America for all people might be. Then it was gone. It took exactly ten years, the decade of the 1960s, for all of it, the rise and the fall of it. If we could but understand what happened, what America did to the movement, then we might know better what to do in the name of decency now and in the future.

Chapter
TWO

From my notebooks:
A middle-aged woman, plainly dressed, her face showing in lines and creases a life that has been harsh, hard, looking like so many Negro maids I have known, on leaving the church that first night Dr. King spoke: "He talk so soft."

From a taped interview in 1964 with Bernice Reagon of Albany, who went on from the movement there to become one of the South's foremost Negro folk singers, and with Cordell Reagon, one of the first SNCC workers in Albany, later a part of the SNCC Freedom Singers group:

Cordell Reagon: "The songs played a significant role in Albany. Without the songs, the Albany Movement could not have been. They sang these songs on the [picket] line and off the line, day in and day out, and went to bed humming 'We Shall Overcome.' Everybody—they put themselves into it. They don't follow a set pattern . . . Most people would be ashamed to involve themselves in something like this, because they think it's kind of barbaric. I mean, a lot of people do. But down there it's a very common thing. They don't feel ashamed that they are letting the inner part of them out. So they have . . . they have an advantage over most Americans. They can do it, you know . . ."

• • •

In the mass meetings, the intonation of the word "Well." First heard by me in Albany, most eloquently. In the audience's responses, amid the cries of "Amen," "Yes," "All right, now," "Lord," "Yes, Lord," the single syllable sounding from some single strong soul, often an older man: "Well."

All different meanings put into the saying of "Well" by the tone, the manner of speaking, sometimes bitten off, almost harsh, sometimes almost crooned, and by inflection. "Well" (quietly) in affirmation. "WELL" (crackling out) in strong affirmation. "Well?" urging the speaker to continue, to tell more, helping him build interest and to reach his own heights of eloquence. "Well" in sorrow over something cruel or outrageous told. "Well" in joy. And "WELL" in righteous anger. "WELL" most often of all in affirmation, agreement, support: "WELL . . . Well."

A convention of Negro religious services, this responsive "Well," and in the mass meetings an important part of the musical, poetic effect, of the impromptu eloquence and the attainment of so much unity and communion:

" . . . Well."

"We must *(well?)*

Attain *(yes)* a status of dignity *(amen)*

Freedom and justice. *(amen) (WELL)*

We have mounted the cross. *(well)*

We have felt the presence of the spear in our side (WELL).

We cannot turn back. *(WELL)*

WELL . . .

Well.

Chapter
THREE

I HAVE ONLY BEGUN to move in this most southern of quests, seeking back into my mind and lost time for what went wrong, and already am embroiled in, in danger of perpetuating, one of the most mistaken, most harmful notions of all about the southern movement: that it failed to accomplish anything.

Question from a northern friend, sympathetic to my quest: If the laws don't change the situation and voluntary movements don't, then what are we left with?

Answer: Oh, but things were changed . . . We are left with something entirely different from what was . . . in the South . . . It is a northern misconception, this one that the southern movement accomplished nothing, a part of the basis for northern despair and despairing rationale of revolution among some blacks and the young of both races . . .

When I lament something lost, something gone wrong with the civil rights movement, I lament not a failure to get results, but something nearer the opposite. I lament that a thing that was alive in the movement, in the Negro people of the South, which in five short years overthrew a whole ironbound system of legalized, institutionalized discrimination, somehow in the process of this great achievement ceased to be galvanized, utilized any longer.

Not that nothing was accomplished, but that so much was —which suggests that even more might have been . . .

The difference in southern and northern reality, southern and northern mind-set, is crucial. John Lewis, chairman of SNCC during its great days, spoke in 1970 of the southern roots of the movement:

"Redemptive love was the heart of the movement, the appeal to the best instincts of human beings. Redemptive love came naturally to Negro Southerners. The role and place of the Negro church was the idea of salvation. Many Negroes, young and old, were involved in the movement out of a strong moral, religious feeling, conviction. Sharecroppers, poor people, would come to the mass meetings, because they were *in the church*. People saw the mass meetings as an extension of the Sunday services."

The movement was a southern thing, founded in southern psychological reality; it struck at the roots of internalized perceptions of self and society by white and Negro Southerners, jarring loose to varying degrees the bedrock attitudes and habits of mind instilled in these Southerners with all the force of childhood conditioning. It destroyed an unjust system of laws and, with this, opened a way out for all Southerners from a mind-set, a psychological situation that was hurtful and crippling. To know how much, indeed, was accomplished, to savor something of just how much power, force for social change was abroad and working, is to go back and feel the quality and texture of life in the South before the changes came, to re-enter the southern psychological reality of the pre-movement days.

I make the effort to move myself back there, back through all the jumble of memories and impressions of the typical southern enmeshment of one's own white existence with the lives, the personalities, of countless Negro people—those ever-present black visages through a white southern lifetime—seeking back there, to the dimmest memories of babyhood, the way things used to be.

How did it used to be in the South before the movement

came to change psychological reality and, in the process, most tragically, came itself to be changed, too? How did it used to be? From a journal I kept in 1964:

> "Nigger-lover" and "hate group" are names that we call each other in the South. I grew up and have lived in a society for which these two epithets contain most of psychological and semantic truth. The yin and yang symbol of hate and love curved about each other falls apart in the South. The present generations of white and Negro Southerners grew up with a terrible knowledge about one another: It is forbidden to love. Where this is so the effort of individuals to violate the commandment seldom finds the depth, the truth contained in the symbol. The effort of the white to love the Negro, of the Negro to love the white, crippled by cultural conditioning, too often results in a saccharine and surface love—robbed of the intertwining and balancing ability also to hate. And the overt hate shown by white Southerners for black ones, and the more usually covert hate of black ones for whites is that most ugly manifestation of human pathology, a murderous and juiceless animosity uncushioned by a corresponding potential of love—a cold and inhuman kind of hate. Such love, such hate tend to be amorphous, and not unlike.

But even as I wrote so surely, memories out of all my growing up and starting a career in the South crowded in to belie—or at least modify—what I said. How did it used to be?

Shadows in a dimness are first memories. Presences of two playmates when I was only two or three—Negro playmates. One memory: We were playing in my house, and one of them, tallest of the three of us, stood on tiptoe at a brick fireplace, trying to reach up to something on the mantel that had caught his eye, pulling at some paper there or something, and suddenly, all the bricks of the fireplace came crashing down as he tumbled back. It was a fine, loud, exciting moment of destruction, a cracking of the brittle surface of the middle-class seemliness there in that house where I lived. None of us was hurt, and, in the adult hubbub—black and white—over what had happened, that was the chief consideration. How much do such early experiences, recallable and unrecallable, influence a man's later life? Sometimes they would sing in the movement churches a variation of the spiritual about Joshua: "And the walls'll come tumblin' down . . ."

I remember the first-name adults. Very early, "proper" southern children are taught to say "sir" and "ma'am" to adults, and to address them as "mister" and "mizzes." It is one of the better parts of our heritage. But then the ugliest part: "Good morning, Mister Banks," I said proudly to the Negro paddler come to go fishing with my father. Very early you learn that the rules don't apply to the adults who are black: you do not "ma'am" the cook in the kitchen, though she may be closer to you, love you more, than nearly anyone else—and in special ways, attuned perhaps to the fact that neither of you is burdened with being called "mister" or "mizzes," closer than your own parents. I remember Mamie and Ruth and Mabel and Anna. And Jim and Lucius. Lucius coming on that outrageous morning when it snowed so deep the very streetcars would not run, walking with his feet tied up in crocus sacks all the considerable way from his part of Atlanta to take care of his white folks on Virginia Avenue, to make his rounds of the basements to build up the badly needed fires in the furnaces he had banked the previous evening.

Lucius. My home was a fatherless one then; such models of real manhood were all too rare.

And I remember the cook in the kitchen of oilcloth and kerosene stove at the home of a friend (during the year of first grade that I lived in Albany) saying very seriously and patiently to four of us children, one of whom had called her "nigger": "You don't say it that way. It is pronounced Knee-grow. Knee-grow." (I have witnessed the lesson in pronunciation and other points of etiquette being given to a moderate politician making his first foray into the "Negro community" for votes and have heard it often delivered with relish by Negro Southerners to white moderates, white office-holders, others who needed it.)

I remembered ever after the right way the cook in my friend's kitchen said to pronounce it. But no one else said it that way, not even the teachers in school. So, like those adults who even yet find themselves being shamed with the lesson in pronunciation, I used to say "Negra" on up until I was a newspaper reporter and began to move in circles where the correct pronunciation was commonplace.

It was more comfortable to be with the first-name adults, but sometimes, too, more disturbing. I have the dim memory of Mabel, when I was three or four, "tending" me, taking me on walks—walks across the boundaries of white and black in the small-town South. I remember from then, always recognize it and date it back, the smell of wood smoke in old houses; I associated that fine, pungent smell with Negroes until I was grown (for "proper" whites used coal in their fireplaces). Dimly, dimly I remember one room of one of those wood-smoke-smelling houses, with an old, old lady in it, remember sitting with her and Mabel listening to hopping, tinkling notes —jazz, I'm sure, that music and the plaintive twanging of "hillbilly" country music absorbed by southern children almost from birth. The labels on the records were pretty—bright reds and purples—and the phonograph arm had a gleaming metallic look.

Out on the streets during those walks the big men who worked on garbage trucks and who, that early in my southern growing up, had become more or less faceless, interchangeable, the "garbage men," suddenly became personalities to me, waving at Mabel and hollering to her. Perhaps I perceived a superior sense of community, and perhaps for the first time, so early, began to know that all was not perfect in my parents' world.

But mostly it was comfortable, familiar, being with Negroes. Communication was easier. They were more inclined than "proper" white adults to admit to a child that they, too, knew of that nether-world of cuss words and sex that in the lingering Victorianism of the South of my growing up came quite early in life to fascinate us, frighten us, torment our consciences. We were seven years old and told the cook in the kitchen about my friend's little brother of four who had taken to going around yelling at people "I'll fuck you down," and she chuckled appreciatively, tolerantly, and it was comforting to have such adult reassurance that it *was* funny and that the word existed in the adult world, too.

How we longed for adults to accept and make commonplace all that secret world of sin and sex and cussing. We told the story to my friend's father, and my friend got a whipping. "Colored people are childlike"—so goes one of the stock slurs of southern racism. So much truth opposite to what is intended is contained in nearly all of those slurs. Only now, as the nation, the "civilized" world begin to understand how much humanity people deny themselves by denying their childhood, being ashamed of the child that lives buried and stifled in every adult, does the statement that the slur makes take on proper meaning. How much better off in the essentials of the human condition the "colored" really were. No wonder we children felt more comfortable around them, could communicate better with them.

"Why, we love our maid, and she loves us. She's like one of the family," the white southern segregationists still say—and usually in the next breath assure you that she certainly would have no part of integration. (One of the classic, true stories of the movement was of the family in a small Mississippi town so assuring a guest about their maid and then turning on the television news and seeing her, sure enough, on the front row of the mass meeting of the town's current "racial crisis," singing and clapping fervently.) But there *was* love in the relationship of many Negro servants and their white folks, and it still exists in some cases. (The old lady in the faded finery of a coat, unfashionably long and, because she is shrunken, loose and baggy on her, walks ahead in the supermarket aisle, and the Negro woman, equally ancient, equally aristocratic, walks just a foot behind, and their eyes, old and tired, are concentrated on the task of shopping, are oblivious to the younger world of housewives and crying babies around them, and the white one selects the cans slowly and carefully as they go along the aisle, and hands each back to the Negro one, who approves it and then places it carefully in the shopping cart.) But there is less of the relationship in the first place; in urban centers of "high" wages (still below the paucity of the minimum wage) average and below-average families that once knew the leisure-class benefit of a full-time cook now have a once-a-week cleaning woman, if any servant at all. And the Negroes mostly now sternly make the relationship a business, not personal, one.

So much of the old partnership was held together by the black half of it, by the black willingness to overlook the injustice of the whole southern social system's discrimination against Negroes in everything from birth to the grave, not the least of it the discrimination in education and in employment, which made domestic work about the only occupation possible for all but a few Negroes. They overlooked the injustice and were, as part of the cruel system, indeed grateful for regular work, decent working conditions—which meant tone of treatment more than the matter of wages and hours, since cooks commonly would work seven days a week, with two afternoons —Thursday and Sunday—off, having to miss their own Sunday morning church services in a culture where religion figured even larger than in the white one, in order that their white folks might go to worship glassy-eyed from a larger-than-ordinary breakfast (waffles with eggs and sausages) they did not have to prepare and come home from feasts of the spirit in their all-white Houses of God to a lavish and perfectly prepared, beautifully served, traditional Sunday dinner of fried chicken with rice and gravy and four vegetables and hot biscuits. (We ate dinner at noon and supper at night in the South of my growing up.)

Did we ever give it a thought, that the cook who so spent her Sunday mornings then had to wash all the dishes of the feast before going home to feed her own family—the cook who

was present from before breakfast until after supper the other
days of the week, doing all the labor of the household, including light and heavy house-cleaning and even washing clothes
and linens (with a washboard in the kitchen sink) and ironing
them and often tending the children, being nursemaid to
them, that she did all this even while her own children might
run wild in the alleys of the slum where the low pay of her job
forced her to live?

Few of us even thought about it. And how, *how* were we
able to achieve such insensitivity, such cruelty, with never a
pang of conscience? "Why, we love our maid, and she loves
us," was the way we did it, and, sad to say, for a long, long time,
that love did exist. She took care in the cooking of the big
Sunday dinner, was concerned that it be just right and was
proud in the serving of it, with great style and gracious acknowledgement of compliments, in a lacy apron and starched
"maid's" dress if company were come. It was a pitiful, patched-
together good that we clung to, black and white, the cook and
her white folks, and from our side of it, the white side, it was
held to with the same ability we displayed in other areas of life,
a compartmentalizing ability to shut out from consciousness
the bad and the evil, to will that reality was anything we were
willing to mention in our laughing, exaggerating, bantering
talk, and to make unreal anything that we were unwilling to
mention.

Sympathetic magic . . . The word was the thing it referred
to; by not mentioning the word, we were able to convince
ourselves the thing did not exist. We never mentioned (and we
still don't often, but with less ability to believe in the magic
of it) that the fried chicken was skimpy, skinny, that the table
linen was becoming worn, that a sot sat at the dinner table, that
cancer ate inexorably on in the back bedroom, that the black
woman every minute that she served and loved us, as we in our
way loved her, was, from the first breath she ever drew onward
to the last, cheated of her birthright. We did it best when
company was come, especially strangers. ("Why, law', Rachel

makes the best biscuits in the whole world, doesn't she? Take some more. Take two.") But we did it even when we were there alone, her and us, never conceding, never speaking the secret knowledge in her and us of evil in the situation, evil brooding over us, ever treacherously threatening that giddy and gay talk which, by its sheer will, kept the wretched, patched-up thing alive—if only for just a little longer. And it was so hot anyhow, and we were so full of those incomparable biscuits and iced tea and sweet potatoes with marshmallow topping and coconut pie. We clung to the saccharine aftertaste of the skimpy good that had once been there, even after all of us, she most of all, out in the kitchen silently polishing the silver, knew it was all over. She continued for a while to acquiesce, did her part in the deception, indulged in the magic, even adding some of her own—a particularly wistful kind.

I listened to a most beautiful and heartbreaking version of this on a night of the White House Conference "To Fulfill These Rights," that indulgence of the Johnson Administration in 1966, in much the same sort of southern sympathetic magic as regards the old civil rights movement. I sat—after the mockery of the appearance of the President, who had presumed earlier to say "We shall overcome"—with one of the wisest of the South's grassroots Negro leaders, Mrs. Helen Howard, of Atlanta, an effective and most militant organizer of poor people. We drank and talked until dawn—droning, slurred southern talk to push away the immediacy of the hurt and evil of that conference. She told me about the days when she worked as a "domestic," as a cook, told me of each of the families she worked for, saying the last names of these families and then the names of each person in the various families lovingly and nostalgically, and with pride in the people of them, in the way this child she cared for from birth turned out and in the success of that lawyer whose bride she served when he was young and struggling. She had long since realized she could never, with dignity, do such work again. But she had no bitterness about those times, only regret. She said that some day she would write

a book. It would be *A Tale of Two Families*. It would tell of
a good black woman who served a white family, while starting
and raising her own, and would trace the parallel problems and
triumphs and losses of each family, she the only link between
them. And it would tell of the black woman's great hope, her
undying dream: "You see, she loves both families, loves them
so much. And what she wants, what she would give her whole
life for, would be for them to come to love each other, her two
families, the way she loves each of them." She said it was like
having her soul torn in two, that endless separation of the two
families she loved.

It was the many like her who, finally, regretfully, knowing
full the largest dimensions of the tragedy of the thing, ended
it. They found other work. By the hundreds of thousands, they
left the South, took the family of the flesh off to Detroit and
Washington and New York, severing the connection with that
other family.

Of those who left the South, one was Rachel who, from the
time I was ten and came from the wilds of south Georgia to
live in Atlanta until I was eighteen and got drafted in the
Army, was my friend and confidante, was, in the old and true
sense of it, like a second mother (and sometimes father, too)
to me. She left while I was in the Army and came back once
to visit after I got home. She was dressed in fine clothes and
came in a fine automobile and told us about her husband's good
job up there in Detroit. She sat on the bed in my grand-
mother's room, welcome in that most intimate of rooms, but
not in the formality of the living room, and we all gathered
about her, so glad to see her, so honored that she had come.
She still laughed as she used to, genuinely, and she still wrinkled her forehead and nose in an eloquent frown of appreciation and criticism of life. It was just so good, I remember
feeling, to see her. She looked so much better off materially,
and not diminished spiritually, and in the face of her laughter
and genuine robust joy at visiting us, we seemed frail, I felt, and
found out.

That was the way it used to be, a white Southerner's perception of the flesh and feel of the tragedy. Beneath this, less than this and yet more, were the law and the vaunted customs, all of the complicated abstract system that made us the way we were—so cruelly separated, yet so wistfully close. The law and the customs were the unshakable foundations for the injustice and the cheating of the black people, those first-name people, over and over, through every minute of their lives. Black people have told that part of it in every way of human communication, including great writing and greater music, have made the world know the legalistic, political, economic and human dimensions of what they experienced in the South.

We knew, too, of the atrocities—farm and sawmill peonage, chain-gang cruelty, casual killing, rape, lynching. I was fortunate (or existentially unfortunate) enough never to have lived where these things might have been seen, but I know many white southern men and women of my own age forever marked and haunted by having witnessed a lynching on some drear courthouse lawn in some decrepit country town, or having heard the screams of pain of the helpless victim of a beating. The closest I came to this was seeing police, once, grimly and mechanically clubbing the life out of a giant of a drunken black man on a downtown Atlanta sidewalk. This was when I was in high school, expecting soon to go and fight the Nazis, but no account I had read of the gas chambers, the concentration camp horrors was as real to me or as lastingly influential on my life as that scene.

Lynching had mostly abated, anyhow, by the end of the 1940s, in part through the work of the Association of Southern Women for the Prevention of Lynching (an organization of some exceptional examples of white southern womanhood) and by a general taming down of life in America. When one did occur, most of us read of it as we read of other atrocities the world over, a feeling of unreality, even unearthliness to it. The racist violence in reaction to civil rights efforts was a brutal onslaught, a part of totalitarian repression. But, as barbaric as it has always been, violence was not the most salient, most prominent ugliness of the South's racism.

It was the everyday cruelty, the ongoing grinding down of people, the hopelessness more than the physical helplessness, the petty and banal cruelty and the terrible economic disadvantage, which should have been apparent to even the most blind, most bigoted of us.

How blind we had been made to be. I was far into my involvement with the movement before a mass-meeting speaker made me understand the simple physical inconvenience of "White Only" rest rooms. I had thought of it as merely one more indignity, one more callous cruelty that told Negroes they were not fit to drink the same water, use the same toilet as whites—this overlaid with the white middle-class's morbid preoccupation with disease and racism's conviction that disease flourished and assumed exotic forms among Negroes.

While I was in high school I worked on Saturdays and during the summers at a men's clothing store in a cheap section of town, catering to poor whites and Negroes. I can still see the old Negro man who came in one evening and, with big, work-thick fingers, picked through the selection of our Sunday "dress-up" felt hats, and finally, painfully, reaching a decision, took one down and then, with a dignity to the indignity of it, reached slowly into his overalls pocket, pulled out some tissue and carefully lined the band of the hat with it before setting it on his grey head and stood, head cocked, to see in the mirror how it looked on him. The movement ended, for the most part, this kind of spectacle, so demeaning to him and to us. But it was not able to build as much as might have been expected on the good that there was in interracial dealings within the evil system that existed before.

Our store's situation offered more insight than most others into the good that was there, because the integration that existed in the store was not the familiar kind involving servants. We had two Negro tailors who were crucial, of course, to the operation of the store, and who were treated accordingly—at least tacitly. The main thing about the relationship of us whites with the two black tailors was that, entirely unconsciously, in the logic of the work situation, with naturalness, we treated one another as individuals, not as white man and Negro; we were integrated—far more than in many of those situations of self-conscious integration made possible by the movement for sophisticated, middle-class Southerners of today. The logic of the situation was this: In such a matter as whether or not a certain alteration was possible (and we clerks, confronted with sizing gaps in the inventory, were capable of promising wild prodigies of alteration to the customers), the word of one or the other tailors was law, never questioned. For their part, knowing that they worked with men with families to feed on a skimpy commission, the two tailors would stretch the limits of possibility in their craft so that a sale might be made, performing, sometimes indeed, prodigies. Such workaday desegregation has since become far more common in the South, with the civil rights law's demand for integrated hiring, and one of the more hopeful results in the big and little stores of the cities and the towns has been this kind of un-selfconscious interaction of lower- and lower-middle-class people with common interests and problems thrown together every day in the routine of their work.

There was more to that situation in our store. One of the tailors was a massive man of much dignity, who at the time was putting the last of six children through college. We whites were proud of him for that. Proud of him and, if I can find a way to express the feeling of it, proud of the South for it—the South and its "progress" and Negroes and their "progress," things having come to the point where this man could get six children through college. This suggests an uneasy awareness that things had been wrong, grievously wrong, and in this we were, if only in unspoken assumptions, a far step ahead of the South's past generations, which were able to convince themselves that Negroes were undeserving of any advantage and incapable of being educated. But there was something else, more important, in the pride. The white clerks of the store, like the tailors themselves (and the store owner for that matter), had not been to college, were only a little less blocked in their youth of any hope for such a thing as the two Negroes. And they all hoped to get their children through college, like the tailor had done. I don't want to overestimate this, or romanticize it, but I do know that there was more than just unconscious awareness of how all of them, black and white, had been cheated of a chance and how, in seeking something better for their children, they were, black and white, possessed of the same, not conflicting, interests.

I doubt that any of the white clerks would have even considered the idea that once through college (or even should their own not get through college), the tailor's children might have an equal footing with theirs. But I never sensed any animosity toward the tailor for being able to do what they must often in the wakeful nights have doubted their ability to do, never felt that they considered him "uppity" in his ambition for his children—as they likely did feel toward Negroes of similar superiority whom they did not know. As men make their inevitable judgments between the worth and character of one and another, I don't think there was any doubt among any of the white clerks that the tailor was a man of a higher capability than any of them. They would not admit this of course. But it was implicit in the inter-relationships, the workings of the organization.

One other part of the life of the little store suggests unacknowledged common interests of black people and white. The strongest, most fervent bond between the people of the store, between the two races in there, was the constant preoccupation with, and enthusiasm for, the local, entirely illegal, lottery operation—"playing the bug." The work of such a store is at best dull, a dreary routine; I knew this from a few days, summers of it. The others had spent their adult lives in the long hours of it—ten, twenty, thirty, forty years, day in, day out. What time away from it they had was fraught with the anxieties and frustrations of impecunious middle-class striving. How little of joy they knew, of the stretching forth of self to higher feeling. But each morning they could rise with the hope of "hitting the bug," and that hope lit up the drear hours of the long, dull day. They bet on the permutation of figures in the closing total of each day's stock market (illegal gambling on the outcome of legal gambling); so it was not until the end of each day that the hope was doomed or—blessed rarity!— rewarded. At least, nearly always the hope was fed for the next day by some near miss of one or another of the store's people. And they all had the example, right on the street, of a butcher who had hit so big as to be able now to own his own shop instead of working in another man's, the dullness of his long days at least better rewarded. Some day maybe society will recognize and proclaim the great good that the lotteries which abound in the South have given to so many people with empty and struggling lives, the one bright ray of limitless hope that shines through all the dreary day. Without its being planned that way, and as far as I know never acknowledged for it, the movement, I think, offered those Negroes who became caught up in it relief, sanctuary, if even for the short time of a mass meeting or a march, from much the same thing—the oppressive dullness and hardness of struggling lives. The movement offered a higher order of thing, and the hope it held out was most significantly different—permanent delivery from, rather than a more favorable form of deadly dullness.

I learned so much in that store that only later, when I knew the movement, I would come to understand. One day as I sat with two other of the clerks talking with the store owner, he suddenly stiffened as he sat on the high stool behind his cash register, his eyes drawing into the top of this head, and pitched forward. It was not one of us who moved first to him, but the Negro tailor, George, in this instance superior in the strength in his big shoulders, who, weeping, lifted him up and held him like a child in his arms, while we waited for the ambulance, the doctors to come and pronounce him dead of a stroke.

We never fully know one another. The constant theme of art, all effort to understand the mystery of life, to probe its deepest tragedy resolves to that saddest of statements—the loneliness of existence. In the South, in such a situation as that at our little store, we dwelt not just in the natural confines of that universal kind of human solitude, striving in the pitiful efforts that people make to reach out to one another, find comfort, solace, the meaning of self, in one another, but in our day-in and day-out dealings with those two black ones in our midst, we knew and, in ways most hopeful of all that I know about the South, its white people and its black, strove against man-created barriers toward that little bit, the tiny touch which is all that is possible for one lonely mortal to have of another. The persistent, pathetic effort to reach others with love is man's most magnificent impulse; the imposition of such a system as that which used to be, in the South, deliberately setting up barriers to this already most difficult of all things to do, is surely insane, surely the worst sin. The southern movement set out to heal the insanity in southern society, to end the sin of it, to allow expiation of it. Instinctively, at its start, before it changed, it sought not merely to right the terrible wrong, but to build on whatever good there was in the thrustings of both races against the artificial barriers to fellowship. And, in so doing, I do believe, the movement penetrated for a time, sent a feeble, flickering light for a time, into that darkest mystery of all human existence—the separation of each of us from all the others.

Chapter
FOUR

I WENT in the summer of 1970 to meet Mama Dolly Raines. She was the first Negro in the South to take in white movement workers, let them live in her home (this beginning in 1962). SNCC field reports spoke with fondness, love, of her, an old woman at the time—about her standing "tiny and straight" to speak inspiration at a mass meeting, about the sanctuary of her home, her care, feeding them sassafras tea. The same reports spoke of the effect of this unprecedented thing in the rural black belt of whites living among Negroes, trying to develop voter registration organizations, of the panic and terror many Negroes felt to see a voter registration team, black and white together, at the door—and of the local whites' violent indignation.

Charles Sherrod took me to Mama Dolly's little farm, near Leesburg in Lee County—"Evil Lee," fully as dangerous in the early 1960s as any in Mississippi. I saw the neat little white farmhouse, freshly painted, with blue trim, framed in two big oak trees, with a cornfield behind, this haven which more than once had been threatened and terrorized by whites.

She gave a whoop and a wonderful laugh when she saw Sherrod and came out on her porch to hug him. They talked together about the old times—and at one point, in a discussion

of recalcitrance, still, of local whites, leaning back in her rocker
on the little front porch, fanning herself, she said:

"I don't see how come we can't live together in love—and
just be people."

Chapter
FIVE

I HAVE SPOKEN of insights that came to me only long years after my working in the store. Back there in those days of the way things used to be there was a faint knowing of love in a land where it had been forbidden to love. But there was far more of numbness, of raw insensitivity, of vague unease about injustice, but almost universal acquiescence in it—on both sides of the color line. At the store and in the South of my going to college and starting a career, we still knew, all of us, black and white, the exact dimensions of the advantaged position of the white over the black. Amid all the common injustices of American life that for the most part remain today, we lived with a superimposed, larger injustice that debilitated Negroes at the core of their lives, and less harshly and less obviously blighted the lives of whites, whether they knew it or not. Why was there the almost universal acquiescence in it? It just seemed so permanent, so unchangeable, like the truly immutable conditions of life. You might not like it, but you struggle along despite it.

I started work on the Atlanta *Journal* in 1952 and saw and sensed a little of the foreshadowings of the mighty upheaval about to come in what seemed the immutable order, caught hints of something in the air. I remember being startled at one of the first meetings of the Fulton County Commission I covered to see how politely, deferentially, its members treated a delegation of Negro citizens come on some complicated zoning business. The way the politicians in the center city of Atlanta behaved was a most vivid object lesson in the importance of Negro franchisement, for Atlanta had been one of the earliest among southern cities to allow Negro registration. Before, I had been only in suburban city and county meetings, where few Negroes had been able to register to vote, and treatment of Negroes was in the worst tradition of the South's ignorant and bullying, courthouse-ring politicians.

Many of the politicians and courthouse hangers-on, as well as lawyers, in those suburban places I had covered talked the South's most vicious, ugly racism, consumed, some of them, with the subject, delighting in Rastus jokes of the genre, mindlessly keeping racism stirring in their communities, in civic club conversations and the like. With them, too, there was a sense of something in the air—ominous, dangerous. They were not, for the most part, fanatics, but were far beyond the casual racism of most Southerners and seemed to get real psychic pleasure from dwelling on the subject, from the ugliness of their talk. The few liberals or moderates seldom spoke out on race, avoided the subject as a part of political prudence. I was assigned as one of the paper's state capitol reporters in early 1954, and there the talk was even more vicious, more prevalent, indulged in up to the highest levels of the government. Herman Talmadge was governor, having won office largely on the skill of a whisper and smear campaign that branded his opponent, the New Deal liberal Ellis Arnall, a nigger-lover and South-hater. The memory and spirit of Herman's father, old Gene Talmadge, one of the worst of the South's old-line racist, pseudo-Populist demagogues, was still strong in the state capitol. Fanaticism was more frequent there. I remember one intense young man, later to become a Superior Court judge with all the unbridled power of that office, who spouted something close to Nazi racist philosophy in frenzies that seemed uncontrollable.

They were waiting there in 1954 at the Georgia capitol for that something I had sensed in the air; they knew its name, cursed it and condemned it before it ever happened. When it came, on one of the first of the fateful Mondays of United States Supreme Court decisions, the racism that had dominated private conversation at the capitol become the main subject of the official and political pronouncements and the chief concern of public policy and administration, and this was true down the lines of county and municipal government across the state and over the South.

The way it used to, and seemed it would always, be was to be no more. I knew this, but knew it in negative ways, knew its meaning only for the white South which, in the conditioning that we all had of the immutability of the old ways, seemed mostly to augur a worsening of an already sick political and social body. In politics, as in our personal lives, we had considered things well off if racism were not put into words; if the subject was avoided, it didn't exist. Now racism, opposition to the momentous school desegregation decision, was the issue in political campaigns across the South that summer of 1954 and overall, the quality of elected leadership, never very high, worsened. That early, one could begin to sense what was later to show shamelessly, the utter shabbiness and collapse of nearly all white southern leadership—political, professional, business and spiritual—openly displayed in the sham of "massive resistance" to the school decision. (A scene that summer on a south Georgia courthouse lawn suggested it all, surrealistically: An aged candidate for governor standing in the 90-degree sun wearing a heavy wool suit, unsweating, unperturbed by heat so murky you felt yourself underwater, telling his "three school" plan to avoid desegregation. One school would be for whites, like always, and one for the colored, the way they wanted it, and a third would be a mental institution for anybody crazy enough to want his children to go to an integrated school. All the schemes and waste and false promises of massive resistance were implicit, all the jack-booted authoritarianism, complete contempt for human rights and civil liberties, the feel of totalitarianism and concentration camps that are the natural expression of racism as a part of a political movement.)

Most of the sense of something in the air during the next few years had these negative, frightening tinges. The feel was of impending catastrophe, irreconcilable conflict, strengthening of the worst anti-democratic forces in the always undemocratic South. Southern fatalism, the conditioned feeling that race relations could not change, continued to work on us. Events like the bombing of the school in Clinton, Tennessee, and the sending of troops to Little Rock had a calculable effect on southern moderates. They would have come finally to acceptance of prevailing liberal sentiment favoring integration. But with each new development, like Clinton, they would slide back—not into racism, but into a frightened reflex crying that now things had gone too far, now calamity would surely consume the South. Then, slowly, they would move back toward the liberal position, and at about the time they had attained it, something like Little Rock would set them back again.

But as the anti-democratic forces in government became stronger, more open, I became, and I think many other white Southerners did too, at least more fully aware than past generations of how southern politics, southern government all along had violated democratic theory and failed the people in the most basic of duties. We were closing the gap in our own minds that Myrdal had noted: fervently supporting democratic theory at the same time we allowed our governments to be antidemocratic and repressive—not merely in racial practice but in such a thing as the watering down of city votes, the need for reapportionment. So, against all our conditioning to hopelessness and against the Eisenhower years' cottony feel of inertia, we began to believe that somehow, because we were more aware of how bad our governments were, the situation would have to be improved. We could feel this about government, if not yet about race.

I missed almost entirely another something that was in the

air in those same years. Most white Southerners missed it. Their having grown up in the South of the way things used to be made it almost impossible not to have missed it. I sensed it dimly, but with no comprehension of its implications, once when I went to cover a speech by Adam Clayton Powell (regarded by my city desk as a sort of archfiend, but a newsworthy one) before a Negro audience in Atlanta, and was startled not so much at his wild insistence that Negroes had the same rights as white people, but at the fervent response, the glad assent of all those Negro Atlantans, those faceless, familiar black people in such unfamiliar behavior.

Also, in the drear winter of 1955–56, the television screen was lit with that then-strange, now-familiar vision of Negro Southerners in non-violent protest, marching, singing, praying in the Montgomery bus boycott. We were then, without knowing it, into the era of electronic perception of the world and our own history. My memory of Montgomery is mostly a composite of those flashing images of huddled-together black people, reminiscent of photographs of India's masses moving under Gandhi's leadership, a flash of hope, something indeed changing in the unchangeable South, something new, innovative in America.

Like most white Southerners, I had no awareness at all of the background of struggle for Negro rights which, in one form or another, had never ceased since Reconstruction, and which culminated in the school decision and Montgomery. A chronicle of that 100 years of struggle in the South would compare with any of the epics of world history where the will of a people to find freedom was unkillable. Vernon Jordan, formerly a southern field secretary for the National Association for the Advancement of Colored People (NAACP), later director of the National Urban League, recalled for me in a 1966 interview, with a sense of awe and fond pride, what he knew of the reality of the work of the NAACP and its offshoot, the Educational and Defense Fund, Inc. (the "inc fund," whose lawyers fought the school suits) during the long dark years leading up to 1954. Support from the Negro people of the South was as fundamental to that struggle as to the more dramatic ones of the 1960s. The work through all those early years (and continuing through the 1960s) of Mrs. Ruby Hurley, director of the Southeastern Regional Office of the NAACP, and the early efforts at voter registration across the South directed by W. C. Patton stand as monuments of the organization's importance to the South. Many of the sit-in students were members of NAACP Youth Councils, but these Councils subsequently became less active.

The preacher, the mortician, doctor (if any), dentist, merchant, beautician, Vernon said, were the people in the Negro community who were the backbone of the old NAACP—people with independent means. It wasn't a matter merely of having money. Those with means whose income was dependent on white power were, sadly, not of the movement. "Go into a town and talk to the Negro principal, find out who his enemies are, and *they* are the leaders," he said of those times.

Preachers, especially country ones, might be conservative, he said, but the church was always the meeting place. People could do things, say things, in the church with security. Whites, by tradition, and probably through ignorance of what went on in the churches, generally respected their sanctuary.

"I have organized NAACP chapters after a funeral," Vernon said. "Funerals were social functions, and they were in churches."

The fraternal orders and women's groups were involved, he said. The fraternal orders began as burial societies for people without access to conventional insurance. "Their day is passing," Vernon said, "but never put them down. They were everywhere—even where the NAACP was not."

Prior to the 1954 decision, NAACP membership was large in the South. People paid their one-dollar membership fees and hid their membership cards in the family Bible. But after the school decision, membership declined—mostly because of intimidation. The whites had found out what the NAACP had been up to all those years—and used the many advantages and

lahassee, Florida, in 1956, attempted abortive bus boycotts of their own.

And mostly I missed the other part of the good, of the hopeful that was all around me, was the real tang of what was in the air in the last half of the 1950s. Young Negroes from many different parts of the South have told me about it. One young man remembers hearing Tom Mboya speak at Fisk University in Tennessee, and says that his speaking at colleges across the South stirred black youth to a sense of world change, a realization that "they were part of a worldwide struggle of young black people to control their lives and their countries."

This ferment among the young was as disparate, unplanned and spontaneous as the building of the little action groups by adults. Here and there were foreshadowings of what it was building to—even in the precise form of the sit-ins. Members of NAACP youth groups staged sit-ins in the border states of Kansas and Oklahoma during 1958, and young Negroes led by CORE attempted them, with little success, in Miami, Florida, in 1959. Through 1959 in Nashville, a group of students, mostly Negro but with some whites, met regularly in a series of workshops in non-violence. The group was remarkable for the number of leaders it later provided to the movement, including John Lewis, Cordell Reagon, Bernard Lafayette, Marion Barry and Diane Nash of SNCC, C. T. Vivian and James Bevel of SCLC and James Lawson, an influential young minister who appeared and reappeared in the movement, emerging as a key leader in 1968's tragic events in Memphis.

John Lewis recalled that the Nashville Christian Leadership Conference and the late A. J. Muste's Fellowship of Reconciliation initiated these workshops. The Reverend Glenn Smiley represented the latter in the South and participated in the workshops. They started, John said, with discussions of philosophy and theory about non-violence as a discipline. Desegregation didn't come up in the discussions for several months. "We talked about the historic Jesus and Gandhi—and finally came the time to make it relevant." (Three years after those important meetings, as a reporter in Albany, I met and chatted briefly with a mild-mannered white man who said he was a minister from the North and was there to observe the demonstrations. I noted his name down in my notebook: "Reverend Glenn Smiley, minister with the Fellowship of Reconciliation," with no knowledge, then, of the important contribution he had made to the southern movement, to the history that had led up to those moments of beautiful non-violent confrontation we were observing.)

The Nashville group attempted a version of the sit-in (seeking service at department store restaurants, leaving peacefully when refused) in November and December of 1959, three months before the historic sit-in at Greensboro, North Carolina that set the movement in motion. Nashville remained a center of the youth movement during the next few years, and the depth of the involvement of the group there in the philosophy and techniques of non-violence was to be influential across the South.

In 1959 James Baldwin predicted a chain reaction of rioting that would begin in a single city and "spread to every metropolitan center in the nation which has a significant Negro population."* He thought the rioting would start in the South, selecting Atlanta as the most likely city. Instead, the sit-ins erupted—but with the same chain reaction effect in the South. The first one, in Greensboro, occurred on February 1, 1960. By February 25, students had sat-in at nine other North Carolina cities, six cities in Virginia, two in South Carolina, two in Florida, two in Tennessee and one in Alabama. In the next two weeks sit-ins had spread to all the southern states but Mississippi, students from more than forty Negro college campuses in all having participated. For a year such demonstrations continued to proliferate and evolve new forms. In like manner,

*James Baldwin, "Nobody Knows My Name: a Letter from the South," originally published in *Partisan Review*, Winter 1959, and in *Nobody Knows My Name* (New York: the Dial Press, 1961), p. 114.

marches and boycotts involving Negroes of all ages began to spread across the South after the first such campaign in Albany in 1961 and 1962, and even more so after Birmingham in 1963.

When this great release of Negro discontent and energy broke forth, I was *Journal* city editor and I knew the sit-ins mostly as a terrible tactical problem of coverage for an understaffed paper. But I did get a sense of what they meant from hearing about them from my reporters. Calling me from the scenes of the sit-ins to say what their stories would be that day, these tough-minded and competent, objectivity-seeking professionals became uncharacteristically, unprofessionally emotional. More than once, one of them choked up and was unable to speak when he called in. They would tell me afterward, in the way of newspapering, with all the depth of feeling and meaning that we don't get into the stories, what really happened at the scenes they had written about.

I did, finally, during the summer of 1960, get to see firsthand something of what the sit-ins meant. Filling in for Claude Sitton, who covered the South then for the *New York Times* and was out of town, I went out to do a story. Dr. King had been freed from the Reidsville State Prison where he had been sent on the flimsy grounds that his participation in an Atlanta sit-in had violated conditions of his "parole" in suburban De-Kalb County on a minor traffic charge. (DeKalb was one of those suburban centers of racist politicians that I had covered.) John Kennedy had called Mrs. King in sympathy, and Robert F. Kennedy had helped "persuade" the suburban judge to release Dr. King—moves considered instrumental in Kennedy's eventually winning the election. (Later that night I heard Dr. King's father, a lifelong Republican, tell a cheering crowd he was a Republican no longer.)

I went out to the suburban county's airport to meet the private plane bringing Dr. King home. I had never seen him before, this man near my own age, already world-famous. He was younger-looking than I had expected. My notes said: "A look of vulnerability about him—not softness, not naïveté, but

somehow hurtable." I followed the big black car taking him to
his father's church, where he was to speak to those welcoming
him back home. When we reached the county line separating
DeKalb from Fulton, his car stopped, and the rest of us trailing
him pulled in behind. Negro students, maybe a hundred of
them, stood just inside the Fulton County line, refusing to
cross over into the nefarious DeKalb, come to welcome their
leader. It was my first sight of the notably neat, orderly, well-
dressed Negro students of the sit-ins. They stood in a long line.
It was dusk, and a full moon glowed on their silhouetted forms.
Dr. King got out of his car and waved to them, and they
responded by beginning to sing: "We Shall Overcome." I
stood listening there in the moonlight, a soft wind breathing.
"Deep in my heart . . ." Their voices were so young, clear—
and so unafraid. "I do believe . . ."

I had not heard the song before, did not catch all the words,
but did feel all through me the spirit of it, its force and its
meaning. "That we shall overcome some day . . ." I stood on
the shoulder of the road, listening, and out of a lifetime of the
way it used to be, out of knowledge of love forbidden, the
hovering, hidden, unspoken knowledge of evil and wrong, out
of all my life of acquiescence in the evil and *their* acquiescence,
Negro acquiescence, our mutual acquiescence making the evil
seem immutable and the South hopeless, and, most of all, out
of all I knew of the striving of Negro and white Southerners
to reach each other, love each other through barriers of evil,
the potential for good in such strivings—out of all my southern
experience, I listened and heard them saying in the song that
the way things used to be was no more, was forever ended. And
knowing all that that meant for them, and for me, I cried. I
cried for the first time in many years, cried unabashedly, cried
for joy—and hope.

Chapter
SIX

THEY ALWAYS STOOD UP to sing "We Shall Overcome," with
arms crossed in front, hands clasping the hand of the person
on either side, the hand clasps forming a chain of all those
gathered together, in the churches, on the streets and sidewalks
of the demonstration confrontations, in the jails, wherever the
movement manifested itself, swaying from side to side, forming in their unity and communion something larger, greater
than the sum of their number, ordinary people finding in each
other and within themselves things, qualities they never knew
they possessed.

I heard the song that night on the road shoulder and it
entered, invaded my life. I think back to how much effect it
had on me . . .

I became increasingly impatient, intolerant of all those who
had not harkened to it, moderate friends spouting fashionable
cant, racist neighbors. People I had tolerated, enjoyed in one
way or another, became offensive. I had always enjoyed, for
example, knowing and communicating with southern politicians on their own entirely amoral level. They are, many of
them, charming and beguiling fellows, if for no other reason
than that they are free from much of the hypocrisy and pre-
tense that binds and sours their contemporaries in business and

the professions. But after hearing the song, after having seen a few towns in the grip of their cynicism delivering cruel blows to the great morality of the movement, I lost my taste for them, could never again stand around with them talking their language of tricks and evasiveness and laughing with them their cynical laughter at the rest of the world out there.

The song, the mass meetings, not only made the commonplace rituals of the society I lived in, the white society, seem pale by contrast, but spoke a condemnation that made them, too, unpalatable. When was the first time that, singing "The Star Spangled Banner" (and we sang it in the South with fervor and emotion, just as we sang "Dixie," not seldom finding the same meaning in both), I looked around and saw no Negroes there and quit singing? It is difficult now to reach back to the feeling of how strong the grip of our southern conditioning was, to realize that it took an act of will and came as a shock to see that what we regarded as the functioning of the full society—club meetings, baseball games, the PTA, parties, lectures, concerts, government meetings, courts, and even, singing "Blest Be the Tie That Binds," the Sunday morning church services—were the workings only of the white society.

When, as a reporter, I used to feel particularly low about the surface depravities that my job required me to watch and describe (what few Americans have ever had to look on while a young, lower-class husband with his pompadoured hair and cheap sport shirt and slack mouth, with weeping wife and dirty-mouthed baby in tow, is sentenced to jail for passing bad checks?) I would find myself a story about kids and gain renewal in the freshness of their voices and honesty of their eyes and energy of their uncowed humanity. But even a Boy Scout Annual Awards Banquet, with all its three-fingered saluting and bluff barbarism and covert slugging of one another on the arm, all its singing and hollering sentimentality, diminished when you had heard the song and remembered the faces in the mass meetings of long-headed, solemn-eyed Negro boys of this same believing and brave Boy Scout age and understood the hurt done to belief and boyhood in both races by the absence of black ones at such banquets in the South.

It was, of course, a process of alienation for me, alienation from the South and the society I was raised in and thought I knew with the intimacy I knew the darkest parts of the house I grew up in so that I could walk its crooks and corridors and dodge its dangers of barked shins without needing to see or slow down. Suddenly in the South I was seeing what I had not needed or not dared to see before. And the alienation from white society drove me more and more often to the movement, deeper and deeper into its meaning.

The deeper I moved into the meaning of the song, the more it became central to my own life, I got from it an increasing sense of that joy and hopefulness that filled me when first I heard it. I have suggested that the movement pushed beyond cultural norms. I think it imbued many of us in this way with a vision of what mankind and society might be beyond anything that our culture would have allowed us to believe in.

During the Selma, Alabama, campaign in 1965, an interracial group of ministers attempted one day to conduct a service in one of the white churches, and were forbidden its use. They conducted the service on the sidewalk outside, and at its end joined hands and sang "We Shall Overcome." Their northern accents, their high-church rendition of the tune made it sound tinny, unmusical. But the belief and, yes, the joy in their voices bring tears to my eyes again years later, hearing them on a tape-recording.

Now, late into the night, some whiskey at hand, I listen to such tapes, and despite myself (knowing that the song is seldom heard any more and thinking I have absorbed the reasons why), when its words come pouring forth, "The truth will make us free . . .," "We'll walk hand in hand . . .," and, most of all, "Black and white together," I feel the old, choked, aching joy and, for a second, the old leap of hope, boundless hope. "We *shall* overcome . . ."

I had heard the song in one of its purest outpourings—from

the sit-in students in 1960—but saw little else of the sit-ins and nothing of the freedom rides, and can only testify to its strength ("I know that I do believe . . .") from what those who were there remember.

After the freedom rides I did begin to hear the song across the South, following the rise and the fall of the movement during the next eight years. The chronology was as follows:

In late 1961 and 1962: the great Albany campaign, which established Dr. King and SCLC on the course of community-wide demonstration campaigns ("We'll all go to jail/ We'll all go to jail . . .") that were to win the legislative victories of the movement and saw SNCC begin its important voter registration and community organization work in the recalcitrant, murderous black belt. ("We'll walk hand in hand . . .")

In 1963: in Birmingham ("We are not afraid . . ."), where the 1964 Civil Rights Act victory was won, where the police showed the brutism of racist repression to the nation, the police dogs lunging at defenseless Negroes, the streams from the fire hoses strong enough to knock an eye out shot point-blank into crowds of teenagers and children (a girl knocked off her feet, rising as the water still poured on her, her head thrown back, staggering somehow forward a few feet against the stream before falling again) ("We shall overcome . . ."); and on the ill-fated Freedom March undertaken by staff workers of SNCC and CORE, one of the most pure, perhaps the last pure manifestation of redemptive love from those two organizations ("Black and white together . . ."); and from the buses departing Atlanta for the March on Washington, the song ringing out from busloads of those eminently respectable, middle-class Negro people I had come by then to feel I knew, whom I respected and loved ("God is on our side / God is on our side / God is on our side to-day"), from whom the newspaper pundits and national government itself feared rampage and violence in Washington.

I heard the song that fateful year, also, at places where people of the movement mourned the murder of their own

("We shall overcome . . ."): Medgar Evers in Mississippi, four little girls in a dynamited Birmingham church; and mourned the murder of John Kennedy, culmination of that frenzy of violence which, in part at least out of the expectations of press and public, had built in America year by year of the movement's life.

I heard the song during those years, 1961 to 1963, in voter registration meetings also, some beleaguered, threatened by terrorist and police violence ("We are not afraid . . ."), and heard it in churches in remote places where movement goals were slight, once in Brunswick, where great gains were made without ever resorting to the ultimate weapon of non-violent demonstrations, the people there singing it in its original version, a Baptist hymn, the cadence slower:

> *I will overcome*
> *I will overcome*
> *I will overcome*
> *Someday . . .*
> *I will wear my crown*
> *I will wear my crown . . .*

In 1964: in St. Augustine, Florida, last of the great campaigns against segregated public facilities, ending with the passage of the Civil Rights Act, a place where the link between lower-class white racism and affluent-class right-wingism showed plain, and the threat therein to America ("We are not afraid . . ."); in the freedom schools and churches in Mississippi ("Black and white together . . ."), where the northern twangs of white college students blended falteringly with the familiar southern tones of Negro Mississippians, the students in a strange, dangerous place (the violence had taken three lives before their work even started), finding solace in the song as so many Negroes before them had ("We are not afraid . . ."); and on television from the Democratic National Convention in Chicago, where the Freedom Democratic Party of Mississippi went with such high hopes ("We shall overcome . . ."), with faith in real democracy, only to find themselves ensnared in manipulative politics—place of betrayal by supposed friends ("We'll walk hand in hand . . .") which ever after was cited by the young activists of SNCC and CORE as the turning point of their faith in the movement and non-violence, the end of their faith in America.

In 1965: at Selma, Alabama, where the Voting Rights Act victory was won ("We shall overcome . . ."), where the movement organizations showed the effects of years of being worn away by the ongoing processes of southern racism and normal America, where the violence ("We are not afraid . . .") raged on, but the people, their silhouetted forms in a symbolic photograph huddled on the Edmund Pettus Bridge, held firm ("Black and white together /Black and white together / Black and white together / Today"); and triumphantly and joyously ("God is on our side . . .") in Montgomery, Alabama, at the end of the Selma-to-Montgomery March before the state capitol building with the Confederate flag flying on the capitol grounds and the American flag waved in the hands of thousands of marchers, as Dr. King made one of his most important speeches ("The truth shall make us free . . ."); and even, with all the victories won, at a little decrepit church in one of the poorest parts of Atlanta where efforts to organize for self-help ("We shall overcome . . .") soon degenerated into the people's quarreling with one another, in the midst of which a middle-aged man, lean and angry, told them to quit fighting among themselves, and said for his part, jobless and with hungry children at home, all he wanted to do was kill white people. And Watts came soon after.

In 1966: loud and empty, a mockery amid tasteless splendor and disillusionment at the White House Conference "To Fulfill These Rights," at which President Johnson told us that "We are moving and we shall not turn back," echoing a freedom song, even as, earlier, he had declared in a speech at Howard University that "We shall overcome" (". . . overcome")—this cunning and manipulative President, the personification of so much that is considered normal and correct in America and which helped wear down and eventually destroy the movement (". . . overcome"); and, most sadly, only a few months later, faintly ("We shall overcome . . .") on the route of the Meredith March in Mississippi, in the little churches where the people sang it with the same simple, sweet faith the movement had known all along, only to be drowned out and eventually silenced by the cry of "Black Power," raised on that march for the first time.

In 1967: we heard the song hardly at all, even in the outposts still operating for voter registration or in the rare instances where poverty programs were working in the spirit of the movement. In New York some of the deepest meaning of the song ("We are not afraid . . .") was expressed by Dr. King in his courageous address at the Riverside Church on April 4, condemning not only America's role in the Vietnam war, but its general warlike posture around the world ("God is on our side . . ."); and in Chicago people sang it bravely, but futilely, as SCLC led demonstrations that revealed the existence of white racism's violence in the North ("We are not afraid . . ."), but revealed also the enormous difficulty of accomplishing in the complexity of a great northern city even the surface kind of gains the movement had made in the South. Black children, in its spirit, went into the previously all-white school in Grenada, Mississippi, and white men beat them with chains. SCLC led protests there against the outrage.

In 1968: at the Poor People's Campaign in Washington the gathered thousands did sing it, but listlessly, and movement sophisticates from North and South smiled condescendingly and mocked it ("Deep in my heart I know . . .")—and that was after, in Memphis, Tennessee, it had been heard during a garbage strike, soaringly in the old spirit ("We shall overcome / We shall overcome / We shall overcome / Today . . ."). Middle-class leaders and the people in this place that never developed a movement were suddenly caught up in one in behalf of impoverished and exploited workers not yet helped by civil rights gains ("We shall overcome . . ."), and Dr. King, hearing of the old spirit of the movement stirring, went there and met the violence that all along had haunted the movement, which it still tried to avoid and resist, and . . . they sang it at his funeral in Atlanta ("We'll walk hand in hand . . ."), but who, even in the instant's lift of the music in the heart, could at such a time believe? They had sung it the night the news came of his death—hushed, stunned little groups in all the southern locales where the song had hinted a fresh, better life for people, had sung it in the little shacks with his picture, along with Jesus's and that of John Kennedy, tacked to the walls. Seated in the dark we were, nine or ten or us, unable still to cry, clinging to each other's company. Finally we reached out hands to each other as once it had been done in the churches, humanity linked as it always has been, each to the other, to all, and we sang all the verses of it:

> We shall overcome
> We shall overcome . . .

in all our grief and despair and hopelessness.

Hopelessness, then, had come full circle in nine short years. How many Americans, black and white, North and South, had, like me, begun the decade in hopelessness at the feeling of immutability to the many injustices and indecencies of southern or American life, and then had felt themselves lifted with the movement, the dissemination of its spirit of hope and joy, only to be plunged at the decade's end by Dr. King's death, which symbolized the death of the movement, to a hopelessness beyond hopelessness, like a man who has tasted for a little time true happiness and then lost it?

Was it better not to have known hope at all?

No. For

> Deep in my heart
> I do believe . . .

Chapter
SEVEN

FROM MY NOTEBOOKS *(Albany, Summer 1962):*
  The preacher, eyes tight shut, arms lifted, pronouncing the benediction as the church full of people hummed "We Shall Overcome":

> *For Thou art our God*
> *We are Thy people*
> *We will bear it in the heat of the day*
> *And we'll bear it in the cool of the evening*
> *For when the dawn breaks eternity*
> *We will see freedom*
> *Over there.*

(amen. well)

> *We shall overcome*
> *Some day.*

Chapter
EIGHT

I HAVE SET OUT a chronology of where the song was sung during the 1960s, naming a year and an event (1960: the sit-ins, 1963: Birmingham, 1966: the Meredith March). But the sit-ins continued into 1961 and were going on in scattered parts of the South until passage of the 1964 Civil Rights Act, and have since, until this very day, been revived in instances of violation of that law. For every Birmingham or St. Augustine, a thousand as brave and traumatic campaigns were going on in town squares and city main streets across the South, and they still occur in the 1970s, a part now of the repertoire of citizenship for Negro Southerners. During the late 1960s and early 1970s, in places that were passed over (and there were many) during the great days of the movement, some outrage could set Negroes into motion, and in such a late-coming of the movement to a town, the whole history of the rise and fall of it would be repeated—from ecstatic spirit at the beginning through various kinds of betrayal to ultimate disappointment, despair, talk of violence.

This happened in Memphis. It happened in a week's time in Orangeburg, South Carolina, a place not altogether passed over (mass marches were fought with fire hoses there in 1963), but revisited by the movement in 1968. College students started sit-ins at a still-segregated bowling alley, singing the old

freedom song "Ain't Go' Let Nobody Turn Me 'Round."
Police beat some of the non-violent demonstrators, and in
anger students broke some store windows. Tensions increased
and, at the end of the week, a crowd of students gathered on
the college campus, some threw rocks at passing cars, and state
police, over-armed and hysterical, mistakenly believing one of
their number had been shot, fired point-blank into the crowd,
hitting screaming students in the back, on the soles of their feet
as they tried to crawl away, killing three students and whatever
was left in the rest of any kind of hope or faith in America.

The movement was, and continued to be, diffuse, full of
parallel and non-parallel thrusts and developments, not the
neat, ordered line my chronology has suggested. Yet there was
an order of development, the progression contained in foreshortened time in the tragedy of Orangeburg, and my listing
of time and event traces it, as now I trace it, and retrace and
retrace, seeking through each year, each event all the things
that happened, the changes, the influences, the human interac-
tions and nonhuman ones, the underlying truth of what America did to the southern movement.

Time and event . . .

1960: the sit-ins and the founding of SNCC
1961: the freedom rides and their influx of northern influence
1961–62: the Albany Movement
1962: the beginning of voter registration and community organization efforts
1963: the Freedom March, the Birmingham Movement, the
March on Washington and the murder of children in Sunday
school and the murder of leaders
1964: the St. Augustine Movement, the Civil Rights Act, the
Mississippi Summer, the Freedom Democratic Party challenge
1965: the Selma Movement, the Voting Rights Act
1966: the White House Conference "To Fulfill These Rights,"
the Meredith March and the cry of "Black Power!"
1967: the end of SNCC and CORE in the South, SCLC's
work confined mostly to Chicago

1968: the Memphis Movement, the murder of Dr. King, the
Poor People's Campaign
1969: the movement disassembled, beginning in disparate local
strugglings to build strength not dependent on national leaders
or organizations or anything else from without

Over and over, back and forth, in time and my own memory,
I trace that same line of year and event, of rise and fall,
thinking surely this time I will find the secret, the certain
knowledge of what was done to the movement—so that if its
spirit should rise forth again in the South, a warning might be
sounded against letting that thing happen to it again.

Part Two

THE RISE OF THE MOVEMENT

Chapter
NINE

To BEGIN ONCE MORE at the beginning: the sit-ins and the freedom rides.

I did not see either, and now I go back and read the newspapers and the serious reports and studies, and in a sense I am where the rest of America was in 1961 and 1962, when the movement was launched by the energy and fresh hope of youth, was at its most innovative. And what I find, what I read, sounds so much like what we read about everything else, tells so little of the energy, the fresh hope, the creative force. The media, through all the time and event of the movement, were one of those forces from everyday America which most influenced the movement, and of all of them were probably the most obvious, their effect easiest to see. This was especially true of the sit-ins and freedom rides—because they were so original, so different from the normal in America. To see what the media did to distort perception of the sit-ins is to understand better how America, seeing the movement mostly through the media, failed through the decade of its history ever to fully understand it, appreciate it—and how this failure to understand and appreciate the movement's best qualities, its highest meaning, was one reason the movement itself was to lose much of its faith in itself.

I asked John Lewis in 1971 for his appraisal of the role of the press. He began by saying that black nationalists had called the Negro church the greatest hindrance to black advancement. "Some of us say it was our greatest strength." Television and the press, similarly, he went on, were caught up in other values of an electronic, photographic age. "Any time there was some violence, we would get a story on television. But when we were involved in in-depth experiences, when people gathered to express feeling, spirit, like in the non-violent workshops, there was no press. There was seldom an in-depth story on things like when white people really did change."

He went on: "Only a few reporters really understood what was going on. They grew up in the South and became friends of the movement, an asset. They were even an extension of the movement—they identified with it. But it's hard to find that now. Those guys are in other parts of the country now."

In the early movement, he said, everyone was surprised that what they were doing was making news. "There was no conscious effort to get in the papers or on television." But later there were maybe times when demonstrations would in part be held for the coverage they would get. Image consciousness developed. (Another movement veteran commented that SNCC never understood how to play the press game. Even CORE did that sometimes, he said.)

John Lewis ended by saying that though the press influenced the movement, it did not cause people in the movement organizations to violate certain principles—including freedom of association, despite considerable red-baiting by such syndicated journalists as Robert Novak and Rowland Evans.

No wonder the sit-in students were surprised that they had attracted the attention of the press. Southern newspapers (and how many northern ones?) did not then (and not much now) cover events important to Negroes—their births, weddings, deaths, or their meetings, political activities, business affairs. About the only thing that they covered concerning Negroes was news of crime, news of violence. In justice to them (and the rest of the press), I am sure that part of the attraction to the sit-ins was their man-bites-dog quality. But the habit with Negro news was to look for violence, and the southern press shared with the northern one an inordinate interest in violence anyhow.

So much is happening so fast that the mind cannot contain all of it, cope with it, and desperately seeks systematizing, correlating characteristics. So much that is happening is horrible; we need mechanisms for avoiding the full impact. So much that happens can be correlated, systematized in terms of conflict and violence, and conflict and violence can be treated impersonally, abstractly, so that they do not seem real. In these ways the media process what is happening, so that any phenomenon, no matter how complex, how unusual, can be seen in a few fast moments on television or comprehended from a fast reading of the front page and automatically identified, classified and fit into previous theory or prejudice . . . and then dismissed from the mind. Just one more damned thing. Sometimes the raw material of news is so different from conditioned expectation, so unfamiliar, that it has to be forced, crammed, squeezed into the bite-sized familiar, the everyday dosage of unreal conflict and violence. The sit-ins and freedom rides were this way, and the distortion that resulted from processing them was crucially harmful, because the thing that was most distinctive about them, unfamiliar, was their approach to conflict and violence.

The best of local coverage and of northern correspondence was sensitive to, and sympathetic to, the deepest meanings, that which was so different. But even these emphasized surface events and viewed conflict in the familiar terms of winning and losing and how much violence. The wire services, upon which most of the nation depended for understanding the sit-ins and freedom rides, seldom got away from the surface, the context of the familiar, imposing their rigid news-writing formulae (far more rigid than those of most newspapers) on things that fit no formula.

The Associated Press story carried by the Chattanooga *Times* on February 3 took only seven paragraphs to announce the thunderclap of the beginning of the movement. Most of the essentials of future coverage, what was deemed important, were in that story, including the sense of hovering "disorder," and emphasis on winning. (It mattered not how you played the game.) The treatment:

> GREENSBORO, N.C. (AP)—A group of Negro students—at one time numbering up to 27 men and four women—sat down at a 5- and 10-cent store lunch counter Tuesday in an attempt to obtain service and break racial barriers.
>
> They failed.
>
> But one of the students said the group is "prepared to keep coming for two years if we have to."
>
> The students are enrolled at North Carolina A. & T. College.
>
> [The] . . . Atlanta . . . district superintendent for the store . . . said, "We haven't refused anybody service. Our girls have been busy, and they couldn't get around to everybody."
>
> Two police officers checked the store several times during the day. They said their only interest was to prevent any disorders.
>
> The demonstration apparently began Monday when four freshmen students from the college sat down in the dime store about 4:30 p.m. and stayed until the store closed at 5:30 p.m.

The story, either as originated by the wire service or edited by the paper, tells nothing of the important rationale of the sit-in. The store official's statement that the waitresses were too busy was palpably dishonest. Allowing such statements to stand unquestioned had a lastingly damaging effect on public understanding of the movement through its history. It was part of a larger perversion of journalistic objectivity—the implication that because there were two sides to the civil rights question in the South, the moral issue involved was subject to the normal conventions of democracy, to majority rule, compromise and the like. Real objectivity would have made clear that integrationists were morally right, segregationists morally wrong.

The United Press International version carried by the *New*

York Times on February 3, 1960, did name the store and did allow the students to try to explain their rationale. But the limitation of news-writing technique clearly, in this instance, hampered communication. The treatment:

> GREENSBORO, N. C., Feb. 2 (UPI)—A group of well-dressed Negro college students staged a sitdown strike in a downtown Woolworth store today and vowed to continue it in relays until Negroes were served at the lunch counter.
>
> At 12:30 p.m. the group filed out of the store and stood on the sidewalk in this city's busiest downtown street. They formed a tight circle, threw their hands into a pyramid in the center and recited the Lord's Prayer.
>
> The spokesman said that "another shift" of students would carry forward the strike, and it would continue "until we get served." "It will go on all week if necessary," he added.
>
> He described the protest as a "student movement," but not connected officially with either the state-supported A. and T. nor Bennett College, private Negro school here.
>
> The Woolworth store was chosen for the demonstration, he said, because "we drop in here before or after a movie and buy a paper or pencil or a newspaper—it's very handy for that."
>
> "We say if we can buy one thing, why can't we buy another?" he declared.

Little of the bravery, the effort of will involved in Negroes' so affronting their conditioning, the way things used to be, comes through, little of the collective or personal beauty of such a moment as that of the sidewalk prayer. And nothing of the culture-challenging originality of that first sit-in, based, as later accounts revealed, on the four freshmen's reading of Myrdal and Lillian Smith—and Gandhi. This is the level of distortion most serious to contemplate—not deliberate, not biased, but cultural, a result of the mechanics of competent news reporting as it is practiced in America.

How much more of the significance of the event, southern reality suddenly challenged, was caught in a story by Albert L. Rozier, Jr., in an extra edition of the student newspaper (*The*

Register, February 5, 1960) at the Agricultural and Technical College:

Four freshmen students of this institution started Monday afternoon what they termed a "passive demand for service" at the lunch counter of a downtown five and dime store.

According to Ezell Blair, leader of the group, he and three other students—Franklin McLain, David Richmond and Joseph McNeill—went into the store at approximately 4:30 p.m. on Monday, purchased small articles from a counter near the lunch bar and took seats at the lunch counter.

Following is a dialogue of the initial conversation between Blair and the waitress behind the counter:

Blair: "I'd like a cup of coffee."

Waitress: "I'm sorry. We don't serve colored here."

Blair: "I beg to disagree with you. You just finished serving me at a counter only two feet from here."

Waitress: "Negroes eat on the other end."

Blair: "What do you mean? This is a public place, isn't it? If it isn't, then why don't you sell membership cards? If you do that, then I'll understand that this is a private concern."

Waitress: "Well, you won't get any service here!"

After this conversation, said Blair, the waitress left them and went to the other end of the counter.

Immediately following this conversation, however, he stated that a Negro girl, a helper on the counter, confronted them, saying, "You are stupid, ignorant! You're dumb! That's why we can't get anywhere today. You know you are supposed to eat at the other end."

After this brief encounter, the students said they were completely ignored. When they asked questions they were not answered.

"I told the waitress we'd sit there until we were served," said McNeill. "She said nothing. Policemen came in and stared at us and walked up and down the aisle, but said nothing to us. We figured it was an effort on their part to frighten us away, but we stayed until 5:30, when the store closed," he continued.

The group said they tried to talk to the manager of the lunch counter and, when they were refused audience, asked to speak with the manager of the store, but were denied this, too. They said that during the entire time they have been there, they have not so much as seen the manager.

The next morning, Tuesday, February 3, a group of approximately twenty students—including the freshman initiators of the demonstration—returned and took seats at the counter.

They entered the store at 10:30 a.m. and remained throughout the day. They were not served, the waitress stating that "it's a store regulation—a custom."

Blair stated that the demonstration was originally planned for two or three weeks; but that now, "We are preparing to continue to sit for as long as necessary—until we are served."

As the sit-ins began to spread across the South, news coverage continued largely to ignore the most extraordinary thing about them—non-violence—and continued to emphasize violence. Since at first there was not even white violence to report, this meant emphasis of hints of violence, threats of it. An AP story in the Greensboro *Daily News*, February 9, 1960 told in the first two paragraphs of the spread of sit-ins to Durham and Winston-Salem, with four white students from Duke participating at Durham. Without elaborating on this most hopeful development, the story told in the third and fourth paragraphs of bomb threats by whites to stores in Durham and Greensboro, and of how in Greensboro "the pressure of white hecklers threatened to make the situation explosive."

News stories are written in such a way that, theoretically, they can be ended at any paragraph; facts are supposed to be given in descending order of importance and then elaborated on in the same order. Editors under deadline pressure will lop off the bottom of stories without reading them. Thus the mechanics of fast-speed journalism contributed to distortion; all too often what was really most important about the sit-ins was relegated to the bottom of the story, while the part that most papers would use was concerned with phenomena well within cultural norms. The Norfolk *Journal and Guide* of February 13, 1960 carried a UPI story on the continuing sit-ins in

Greensboro. The top was concerned with the bomb threat and
the presence of Ku Klux Klansmen and white teenagers at a
sit-in, serving to "create a potentially explosive situation." Almost at the bottom of the story, which was a full column long,
these facts emerged:

> Lending support to the demonstrations were students from
> (white) Woman's College and young white men who identified
> themselves as students from Guilford College, a small Quaker
> school near here, and Greensboro College. A man who said he
> was a Guilford student explained he was on hand to see the
> demonstration so he could report to the Society of Friends head-
> quarters in nearby High Point.
>
> One of the white girls from Women's College said: "I have
> a moral obligation to support this movement." Miss Marilyn
> Lott, 21, of Washington, said, "I am fully in agreement with the
> ideals of these students, and I have every intention of standing
> with them in this."
>
> Another white girl, Miss Genie Seaman of Orlando, Fla.,
> refused to order food at the counter because "there seem to be
> a few people ahead of me."

The *Journal and Guide* is a Negro newspaper and could be
expected to lavish a full column on sit-ins. But what of readers
of other newspapers dependent that day on UPI for their
understanding of the important southern history being made
in the sit-ins?

Sit-ins occurred in Charlotte after Winston-Salem. What
did anyone in America learn in casual news coverage about
what it meant to a man like Dr. Rufus Perry, president of
Johnson C. Smith College, a small Negro institution in Charlotte, when his students joined the movement?

"I had anticipated it," he told me during an interview in
1964. "It occurred on a Monday; there had been a panty raid
the previous Thursday. I knew what my position would be.

"For thirty years as a Negro educator, I had been involved
in teaching human dignity, Christian brotherhood, the princi-

ples of freedom. When these young people went out, I certainly could not say to them, no.

"I said, 'Let us maintain the educational objectivity of the institution, which also seeks these rights. Don't disrupt the institution.'

"I sought to give guidance. I never attempted to stop the demonstrations. I told others, 'If you try to stop it, you're dead.'

"There was fine rapport with the police department from the chief on down—even with the merchants. Negotiations with the merchants were conducted on a first-name basis. We got plenty of threats—bomb threats, and so on. We ignored them. If it came, we had to suffer the consequences.

"I cautioned students about arrests. I told them it could hurt them in the future—if one wanted to run for political office, for example. At that time we didn't talk about deliberately getting arrested. Only three students were arrested. Two of the cases were dismissed, and the third student didn't even get a fine.

"The students had support from large segments of the whites. Prominent white people withdrew their charge accounts from the stores involved.

"I insisted always that the students conduct themselves as ladies and gentlemen—and they did. Their poise in the face of profanity, being spat upon . . . I don't know whether I could take that.

"It was possible then for the first time for the nation to see the results of the sound, wholesome training in Negro colleges of the South. What the students were doing reflected that which has been deep in the educational philosophy of such schools during the ninety and ninety-five years they have been in existence."

That is not exactly the kind of insight that the media pointed out to America about the sit-ins—no more than the media interpreted the instances, so fragilely hopeful, so portentous in light of the way things used to be, of white support where it did exist.

Instead, by mid-February the media had the first paragraph (most important fact), the headline, that convention and cultural norms had led them to look for all along. From the Atlanta *Journal*, February 16, 1960, the treatment:

LUNCH COUNTER 'SIT-DOWNERS' IN FIRST CLASH

HIGH POINT, N. C., Feb. 16 (AP)—The first outbreak of violence has been reported as the demonstrations against lunch counter segregation spread in the South.

Two weeks after the first demonstrations protesting segregated eating facilities began at nearby Greensboro, High Point reported a fist fight Monday between whites and Negroes in a milling crowd of 75 in front of an F. W. Woolworth Co. store. Police quickly subdued the participants.

Earlier, at a suburban shopping center, white boys taunted and threw snowballs at Negroes who sought to occupy seats at the lunch counter of another Woolworth store . . .

This is all the reader learns in this version about the historic "first" alleged violence in the sit-ins. The story implies—but does not back up with descriptive facts—that the violence was mutual, rather than, as usual in such cases, unilaterally white. But anyhow, there it was—the predictable, the familiar. It wasn't much of beginning: snowballs, an alleged fist fight. But the media made the most of it.

How different the reporting might have been—and American reaction to the movement. Suppose wire services and most newspapers had been capable of as high-level reportage as the following (February 17, 1960) by Gene Roberts, then of the Raleigh *News and Observer* and later one of the most skilled of the *New York Times* southern correspondents:

DURHAM— Hundreds of Negro adults Tuesday night signaled their willingness to boycott chain stores operating segregated eating facilities.

They offered to support a growing student sitdown protest as the Rev. Martin Luther King urged a united front—both whites and Negroes—against all segregation.

King, who led Montgomery, Ala., Negroes in a boycott against segregated city buses, repeated this phrase time and time again:

"We just want to be free."

Each time the words brought applause from a predominantly Negro adult crowd of 1,200 attending a rally here in White Rock Baptist Church.

"Let us not fear going to jail," King urged. "We must say we are willing and prepared to fill up the jailhouses of the South."

But he cautioned: "Our ultimate aim is not to humiliate the white man but to win his understanding." This also brought applause . . .

Minutes before King addressed the rally, a Durham Negro minister, the Rev. Douglas E. Moore, pastor of Asbury Temple Methodist Church, asked the crowd if it was willing to be part of a "mass and mammoth attack on segregation."

"How many," he asked, "would be willing to give up Easter outfits . . . to help finance our work?"

And he said: "I wonder how many would refuse to patronize the merchants" who are unwilling to serve Negro sitdown participants.

Almost all of those in attendance stood to indicate their willingness.

The crowd for the most part was made up of Negroes 30 years old or older. But there was a liberal sprinkling of young Negroes and an estimated 50 whites in the audience.

The crowd filled the church and spilled out into the courtyard. Hundreds stood or sat on the floor to hear King.

There was no room even for standing, 15 minutes before the 8 p.m. rally.

King termed the current student sitdown protest which has struck dozens of chain stores in the South "one of the most significant developments in the civil rights struggle."

"Segregated eating facilities," he said, "are the Negro's burden and America's shame."

He said the Negro has made it clear that he will not be satisfied with token integration or segregation in any form.

And he said that if the sitdown protest is a victory, "it will not be a victory for 17 million Negroes, it will be a victory for democracy."

He urged repeatedly that the "struggle for equality" be one of non-violence.

"I am still convinced Jesus was right," he said.

"I can hear him saying, 'He who lives by the sword will perish by the sword.' "

"I can hear his voice crying out, 'Love thy enemies.' "

"How long must we suffer?" he asked.

And then he answered, "Not long, not long."

"We don't want black supremacy," he said. "That's as bad as white supremacy." Many in the audience shouted, "So true."

King urged all those present "to go out with a little song on your lips. Keep saying we just want to be free." . . .

Commenting on Atty. Gen. Malcolm Seawell's statement that sitdown incidents could have devastating effects, King said, "The continued existence of segregation in any form in North Carolina and the United States can have a much more devastating effect than the sitdowns."

"The state of the world does not allow us the luxury of an anemic democracy," King said. He added that students were only asking that they be treated with the same respect "that the people in the trade have for dollars."

A corps of photographers and newsmen followed King as he toured the dime stores which closed their lunch counters after a student boycott last week . . .

Noticing the newspaper photographers and television cameramen, an unidentified store employe made a rush for one, and the lensmen took to their heels.

Both King and Abernathy immediately left the scene.

A WTVD television cameraman, Ed Gray, was on his way out the door when a policeman attempted to confiscate his camera and asked him to step inside. A Negro photographer on an assignment from the *Carolina Times* had his camera taken.

Store officials and police spoke to both photographers, and the WTVD cameraman retrieved his camera. The Negro photographer, C. C. Burthey, was detained by police and store officials until a Negro lawyer advised Burthey his film could not be confiscated unless a warrant were issued.

Burthey was advised to take his camera and film and leave the store.

A crowd gathered in the store as officials and policemen talked to photographers . . .

That was what America for the most part missed—the spirit of non-violent militance, redemptive love, dignity, the strength of the preaching and the responses of the people. The "violence," skirmishings over cameras, is where it belongs, in proper perspective, at the bottom of the story. Sportswriters and announcers maintain this kind of perspective; they don't drop coverage of the ball game to dwell on a fist fight in the grandstand.

As the sit-ins continued, they were soon adapted to another distortive convention of news-writing, the "roundup." This is the way papers and especially wire services formularize coverage of recurring, widespread events. As they would "roundup" the weekend's traffic fatalities in a state, devoting a paragraph to each (making unreal the horrible), they would "roundup" the demonstration news of the day, with the same dehumanizing effect. From the Chattanooga *Times*, April 12, 1960, by the Associated Press, the treatment:

—More sitdowns and arrests Monday marked the start of the 10th week of demonstrations aimed primarily at traditionally segregated lunch counters in the South.

About 100 Negroes staged protests at four stores in Concord, N. C., and six of them were arrested.

So much for the brave and beautiful in Concord. And:

In addition, plans were announced for an Easter weekend meeting of Negro college students from 40 communities where integration demonstrations have been held.

The Rev. Martin Luther King Jr., a Negro integration leader now living in Atlanta, said the sessions at Raleigh, N. C., might lead to development of a selective buying program as well as formation of a Southwide council of Negro students battling racial segregation.

SNCC was founded at that meeting . . . So much for the implications of the founding of such a southwide council of Negro students.

Five Negro college students pleaded innocent when arraigned before Pulaski Circuit Court Judge William J. Kirby at Little Rock on appeal of charges stemming from a lunch counter demonstration on March 10. Trial was set for April 27.

The students wore typewritten badges on the lapels of their jackets reading: "I am wearing 1959 clothes with 1960 dignity. I refuse to patronize segregated stores."

At Augusta, Ga., Pvt. George Johnson, 22, a Negro stationed at nearby Ft. Gordon, was held for trial in City Court after a hearing on a charge of refusing to leave a white restaurant at the Trailways bus station where he sought service unsuccessfully Saturday.

No mention of the interstate commerce implications of such refusal in a bus terminal, a federal law breach that was to lead to the freedom rides. On with the roundup:

A spokesman for the National Association for the Advancement of Colored People said an attempt by Negroes to secure access to the Danville, Va., public library would be taken to federal court.

The roundups did, in a haphazard way, give a sense of the diversity and scope of the movement. Even so, astute observers felt the need finally to better inform the public of just how widespread, how big in impact the movement had become. On a higher level this kind of reporting was not without distortion either—in its emphasis on things rather than the people and spirit of the movement. From a special report to subscribers, "The Student Movement: A Recapitulation," (Atlanta, Southern Regional Council, September 1961), the treatment:

. . . The movement, first begun as a protest against segregated lunch counter facilities, has, in the year and a half, embraced parks, swimming pools, theaters, restaurants, churches, interstate transportation, voting registration, libraries, museums, art galleries, laundromats, employment, beaches and courtrooms.

The economic boycott, a natural by-product of reluctance to buy where not served, soon emerged as a powerful—and successful—means of achieving equal facilities and equal treatment.

. . . At first spontaneous, the sit-in movement has gradually become directed through the students' own organizations and adult direct-action groups.

In many cities and states the sit-in movement elicited favorable responses from segments of the white population which had hitherto been silent.

Non-violence and direct action remain the philosophies upon which the sit-in movement is based. Among many students there is, understandably, an undercurrent of desire to defend themselves against physical attack; but, nevertheless, the willingness to suffer and endure provocation is prevalent . . .

The year-and-a-half sit-in activity has penetrated racial barriers in public accommodations with unprecedented speed.

. . . Since February 1, 1960, each southern and border state, as well as Nevada, Illinois, and Ohio—20 in all—has been affected by protest demonstrations.

Over 100 cities in the South and in the border states have had sit-ins or other forms of direct action.

An estimated 3,600 students and supporters—in southern and border states—have been arrested.

At least 70,000 Negroes and whites in those states actively participated in some way; this figure counts persons who sat-in, picketed, marched and attended mass meetings (sometimes in the face of intimidation). It does not account for thousands of others who supported the movement by letters to the editor, financial contributions and expressions of moral support . . .

This was written before the Albany Movement ever began, and it reflects a concern that, after Albany, was to become an over-concern with tangible results, an imposition of pragmatic, liberal thinking on what was not only a deeply spiritual expression, but also a quest for new ways of thinking and seeking change. The late Thomas Merton was the most aware, I think, of the few commentators who did appreciate fully the new directions embodied in the movement. I can remember my excitement in 1963 to read magazine versions of what was to be in his book *Seeds of Destruction*, feeling he was articulating what I had only dumbly felt, and that his voice would surely be heard over all the tumult of strategic, violence-content, pragmatic analysis of the movement, that at last America would understand that:

> These Negroes are not simply judging the white man and rejecting him. On the contrary, they are seeking by Christian love and sacrifice to redeem him, to enlighten him, so as not only to save his soul from perdition, but also to awaken his mind and his conscience, and stir him to initiate the reform and renewal which may still be capable of saving our society . . .*

But, looking back, I see that he probably understood all too well why America could not attend either his or the movement's message:

> . . . If they are forced to listen to what the Negro is trying to say, the whites may have to admit that *their prosperity is rooted to some extent in injustice and in sin.* And, in consequence, this might lead to a complete re-examination of the political motives behind all our current policies, domestic and foreign, with the possible admission that we are wrong. Such an admission might, in fact, be so disastrous that its effects would dislocate our whole economy and ruin the country. These are not things that are consciously admitted, but they are confusedly present in our minds. They account for the passionate and mindless desperation with which we plunge this way and that, trying to evade the implications of our present crisis.*

*Thomas Merton, *Seeds of Destruction* (New York: Farrar, Straus and Giroux, Second Printing, 1964), pp. 45–46.
*Merton, p. 48.

I. F. Stone was another who was early aware that America was missing most of the point of the movement. He wrote in *I. F. Stone's Weekly* (Washington, D.C., June 4, 1962):

> . . . Everywhere else in recent years terrorism has been accepted as a justifiable weapon in liberation struggles. From Palestine and Cyprus to Algeria and Indonesia, the knife, the bomb, the nocturnal attack, haphazard violence often at the expense of the very people being liberated, have been taken for granted.
>
> Here in the United States the struggle against the imposed humiliation of the Negro has been carried out in Gandhi's spirit, with successful non-violence. History will record it to the honor of the Negro and of our country, but too few are aware of it today.

I seek back to what most Americans never were aware of. I was not there, and those who were have known so much despair and disillusionment in the ensuing years. Mrs. Jay Brothers participated in the 1963 wave of sit-ins in Nashville—not as a leader and, at twenty-three, older than the high school and college students in the group, some eighty-five of them. They were seeking service in the Morrison's cafeteria and jobs and integration of lunch counters at five and ten cent stores. She talked eight years later of some of the things that happened.

"We came out of one store and were waiting for a ride back to the [Fisk] campus, and I sat down on the curb. I was eight months pregnant. A lady walked up, one of the clerks in the store, and she recognized me—and walked up and kicked me in the side. The others tried to get a cop to arrest her. He threatened to arrest us for disorderly conduct. They did later —me included. Sixty of us . . .

"I couldn't have done anything about it if I had wanted to —it almost knocked me out. But I wouldn't have hit her back if I could—not then. I would now. I don't have the guts I had then . . .

"We didn't really get angry at that age. It was just fun. We more or less were having a good time . . . I don't think we could have gotten angry then. The people who attacked us were just

sick. I wasn't in on the hard treatment. Jail wasn't bad. I never
was hit on the head with clubs . . .

"I couldn't do it now. I couldn't be that non-violent. My
patience wouldn't last. Maybe I've gotten too old. I couldn't
stand to be called all those dirty names . . . harassed . . . all that
sort of stuff. Bottles thrown at you . . . beer cans . . . and just
duck and dodge. If I didn't know now what I do know, and feel
like I do now . . ."

She said the group feeling, the cohesion were wonderful.
Had she ever known anything like it before or since?

"Never."

And: "There's still a lot that needs to be done in Nashville."

I sit listening to people who were there trying to recapture
the almost lost feel and fleshing of mighty events. Bernard Lee,
still a stalwart of SCLC ten years later, tells of leading the
sit-ins in Montgomery in February 1960, when he was a student at Alabama State College there. Things were as rough in
Montgomery as anywhere in the South; at one demonstration
Klansmen hit students in the head with miniature baseball bats
provided for the purpose by a local lumber company.

"Dr. King was in Atlanta by then. Reverend Abernathy was
still in Montgomery. He was more responsible than Dr. King
for my involvement. We had heard about Greensboro, and
some students invited me to a meeting at Reverend Abernathy's house. He decided for some reason that I should be the
leader. From that time on I've stayed with it . . ."

I don't want to intrude questions, reporter questions, skilled
processing questions that would draw out details of head-
cracking and heroism, and draw Bernard Lee away from his
memory's holding of what was important to him about the
experience, worth recalling.

He goes on in a voice increasingly edged with the emotion,
exhilaration, attached to a time in the mind so far back,
reached back to after so much else has happened. (He was
among the few who were with Dr. King all of the last day of
his life, until Dr. King left Bernard's room in the Lorraine

Motel to go to his death on the balcony off his own room . . .)

"Dr. King came to speak during the peak of our demonstrations. There were four thousand students at the meeting, nearly all the student body. It was our first real meeting. Everyone was impressed. He endeared himself to that generation of students by being with us in the sit-ins . . ."

What was it like to Bernard Lee, raised in Virginia, going to school in Alabama, suddenly catapulted into America's most innovative social movement, into strife and danger and a vision of limitless possibility? "By coincidence, I had just written a term paper on civil disobedience and non-violence—had read Gandhi for it."

What was it like? "Even today, I can still feel back to the way it was. It made me so proud . . . I never had to think about whether to get involved. We were clean-cut, well-dressed, non-violent. All seemed right . . ."

What was it like? To get back somehow to the events, the emotions, the actuality . . . I am already in danger of perpetuating another kind of distortion, an ascribing of saintliness, of superhuman good to those entirely human, often ordinary, young Negro Southerners of the sit-ins. The damage already done by this dangerous distortion is evident all about: It imbued the movement in the eyes of others who might have supported it or emulated it (and maybe some of those who were actively involved in it) with a feel of the impossible, something unattainable by ordinary mortals. Even worse, it interfered with seeing the movement's people, the South's Negro people, whole, seeing them as fully functioning people, prey to all the emotional stresses, all the cultural counterforces that anyone in the role they had assumed would be. There was a white view of black people which was only the other side of racism's seeing Negroes as all bad. It saw them as all good, ignoring the humanity of individuals just as thoroughly as racism does.

They were not saints, not geniuses, these young Negro men

and women of the sit-ins and the countless others of the movement through its history. That they moved for a time with the spirit, the kind of vision that goads and guides saints and geniuses, was the miracle, the precious extra-cultural thrust of the movement.

Cordell Reagon was involved in the first round of sit-ins in Nashville in 1960. Here is how he recalled his own motivation and his development afterward:

"When demonstrations got started in Nashville, they excluded the high school students—which I didn't like. They never asked us to participate, and when we tried to they wouldn't let us, because they would say that we were too hotheaded, disorganized and . . . too young, you know, that we couldn't discipline ourselves.

"So about sixty students got arrested in Nashville, and they had a march—on city hall. They didn't ask the high school students to stay out of school, or anything. They just excluded us again. So myself and two other fellows, we organized in the high school and had a walk-out and went downtown and marched with the rest of the people. After that the college students started looking at us and invited us to participate in the sit-ins.

"I . . . really, I thought it was exciting. I was just doing it. It was a challenge for me, because we were excluded. I don't like to be excluded from anything. After that, I got very involved in the movement. I think the real change came about during the freedom rides."

Leon Hall, a stalwart in SCLC's Alabama work, recalled in 1970 during an interview how he entered the movement by becoming involved in a sit-in in Montgomery in 1962.

"I was in the ninth grade. I was a chief thug—you know, hanging around hamburger stands, hanging on the corner. I got tricked. James Bevel and James Orange [adult SCLC workers] came up and said we were being exploited. They said we were paying thirty-five cents for a hamburger, when you could get them for ten cents at the Krystal. They got us in a car, and we went in the Krystal. There was an uproar: 'Throw the niggers out.' They beat us up.

"Bevel and Orange knew that was how to get us involved. People heard about it. Everybody knew us, because we were the hoodlums, you now. It made them mad. I never had so much prestige in my life. Two-thirds of the high school student body attended the mass meeting that night. The more they busted our heads, the stronger we got. The school board put me out six times.

"I got hooked up in the movement that way. A lot of kids over the South did—the same way. I've done the same thing around the South . . ."

The two adults, Bevel and Orange, operated here with a sureness, a faith extraordinary for our times, as did Leon when he later tricked youngsters himself. But, as with SNCC workers later when they jeopardized Negroes by their very presence in a community, by mobilizing them to try to register to vote, they were not really playing with human lives. Implicit in their self-assurance was a negative knowledge: that nothing in which they might be responsible for involving such Negro Southerners could be worse than their living a lifetime under the conditions of the way things used to be in the South.

I sit now, filled with the sense of the full human dimensions of what at the time seemed saintly and superhuman, listening to a tape-recording of an interview with Weldon Rougeau, who spent fifty-eight days with a fellow member of CORE (they were nineteen and twenty respectively) in a solitary confinement cell in Baton Rouge, Louisiana, waiting trial on charges of anarchy (punishable by ten years at hard labor) for their leadership roles in local sit-ins. The interview took place in 1964, some three years after the ordeal. Not saintly forebearance at all comes through in the interview, but the entirely human, conflicting feeling anyone would have in such a circumstance.

Not saints, not superhuman, not doing the impossible—and yet full of faith in what they were doing, a faith in its ultimate worth that is beyond anything most of us have felt. This young man near the end of our interview told me he planned to leave soon, to go North to finish college.

Then he said, "I feel that I'm going to come back to the South. I'm definitely going to expose my son to the movement at a very early age. I want him to learn something about it. I want him to be a part of the suffering . . ."

Chapter
TEN

How SHALLOW, compared with such hints of the reality of the sit-ins, were the news stories about them, processing them. The expectation of violence by the media was better rewarded by the freedom rides. They provided the kind of all-out violence from whites that made the movement big news, the familiar kind. Also, they provided a focal point for feeding the national fascination with violence that the sit-ins, going on simultaneously and for months across the South, never did. All you had to do to see the show was to be where the first two freedom-ride buses went.

The Southern Regional Council traced their course in a report, "The Freedom Ride, May 1961," published May 30, 1961:

> March 13—Announcement by C.O.R.E. of Freedom Ride.
> April 28—C.O.R.E. wrote to President Kennedy, informing him of plans.
> May 4—Ride began from Washington; arrived in Richmond.
> May 7—Arrival in Danville (Va.); dispute over restaurant service settled quietly at Trailways terminal.
> May 8—Arrival in Charlotte; arrest of one rider for trespass while demanding shoe shine at Union Bus terminal.
> May 9—Arrival in Rock Hill (S.C.) and attack in Greyhound terminal; white waiting room at Trailways terminal was closed when bus pulled in.

> May 10—Defendant in Charlotte trespass case acquitted. Two riders arrested in Winnsboro (S.C.) and released after several hours; charges dropped.
>
> May 12—Arrived in Augusta (Ga.); used all facilities.
>
> May 13—Traveled through Athens (Ga.) where all facilities were used, and arrived in Atlanta; restaurant closed at Greyhound station.
>
> May 14—Some riders were served at Trailways terminal in Atlanta. Entire group left for Birmingham, riding in Trailways and Greyhound buses . . .

These phases of the freedom rides, with little violence, little disturbance, were only routinely noted in northern and southern papers. No great effort was made by any of the media to emblazon in the public mind the single, simple message of the freedom rides—that systematic segregation of seating on interstate buses traveling in the South and of facilities in bus terminals along the route violated the U.S. Constitution and a specific Supreme Court ruling. The *New York Times* in some of its main stories on the freedom rides gave such inadequate explanations of their purpose as "testing the state's segregation laws."

But when, in Anniston, Birmingham and Montgomery, Alabama, white mobs attacked the freedom riders, they became big news. Television told it, and newspapers, including the nation's most responsible, afforded the story the kind of coverage reserved for the most important of events— front-page, banner-headline stories with photographs, inside-page feature and interpretative stories. Thus the freedom rides achieved a prominence in the national consciousness that the sit-ins (which were gentler in tone, more purposeful, and almost entirely an indigenous southern movement) never did. Not the least part of the difference was the frantic activity of the administration in Washington to stem violence once it had started, threatening to send in the U.S. Army, negotiating with state officials behind the scenes. (Alabama Governor John Patterson finally called out the National Guard.) If such energy had been put into protecting the rights of the sit-in students or even enforcing the court decision on bus facilities, the violence might never have occurred. But occur it did, and American media knew how to handle it, just as the American public knew (or thought it knew) what it meant.

Sample headlines and first paragraphs suggest the tone and scope of the treatment:

PROTECTION FOR RIDERS
ASKED BY ATTORNEY GENERAL
FBI Investigating Attack
On Group Riding in South

BIRMINGHAM, ALA. (UPI)—A group of whites and Negroes touring the South in a methodical test of segregation in bus terminals said Monday it would continue despite two incidents Sunday of overt violence . . .

Some members of the group were beaten by angry segregationists Sunday at a Trailways bus station in Birmingham, and a Greyhound bus carrying other members was burned Sunday, apparently by a fire bomb, near Anniston, Alabama.

—The Atlanta *Daily World,* May 16, 1961.

This historic city was quiet but tense today—a sharp contrast to bloody racial rioting which brought martial rule . . .

—The (Montgomery) *Alabama Journal* May 22, 1961.

U.S. STEPS UP ALABAMA ACTION,
ARRESTS 4, SENDS MORE AGENTS

—The *Washington Post,* May 23, 1961.

WASHINGTON, May 22—Attorney General Robert F. Kennedy ordered 200 more Federal marshals into Alabama today to help prevent new racial violence.

—The *New York Times,* May 23, 1961.

11 'RIDERS' LEAVE CITY ON BUS
AFTER EATING AT WHITE COUNTER

—The *Alabama Journal,* May 24, 1961.

12 'FREEDOM RIDERS' ARRESTED
AT BUS STATION IN JACKSON, MISS.
Police Quickly
Take Action
—The Atlanta *Journal*, May 24, 1961.

That traces the essential parts of the freedom-ride saga in its "big news" stages, Alabama violence and Mississippi police-state violation of constitutional rights. Was it really such big news, and did the press really get the story? If news is when a man bites a dog, was not the absence of violence in other parts of the South more worthy of note than the predictable depravities in the South's two most racist states?

I don't think it is too harsh a judgment to say that the media, when confronted with domestic violence, have increasingly been subject to an hysteria which often blocks their own techniques for maintaining balance and perspective in reporting. I have known this hysteria as a newspaper reporter and city editor myself; all of one's training and judgment is terribly strained by the intensity of emotion and urgency of action when some drama of modern-day antagonism and savagery is breaking loose before you. The need is not, of course, to pretend, as some southern papers were wont to do, that nothing at all had happened, but to find a perspective that allows something more than the simple telling of violent deeds, wallowing in the details of them with pornographic explictness, a perspective for assessing, interpreting, even understanding the violence.

Examples from the most respected of national newspapers indicate the degree to which professional journalists failed this responsibility in the freedom rides. The feature stories accompanying the main news stories—this overabundance of coverage itself a part of distortion—suggest the tone of the hysteria and the difficulty of resisting it. From the *Christian Science Monitor*, May 22, 1961, the treatment:

MONTGOMERY, ALA.—Newsmen were harried and attacked trying to cover mob violence here.

The crowd turned on newsmen and photographers to such an extent that some out-of-town press representatives returned home rather than face the danger of unrestrained hostility shown by the mob and other white groups reported to be roaming the city.

Several newsmen, long experienced in covering racial troubles in the South, reported they had "never seen anything like it."

From the *Washington Post*, June 13, 1961 (part of a series), the treatment:

Alabama, which for the past seven years has been sowing the wind of race hatred and lawlessness, found out in recent weeks how inevitably comes the whirlwind.

Violence by white thugs broke out at a bus station in Birmingham, on the outskirts of Anniston and in a bus station and outside a church in Montgomery.

Beatings administered to "Freedom Riders" and Negroes caught in the mob were brutal beyond belief.

Bands of white men backed by shrieking, profane women slugged, kicked and stamped on their victims. They used iron pipes, bats, bricks and chains. Caught up in a frenzy of hate, they were without mercy. In Montgomery, the injured and the unconscious were left lying in the street. The police turned their backs.

The mobs reflected the irresponsibility of state and local officials who have advocated defiance of Federal law, who have preached disrespect for the courts and who have campaigned on platforms to deprive Negro citizens of their Constitutional rights . . .

Both articles are nice expressions of righteous indignation, but serve little purpose beyond underscoring and reiterating the already well-reported fact that a mob of frenzied whites did indeed attack the freedom riders. (The scrupulous use by both northern and southern papers of quotation marks around the term freedom rider is one more of those minor instances of an implied objectivity whose effect was the opposite, a calling into question, one supposes, of the riders' claim to the term, freedom; the *Alabama Journal's* use, in the May 22 story, of "so-called 'freedom riders' " seems doubly to question the claim. Another paragraph from that story abandoned even this kind of ostensible objectivity. "Patterson in his proclamation of martial law," it said, "still insisted that the self-styled 'freedom riders'—he called them 'agitators'—were to blame for the race rioting because of their insistence on testing bus station racial barriers." "So-called," "self-styled" . . . Those familiar with southern editorial pages and letters to the editor columns would recognize these as the epithets they had come to be. A "so-called, self-styled" liberal, or whatever, was something like a revolving son-of-a-bitch.)

The *Washington Post* series installment went on at some length to substantiate its discovery that Alabama politicians of the stripe of then-Governor Patterson had indeed been openly engaged in the ancient southern practice of racist rabble-rousing. But the article did not altogether prove its assumption of a causal relationship with the violence to the freedom riders. Why, it might have been asked, didn't such a whirlwind ensue in Virginia, the homeplace of massive resistance, or in Georgia, whose governor at the time had campaigned on the promise that "not one, no, not one" Negro child would ever go to school with a white one? Even more to the point of a real understanding of the impact of the movement on the South would have been an attempt to understand why violence was so much more ferocious in Alabama against the freedom riders than against the sit-in demonstrators, whose ostensible goals—integration of public accommodations—were the same.

At least part of the answer is grounded in white southern racial attitudes, historical memory. More than one ordinary white Southerner, casual in his racism, come by it from cultural conditioning, looked at the impressive courage and decorum of the sit-in students and said, "Well, hell, I don't like it, but to tell the truth, if I was in their place, I'd be doing the same thing." How much was there, never spoken, as such things were never admitted in the clothing store where I worked, of knowledge that the struggle of the Negro students, the very audacity of it, was of the kind, and against much the same forces, that white Southerners needed to make, too? And how much of secret fear among the whites that they were just not up to doing what these Negroes were doing?

Interestingly, it was the notably right-wing, segregationist Richmond *News Leader* under James Jackson Kilpatrick which, in an editorial (February 22, 1960), paid the classic grudging tribute to the extraordinary qualities of the sit-in students:

> Many a Virginian must have felt a tinge of wry regret at the state of things as they are, in reading of Saturday's "sit-downs" by Negro students in Richmond stores. Here were the colored students, in coats, white shirts, ties, and one of them was reading Goethe and one was taking notes from a biology text. And here, on the sidewalk outside, was a gang of white boys come to heckle, a ragtail rabble, slack-jawed, black-jacketed, grinning fit to kill, and some of them, God save the mark, were waving the proud and honored flag of the Southern States in the last war fought by gentlemen. *Eheu!* It gives one pause.

Part of the white attitude toward the sit-ins was the old one of "these are our niggers—we can handle them." But the freedom rides brought outsiders, and in two of the forms most feared and hated in the white southern racist consciousness: the "uppity" northern nigger and the white northern agitator. That the latter affronted middle-class standards with beards and unconventional dress (as home-grown hippies to their peril were later to do) didn't help matters. The same fear and hatred gripped white Mississippi with murderous hysteria in anticipation of the arrival of the 1964 Freedom Summer volunteers from the North.

White Southerners on the side of the movement might well have indulged a degree of the traditional fear of outsiders. The freedom rides not only launched CORE as a large-scale organization of the movement—one effect of which was to increase competition among organizations that was to prove so costly to the movement, offset, of course, by the great good CORE did, especially in Louisiana and Florida. But they also brought into the southern-based organizations, especially SNCC, a northern influence, people with no grounding in the reality of white and Negro inter-relationship of the way things used to be, which was the basis of the best, highest spirit of the movement. (Not all the Northerners in the movement, of course, were incapable of catching its southern spirit.)

Southern psychology, however, doesn't fully explain the continued escalation of violence to the movement, outsider and indigenous alike, in subsequent years. Could the media's interest in violence, expectation of it, over-reaction to it, have had anything to do with that? The *Post*'s listing of the arsenal of mob violence (iron pipes, bats, bricks and chains) during the freedom rides is interesting both as an index of how far things had moved from the sit-in snowballing and fist fight in North Carolina, but how far they were yet from the bombs and bullets that were to come.

It is well documented that the violence, private and official, over the years had its erosive effect on the civil rights workers and on the spirit of the movement. Less noted was the effect it had—especially in the early, formative time of the sit-ins and freedom rides—in imparting a seriousness of purpose, a sense literally of life-and-death struggle, to the young Negro Southerners of the civil rights organizations. This has to be taken into account in trying to understand the extreme effectiveness of those young people. They were risking their lives; their belief was that important to them. Those not willing to become civil rights workers (and I have talked with many who were in the sit-ins while in college, but couldn't see themselves continuing in the struggle) were not, in my opinion, either more or less balanced than those who did stay in; but obviously the latter were a special kind. And when they were most effective, their serious willingness to face violence was of a special kind. They talked, awed, back then, of how non-violence really could defeat violence.

"I think the real change came about during the freedom rides," said Cordell Reagon. He went on to describe his own coming to the seriousness of purpose of a full-time civil rights worker:

"I went on a freedom ride from Nashville to Jackson, Mississippi, and got arrested in Jackson, and spent . . . oh, I don't know . . . thirty-nine or forty-nine days in jail. And witnessed . . . you know . . . a lot of police brutality, real brutality, the type of violence that I had never seen before, except in gang fights around Nashville and stuff like that.

"Like . . . policemen using cow-prodders. See, they say that police first started using cow-prodders in Birmingham. Well, that's not true. They were using cow-prodders during the freedom rides, because there was one incident when we were first transferred from the county jail to Parchman Penitentiary.

"There were two pacifists on the truck. They refused to get out of the truck. They refused to cooperate at all. The truck came up to, I guess, about my neck—it was a very high-bed truck. And the policemen walked up and pulled 'em down to the ground, dragged 'em through a big puddle of mud, over a big slab of rough concrete and into the prison, where all of us were standing. We had to strip down completely, take all of our clothing off. Then the two fellows refused to take off any of their clothing. So they used cattle-prodders on them. They put the cattle prods up and down their bodies, you know, about thirty times—which left black marks all over their bodies. They still refused to take off their clothing, though. So they tore their clothing off of 'em, beat them and took 'em to the cells.

"A lot of things happened down there. This was just one incident. These two went through more than anybody else. They were taken out of their cells once again. Their heads were beat up against a concrete wall, and a lot of other things happened to them. But all of us went through literally hell down there—being put in solitary confinement, finding glass in our food . . .

"So I guess that's when I got . . . really got involved in the movement. That's when I stopped thinking it was just something exciting."

Even where the attempt was made to put non-violence into perspective, distortion occurred; the extra-cultural qualities were difficult to express in cultural terms, and the unfamiliar nearly always got bent and squeezed into familiarity. I know of no better example of this in serious efforts to write about the freedom rides than the following, which, as it so happens, I wrote in 1963. From "Direct Action in the South" in *New South* (Atlanta, Southern Regional Council, October–November 1963), the treatment:

> A little more than a year after the sit-ins began, CORE announced on March 13, 1961 that a small biracial group would travel on interstate buses from Washington to New Orleans to test racial discrimination in interstate travel terminals.
>
> It was no secret that many had segregated waiting rooms and lunch counters. This was despite Interstate Commerce Commission and Supreme Court rulings, including a Richmond case in 1960 which had found discrimination to be in violation of the Interstate Commerce Act . . .
>
> Trouble began in Alabama. A mob met the . . . bus six miles outside Anniston. They slashed its tires, and it fled on flats for six miles. Then the pursuing mob threw fire into the bus, destroying it. Passengers escaped serious injury . . .
>
> . . . [Another] bus encountered a mob at Anniston, but made it into Birmingham. There the freedom riders stepped from the bus into the violent crowd and were savagely beaten. One required fifty stitches for injuries to the head.
>
> Birmingham police were warned by the Justice Department to expect violence when the bus came. Police did not arrive at the bus station until ten minutes after the bus did.
>
> Thus received, the original thirteen freedom riders took a plane to New Orleans. But they were followed by many more. In all, more than 1,000 persons made freedom rides. CORE,

SCLC, SNCC and the Nashville Student Movement sent riders and formed a Freedom Riders Coordinating Committee.

From jeers to beatings, the subsequent waves of freedom riders ran into trouble—again mostly in Alabama . . . Mobs and tensions built so high in Montgomery on May 20, 21, 22, that President Kennedy ordered some 600 federal marshals into the city for its own protection and that of the riders.

For the lap of the journey from Montgomery to Jackson (Miss.), a new pattern developed. The riders were heavily guarded en route, and then, when they stepped off the bus in Jackson, they were arrested. As fast as they might arrive during the ensuing weeks, they were taken to jail. . .

. . . The freedom rides seemed to many to go beyond the needs of the moment in order to antagonize white Southerners. Even people sympathetic to the goals of the riders became critical of their tactics, particularly the continuation of the rides after the Attorney General had commenced the government's action [ICC rules prohibiting discrimination in interstate facilities] . . .

This brought the South, and indeed the nation, up against the question of the moral and legal validity of non-violence that provokes violence. A June 1961 Gallup Poll showed that while a majority of Americans approved of ending segregation in interstate travel, 64 per cent disapproved of the freedom riders' methods, largely on grounds they "were causing too much trouble."

Thus the almost solid sympathy for sit-ins outside the South, and a certain grudging admiration from even die-hard southern segregationists were reduced . . .

What concept of the freedom rides did America get from such coverage? What did America know of the southern Negro support, for example, of the freedom rides and their aspiration? What did it know of the contrast between movement attitudes with, on the one hand, the cynical maneuverings of state government, and, on the other, hard-nosed exercise of too-late power by the federal government? What did it know of the meaning of the freedom rides in the hearts of the people who undertook them? What were they really like?

John Lewis evoked the churning chaos of the freedom rides, their spirit, their moments of greatness, as well as their violence in a taped interview in 1967 for the Civil Rights Documentation Project. He had been scheduled to go on one of the first two buses, but was delayed and, while en route to catch up with the buses in Birmingham, learned of the burning and beatings. CORE spokesmen had announced that no further freedom rides would be attempted, because they were too dangerous. He went to Nashville, where various elements of the non-violent movement group strongly urged continuing the rides.

". . . We got together—Diane Nash, James Bevel, C. T. Vivian, Jim Lawson. We just started talking that this ride has got to continue. It must not stop. We cannot let it stop . . . So we started talking with the Nashville Christian Leadership Conference—all these ministers—that we needed this money in order to continue the ride . . .

"They were saying 'You cannot go. We cannot give you this money to go. You're just asking for death; this is suicide. It would be suicide to go.' . . .

"Then we started convincing some of the other ministers and some of the other adults, and they said, 'If you want to go, go.'

"Tuesday, we met. Bevel, by that time, became the chairman of the local group in Nashville. It was his job to appoint the people to continue riding. Nashville is supposed to be so democratic, where people try to reach a consensus on everything and sort of wait and carry for a decision. I don't know why, but somehow, so many people wanted to go that Bevel had to make the decision to appoint ten people to continue the ride. So he appointed ten people.

". . . That ride started on May 17, Wednesday. That was the anniversary of the Supreme Court decision. It was May 17, 1961, at six-thirty Wednesday morning. I remember that very well. There were ten of us. Three young ladies and seven fellows, two whites—one white girl, a student at Peabody College, and a white guy, an exchange student at Fisk."

They got to a railroad crossing just outside Birmingham, where police boarded the bus, arrested the young white man and a Negro youth who were on the front seat and told the rest they were known to be freedom riders on the way to New Orleans, with stops in Birmingham, Montgomery and Jackson, Mississippi.

"So we drove into Birmingham, and they wouldn't let us get off the bus . . . They put newspaper and cardboard all around the windows to keep the people outside from looking in. Reverend [Fred] Shuttlesworth and some of the other ministers met us at the bus station, but they still wouldn't let us off. So finally, some of us stood up and tried to get out, and the cops got on the bus and just started knocking people down and sticking people with billy clubs and things . . . All the other people were still kept on the bus also. All these other people—regular passengers."

Finally, they were allowed off the bus and into the white waiting room, where all facilities, including rest rooms, were closed. They had decided not to stay the night in Birmingham, and tried unsuccessfully to get connections to Montgomery. After some five hours Police Commissioner Bull Connor and Mayor Arthur Haynes came and placed them in "protective custody." They had not eaten that day, and fasted that night and the next day and night in jail. Around midnight of the second night in jail Bull Connor came and told them he was sending them back to Nashville.

"We went limp. That's the only time we went limp. They literally picked us up, because we said, 'We're not going unless we go by public transportation.' We said, 'We came here by bus and we can go back by bus.' "

The seven of them (three had avoided the jailing) were placed in black limousines and, with cars before and behind, they were driven to the Tennessee line and put out on the highway.

Along the way they talked with Connor—"jovial, gracious" talk. "We told him that when we got back to the college campus . . . we would have breakfast with him. Things like that. He was very talkative. They [Connor and other whites in the car] never got bitter or dirty and nasty during the whole thing. It was just amusing. 'Yes, I'll be glad to hear your views.' Things like that. We started talking to him about the philosophy of love and non-violence that didn't allow us to hurt anybody. Why did he arrest us? Why did he lock us up like this? We didn't violate any law. He could be charged with kidnapping or things like that . . ."

They were near a small town when put out, found a Negro home in it, knocked on the door and asked for help. The family had already heard about them. "They were nervous. They were really frightened. The old man and his wife, they were really frightened. They didn't know what to do and at the same time they wanted to be helpful. So we got in, and the man went to different stores—about three or four stores—buying food from different places to keep the people in the community from being suspicious. He said, 'If anyone asks, say you're my cousins from Nashville, who came down to visit me, my sister's children.' So we all had something to eat, first time we'd had something to eat since Tuesday night. It was early Friday morning."

They called Nashville, and a car came to take them back to Birmingham. As they neared that city a radio news broadcast told that they were returning and described their car. They went in by back routes, found Reverend Shuttlesworth's home and ate fried chicken with him that night.

Then they tried to board a bus for Montgomery. The driver told them he feared for his life. "So we started singing there on the sidewalk, and then the bus driver started singing and kept on singing. A big mob came up outside of the waiting room, outside of the bus terminal. Police came down with dogs and forced them back to keep the mob from getting to the bus station."

All night they tried in vain to get a bus driver to let them board. Reporters told them Attorney General Robert Kennedy was pushing city officials hard to get the riders on a bus. "Some of the press people there were keeping us informed on what was going on. They were sort of pro-movement types."

The next morning a bus did take them aboard, along with other groups, white and black, from the North as well as the South. State troopers and a private plane followed the bus, but both disappeared just outside Montgomery. Then they reached the bus station.

"It was so quiet. Since 1957 I'd gone through that city many times, through that bus station many, many times and never seen it before like that. That bus station had become a ghost town, that whole area. It was an eerie feeling. Complete silence. There were no cabs around that you could see. You couldn't see any other buses. Not anything."

The police station was about five minutes away, but no police were there.

"We stepped off the bus, and it was a matter of minutes, three or four minutes, until people just started pouring out of the station, out of buildings, from all over the place. White people . . .

"Reporters converged on the bus station also. At first they just literally beat the reporters, just took cameras. One guy— I'll never forget—he was an NBC cameraman who had been with us back in Nashville, back in 1960. They took this camera from this guy and they just dropped it on him. Just smashed it on him, knocked him out . . . Then they just started hitting people going and coming, all the reporters."

There had been barely time to get the girls out—into a cab driven by a Negro who feared taking two of the girls, who were white, but finally did so. Some of the group jumped over a railing and were given refuge in the basement of the city's post office by the postmaster who held a door open for them ("the white postmaster in Montgomery, Alabama"). And a white couple tried to protect two of the white girls. John Siegenthaler, representing the President of the United States, tried to protect the two white girls, and was attacked.

"He tried to protect these two young ladies, and he was knocked unconscious. He was beaten to a pulp by the mob. The two girls ran into a church, and the secretary at the local Presbyterian Church opened the doors and really spared the lives of those two young women.

"While we were standing there trying to get away and couldn't, they started beating on us. And I had a brief case in my hand, and they took this brief case . . . They hit me in the head with it and just tore up the brief case completely. It left a large gash, a cut, in my head. The scar and things are still there. I was knocked out—well, I was knocked unconscious and left lying on the street there." (He had a brain concussion.)

Lying there bleeding, he was handed a state court injunction forbidding interracial travel in Alabama. When he was able to get to his feet he saw a white member of the group.

"This guy Jim Swerd . . . was beaten so badly that I didn't even recognize him. I didn't know who it was. He was just standing there. We both were just still bleeding. He was bleeding all over, and blood was pouring out of my head."

In the midst of the beatings, Floyd Mann, then-director of the state patrol, came on the scene and fired a shot in the air and cried out that there should be no killing. "I guess that shot and several other shots in the air by Floyd Mann saved quite a few people that day from being actually killed."

John and several others, including Jim Swerd, whose spinal cord was injured, were finally taken to a hospital. And: "See, we couldn't account for people. There were twenty-one of us, and we couldn't even account for what happened to all of the people. There was no way."

Finally, coordination was achieved by Diane Nash, who took calls in Nashville from members of the scattered group and told them all to meet at Ralph Abernathy's church.

"But that was not where we met. We met at someone's home . . . We went from there to a church outside Montgomery, a Methodist church, where Martin King and Ralph Abernathy met us late Saturday night, like it was almost midnight

... We made plans for a mass meeting that Sunday ... night."
Then they dispersed to various homes to hide out from arrests
under the injunction. The Montgomery Improvement Association, the old bus boycott group, still active, still holding weekly
mass meetings, sponsored the mass meeting that Sunday night.

"At around five-thirty or six o'clock the church was packed
already with about twelve hundred people, and the meeting
wasn't supposed to start until eight o'clock. Before the meeting
could get underway, a mob gathered and started burning cars
and beating up people out in the park in front of the church.

"I think Martin Luther King got in contact with Bobby
Kennedy ... Later that night, I believe, President Kennedy
deputized all the federal marshals in the city of Montgomery.
Then people in the church started singing. Fire bombs and
stench bombs started coming into the church through the back
windows; people started throwing into the church. It became
very bad. Some of the people started panicking."

A National Guard official came in and announced martial
law had been declared and that the people could not leave the
church. They spent the night there, some twelve hundred of
them, and were carried to safety the next morning in National
Guard trucks.

On Monday and Tuesday the freedom riders rested and
recuperated; new ones came into Montgomery, including a
group from Howard University in Washington, whose number
included Bill Mahoney and Stokely Carmichael. John, Dr.
King, Dr. Abernathy and James Farmer announced at a Tuesday press conference that the rides would continue.

No one was arrested, and Wednesday the National Guard
escorted the group to the bus station where they were served
food without trouble. A National Guard general spoke to them
when they got on the bus, saying it would be a dangerous
journey, but he thought they could make it. "I wish I could
remember the general's name ... He was a good old man who
liked to do the right thing, I think."

With a guardsman on board, a convoy of them behind, a

truckload in front and a helicopter overhead, the bus, normally scheduled but carrying only freedom riders, drove without regular stops to the Mississippi line. "We went through Selma. That was the first time—I think it was at Selma, a lot of people gathered out on the highway at a filling station . . . We didn't stop at any of these stations . . .

"They carried us fast, very fast. People threw rocks and stones at the bus. And each time this bus would stop on the highway some place, those guards would jump out of their trucks and they'd go stand over to the wooded area, just like that. And they were pointed and ready. And the helicopter would stop and circle the bus. When we got to the Alabama-Mississippi state line, the Mississippi guards and another helicopter took over and did the same thing."

They arrived in Jackson in late afternoon. "The driver got off; we got off. We walked into the waiting room, the so-called white waiting room, and just walked. Some people went into the rest room; other people went into the restaurant . . . Other people were sitting there waiting for buses. Other white people, press folk, guards, were all around, and police dogs.

"[A police officer] said, 'Keep moving.' No one stopped; we just kept moving.

"He said, 'You're under arrest.' Just like that."

They were found guilty of trespassing and sent to Mississippi's dread Parchman Prison Farm under sixty-day sentences. ". . . When we got there, we sang freedom songs. We used to rock the jails in Mississippi those nights we stayed there, singing. The prisoners downstairs used to sing with us."

And: ". . . The freedom ride didn't stop with that bus. Hundreds and hundreds of people from all over the South and professors and students from universities [from all over the nation] joined the rides."

What was it really like? The mind has its own private ways of processing public events, and these people who experienced the sit-ins and freedom rides obviously do not have now quite the same kind of perception of them that the press and the somber-sided studies did at the time they were occurring. In thinking back to it, retelling it, those who were there include the materials that so fascinated the press at the time—the drama of the confrontations, the violence (and how much more strongly the cruelty and savagery of southern white racism comes through in their memories than in the most blood-drenched photography and newspaper prose of those times), the strategy, the statistics, the winning and the losing. But their memories contain so much more that the press, the studies, the general public missed: of feeling so right in the doing of it . . . of whites who saved Negroes from the mobs . . . of the ability to distinguish an occasional good old man who wants to do the right thing in the midst of so much evidence of evil in white people and the all-white governments . . . of the bus driver who joined in the singing.

I worry that I am romanticizing, imposing my own southern bias and wistful, desperate hoping on such things as these memories of the reality of the sit-ins and freedom rides. I see in such accounts of what it was really like so much evidence that the participants really did believe in that entirely southern stratagem of trying to change white attitudes and feelings, and so many hints that they were succeeding—or had more chance of this kind of success than anything written at the time would concede. I keep asking people who were there if I am wrong about this, if I am wrong in thinking the theme of redemptive love was so much a part of those early events. They assure me I am not.

"There was this very strong feeling we could change the hard-core segregationist attitudes and feelings," John Lewis said, when I asked him. "There were just a great many young people who believed in that hope—what we later came to call the beloved community."

The media not only failed to capture that and convey it to America, it failed even to communicate fully the most salient point about the violence to the movement with which it was so fascinated—that through the years of the movement, the violence was nearly always unilaterally white. Americans were accustomed to, conditioned to, mutual violence. If the fragmentary vision on the TV screen showed whites hitting blacks, then the assumption was that blacks had hit, or would hit, whites. I can remember the over-reaction, the fear in store owners, police, bystanders, reporters (sometimes myself not excluded), when they saw a column of non-violent demonstrators coming. Given normal American responses, given the countless grievances Negro Southerners had, it was almost impossible not to expect violence from that marching column. The philosophy of non-violence may have been grasped by media and public, but not this kind of psychological reality. How important an achievement non-violence was in the face of it.

Most white Southerners and probably a portion of southern-conditioned Negroes tended to see the white violence to non-violent demonstrators as a natural response, cause and effect. (How much of this was shared in the North?) Negroes put themselves where they were not supposed to be, where their presence provoked the violence-prone; naturally they got hit. This was part of the national (and my own at the time) trepidation about the freedom rides. At its best, this was expressed as fear for the demonstrators, a feeling they were risking too much danger. At worst, it was the feeling that the demonstrators were to blame for the violence they attracted to themselves, that they got what they deserved.

In such ways America, North and South, through its perception of the movement via the media, had a blurred, if not entirely wrong, understanding of non-violence and violence. In the South many white people spoke of the most beautiful, most peaceful demonstrations as "riots," and this was translated into public policy—unconstitutional arrests and police harassment. Headlines proclaiming "racial rioting," when actually white rioting had occurred, contributed to such misapprehension. Headlines speaking of police arresting demonstrators, as though in a normal context, contributed to the feeling that non-violent Negroes were indeed at fault. Perhaps it is giving white Southerners too much credit for concern with civil liberties to suggest that had they been better informed, public policy and the ultimate fate of the movement's original goal might have been different. Perhaps, even if the media had done their duty, white southern guilt and phobia, the belief that Negroes are inherently ferocious, would have blinded them to the truth. But they had the right to have had a chance, at least, to be better informed—as did the rest of America.

Soon enough came real Negro rioting, the northern ghetto rioting, and finally mutual violence, at first, in its black expression, mostly verbal, but eventually, as with the Black Panthers, with weaponry. The Southerners who thought the demonstrations had been riots (and however many Northerners shared the delusion) were understandably not too surprised by the northern riots. And an escalation in the repression of demonstrations, with little distinction ever made between non-violent and violent, seemed neither to surprise nor concern most Americans. It was just more violence.

Eight years after the first sit-in "fist fight," the Orangeburg students were shot and killed with impunity. The state police who shot into that defenseless crowd had been at least encouraged by past "law and order" exhortations of high state and national officials, past "get tough" statements against demonstrators and/or rioters. Two years after that, after escalation of irresponsible verbal attacks on student dissenters by Vice President Spiro Agnew and others, including the President himself, the National Guard fired on students at Kent State University in Ohio, killing three, and police fired on students protesting the war, the Kent killings and conditions at Jackson State College in Jackson, Mississippi, killing two. Black (at Jackson State) and white (at Kent) together, they seemed to have become fair game.

In all three instances, the police massively over-reacted to the students' own versions of violence—rock-throwing at Orangeburg and Jackson State, arson at Kent. In all three instances, police claimed, but did not prove, far more violent provocation—sniper fire. Talk of violence, violent rhetoric, charges of violence, minor violence, murderous violence . . . demonstrations had been, somehow, moved into the mainstream context. The expectation had been there from the beginning of the sit-ins, in the processing of them.

Chapter
ELEVEN

EVEN IN ITS OVER-EMPHASIS of the violence done to the movement, the media missed much that was pertinent about that violence, much in terms of the way things used to be that might have made the rest of the country understand better what extraordinary things were occurring in the South. The jail experience is a prime example.

From my private journal, 1965: "The jail experience was central to all the movement, the symbolic ordeal, the mark of the highest honor. It had special symbolic significance for Negro Southerners who had, all of their lives, known the white-controlled laws, courts and jails as a threat hanging over them, a means of coercion, part of the apparatus of control, oppression. To get yourself deliberately into the toils of this dread thing you had always sought to avoid, to turn it about and use it to force change was an act not only of high courage, but of important personal, psychological meaning. You were ending within yourself one of the chief causes of acquiescence to an unjust system. For the Negro middle-class of the South—and most of the students of the sit-ins and freedom rides, though not most of the people of the later mass marches, were middle-class—going to jail also signified defiance of that Negro southern code which distinguished the middle-class not so much in economic terms (for nearly everyone was poor), but by such criteria as whether or not one had been to jail. The young Northerners who braved the jail experience may have had more lurid fears and fantasies about white southern law enforcement, but they could not have had the kind of personal trauma, the special conditioning against it that Southerners did . . ."

The impact on Southerners of the jail experience is worth exploring for what it tells of the reality of what the movement was up against (so that we may understand real bitterness, alienation, and the giving up of ideals and non-violent methods by some), and also of what it tells about a special kind of unreality born of southern conditioning that makes the willingness of thousands to brave the experience seem even more majestic than ever.

In Albany, a year after the great demonstrations there, Reverend Samuel Wells was still leading little groups in demonstrations, just as he had been vainly leading Negroes to try to register to vote for years before the movement ever came to the city. He told in an affidavit what happened when he was arrested on July 8, 1963:

> . . . Then the captain, the uniformed officer, caught me by the arm and told me to follow him. I did not feel that I should cooperate with him in such an arrest, so I went down on the pavement of the streets and lied there until the detective on my right caught me by the right wrist with his left hand. With his right hand, he grabbed me in my groin. With the first hold he only caught me in my pants. Then he reached down into my groin to get a hold on my genitals and they lifted me by these two holds, carrying me in the alley about halfway between the door and the street . . . Then we were nearing the cement steps of the entrance into the booking office. I began watching the steps as we neared them, because I was afraid that they would throw me up against the steps, as the same detective had swung me there before, at another time, with the help of two other men, and I landed across the stomach of a fifty-nine-year-old woman.
>
> "You better look because we'll throw you up against those

steps," he said, when he saw me watching the steps. Then, dropping me at the door inside, and looking to see if they were ready to book me, the two again picked me up, to carry me in, dropping me on the floor and asking me to get up and give the officer my name and address. Again I failed to cooperate. Then the two picked me up and threw me against the bars of the office. I gave the officer my name and address and age.

When he said, "That's all," I again fell back on the floor. The two picked me up and carried me into the area where the whites are locked up, because you have to go through this area to get to the place where they lock up the colored. Then again in this area where they lock up the whites, they threw me again on the floor. During this time I made it clear that I had been hurt by the detective and the officer who purposely picked me up by my genitals.

The detective's response to this was, "What do you want me to do about it?" As I continued to lay on the floor, I told him, "I will see you around the corner of justice, because injustice will not prevail always."

Then the same two officers carried me down into the area, where they threw me into a cell so that I fell flat on my back with my head out the door of the cell. One of the officers kicked me upside the head and after this I rose to my feet. The officer backing up putting his hand on his gun told me to stay in the cell.

I told him, "I do not want to come out the cell, because there is more power in the cell than there is out there where you are"*

Frank Holloway, a student leader in Atlanta demonstrations, describing his adventures during the freedom rides, told what happened on a Mississippi prison farm:

. . . When we got there we met several men in ten-gallon hats, looking like something out of an old Western, with rifles in their hands, staring at us as if we were desperate killers about to escape. This tickled me, and I had to smile. Here we were, non-violent freedom riders, who had come to jail to stay there,

*Affidavit from Reverend Samuel Benjamin Wells, July 12, 1963, to Slater King, Notary Public. Reprinted by the Student Non-Violent Coordinating Committee.

and they led us through a tunnel of men holding rifles to prevent our escape. They locked us up in the farm jail. Soon they took us out to a room, boys on one side and girls on the other. One by one, they took us into another room for questioning before they gave us our black and white stripes.

There were about eight guards with sticks in their hands in the second room, and the freedom rider being questioned was surrounded by these men. Outside we could hear the questions, and thumps and whacks, and sometimes a quick groan or a cry, when their questions weren't answered to their real satisfaction. They beat several Riders who didn't say, "Yes sir," but none of them would Uncle-Tom the guards.

Rev. C. T. Vivian . . . was beaten pretty bad. When he came out he had blood streaming from his head. They took him to the penal farm doctor, who apparently patched him up so he looked like he had not been beaten when we saw him again.

We could hear somebody slap a girl freedom rider and her quick, little scream—I guess it was knocked out of her. She was about five feet tall and wore glasses, and they beat her because she wouldn't Uncle-Tom them or behave in a subservient manner.*

Bill Hansen gave the following account of the time in Albany when his jaw was broken during the jail beating:

"I was the only civil rights prisoner in the white section. I had a technique for dealing with white prisoners. I would go in and look at everybody—but never be over-friendly or look afraid or hostile. I would just be bland. I never had any trouble before. You can't live in a cell with other people and not be friendly. You hate the same things.

"Anyhow, you give them no excuse to get angry with you. And when I would get out, I would take messages to their wives, or whoever they wanted me to.

"This time, I was sitting on a little step by the cell door. A guy came in. I glanced up at him, and then went back to what I was reading. The next thing I knew he hit me on the side of

*"Travel Notes from a Deep South Tourist" by Frank Holloway (*New South*, Vol. 17, no. 7, July–August 1961), p. 8.

the jaw. I blacked out and when I came to, he kicked me in the face. I could feel blood; I passed out.

"When I came to, I could hear Jim Forman [SNCC executive secretary] in the street yelling up at Charlie Jones in the jail. I yelled that they had beat me up and to come get me out . . ."

The scandal of illegal prison brutality has been a national one; if Negroes generally through the years, and the people of the movement most of all, were favorite targets for it in the South, they were not the only ones. As in the rest of the country, poor whites, any powerless people, remain vulnerable to such treatment, with virtually no means of redress. Young people—hippies, pacifists, campus demonstrators—have come in for it in recent years. Here was one more terrible sickness in southern, national society that the movement never overcame, never really even began to work on when it was most effective—as crucial as any of the many such sicknesses that required social action of the movement's calibre in the 1970s. Many of the sporadic, spontaneous demonstration campaigns of the late 1960s and early 1970s were over just this issue.

At about the same time that Dr. King was writing his famed "Letter from the Birmingham Jail," a then-obscure leader in a small black-belt city was writing a letter of his own from jail. He scrawled it on ruled paper with a ball-point pen. Some of the pages were not filled, some torn in two; the letter broke off in mid-sentence after eleven pages. It tells many things about the jail experience, but most of all it allows the opportunity to see radicalism being forged in the mind of a man, independent of and—one suspects—immune from, superimposed dogma, something more grounded in reality than the radicalism of the New Left and Black Power that came along later. The letter:

I ONLY W̶a̶n̶t̶e̶d̶ WANT TO BE FREE

I write these words from t̶h̶e̶
from a dirty, c̶e̶l̶l̶ stinky, roach filled

Bed Bug bitting cell in what they call
the Hole of the . . . county jail.

2

I was placed ~~here~~ in this cell by my own
Government. The Government that I
fought for on foreign soil. This almost
cost me my life. I am 40% Disable to
day. Yes I draw 2 little checks, but
~~can~~ you can't pay a man enough money for his life? No,
all the money in the world could
not ~~buy~~ compensate for the agony
and pain my body go through ever
~~and all~~ winter, ~~long~~, and ~~many~~
many, many rainy days. Yes, ~~when my~~
~~pelvic/ girdle~~ doctors described my left
pelvic condition as having been busted,
healing left spur formations which
cause pain. My leg was described as
a compound fracture. My shoulder as
being dislocated. My side as having seven
broken ribs. I don't remember the
description of my teeth, but I know
all of my front teeth (8) was knocked
back into my mouth. I believe they
described my head as busted cranium. Well,
this all happen in Germany during ~~the~~

3

World War # II. I was there because,
I ~~wanted~~ Americans to be Free. Yes,
the Government that I went to war
for, jailed me like a murder, rober,
rapist etc. Just because I want to
be free.

4

I been here 36 hrs. Now its frightening
to hear "my mates" talk about their
crimes. They ask me, "Mate what wrap

take"? Meaning what crime have I com—
mitted. I answer by saying, I only ask to
be free.
My cell is down in the hole. Its damp,
dingey, with out light except ~~that~~ the
little natural light that penetrates
through a window one story from the ground.
The odor is most foul, ~~but~~ ~~you~~ foul enough
that my smelling senses have not
sensitize after 36 hours. All of this, just
because I want to be free.

5

I don't like this place but its nothing
I can do about it. I spent most
of my time praying for my wife,
~~and~~ five children, and followers. I have
tried to hate but I can't, cause its
not Gods will. I just want to be
free.
After that unknown white woman took out the
warrant for my arest. After that
white (blind) judge issued the warrant
for my arrest. After two unknown white
deputies showed up at my home 3:00
A.M. in the doom of the night &
arrested me. I prayed to God, don't let
them kill me. After the two deputies
enter my home & told me to come
with them, I ask their names & time
to call a lawyer that maybe could tell
me they was real deputies and not
murderers. I could not find one lawyer
who knew them. After a while they
yelled out, "Ok. You've had enough

6

time, Less go." I told my wife to
keep trying to find a lawyer and not
worry about me.

As I started out the door, my 7 year
old son ran to the door & ask with
fright, Daddy where are these men taking you? I answered with peace, I
have to go out for a little while, I will
soon be back now. You be a good boy
& go back to bed. As I went out the
front door I realize, I could have
been going to meet death. This has
happen to many Negroes. I got into
the car with these two unknown
white men as if they were my friends.
I had made up my mind, if I must
die I will die like a man. I knew
they were taking me some where, because I want to be free.
As they drove back toward town, I said
to myself I am glad I decided to come

7

peaceful. If they are going to do any
thing to me, I would rather it not
be done in the presence of my wife
& children. I thought about the murder
of Meger Everets in Mississippi. He was
shot in the back & killed because he
wanted to be free. I said to myself,
if they kill me it will be because
I want to be free. I wondered how
many Negroes will the federal government allow the white folk kill just
because we want to be free.
As we rode along I watched every
corner & direction the car took with
exactness. ~~One mind said to me, if
they turn a corner or go~~ I got
tense and more afraid as the car
travel. I had one mind to jump out
the car at the next corner. Then, I

remembered this is one of the tricks whites
have used for many years. Allow the Negro to run & shoot him dead. I made

8

up my mind, if they shoot me it will
have to be from the front. Then, I
remembered the one thing I could
do was to pray. Silently I started talking with God. As I talked with him I
could observe his presence. I asked him
to protect my wife and children
from all harm & danger. You see,
there have been times, because a
black man just wanted to be free,
~~We would be arrested~~ & the whites
would arrest him & then bomb
or set fire to his home. I prayed
this would not happen to me, just because I want to be free.
I wonder how long the American way of
life can endure. How long can this so-
call Democracy prevail. How much time
does the Communist need to ~~tell the~~ prove to the whole
world how unjust, how unfair, how ~~undem~~
undemocratic, how unchristian the ~~America~~

9

American way of life is to every ~~man~~ one
of her ~~colored~~ Negro citizens. Even though they
fight & die in wars to protect America;
they obey her laws; they till the soil & cultivate her farms; cut the forest into
timber & build her towns; ~~accepther/~~
~~poor education (in comparison to that~~
~~which is rated good for whites);~~ accepts
a second rate education; live in her
slums; do her domestic work; allow the
mongrelization of their race; denied
decent jobs; victims of police brutality;

v̶i̶c̶t̶i̶m̶s̶ o̶f̶ denied justice in the court
rooms; a̶n̶d̶ exploited by partisan politics,
j̶u̶s̶t̶ b̶e̶c̶a̶u̶s̶e̶ jail without just cause, they
are the last one hired and the first one
fired, we just want to be free.
As I sit here in the confines of this little dirty
dim cell (I can touch both sides with the palms of both
hands), wishing for a cool drink of water,
with only the presence of all mighty God,
I can't help from shedding tears & saying
at least they didn't shoot you through the

10

back. As I hear the prisoners in the
other cells discuss their brutal crimes,
I ask God why must I be
housed with them? I received an answer,
my only begotten son, Jesus Christ was
crucified & died among thieves. Now
I know the price one must pay for
wanting to be free.
Upon the walls of this cell I see the name
of a Negro that is common to every
[one in town] . . . who
was last arrested for raping one
white woman & murdering another. I
take it, [he] was housed in this
cell. At his trial, they proved he had lived
a lifetime of vitcious crime.
(r̶o̶b̶b̶e̶r̶y̶, t̶h̶i̶e̶f̶, c̶u̶t̶t̶i̶n̶g̶ & s̶h̶o̶o̶t̶-
i̶n̶g̶) Now, I wonder was he guilty? Even if he
executed the acts, who was guilty? Could
i̶t̶ h̶a̶v̶e̶ b̶e̶e̶n̶ a̶ c̶a̶s̶e̶ w̶h̶e̶r̶e̶ t̶h̶i̶s̶ m̶a̶n̶ h̶a̶v̶e̶
b̶e̶e̶n̶ d̶e̶n̶i̶e̶d̶ the American way of life
that jailed me because I want to be

11

free, be guilty. Is it possible for me
to learn to hate the American way
of life and retalliate by trying to

destroy it by crime & violence? Is it
human for a man to protest that
which tries to destroy him? Well, on
the wall of this jail cell I can glimpse
a figure in the shape of a cross and
beneath it is scratched GOD IS GOOD.
I wonder did [the rapist] do that.
Any way, I am happy its here, because,
at this moment I have mix emotions.
In the top of this cell is a figure
like a heart. Looks like it was drawn
with a shoe heel. Inscribe with what
probably was a hard match stick is,

Chapter
TWELVE

THE WRITER of the letter from the small-city jail smuggled it out to a reporter in the hope that it might be printed in a national newspaper. Much of the failure of the media toward the movement is summed up in the response of an editor to the suggestion that it be reproduced in full in the paper: "Thanks, but we don't believe we can use this as a letter . . ."

When it is known that the police in that particular city were rather noted for being better than most southern ones, the letter takes on a whole new, poignant significance. It helps explain why the threat of filling the jails was never the weapon in the American South that it was in India under Gandhi. Negro Southerners had not the cultural, philosophical life-view that made such sacrifice more natural in India. And though many were literally starving, most were not down to that sheer edge of desperation which in India meant that masses of people could feel they had nothing to lose in the sacrifice. Another practical consideration: Many Negro Southerners, because of discriminatory justice, in part, had paroles or previous convictions which would have made going to jail for civil rights very costly. But beyond all that, enough evidence of inhuman treatment, indeed of murder, in the jails existed to justify the fear expressed in the letter. Such things as lack of full support for the strategy of filling the jails probably helped push the movement into one more of the standard cultural patterns which so debilitated it. This is a pattern for which political science has not yet a comprehensive descriptive term; it involves what has come to be called the scenario, a staging under rigid control of what seem to be spontaneous events. We saw this happen with enemies of the movement—when, first, Ross Barnett as Governor of Mississippi was allowed to seem to resist integration of the University of Mississippi (and things got out of control with a calamitous white riot ensuing), and when George Wallace as Governor of Alabama was allowed to stand in the schoolhouse door against integration of the University of Alabama and launch his dubious national political career.

With the movement, complicity with the Federal government in the staging of direct-action scenarios was, I think, for the most part far less controlled, less worked out in advance. It was more a matter of being able to anticipate responses, to know what must be done to elicit certain responses, and going through the necessary symbolic motions—as in Birmingham in 1963, when massive demonstrations ostensibly over local grievances pressured President Kennedy to propose civil rights legislation, and as in St. Augustine in 1964, when similarly localized demonstrations pressured Congress to pass the legislation. The movement knew what the liberals in power in Washington wanted, what they did not want and, increasingly, to the movement's great detriment, it allowed itself to be influenced by this kind of knowledge. Other ways in which such manipulation occurred become clear in an examination of the organizational structure of the movement and what happened to the organizations after the freedom rides.

Southern organizations speak the metaphors of the South's tangled ideology and even reflect the untended wildness of much, yet, of the landscape. And southern Negro organizational structures are, if such is possible, more ramblingly complex, unpredictable and full of schisms than the white. Only with some appreciation of this, of how, in its Baptist Churches, the white South maintains a sort of controlled chaos and anarchy with no one church beholden to any other or any superstructure, and of how, in the smallest of humble Negro churches, there are cliques and cliques within cliques, forever wrangling, only with patience and a kind of fondness for this can one make much sense of the organizational aspects of the movement.

Obviously, in the sit-ins and freedom rides, the different organizations worked together beautifully, with improvization, spontaneity. SNCC, SCLC, NAACP Youth Councils, and CORE sent forth demonstrators; SCLC and the NAACP provided bases and wise consultation; the NAACP Legal Defense and Educational Fund came in with attorneys and legal maneuvers; the local churches, the local organizations, the local leaders were available in various supporting roles. Behind the scenes, these diverse elements might be involved in all kinds of rivalries and differences of opinion; but in the crises they overcame their differences and were remarkably effective.

This kind of informal cooperation and overlapping of leadership among the organizations was what, often, people meant when they referred to the southern movement—a coalition of organizations working in more or less specialized ways, more or less together, toward the same goals. But only if one thinks of these organizations in terms of the support they had from the mass of the Negro people of the South, only if one knows that the movement was far more than the few people who were the leaders and staff workers of the organizations, only if one realizes that the real solidarity, the strongest impulse to cooperation was with the people, does one begin to get the feel of what the movement once was and, with important potential, continues to be.

The "professionals," Dr. King and Dr. Abernathy and the freedom riders themselves—they were part of the movement there in Montgomery during the crisis of the freedom rides. But they would have been meaningless without that other, greater part—the local preachers and the Montgomery Improvement Association, the twelve hundred people at the church two hours before the mass meeting was to start, ready for what might come, ready to hide the freedom riders in their homes. The movement impinged on the everyday life of the average Negro Southerner, and a solidarity that had always been implicit, but never utilized, began to emerge. Frank Holloway, in "Travel Notes from a Deep South Tourist" (p. 4), gave one example:

> One thing that made us feel rather good happened at Tuskegee, when the bus picked up some Negro passengers, who went to the rear. A couple of minutes later a Negro man came up and sat by Harold. He told Harold that he noticed us sitting in the front when he got on and that he had never seen this before in Alabama. Then he said it came to him we were Freedom Riders, and that he felt an obligation to us and himself to join us in the front, although he was afraid to. He also said he didn't exactly go along with that non-violence jive the students were practicing. So for the remainder of the trip we talked to him about non-violence in opposition to violence.

Even more basic was the spirit of that old couple in the town where the freedom riders had been put out by Bull Connor. The man and his wife were frightened, but had no thought other than to risk not just momentary safety, but their future existence in such a little town by taking the young people in. That was the movement. It had existed a long, long time, and continued to exist after the movement was proclaimed dead, and the most exciting organizations—SNCC and CORE— were departed from the South.

SNCC was the most exciting, and most important, now, to consider. I think its main importance transcended the South and civil rights. For it set the style and tone, or rather expressed the style and tone for a new generation's approach to politics and social change around the world, young people who thought they had come to a complete break with the techniques and attitudes of the past and believed they could change conditions against which the old techniques and attitudes could not prevail.

CORE and SCLC had something of the same style and tone, and many young people of the same spirit as SNCC, but they operated out of a more standard organizational base, with standard bureaucratic tendencies and concerns. And older people remained an influence in them—James Farmer himself and such a wise and seasoned man as Richard Haley, also of CORE.

SNCC's distinctive qualities stemmed from a crucial decision that was made when it was founded. This was at the conference of those who had participated in the sit-ins—student activists from over the South—that was held during the Easter weekend (April 14) of 1960 in Raleigh, North Carolina. These young activists decided then that their Student Nonviolent Coordinating Committee would be entirely independent from the other civil rights organizations and would be controlled and run by the young people themselves. (It was formed as a "temporary" organization to coordinate the sit-ins and other student protests, but in less than a year had established a permanent office and had some full-time workers. Atlanta was selected over Nashville as headquarters; Marion Barry of the Nashville Student Movement was elected chairman; John Lewis succeeded him in 1963.)

Some of the people at the conference, apparently including Dr. King himself, hoped the new organization would develop into a youth wing of SCLC. But powerful and persuasive voices were raised against this, most notably those of Ella Baker and James Lawson. Mrs. Baker had been the first executive director of SCLC, and was instrumental in calling the Raleigh Conference. Some in SCLC were to say in later years that one reason for her stand for a separate SNCC was that she was bitter at having just been dismissed as executive director in deference to the notion that the job required a man. Other people who were at the conference say the reason for her dismissal was the stand she took.

Southerners, loving gossip, endlessly hash over such human

and personal aspects of important events. But in the grip of my own preoccupation, my southern quest back into lost time for first causes, fatal turning points, the important thing is not why Ella Baker did what she did, but what it was she did, the important consequences of SNCC's being separate for SNCC and for the movement—and eventually for the youth movement. The loss of her influence, notably humanistic and creative, in SCLC was also important, maybe crucial to movement history.

Certainly it is clear that she spoke out of an extraordinary understanding of, and empathy with, the young people at the Raleigh Conference. (She was in her fifties at the time.) She had the profound insight that they needed to be free from the pressures and forces that operated in existent organizations, that their youthful spirit and idealism ought to have a chance to continue to be expressed as freely as possible from the influence of older people, an influence which, however seasoned and wise, was, by human nature and the special circumstances later labeled "generation gap," bound to be less idealistic, less exuberantly pushing at the boundaries of a culture. (Ironically, she was, herself, to remain a strong and beautiful influence on SNCC through its brief, important life.)

Subsequent history of SNCC and SCLC relations is a striking specific example of the difficulty of escaping cultural norms. In getting free ideologically and spiritually from the more standard organizations, SNCC became from the very beginning enmeshed in something quite similar to standard American rivalry and enmity with the other organizations, especially SCLC. Criticism of them was silently implicit in the decision to be separate, and John Lewis recalls that it was not all silent. In part, the decision grew out of unhappy experiences with the other organizations during those first months of the sit-ins.

Certainly the rivalry between SNCC and SCLC, their philosophical, tactical and tonal differences, weakened effectiveness of the movement. SNCC was superbly skilled at

organizing, galvanizing Negro communities for action, making
them capable of truly great direct action. And SCLC was just
as skilled at utilizing such spirit, building out of it great campaigns aimed at achieving specific goals. They worked together
by happenstance mostly in the two most beautiful movement
campaigns—Albany, with its great release of the spiritual
power within the people, and Selma, with its great stirring of
the rest of the nation. SNCC in both instances laid the groundwork; SCLC developed and directed the campaigns. Suppose
they had been able to do this more often, and not by happenstance, but with concerted planning, calculated choices of
places to campaign, combining not just skills, but different
kinds of knowledge of weak points in segregationist armor and
strategic advantages. Suppose beyond that they had been able
to plan together the direction in which the movement would
go, instead of, as it was, each often pulling it in different
directions, and both, willy-nilly, pulled and pushed by the cultural forces. The movement was to become bogged down in
strategic concerns, mostly mainstream maneuvering; if SCLC
and SNCC had worked together on a concerted strategy, it
might have been truer to the movement's southern roots and
its early innovativeness.

SNCC came to accuse SCLC of exploiting the bravery and
spirit of local movements and of leaving the communities
where demonstrations won national legislation in worse shape
than it found them. SCLC considered SNCC unable to see the
woods for the trees. Its spokesmen urged division of labor—
SCLC seeking conditions southwide favorable to SNCC's localized kind of operation. Both were partially right. Together,
they might have not only won the legislation, but made it and
other laws and institutions work in immediate alleviation of the
problems besetting the people in the movement communities,
indeed all the Negro people.

The new laws proved that it is possible to legislate morality
on the level of practice and custom. But the movement originally had sought to effect personal morality—which, in their

twisted way, southern congressmen, arguing that you can't legislate morality, correctly knew to be the nub of the race issue. America lost the chance the movement seemed at first to offer of a personal resolution among whites of its oldest moral dilemma when SCLC became chiefly concerned with legislative remedies and SNCC broke itself in its personal approach to hard-core white southern racists.

SNCC's greatest strength, its closeness, its faithfulness to the people, might have been imparted to SCLC to temper SCLC's greatest weakness—an increasing tendency to manipulate and use people. And SCLC's greatest strength— a sound grasp of American socio-political reality and an ability to transcend this with something of its own coherent philoso- phy—might have been imparted to SNCC to temper its great- est weakness—an increasing unreality in its approaches to society and politics.

Apart, both seemed to move deeper and deeper into stand- ard, mainstream aspiration and techniques, further away from their innovational origins. Together, they might have more successfully prevailed against cultural forces. I seek back, seek back to what went wrong. It must be just such simple, human things as this: Suppose Ella Baker had remained in her job at SCLC and, with her influence on SNCC, had been able to serve as a bridge between them. Merely to have prevented the bitter enmity that developed between the two organizations would have enhanced the movement considerably, might have saved SNCC.

The strain between the spiritual mode and standard cultural approaches was there from the start of SNCC. But it was creative tension, in balance. Connie Curry, one of the white Southerners who was at the founding conference, recalls that one delegate, a young black man from Virginia, got up in the midst of all the hope and joy and, declaring, "I don't dig all this," told the others what they ought to be thinking about was money and jobs and scholarships for poor Negroes, in effect urging class concerns and racial solidarity. But the new spirit prevailed; that young man was made part of the governing board, in an effort to assimilate his strengths, not reject his dissent.

Miss Curry said her best memory of the conference was of standing in a big circle in the church where they met, holding hands, singing "We Shall Overcome," the incredible feeling of it, greatest of all the many exalted times she sang the song. She said, "I just remember the beauty. We all believed. We thought all was going to be okay." John Lewis said that far more than in reaction to what were perceived as weaknesses in the other organizations, SNCC was founded as a separate organization out of positive motivations—essentially the feeling of strength and solidarity among the young activists. They just wanted to continue to act on their own, to be free, to have their own organization which, in its own ways, would work with the other organizations.

And that unquestionably was what allowed SNCC for a time to be so much, to accomplish so much in the South and to express a tone and style for a new generation worldwide. But the strengths gained from the decision to remain separate contained the seeds of SNCC's destruction. Perhaps the most that the New Left and youth movement might learn from the southern movement has to do with the paradox of how, in cutting itself free from weaknesses in standard organizations and older people, SNCC also needlessly cut itself off from strengths like balance, stability, continuity, perspective, which have always sustained people and organizations.

Another of those turning points I have been seeking occurred within the organizational structure of the movement soon after the freedom rides. This was the decision of SNCC and CORE to devote the most of their energies to Negro voter registration, a departure from their early brilliant development of techniques and tactics of non-violent direct action, leaving the field there mostly to SCLC. Making the decision reportedly traumatized SNCC, dividing its staff in bitter debate. Some had from the beginning sensed the possibilities in political activity among Negro Southerners, Jim Forman, the canny and ever-influential executive secretary, among them. So, too,

133

early documents of the organization indicate, some were aware of the advantages for organization of Negro Southerners inherent in drives for voter registration.

But the decision when it came, by all accounts, was one which, if not forced on the two organizations, was certainly tantalizingly held before them by forces from without. In part, the persuasion came from the Kennedy Administration, and in part from private foundations offering badly needed money if it would be used for voter registration. It was no secret that Robert Kennedy, as attorney general, had looked on the clamor, provocation and violence of the freedom rides with disfavor; he was considered to have been influential in the abortive attempt to call them off after the initial Alabama violence.

Once they had run their course, he and other administration figures strongly urged a great southwide effort to remedy the appalling situation of Negro disfranchisement. They used the strong argument that, without the vote, Negroes would find other civil rights goals either unattainable or ever-jeopardized. Negro registration in 1962 was only 26.8 per cent of its potential in the eleven southern states, as low as 13.4 per cent in Alabama and 5.3 per cent in Mississippi.

Any assessment of erosion of the spirit of the movement, the faith of the most dedicated activists, must take into account the failure of the federal government ever to live up to its basic responsibilities to deal with the southern stratagems of disfranchisement or to protect the rights and safety of the civil rights workers and voter applicants in the subsequent registration campaigns. Promise of more even than the ordinary protection that never came was at least implicit in the inducements to SNCC and CORE to undertake the voter drives. Just as damaging was the failure of foundations ever to deliver as much money as they seemed to promise for the drives.*

*See *Climbing Jacob's Ladder: The Arrival of Negroes in Southern Politics* by Pat Watters and Reese Cleghorn (New York: Harcourt, Brace and World, Inc., 1967) for a detailed account of the voter drives administered from 1962 to 1966 by the Voter Education Project of the Southern Regional Council.

But a perhaps stronger, certainly more subtle and complicated, erosive effect was also at work in the ability of a national administration so to influence and attempt to manipulate a movement which had as one of its main purposes, really, the influencing and manipulation of the government. Ostensibly, the movement was attempting to force reform on government. But that government, in a thing like the urging of voter registration, whether correct in its assumption or not, was privately attempting to set priorities on the reforms sought and establish what methods would be used to gain them.

The danger of such government from behind the scenes, not uncommon in all spheres of American life, was all too apparent in the uses of its power by the Johnson Administration whose actions, if not intentions, were in so many ways seriously harmful to the movement. One example of this: Dr. King had increasingly open access to the offices of the President and other high officials of the Kennedy Administration and he used this when pressured by other leaders and discontented followers. However ill-advised it might have been, he was said to have come to depend on this access to high places. When the access was greatly curtailed during the Johnson Administration he was in serious trouble, and so, too, the movement's whole rationale of non-violence. He had the courage, nevertheless, and I think the greatness to oppose the Vietnam War, in spite of his need for access to President Johnson—which he lost altogether with the stand. Not all leaders in or out of the movement are capable of giving up such power on the basis of principle—hence the insidiousness of the influence in the first place. Not the least of the reasons Dr. King went to Memphis was out of a desperate need to retain relevancy, to demonstrate his effectiveness in the face of his loss of prestige with the administration. That he met his violent death in an effort to prove that non-violence still could work remains—in this context—among the greatest ironies of that tragedy. For unless we impute to the Johnson Administration—and I am not willing to—a complete Machiavellian enmity to the movement's meaning, proof of the validity of non-violence was, at the time, one of the most important things that administration needed.

The Nixon Administration, those in it who reflected the influence of right-wing, Goldwaterish unrealism on the Republican party, did evidence a deliberate will to harm the movement, the cause of civil rights and integration with its use of manipulative power. One example: In early 1970, when Roy Innis, the new director of what was left of CORE, set out to promote among southern black people and white segregationist office-holders his black separatist scheme for black-controlled black schools, he concentrated his first efforts on Mobile, Alabama. Asked by a white southern civil rights worker why CORE picked a place where a long effort to force real desegregation of schools had been stymied by local officials and an unfriendly federal judge, an aide to Innis replied that a high official of the Justice Department had advised that it was a place where black people, because of bitterness, would be more likely than in most southern locales to support the scheme.

Another example of the bad effect of even well-intentioned efforts of officialdom to influence the movement: One reason that Dr. King took SCLC into the ill-fated campaign in Chicago shortly after the Watts riots of 1965 was that Senator Robert Kennedy had criticized him for not giving more time to northern problems. That campaign had a twofold bad effect on the movement. It contributed, with its suggestion that non-violence would not work in the North, to the loss of prestige Dr. King suffered and it drew SCLC people and resources out of the South, where non-violence had proved effective and was still badly needed.

I am in danger of underestimating the achievement, the resilience, of the movement. Despite the pernicious effect of government and establishment influence, Dr. King *was* still able to speak his moral conviction about the Vietnam War and all war—against the strongest thrust of American government and culture. Similar greatness was shown by SNCC and CORE when they did yield to the influence by finally deciding to go into voter registration. For if some expected this to draw the fire out of direct action, to divert the young activists from truly forceful, explosive activity, they did not reckon with the kinds of voter registration campaigns SNCC and CORE would conduct. They chose to go into the most recalcitrant, most violent rural areas to confront racism with one of its worst fears: the demand for Negro suffrage where Negroes outnumbered whites. And they continued to exert some pressure in the streets—something they might not have been able to do without the voter registration money to keep their southern offices alive.

But once more, paradoxically, SNCC's strength contained the seeds of its destruction. The work in the voter projects gave SNCC workers their deepest, most beautiful experience of the humanity and the greatness of Negro Southerners. It also gave them their most painful insight into, and experience of, the worst of southern racism and the horrors of American poverty. They were in more ways than one radicalized by what they found. In one way of saying it (their own), they came to see that all of America was guilty of this worst of southern oppression and neglect of people. In another way of saying it, by knowing the worst of America, they came to expect an opposing perfection which was not there. Most Americans operate with understanding of relative good and evil in the society, not with burning awareness only of the worst evil.

Andy Young, the able administrative assistant to Dr. King and later Dr. Abernathy in SCLC, discussed with me in 1970 what he thought the fundamental differences had been between SNCC and SCLC and summed much of it up in terms of differences in degrees of expectation. He said that when he first became involved in the movement he promised himself to give five years to it. Soon he realized that the job would require ten or twenty years at least. But SNCC, he said, encouraged students to come down South with the idea of changing a whole state in a summer. The impossibility of SNCC's expectations, their inevitable disappointment, contributed greatly to the bitterness and cynicism that eventually destroyed SNCC, he thought.

"We tried to warn SNCC. We were all Southerners and we knew the depth of the depravity of southern racism. We knew better than to try to take on Mississippi. We saw Birmingham as having realistic possibilities, as the reality."

SNCC, he continued, went at the work of the movement with too much intensity, and its staff members broke themselves physically and mentally with never-relenting exertion and stress. On the other hand, SCLC staffers reserved Atlanta, where many of them lived, as a place to relax, be with their families, get away occasionally from the pressures and terrors of their work. (That was one important reason why SCLC seldom became deeply involved in Atlanta's civil rights efforts and crises.)

Many SNCC workers, he said, had ulcers, while few SCLC staffers ever did. Dr. King at his death did not.

"If you think you're going to change everything any day, you can't ever relax," he said.

SNCC, of course, accused SCLC of being soft, its staffers of living too easy.

"It was just a different philosophical approach," Andy said, and he again suggested that much of the difference was in northern and southern understanding of southern reality, SNCC's heavily influenced by northern perceptions.

But Southerners strongly influenced SNCC, too. And if the main thrust of the movement was, as I believe, toward changing America, and if one believes, as I have come to, that the idealism, the beauty of the movement, were periled by America, not intentionally so much as automatically as long as America functioned normally, then SNCC's intensity and rush make sense. Maybe unconsciously, the SNCC kids knew they had to change America before American culture could stifle the innovative and creative, culture-changing forces at work in the movement.

At its height, SNCC was a metaphor speaking the greatest

strengths and beauties of the Negro people of the South, the people of the movement. It did not work fast enough to prevent itself being killed by America. But the movement, the strengths and beauties of its people—were they, too, killed? If one has known the full expression of them, he cannot say that they are forever stilled, or that the power of them did not continue to work on America, even after SNCC was gone, and the movement proclaimed dead.

I seek back, I seek back—and my thoughts inevitably lead me to Albany, the next great movement event after the freedom rides—Albany, where the strengths and beauties were so greatly in evidence, and the forces arrayed against them. There was a height the movement rose to, and then began its fall.

Part Three

GOD'S ALL-*BENNY*

THIRTEEN

Paul   and   Si   —las, bound in . . . jail—
Got no   mon—ey for to . . . go their . . . bail—
Keep your eyes
On the prize—
Hold—on . . .

IT IS HOT SUMMER in Albany, Georgia, the summer of 1962, the summer of the final drama of the Albany Movement. I am in the Shiloh Baptist Church; I sit on the floor beneath the pulpit, to its right, looking up to it on the raised platform, with the three high-backed, red-upholstered chairs symmetrically behind it. The little space between the altar rail and the first pews is tacitly reserved for the press. Six other reporters share the space with me, sitting on the floor, as I do, with legs crossed, taking notes, listening. Two television crews beam their bright lights on the pulpit platform, aim their cameras. Two people operate tape recorders. The people of the movement fill the sanctuary behind us. They are crowded into all the long, light-wood benches and are sitting in the middle aisle between the two sections of benches and standing in the two side aisles, some leaning against the walls or propping hands back on the window seats, and they are standing across the rear of the church and out into the vestibule. They fill the two long

benches set perpendicular to the pulpit on either side of it, the
amen corners, and they fill the choir loft behind the pulpit.
The white plaster walls of the church curve inward toward the
ceiling, gently, gracefully, giving the sanctuary sort of an ark
shape. The wall behind the choir loft is painted blue, and across
it is inscribed: "The Lord Is In His Holy Temple," and beneath
that is a framed print of the Last Supper. I sit in this place with
my head back now, eyes half closed, arms, hands limp. The
open page of my notebook is smeared; sweat from my hands
has blurred the blue ball-point ink where I have written. I sweat
all over, can feel the sweat running over all my body. The heat
is a packed heat, a physical force that hits you when you enter
the church, and by the time I had made my way through it to
where I sit I was wet all over with sweat.

This has become a nightly thing, sitting like this in the mass
meeting at the church, sitting limp, my head back, giving
myself to the sweating, the heat, seeing through sweat-blurred
eyes back through the crowd the many black faces, arms, wet,
too, with sweat, cardboard fans in soft motion in the heat, in
the crowd. They are singing the unaccompanied, hand-clapping music of the movement, and I give myself to the sweat
and the heat and the music, a sense almost of loss of self, of
having blended into all the other sweating bodies and the heat
and the music and the great feeling alive in this church:

> The only   ch — ain
> That a man can stand
> Is   a   ch — ain
> Of   a   hand in
> hand   —
> Keep   your   eyes
> On the prize
> Hold — on
> Hold — on
> HOLD   —   ON—
> HOLD   —   ON—

Keep your eyes
On ˇ the prize—
Hold —on
Hold —   on.

The song sounds within me, slow, patient, like the people who sing it, women with contralto and soprano and men with bass and baritone improvising in each line complex harmony and rhythm against the steady, sure beat of the main body of the song. I give myself to the song; it carries me on like water, a slow and endless current, slowly on, patiently on to the unknown, never-discovered shore it seeks, verse after verse, two leaders, one a man in basso, the other a woman in contralto, improvising interchangeably the lead lines:

Albenny Georgia lives in race
We're goin' to fight it from place to place
Keep your eyes
On the prize
Hold — on . . .

I know what I think is right
Freedom in the souls of black and white
Keep your eyes
On the prize
Hold — on . . .

Singing and shouting is very well
Get off your seat and go to jail
Keep your eyes
On the prize
Hold — on.
Hold — on.
HOLD —   ON —
HOLD —   ON —
Keep your eyes
On the prize
Hold —   on —
Hold —   on.

Jordan River is deep and wide
We'll find freedom on the other side
Keep your eyes
On the prize
Hold — on.

I see the glistening, lean face of Dr. W. G. Anderson up
behind the pulpit, his face transfixed, an ecstasy in it that is
beyond my own passive giving of self to the moment and the
music:

Hold

—on

—

Hold —   on —
Keep your eyes
On the prize
Hold

—on

Hold—

on.

I see in the crowd once more here, there, the beauty of the
young women (and I had never, before beginning to come into
this church for these meetings, noted the beauty of black
women), in the shape of a head, thin, long face, the thrust of
breasts, liquid-soft, large, almond-shaped eyes. I see the chocolate brown of a baby's face with its big eyes staring unblinking
at me.

Hold

—   on
Hold —   on

I see a family. Big man with labor-built, massive shoulders
and arms, black brow creased in the earnestness of singing, and
plump, pretty wife, wearing a cotton dress, face radiant, and

a boy about nine between them, head elongated at the back like African sculpture, and a girl by her daddy, younger, hair tightly braided, staring off, solemn amid all the singing:

> Hold   —   on
> Hold   —   on.

Abruptly it stops, and a speaker has risen to the pulpit, and I am back, struggling against the heat to listen to the speaker, trying to make notes, struggling against the lingering, lethargic feeling of loss of self . . . I am back somewhere short of that mysterious, unknown place the song had been carrying me, somewhere short of it, but never again to be completely re-turned to where I had been before first I heard such music, gave myself to the beauty and the meaning of the mass meet-ings, to the spirit of the movement.

It had begun on that dreary December day in Atlanta. I had just moved into a new house; nothing was unpacked; Christmas still had to be bought for two Santa Claus-aged children. Claude Sitton, reporter's reporter, voice of duty, was on the phone, calling from Albany:

"Aw, man, you can't miss this one."

I had already missed too many. I had been writing a column for six months, and Claude had called from various places where civil rights history was being made. Each time I had a valid excuse not to, and this time even more so. But I still remembered hearing the sit-in students singing on the road-side, and I wanted to go—yet feared to go. I had worked a long time to get the job I had; all that feeling in the song on the side of the road threatened the careful balance and calculated coolness of tone required to keep it. This I knew instinctively.

"What about violence?" I asked Claude.

"It could get rough."

Hell. I was afraid. I was full of the ingrained fear, the unrea-soning fear we all had of white southern racism. So I said I would be there. I couldn't admit to myself such fear, couldn't live any longer with the secret knowledge that because I was scared of the rednecks I was missing the biggest story of my times, the real history, and the something I had sensed of a thing I could believe in—in a deeply personal dilemma of disbelief in an age of unbelief. But I told myself and my paper that the reason I was going had to do with the dire thing Claude said was about to happen in Albany.

"Come on," he had said, "because it looks like the movement is going to break wide open down here."

Thus, within ourselves and pushed by compulsions from without, we resisted the movement and ignored its meaning (which was the very thing that drew us to it), writing of it in conventional terms, doing our part in pushing it toward the conventional, reshaping it, destroying its meaning. Through the two years of miracle and release, spiritual breaking of the lockhold of history and tradition on the minds and morality of a generation of Southerners by the sit-ins and freedom rides, there had been this undercurrent of press preoccupation with the signs of enmity and dissolution within the movement. Wishful thinking perhaps on the part of some, self-fulfilling prophesy certainly, but I think now, looking back on my own part in it, that it was more. It had to do with compulsion, partly personal (that in all of us which is driven to destroy good because of fear of it), and partly cultural (that ingrained awareness of what is important, what is not). Once I got to Albany I found myself all unawares resisting both parts of compulsion, coming close to fearing the good no longer but close to embracing it, coming even to know one of the origins of the fear, the feeling that if you dare allow yourself to believe in anything, you will inevitably be disappointed, even destroyed along with it, and coming, certainly, to know what was really important in what was going on, sitting in the church listening to the music of the people of the movement, not worrying, really, about the bickering and dissension and signs of dissolution among the movement organizations.

In Albany the conflict at the beginning was between SNCC and the NAACP, a struggle in effect for the loyalty of students at the all-Negro Albany State College. SNCC was even more hostile to SCLC when it entered the campaign, and increasingly critical. Some of this was the beginning of the disagreement between the two organizations about tactics and approach to people; some of it surely was SNCC's simple resentment of SCLC's ability to draw attention to itself—from the media, from the American public and, most importantly, from the common Negro people who crowded the Albany churches to see and hear Dr. King and Dr. Abernathy. Some accounts of why the Albany campaign finally collapsed suggest that the people and their leaders, sharing some of SNCC's resentments and probably encouraged by SNCC, finally came to the point where they no longer would support SCLC.*

Marion Page, who had been executive secretary of the Albany Movement, told me in 1970 that this, in effect, is what happened. He said people particularly resented Ralph Abernathy's saying on television in Atlanta, after the second time he and Dr. King were jailed, that SCLC had taken charge of the Albany Movement.

"People who had done the fighting felt they were being given a back seat. We were trying to get up, then, the hugest demonstration ever, but the air went out. We never were able to get up steam again."

He attaches great importance to the version he has told me of why the Albany campaign failed. He sits across from me in his living room and says that he has never talked with any other reporter about this. My training and maybe instinct cry out to seize on what he has divulged, to press him for more details, to concentrate other interviews and research on fully uncovering a new gem of truth. After all, it was in the quest of just such details and facts of movement disintegration that I first went to Albany. That endless time ago. But now I can hold better to perspective. I am not seeking an exclusive news story; I am no historian. I am interested in the fact that Mr. Page (and,

*Chapter 6 of *King: A Critical Biography*, by David L. Lewis (New York: Praeger Publishers, 1970) contains a perceptive recapitulation of the Albany events.

as he says, most of the other leaders) became resentful of
SCLC and, more importantly, that the people did, too, coming
to an end of their most beautiful ability to believe and sacrifice.

I am interested in that change which occurred in the hearts
of the people, the dynamics of it, the causes, the effects. Would
it have not occurred under another leadership? Or if the leadership had not been, as it were, pressed and pushed into strategies
and actions which were irrelevant to the spirit, the natural
expression of the people? If the people themselves, stretching
the limits of courage and energy, stressed, weary, had not been
subject to mainstream (and white racist) disparagement of the
leadership? If the government and society had exercised their
responsibilities to the people and the leadership? . . .

"It was not all a loss," Mr. Page says to me in his living room.
"Maybe it was to Martin Luther King. But the ultimate end
was not the glorification of Martin Luther King. The ultimate
end was to bring relief to the people of Albany, Georgia, and
its environs."

The causes . . . and effects.

Mr. Page is a gentle, older man. He has large hands and uses
them expressively as he talks. I remember him in the frantic
days of the movement as the one who kept going, over and
over, to the recalcitrant and canny city officials, trying to set
up negotiations. I can see him in the church with a page from
a note pad on which were scribbled points for negotiation. It
was one of the times when the white city officials had seemed
to promise to sit down and talk. (At the start, the Albany
Movement asked no more, merely that the city officials sit
down and talk, and throughout this remained a major goal,
never realized during the two campaigns.) Mr. Page that afternoon, I remember, was excited, hopeful. But, as always, the
whites went back on their promise.

"Chief Pritchett and the city attorney would promise things
and then renege," Mr. Page said in 1970. "We dug our teeth
in and held on."

Mr. Page, who was so capable of hope during the movement,

so patient in his seeking of honorable negotiation with dishonorable men, saying now: "I was a naïve little boy from a country town. They put things over on me. But not any more." Mr. Page saying: "The SNCCs here—the original SNCCs—were fine—not like this motley bunch they've got now." Saying: "During the missile crisis, I said it might not be a bad idea to . . . just blow this country up and start over again. I understand Stokely Carmichael, there in the bowels of Lowndes County, Alabama, in that hell hole. They laid it on him. They made him like he is. Eldridge Cleaver the same."

Mr. Page, most bitterly of all, saying: "The Justice Department . . . I was naïve until those birds got through with me . . . They almost made an anarchist out of me. Promise after promise, and nothing would happen. They just played politics, pure and simple. Anything that would upset the white people of Georgia they would gloss over. And at the same time try to placate us."

Saying, finally: "I have roots here. My children. My parents before me. I have no intention of going to Africa. I'll stay and fight it out . . . There were decent white people here all the while. Most of them are products of their environment. They were brought up to believe that 'what I do is all right; if what you do doesn't please me, stop it.' We put an end to that."

These are the things I seek of Mr. Page—the sanity of the movement still alive in such people and no little of its original indigenous, sweet spirit—this, rather than some detail of new truth about the dissension within the movement in Albany; not the details of that dissension, but what it meant, what part it played in the shaping of the movement into the culturally familiar, culturally acceptable. Albany was perhaps the fatal turning point. I am not concerned any more with who might have been right, who wrong in the squabbling there. SNCC and SCLC needed to draw closer to each other in thought and strategy; they still believed in the same things. Instead, in Albany, they began moving further apart, a splitting that continued until, on the Meredith March, they were completely asunder, no longer believing in the same things. And the people who responded so fully, so beautifully, to the movement in Albany and in all the other places it came to (because in Albany most so, but in all the other places to a degree the movement drew its meanings and methods from them, gave expression to indigenous wisdoms)—the people were deserted on the Meredith March by part of their movement, left, like Mr. Page, with mixtures of bitterness and sane understanding and wistful memories.

I struggle now to find what happened in Albany that turned the movement to the conventional, but I cannot fully understand it if I do not keep alive in me the knowledge of what was inside the people, telling of the things that happened, but letting there always be in a part of my mind as I tell it the powerful pounding of the music of the mass meetings as a counterpoint to my words of discovery and analysis, like the humming of the congregation:

> *Keep your eyes*
> *On the prize*

while the the preacher extemporized his poems of prayer.

Reverend Wells, in so many ways the articulate spokesman for all that was within the unlettered, unsophisticated people, told in 1971 what, out of all the practicality and strategy, the concerns of conventionality, in sum, Albany meant to him—and he spoke in terms of the spiritual:

"When it started, I held that America could live and could reign as a world leader if it could find a place for its black citizens. It could live forever. Whenever I came before people, I said that, and I still feel it, still hope it—if I can't always any more believe it.

"I would tell them at the beginning that I loved America, that it was one of the greatest nations in the world, and that I believed that if the people would stand together and let us all go to battle in Albany, Georgia—make Albany, Georgia, the battleground of the whole nation—we would not upset the whole nation with many battlegrounds, but just have one battlefield.

"And then we were arrested ten or fifteen minutes after our feet hit the ground in our first attempt to picket.

"We got a group together and went to Washington. Two cars all the way to Washington—just simple little people. We asked to speak to the attorney general. As usual, the head sent his second-in-command. It's happened every time in the last hundred years. Black men know this is no accident.

"We spoke to John Doar [first assistant attorney general in the civil rights division] and asked for help on the right to picket. That's all we went to ask for. Now you look back on it. Lord have mercy—the right to picket. He said if it was a voting situation, they had the law spelled out to protect us. But it was not spelled out on picketing. I choked the assistant attorney general with one word. I asked him what was meant by the guaranteed rights of the Constitution. I haven't had an answer yet.

"The power structure knew what he told us before we got back. They were ready to lay it on us. And they did.

"They herded us into those jails, while the white community stood across Oglethorpe and observed what was happening. The same people who would sit in those half-million dollar and million-dollar structures every Sunday morning and listen to men of the cloth of God with all kinds of letters behind their names . . . I would tune in on the radio, and couldn't hear a single word from Heaven. I saw more God in the movement than in twenty years in the church.

"I've been a churchman as long as I can remember—and no preacher can convince me that Heaven didn't have nothing to say about what was happening there in Albany.

"The white church, the white community, let us down. The white community was without a heart, without a conscience. My sole reason for demonstrating was to reach the better people—who hadn't thought about injustice before. I don't know what happened. We were depending on the white community. We had faith . . ."

The several streams of movement history that had been flowing through the years prior to 1962 came together in Albany. In the summer of 1961 Charles Sherrod and Cordell Reagon, among the first of the full-time staff workers for that new "coordinating committee" of the non-violent student demonstrations, SNCC, came to the little city, trading and manufacturing center of southwest Georgia (immortalized in the infamy of its earlier role as slave and cotton market center in DuBois' *Souls of Black Folk*). They were joined soon after by Charles Jones. All three were veterans of the sit-ins. They set about trying to develop ties with the Albany Negro community and to begin to develop a community organization as a prelude to doing the same thing in the surrounding, and far more harshly racist, counties. This was the first concerted move by SNCC into this kind of work, a precedent to the voter registration effort in the style that was to make that effort its most important and characteristic work. Ironically, what had started as a pilot project by some of those in SNCC who favored voter registration over demonstrations soon turned into the largest demonstration campaign to that date. (Those who, in the SNCC debate, favored direct action went to practice it in Mississippi—and became famed instead for voter registration and community organization work.)

Cordell Reagon, in the 1964 tape recording, recalled that first SNCC venture into voter registration in Albany:

"I came right out of high school, working with SNCC. SNCC was just getting on its feet when I joined. It was still disorganized. There were only five people—[Charles] McDew, Sherrod, Charles Jones, a few other people. We went down to McComb after I got out of Parchman. And a lot of things happened down there. A man named Herbert Lee got killed during the first few months in McComb. A lot of people got put in jail. I guess all of us at one time or another had been beaten down in that area—by police or by local people. Nothing still has ever been done about that . . .

"After I left McComb, I went to Albany. Sherrod and I went to Albany . . . in sixty-one, and I stayed there a little over a year . . . We planned to work on voter registration in Albany but not extensively, but to work out of Albany into the surrounding counties. We also felt that whatever affected Albany would have some bearing on the surrounding communities. And I think it proved to be true—after we got kids involved in direct action and after we went to jail . . .

"When we first went into Albany, we ran into a lot of obstacles. No place to stay, for one thing. No money in our pockets. We did get a place to stay for a few nights with . . . Mr. King, who is the father of Attorney King down there. We spent those three days at the college—Albany State College—talking to the students, trying to get them involved in some way. And, at the same time, trying to find us a place to stay.

"At that time very few people knew who we were. It had been rumored around we were freedom riders. Within a week's time everybody in the community knew who we were, from the police on down. People would see us walking down the street. They'd cross over to the other side because of freedom riders, you know, things like this. They were just extremely afraid of us, because we represented something that had never been done, that they'd never really given any thought to—because they'd always been in fact in their place . . .

"We ran into all kinds of obstacles. NAACP saying we were taking their members and other people saying we were communists . . . Even Negroes were saying this, you know. So we decided we were going to have to have some kind of local organization to work through. At that time Sherrod and I went to one of the most prominent men in the community that we felt could be trusted. It was Dr. Anderson. And, you know, this is how we worked. We tried to pick out somebody we thought the community would like. We told him what our program was; he was very much interested in our program . . . Most of the decisions were made by the Albany people themselves. And this is SNCC's policy—not to try to set yourself up as any kind of leadership, but to in fact try to be with local leadership and try to serve in some sort of advisory capacity . . .

"We kept stressing that we were not leaders, that whatever they wanted us to do, we would do . . . Eventually we pulled through. I think what really got us through, though, was that Sherrod . . . spoke to the ministerial alliance and also spoke at a mass meeting of the people of the community and told them that we didn't have any money, that the only thing we had was our bodies. They were welcome to our bodies, and they could use our bodies the best way they saw fit. And so this was the thing. We put our bodies on the line . . .

"A little later on, Charles Jones came down. He encountered the same kind of opposition from the local community that we did. But we were finally breaking through those barriers. People were looking at us and accepting us. The way we did in Albany, which I think is going to go down in history, was that we went into that community, we stayed there, and we became a part of that community. We worked with the people day and night . . . See, we had twelve dollars between us when we went to Albany and we lived off that twelve dollars for two weeks . . .

"The people learned to accept us not as . . . field secretaries for SNCC, because we didn't go in there like most civil rights organizations. We didn't go in there wearing neckties. Now I can't say it was because we didn't want to—we didn't have money to buy shirts and ties, and we still don't. But this is the thing: We identify with the community. I basically identified with the students . . . Sherrod basically identified with the local older people, because he was a young minister and made them feel that he wasn't going to tell them anything that was wrong. With this type of combination, I think we worked out beautifully. Charlie Jones—he worked with just about everybody. The people down there really liked him . . .

"I might point out that Dr. King didn't come to Albany until after [many] people had been put in jail. I don't hold this against him. I think you can always use somebody. But people in Albany had their movement. I like to see local communities build their movement and make their movement and carry their burden themselves . . . I tend to think that you need money raised for the cause of the movement, not because you got somebody will draw a crowd."

Mr. and Mrs. Emanuel Jackson took the three SNCC workers into their home. (Both lost their jobs, she as librarian at Albany State, he as assistant circulation manager of the *Albany Herald*, as a result.) Mr. Page let SNCC have an office. (It was fire-bombed by whites.) Mr. Page recalled how they went around talking to people about grievances—lack of street lights and paved streets, fire-bombings of the SNCC office and ministers' homes.

"I had got along all right," he said. "There were no pressures on me. I hadn't ever done anything. But when they talked about police brutality I couldn't ignore it. Before long it would get me, too . . ."

Mrs. Jackson, called Goldie, secretary of the Albany Movement through its existence, recalled early meetings of five or six concerned citizens over the grievances. "We had hoped just to go to the City Commission and get redress of our grievances. But we could never really be heard. The SNCC kids said we had to come together as a group—had to really organize and make them listen." (To hear again the overtones of fondness, admiration, even awe, in the voices of such people when they speak of "the SNCC kids" is to realize anew just how much they meant to Negro Southerners of the movement, how much they inspired the people and called forth the greatness within them.)

The Albany Movement was organized on November 17, 1961, out of the nucleus of concerned citizens. Mrs. Marian King (widow of Slater King, Negro real estate man who, with his brother, Attorney C. B. King, was a stalwart of the movement) recalled in 1970 the small beginnings: "We would get together and talk after Charles Sherrod and Cordell Reagon came around looking for support. I don't recall the issues. But

we would hear beautiful speeches. People were talking about
their grievances against white folks for the first time, were
saying things openly. Certain people spoke more than others
and became leaders. It was all spontaneous . . ."

The officers elected were middle-class and adult, not students. Dr. Anderson was president, Slater King vice-president,
Mr. Page executive secretary, Mrs. Jackson secretary. The
SNCC workers had encouraged development of such an organization, capable of commanding the respect of a whole cross
section of the community, not merely the young people as in
the sit-ins and freedom rides. Presumably, they sought such
community-wide organization (as later they were to do in the
surrounding southwest Georgia counties) as logical to a voter
registration drive. The practice in the surrounding counties
subsequently was to organize first around such issues as paving
and street lights or police brutality, whatever concerned people, and then to develop enthusiasm for voter registration as
the solution to the problems—sending surprising numbers
against white trickery, hostility and violence in futile attempts
to register.

But the direct-action reflex was still strong in SNCC. The
three workers had also become involved in plans of the
NAACP Youth Council at Albany State for a test of the
Interstate Commerce Commission ruling against bus terminal
segregation; the sit-in occurred on the day that the ruling went
into effect, November 1. Police ordered the students out of the
white waiting room, but did not arrest anyone. On November
22 they did arrest five students who sought service in the white
restaurant in the Trailways Terminal. This was followed by the
arrival, on Sunday, December 10, of eight SNCC and SCLC
staff members in freedom-ride style in a "white" railroad car.
They entered the white waiting room at the Union Railway
Terminal, where a crowd of Albany Movement Negroes waited
them.

Thus all previous movement history was joined symbolically
in Albany. SNCC was there experimentally beginning its great

voter registration work; Negro college students were in jail for
a sit-in demonstration; freedom riders arrived and would cata-
pult the Albany Movement into action, with Dr. King coming
to lead it, the first sustained campaign that included all segments and classes of a Negro community since Montgomery.
The goals in Albany were far broader than in Montgomery,
were indeed what the movement would continue to seek for
the next three years—full integration of public facilities and
enfranchisment of Negroes. The two main modes of the movement began, then, in Albany in 1961 and 1962—the pattern
of massive non-violent marches and demonstrations developed
by SCLC, and the slow, patient work of community organization and voter registration that was to become SNCC's mainstay.

"It broke open with the freedom ride," A. C. Searles, editor
of the *Southwest Georgian*, a Negro weekly newspaper, recalled in 1970. "I went down to meet the train. There was no
trouble. They went in the white waiting room. They didn't stay
long. They shook hands with the people in the crowd there to
meet them. Everything was smooth. There were no grounds for
arresting anyone. The crowd decided to have a motorcade to
a church for a rally. The chief [Police Chief Laurie Pritchett]
told [the freedom riders going to a car] to get out of the street
or they would be under arrest. He said they were blocking
traffic. There were no sidewalks. He was just mad. Things had
gone too smoothly. My people just grinned at him . . .

"He arrested them and started three years of upheaval with
that . . ."

In the 1940s Mr. Searles had earned the enmity of local
whites and a death threat for reporting the fatal beating of a
Negro man by the sheriff of an adjoining county. "We used to
have to put 'white' after a white man's name in the paper. Civil
rights. These people just don't know. I was not a radical then.
I still am not."

"The movement's dead," he said in 1970. "I hate to report

it. The only person who could have kept it alive was killed."
He referred to Slater King, killed in an automobile accident.
I asked him what it had amounted to—all the turmoil of the
movement in Albany. He smiled.

"Until 1961 I thought Albany was a pretty good town. I
thought race relations were fairly good. The reason was I had
accepted the patterns—separate waiting rooms, the back of the
bus. I didn't necessarily like it, but I had accepted. In 1961 the
talk became, 'Let's integrate.' It had never occurred to me
before that much could be done about it . . . What did we win?
We won self-respect. It changed all my attitudes. This movement made me demand a semblance of first-class citizenship."

The newly formed Albany Movement responded to the arrests of the freedom riders by calling for mass meetings and
demonstrations. Hundreds of Negroes came forth to fill the
churches, to speak in song and prayer their own discovery of
this new, never-before-dared thought of "Integrate, integrate."
The first mass meeting had been held in November, when the
Albany State students were arrested. Mrs. Jackson described
being there:

"I'll never forget it. It was on a Saturday night at the Mount
Zion Baptist Church. So many came there was no room for
some to sit. They knew about the meeting just from talk
around the community. That night we sang 'We Shall Overcome' for the first time. We are a very emotional people anyway. Two things we knew held us together: prayer of
something good to come and song that tells from the depth of
the heart how we feel about our fellow man. People stayed
there all night long that first time, praying and singing . . ."

As in nearly every place where the song was heard in those
years when it was the anthem of the movement, people in
Albany believed that it originated there. The truth seems to be
that it was introduced in its movement form (revised from a
labor union version) at the Highlander Folk School in the
1940s by Zilphya Horton, wife of Miles Horton, the school's

director. It was sung there, as later in the movement, at the close of meetings and the like over the years. Guy Carawan, a young white folk singer, helped introduce it to movement groups around the South. Mrs. Jackson told how Ruthie Harris and Bernice Johnson (later Reagon), two of the most beautiful voices in the Albany Movement, sat up all one night putting together the words; what they evidently did was add Albany variations to the basic stanzas.

They sent the first demonstration into downtown Albany on the Monday after the freedom-ride arrests on Sunday—people singing and praying, kneeling on the sidewalk in a long line, asking that the arrested students be released. Photographs show the solemn black faces, the ordinary clothes, the fear and exaltation of the moment. Mrs. Marian King was on that first march. "We didn't expect to be jailed for kneeling and praying in front of city hall," she said in 1970. "They took us up the alley, put eight or ten people to a cell, and then moved us to Baker County. We were terrified . . ."

The demonstrations and arrests continued the next day and the next, and on the day after that, the fourth day, I saw them for the first time, entered the Shiloh Baptist Church and sat in the cold and the gloom and heard the eloquence of song and prayer and exhortation from the young woman speaker and followed the march through the drizzle to the Trailways Terminal and watched the arrests there, feeling in me all that emotion and awe and inchoate reaching out to try to understand what I saw. I heard the song that day for the first time since on the roadside with the Atlanta sit-in students. As in all those other places where the people believe they originated the song, there was poetic validity to the belief; it came from within, was not superimposed:

> We'll walk hand in hand
> We'll walk hand in hand
> We'll walk hand in hand
> Today . . .

And one of the Albany verses:

> *We'll all go to jail*
> *We'll all go to jail*
> *We'll all go to jail*
> *Today . . .*

In Albany, and elsewhere when fervor was high, there was, too, a flourish in the rendering of the refrain, an adding, thrusting into it of extra notes which, with hundreds singing loudly, confidently, exultantly, made it, far more than in most singing of it, strong and joyful and imperative, an impetus to action: an added "Oh . . . oh . . . oh" in two lines of the refrain; the first time a long "Oooooh" in the background of the "Oh . . . oh . . . oh . . ." (Leon Hall said, "like pouring out a bucket of stars"):

> *We'll all go to jail*
> *Today . . .*
> *Oh-oh-oh, deep in my heart*
> *I know that I do believe*
> *Oh-oh-oh, we shall overcome*
> *Some day . . .*

I saw the fourth day of demonstrations, and on the fifth day Dr. King arrived and that night the miracle of the crowd's willing him to lead the march the next day occurred. More than a hundred people followed him and Dr. Abernathy to jail that day, and more than five hundred were already in jail and . . . the white officials condescended to negotiate. In exchange for the promise that demonstrations would cease, they agreed to release those who were in jail on property bonds (the charges not dismissed) and to consider Negro grievances at some undesignated time in the future. It was a week before Christmas; Dr. King left Albany, and the press did, too. I went home with the music of the mass meetings ringing in my ears.

And memories, images building within me the awareness— not understanding or full comprehension, just the simple awareness of something entirely new, a spirit suddenly alive in dead America (and my own career-concentrated, deadened sensibilities), full of heady portent, a snapping loose suddenly of bonds in a process that, once begun, could not be stopped until all were gone, not just some of them, but all, so that those of us who had been by history and conditioning completely tied down were to be completely free—whether we wanted to be, could without fear be, or not.

It is so hard now to recapture the feeling of that great time. In an America returned, at least temporarily, to jaundice, cynicism and hopelessness in some ways more profound than in the South of the way things used to be, I have to go back to the raw notes of what people said and did, what they told me, to believe that it really was there. I talked to some of the teenagers who had been in those demonstrations of the first three days. A pretty, fifteen-year-old girl, just out of jail, described her experience and emotions in Albany, Georgia, in December, 1961:

"We marched around the courthouse first. Nothing happened. We decided to go again and got to the corner, and a policeman said we were under arrest. They pushed us into the alley and took our names. They put the juveniles in cells to themselves. I was in the second cell. Then they loaded us on a bus. It was a regular city transit bus, and nobody said anything to us until we got to Camilla. Then they cursed us and told us to get off the bus.

"The sheriff there said to us, 'You're not in Albany any more. You're in Camilla.' That was to threaten us. He said if there was any noise he had something bad for us.

"We were put in a cell designed for six. There were fifty-four girls—and only six beds. There were no mattresses, just steel beds. Some got in the beds, some put their coats down on the floor. We alternated, because the floor was more comfortable.

"They told us not to sing and pray. But we did pray. Everybody prayed real soft. We kneeled and prayed during the night.

"The next morning, at eight-thirty, they asked if we were

hungry. We said yes. Breakfast was a big spoonful of raw grits
and chicken gravy—with no chicken in it—and two slices of
white bread. I just played over mine. They wouldn't come for
the garbage. We asked them to, but they wouldn't. We asked
for a mop for some that had been spilled; they said lick it up.

"They kept playing with the heat—turning it up as high as
it would get and then turning it down. We paid no attention
and kept our mouths closed.

"At three-thirty they asked if we were hungry again. Dinner
was a big spoonful of raw black-eyed peas, bread and raw
fat-back. When I say raw, I mean it wasn't cooked enough—
wasn't cooked good. They told us to keep the wooden spoons
they gave us, that we wouldn't get another for a year and a half.
[She showed me hers—a souvenir now.]

"Late that afternoon, they opened the door for us and asked
if we were ready to go home. They brought us back to Albany.
Nothing was said. The Albany police led us into the courtroom.
We sat on the left side of the courtroom; our parents were on
the right side.

"The juvenile judge read two parts of the Constitution and
told us not to demonstrate any more. He wasted his breath. We
will be back. We went on home as happy as ever—and determined to come back.

"I wasn't frightened at all. I felt I was doing something for
myself and my people. I wasn't frightened at all that night. I
just kept praying. I said the Lord's Prayer, over and over, all
through the night."

A sixteen-year-old girl told much the same story of her experience in another county prison camp. The guards there told
the young Albany Negroes, to their amusement, they would be
in a cell where a man had died, that it was "hainted." He also
threatened to sic dogs on them.

"As we ate, a big black and brown dog was there, and he
sniffed our food as they passed it to us. Within ourselves it hurt
us, but nobody said anything. We stacked all our plates nice
and neat in the shower room."

A senior in high school, she hoped to be a speech therapist.

"Three years ago, I was introduced to a girlfriend who was not able to talk or hear. She taught me to talk with my hands. I am still learning."

Was she angry, bitter about her experience? "No. One day they will realize we are right. We shall overcome. God *is* on our side. All we want is human dignity and equal rights for all people—including my own children when I have them."

From the start in Albany I had abandoned the attempt at orderly note-taking for my column, had instead filled page after page with impressionistic, descriptive jottings full of the discovery, the awe I felt, trying to capture all that was happening, aware that it was too important, too big to be confined to a column:

. . . On the night before Dr. King arrived in Albany, at the mass meeting at Shiloh: The prayer is a chant, repetition of metered lines with rising intensity, crowding of meter, interspersed with sudden shouts, cries. One line shouted: aaa-MEN, aaaaa-MEN, aaaaaa-MEN. Then quietly: Amen. The sanctuary is full; people stand in the rear. A quietly spoken prayer begins:

> Guide them, Lord
> Guide our white brothers
> Guide them, Lord
> For they are grappling with problems
> With which they are unacquainted.
> Make them conscious of the fact
> That men are all equal
> That color does not matter
> To the Lord
> But purity of heart.
> We love freedom
> We love freedom
> We love freedom.

The congregation has joined in, repeating with the preacher: We love freedom. Four little girls, one with pigtails, are on the front row between their father, huge in a black sweater, white

shirt and tie, and their mother, pretty in an orange sweater.
The prayer continues:

> We pray, oh Lord
> That oppression will end
> That domination will end
> That prejudice will cease.
> Thou who
> Overruled the Pharaohs
> Overruled the Babylonians
> Overruled the Greeks and Romans
> You alone is God
> Always have been God
> God in man
> God in love
> May our suffering help us.
> For
> The Lord is my shepherd
> I shall not want.
> He maketh me to lie down beside green pastures . . .

and vigorously, happily, the crowd joins with him in the psalm,
its words becoming song, and at its end the preacher intoning:

> Do you know Him?
> Jesus Christ
> Our son.
> He is my lawyer
> Jesus Christ
> Our son.
> The first man on the battlefield
> And the last to leave . . .

Another preacher gets up to speak: "It is a pathetic and
pitiful sight to see these scores of our young people being
turned loose from the hell holes called jails. They were not accused of carrying knives or razors. Lord have mercy! They just
were walking down the street singing, trying to be happy
. . . We might not be able to supply these youngsters with everything they need. But they seem to have a secret weapon . . .

"I saw two big huskies sitting in the police car downtown, and traffic was snarled. They should have been out directing traffic instead of watching innocent Negroes come there to pray and sing . . . Repeat with me:

> There is a God in heaven.
> God is on our side
> And we shall not fear.

He resumes his telling of the injustices of the situation, an Old Testament prophet crying out: "I glory in the fact that not a Negro has been arrested for carrying a lethal weapon. A thirteen-year-old girl was jailed. What for? For singing! And she was singing not the blues, not jazz, but singing hymns . . .

"Oh, those pore wicked, unkind, uncouth, wicked people who oppose us!"

Another speaker tells of visiting and interviewing Charles Sherrod in the Terrell County jail. There had been a report that he had been brutally beaten. "Oh, no! Oh, no!" the crowd chorused. Then Sherrod was presented.

"Did they beat you up?"

"No. They slapped me a couple of times." (groans)

"It cut my lip." (groans)

"A man named Zeke with a sling on his arm . . ." (This was Z. T. Mathews, sheriff of Terrell County.)

"There was no singing or demonstrations in that jail."

"Did you pray?"

"I prayed to myself." (a murmur of approval)

"I answered him 'yes' and 'no.' I didn't put a handle on it. He wanted me to say 'yes, sir' and 'no, sir.' I was not badly beaten. I was struck twice in the face while under arrest."

A plain man rises to speak, his face radiant. "It is a funny thing," he says. "As much hell as we've caught here in Albany, I still love it. It's home. I love to fish, to pick the magnolias, to pick blueberries. I love peanuts. I like pecans . . .

The crowd murmurs rich, mirthful appreciation after each phrase and bursts into applause when he concludes:

"I want to stay here. I want to raise my children here. I want to live a decent, law-abiding, self-respecting and dignified life here."

Mr. Page, drily, businesslike, gives a brief report: "The boycotts are hurting them. Not only are we staying out of the stores, but the white people are not going downtown because they are scared . . .

"If we keep the faith, this thing can be resolved without difficulty.

"You are, after all, more law-abiding than the rest of them . . ."

Another speaker: "Christmas is almost on us, but I don't feel much like it, do you? Without the spirit of Christ, there is no Christmas."

He tells of a girl who was sent to the Newton jail in Baker County who lost her voice because of the cold. He tells of asking Chief Pritchett if he thought it right to send Albany people to all those other counties. The people applaud, shout.

The meeting moves with an inevitability through such moments—a sense of inner form to it, high moments, low ones, expressions of joy, of sorrow, of mirth, of courage and determination, and expressions again and again of that larger view of life which, spontaneously, out of the hearts of the people, out of their culture, their religion, gave them the grace to have genuine compassion, forbearance, love for their enemies, condemning the sin, not the sinners. Soon the meeting would end, the spirit at its end that of the speaker up there now, concluding his remarks:

"They know they are not going to gain their ends. They need the Lord to come in and touch the hearts of two or three men here in this town. That's what we are praying for."

That was on the night before Dr. King arrived. He did not teach them, build in them, the spirit of forgiveness, the philosophy of redemptive love. He drew it from them, learned it from them, had it, like the SNCC kids, in his own heart when he started back in Montgomery, had it from the same background, culture—and for a time, such Negro Southerners, the many of them and their leaders, Dr. King their ultimate spokesman, were able to transcend the dominant culture of America and the South, were able to resist the compulsions of what America had become.

"All of the people deeply felt what was going on," said Mrs. Goldie Jackson. "The people pushed those of us who were leaders. We were not ready, but they had been waiting. I didn't know that about people before—that they could come together like that . . .

"People who worked in white people's kitchens would say they were ready to go to jail. They would give me their names and then the name they wanted to go to jail under."

My notes of that time contain, too, the elements of American compulsion, not merely the subtle, unseen forces at work on the movement, but the overt, raw resistance to it—the kind of thing that was normal for America, a normality which the movement, for a time, showed, by the contrast of its own spirit, to be insane.

My notes say: A Negro leader who is pleased, encouraged by a report he has that Jack Kennedy is concerned about Albany, has been talking to Bobby Kennedy about it. Police Chief Pritchett calling a press conference to announce that four of those arrested in the freedom ride have criminal records. It turns out that their records are of previous arrests for nonviolent protest. (The list of those who were in jail, unknown names at the time, included people who would distinguish themselves in movement and later New Left history: Bernard S. Lee, James Forman, Tom E. Hayden, John Robert Zellner.) Chief Pritchett, a round-faced, puckish-looking man with light red hair, pink skin, a canny man, a sardonic one, saying: "Outside agitation by people with criminal records is largely responsible for the trouble here." Saying: "The governor called, and I assured him Albany is doing everything possible to protect all citizens and avoid bloodshed. He and I talked to the attorney general and expressed the view that removal from our midst of paid agitators would solve all our problems." (The U.S. Attorney General eventually accepted the assurances of the chief and the mayor that they could handle the situation, despite telegrams and calls from movement leaders pleading for federal action against the unconstitutional arrests. When the truce was finally reached he sent the mayor a telegram of congratulations.) Chief Pritchett saying: "We must avoid mass demonstrations and possible death." Mayor Asa Kelley, a short, studious-looking man with metal-rimmed glasses, his brow furrowed, saying solemnly: "Large numbers of both colored and white people are coming to Albany, their purpose unknown. I have requested the governor to alert the local National Guard unit, subject to the call of the mayor. This is to maintain peace and tranquility of the city and protect the lives and limbs of all citizens, white and Negro. They are now in the process of assembling at the armory. I don't intend to use them except for the purpose of maintaining peace, law and order . . ."

They were not used. Chief Pritchett's police were quite capable of making the hundreds of unconstitutional arrests that ensued, of controlling the whites. At the time, I was struck simply by the contrast, the dramatic contrast between the beauty of the Negroes' spirit, the feeling of their meetings and demonstrations and the ugly, cynical, often vicious, feeling of the white officials, their obsession with force, their phobia about violence. I did not then see the contrast as cultural—the ugly and incessant talk of the threat of violence, so much a part of making the movement familiarly American, of the processing of it, and the singing forth with joy, mirth in the church:

> This little light of mine
> I'm gonna let it shine
> This little light of mine
> I'm gonna let it shine

This little light of mine
I'm gonna let it shine
Let it shine
Let it shine
Let it shine.

All in the jail house
I'm gonna let it shine
All in the jail house
I'm gonna let it shine
All in the jail house
I'm gonna let it shine
Let it shine
Let it shine
Let it shine.

All on Chief Pritchett
I'm gonna let it shine
Ohhh . . . all on Chief Pritchett
I'm gonna let it shine
Ohhh . . . all on Chief Pritchett
I'm gonna let it shine
Let it shine
Let it shine
Let it shine . . .

Mirth was so often a part of the mass meetings. Dr. Anderson, scorning the frequently heard plaint of the whites that the SCLC leaders were outside agitators: "If they're not Albany people I don't know who you can call Albany people. And these are the people who have been engaged in the sit-ins, and the kneel-ins and the wade-ins and the jail-ins and the stand-ins. And when any more 'in's' come, we'll do that, too."

And Ralph Abernathy intoning: "I want every freedom-loving Negro under the sound of my voice—in this church and on the outside—to meet us at two o'clock at Mount Zion and the Shiloh Baptist Church. Do you know where it is? [*ye-eee-eesss*] Now if you meet me down at Mount Zion . . .

And you can't find me nowhere
Then you come on down to city jail
Because I'll be waitin' down there.
If you meet me down at city jail
And you can't find me nowhere
Then you come on up to Camilla
Because they will have transferred me over there.

The incredible contrast of the grim, violence-obsessed whites and the movement people: Waiting the great demonstration that Dr. King led, a long line of police in yellow raincoats, rigid, militaristic, faces a study in grimness, apprehension, fear for some and for others, savagery . . . Chief Pritchett, his face red, excited, standing before the halted marchers, saying: "Does anyone here have a permit for this parade? If not, I will have to place you under arrest if you continue it." Paddy wagons at the ready, blocking intersections, and . . .

In the long line of black marchers, solemnly now, with great dignity, dropping to their knees to pray there on the sidewalk before crossing the line the chief has set and going to jail, two little boys standing side by side, of the believing age of ten or eleven, scared smiles on their faces, going down on their knees together, closing their eyes tightly for the prayer . . . And then, as the prayer ends, and the people rise to face this day's fate and a lifetime's fears in the grim, murderous presence of the police, strongly and bravely, indeed joyfully, the two boys rise and join in the song that rings out up and down the line of people marching off to jail:

We shall overcome
We shall overcome
We shall overcome
Today.
Oh-oh-oh deep in my heart
I know that I do believe
Oh-oh-oh . . .

Chapter
FOURTEEN

WE HEARD LITTLE of events in Albany during the next six months. It was as though I had been in some mystical new land, had seen and sensed the surface of its miracles and promise, and then, as in a dream, was gone from it.

But life goes on in such places where we have known extraordinary experience and then departed, despite that sense we have that it ceases to exist once we cease to see it. The illusion was reinforced in this instance; once I did return to Albany, in July 1962, when I walked into the Shiloh Baptist Church and saw the faces, heard the voices of the movement people, it was as though nothing had changed, nothing had happened, as though no time had passed and, as in a dream, that which had so stirred me and changed my life in December had been held frozen in the intervening months and now with magic, in a moment, had returned to life. The leader at the pulpit with head thrown back, big hands pounding together the joyful beat of the music, the life of it:

> *This little light of mine*
> *I'm going to let it shine*
> *Shine on Mayor Kelley*
> *I'm going to let it shine . . .*

Much had, of course, happened, most of it bad. The white leaders, claiming a great victory over Dr. King, claiming the movement had disintegrated, refused to consider grievances. Police had harassed and arrested boycott pickets and had killed a Negro youth in alleged self-defense. A bus boycott had resulted in the closing down of the bus company. On February 27 Dr. King, Dr. Abernathy and two of the Albany people who participated in the December 16 march had been tried in city court on charges of parading without a permit, obstructing the sidewalk and disorderly conduct. The decision was held in abeyance. In March a trial on similar charges was held in county court for the freedom riders who precipitated the December demonstrations. Charles Sherrod tried to sit in the white section of the courtroom, and a deputy knocked him down and dragged him to the Negro side. Three of the white defendants tried to sit down beside him and were dragged out of the courtroom. (Mrs. Tom Hayden, called "Casey," was pulled over a row of benches.)

On July 10 the recorder's court found Dr. King and Dr. Abernathy guilty on the basis of the February trial. The sentence: forty-five days or $178 fine. With all the flourish attendant on any action of Dr. King's, all the clamor of news coverage, they elected to serve the jail sentence—and the Albany Movement, dormant since December, broke forth anew.

Thus, in an action interpretable only within the cynical context of Georgia politics, the white officials who had, in December, so exorcised "outside agitators" in July deliberately brought the two chief ones of these in the nation back to Albany. Marvin Griffin, one of the worst of the massive-resistance breed of demagogues whose emergence after the 1954 school decision so appalled those of us who thought then that if you don't talk about racial problems they will go away, was running for governor, the tone of his campaign summed up in a promise to brain demonstrators with a sapling pole. He had strong supporters in the Albany officialdom, including James Gray, controller of the media—newspaper and television—

there. It was a reasonable surmise (reached by many) that a main motive for bringing Dr. King back to Albany was that the hubbub that was bound to ensue would reverberate in Mr. Griffin's favor. This would be true not merely in terms of racist voters, but those who liked not to think about the matter, who perceived demonstrations, through the various distortions of the state's generally bad press, as nigger rioting, and would be inclined to support a candidate who promised to take a firm stand, to suppress them.

If the surmise were correct, if the Albany leaders deliberately set off the Albany Movement again as a political strategy, then the depths of the depravity of southern politics are suggested. Not merely were they willing so to attempt to manipulate the Albany Movement (whose nobility they were conditioned not to see, yet which, surely, must somewhere deep in them—if they were human—have penetrated), but were willing to bring down upon their own people, the common run of whites, all the havoc, the alleged danger they were forever ascribing, the undeniable bad publicity that the movement meant. If this were one part of the political cynicism that helped to change, to end, the movement, there is conjecture which suggests a worse form. It was no secret that the Kennedy Administration was appalled to see the Albany Movement resume; a flurry of official action included many phone calls to the Albany officials and a promise to Mrs. King that the Department of Justice would use its influence to obtain her husband's release.

For whatever reason, the role of the Federal government in Albany throughout was never vigorously in support of the heroism, idealism or constitutional rights of the movement people. It was, instead, manipulative, attempting, as Mr. Page pointed out, to please at least two sides at once. On the second morning after Dr. King and Dr. Abernathy were jailed a mysterious stranger appeared at the police station and paid their fines, and they were (despite their bewildered protest) released. No one seems ever to have solved the mystery of that person's identity. Some assumed that the Kennedy Administration was involved. It was a justifiable suspicion—they wanted King out. They had not hesitated in the past to improvise such solutions to problems besetting them. Later, a federal district judge, J. Robert Elliott, issued a highly questionable (quickly reversed by Chief Judge Elbert Tuttle of the Fifth Circuit Court of Appeals) temporary restraining order against demonstrations by the Albany Movement. Judge Elliott had only recently been appointed by President Kennedy. He was an avowed racist, known to be when he was appointed. The standard apology for such appointments (and the Kennedy Administration had a terrible record of them) was the need to mollify southern senators. (Traditionally, senators recommend who should receive such appointments.) Surface cynicism would call for a wry enjoyment of the embarrassment of a liberal administration when such an appointee issued such a ruling as Judge Elliott did in Albany. But cynicism that goes deeper—of the kind that came finally to consume the movement—would not hesitate to conclude that an administration capable of making such an appointment in the first place was capable of conspiring with such a judge to make such a ruling—certainly where there was high-powered political advantage to be gained.

The administration could have been expected then to resist such a cynical stratagem as that of the Albany city fathers in support of Marvin Griffin. It would much prefer to have a moderate like Carl Sanders elected. It is possible, in the grip of the kind of cynicism the movement came to know, to believe that the reason it preferred moderates was simply that they did not precipitate crises like Wallace or Ross Barnett did, and Griffin could be counted on to do, that they did not force forthright action in behalf of civil rights on an administration which felt it needed in the South the support of the fearful moderates as well as the Negroes. But beyond cynicism, the point of all this is that such considerations (and perhaps—let us hope it is so—all of this conjecture about both sides is untrue) apply in the daily ongoing routines of American politics. A liberal administration can be expected automatically to

react against a cynical attempt by racists to exploit as important
and beautiful human effort as the movement. If the idealism
that the movement stands for, the pledges of the administration in support of that idealism and, for that matter, the beliefs
of the racists all get lost, become irrelevant in the process, then
that is what is wrong with America. The movement came to
know this, and however fanciful its versions might be of the
details of the cynical and amoral manipulations of politics and
government, it told in a poetic, metaphorical sense, the truth
—a terrible truth. And the beginning of the movement's reve-
lations of this truth was in Albany.

Andrew Young told me years later how he and Wyatt Tee
Walker urged against a resumption of the movement in Albany
on the occasion of the July jailing. ("We couldn't see any
handles to anything.") But the spiritual strength was still there
then. Ralph Abernathy opposed them, and they came to agree
with what he said: "When you are called on to witness, you
can't always know, can't always analyze what might happen.
You just have to go."

So, through the rest of July and into August, the Albany
Movement wound through its drama—with great effect on the
future course of the southern movement and foretelling in
foreshortened time what was to happen to all of the movement,
the decline from the original high hopes and spiritual feeling
to an eventual disappointment and bitterness, despite which
the people continued firmly and on mostly conventional terms
to struggle. As during December, I tried to thread my way
through the various levels of the reality of it.

But the most meaningful was that of the mass meetings.
Sitting, sweating, giving myself to them. They were so fervent,
so intense, so excited—hundreds of people crowding into the
little churches, sometimes filling both Shiloh and the Mount
Zion Baptist across the street, with loudspeakers relaying the
meeting to Mount Zion. Their voices, blended so forcefully,
vibrantly, joyfully, told the blending of their wills; the music
spoke as one person formed of all the many people, saying

that it was more than all of the many people combined.

They sang one song in July that they had not sung in December:

> *Come by here, my Lord*
> *Come by here.*
>
> *Come by here, my Lord*
> *Come by here.*
>
> *Come by here, my Lord*
> *Come by here.*
>
> *Oo-ooh, Lord*
> *Come by here.*
>
> *Somebody's singin', Lord*
> *Come by here . . .*
>
> *Somebody's praying', Lord*
> *Come by here . . .*

"Ooh-ooh, Lord, Come by here." A young white woman who grew up in Albany told how at a teenage party that same summer they all (all white) sat under the trees one night at the resort, Radium Springs, and sang together: "Kum-bi-yah." In later years, in the new thing of black pride, the good that emerged out of the Black Power rhetoric, black Southerners would sing "Kum-bi-yah," too. In Sparta, Georgia, in 1970, city police tried to stop a mass march protesting school segregation, and when John McCown, the leader, gave the order to pass the police on by the people did it shouting the song "Kum-bi-yah." I had never heard it either way before the summer of Albany, with verse after verse rolling forth in many moods all summer long:

> *Gonna be free, my Lord*
> *Come by here . . .*
>
> *They're bombin' our houses, Lord*
> *Come by here . . .*

> *Somebody needs you, Lord*
> *Come by here . . .*

"Oh, Lord, come by here." On one of the nights early in the campaign in the packed-in heat, the singing built and built. All the favorites from December rang out, the sound like waves breaking against the walls of the church:

> *Oh . . . freedom*
> *Oh . . . freedom*
> *Oh . . . freedom*
> *Over mee-ee.*
>
> *And before I'll be a slave*
> *I'll be buried in my grave*
> *And go home*
> *To my Lord*
> *And be free-ee.*

And:

> *We're on our way*
> *To Freedom Land*
> *We're on our way*
> *To Freedom Land*
> *We're on our way*
> *To Freedom Land*
> *We're on our way*
> *We're on our way.*
>
> *This little light of mine,*
> *I'm gonna let it shine . . .*
>
> *Over my head*
> *I see freedom in the air*
> *Over my head*
> *I see freedom in the air*
> *Over my head*
> *I see freedom in the air*
> *There must be*
> *A God*
> *Somewhere.*

"Over my head I see justice in the air . . . Over my head I see
goodness in the air . . ." Without pause or discernible signal,
after verse upon verse of such a song, suddenly the singers
would shift to another song, the intensity, the music building
from one to the other: "Keep your eyes / On the prize / Hold
on . . ."

> *Hold on*
> *Hold on*
> *Hold on*
> *Hold on*

"Keep your eyes on the prize / Hold on"—and with the
clapped beat suddenly changed:

> *Ain't go' let nobody*
> *Turn me 'round*
> *Turn me 'round*
> *Turn me 'round*
> *Ain't go' let nobody*
> *Turn me' round*
> *Keep on a-walkin'*
> *Keep on a-talkin'*
> *Marchin' on to Freedom Land.*

On this night the song kept on and on: "Ain't go' let Chief
Pritchett / Turn me 'round . . . / Ain't go' let Mayor Kelley
. . . / Ain't go' let Judge Elliott . . . / Ain't go' let Gov'nor
Vandiver . . ." and then over and over:

> *Ain't go' let nobody*
> *Turn me 'round*
> *Turn me 'round*
> *Turn me 'round*

the clapping between the lines becoming increasingly complex, faster, faster and faster, in counterpoint, all kinds of
rhythms . . .

Keep on a-walkin'-YEAH!
Keep on a-talkin'-YEAH!
Marchin' on the FREEDOM HIGHWAY . . .

and then the complex clapping between the lines sounded into the lines, and the song itself, with each verse, became faster and faster, the clapping now through each line with high shouts over the pounding of the words and the clapping, and then clapping only—louder, faster—and then, beginning over it, a unison shout over and over:

FREE-DOM
FREE-DOM

FREEDOM FREEDOM FREEDOM FREEDOM
FREEDOM FREEDOM FREEDOM FREEDOM

a war chant, an unleashing, full expression of the impetus, the will, the excitement—and the joy—of the Albany Movement, and then, at the height of it, the words of the song returned, a mighty shout:

AIN'T GO' LET NOBODY
TURN ME 'ROUND

the clapping as before in all its complexity and fastness through all the words:

TURN ME 'ROUND
TURN ME 'ROUND
AIN'T GO' LET NOBODY
TURN ME 'ROUND
KEEP ON A-WALKIN' - YEAH!
KEEP ON A-TALKIN' - YEAH!
MARCHIN' ON TO FREEDOM LAND . . .

and then the song became

THIS LITTLE LIGHT OF MINE
I'M GONNA LET IT SHINE

with still the speeded-up meter, the complex, fervent clapping:

EVERYWHERE I GO, LORD
I'M GONNA LET IT SHINE
OH-OH EVERYWHERE I GO-OH
I'M GONNA LET IT SHINE
OH, EVERYWHERE I GO, LORD
I'M GONNA LET IT SHINE
LET IT SHINE
LET IT SHINE
LET IT SHINE . . .

"All in the jail house . . .
All in the county camp

I'M GONNA LET IT SHINE

and then the song became;

THE ONLY CHAIN
THAT A MAN CAN STAND
IS A CHAIN
OF A HAND IN HAND

Keep your eyes on the prize—Hold on . . . verse after verse, the joy, the fervor not diminished. At last, with the abruptness that was usual, it ended and a speaker got up and began intoning his own poetry.

Such music cannot be described—or recaptured. It was there. I heard it, was privileged to hear it night after night in the packed-in heat. And even now, hearing it more thinly on tapes, I return to the mystical, inspired and excited, ecstatic—and reverent mood of those meetings. Hear Reverend C. K. Steele, stern-faced older man, the leader from Tallahassee, Florida, come up to Albany to be a part of it all, as he had gone to Montgomery and was part of the bus boycott, going home from there inspired to try it in Tallahassee, never fully succeeding at home with it—hear him pronounce benediction after a long, inspired singing of "We Shall Overcome," the audience humming now the music of the anthem behind his words:

THE HUMMING:

> *we shall overcome*
> *we shall overcome*

THE PREACHER:

Oh God our Father

> *we shall overcome*

God have mercy on all of us

> *some day*

As we come now to the close

> *oh-oh-oh deep in my heart*

Of a very hectic day

> *I know that I do believe*

We come to thee

> *oh-oh-oh that we shall overcome*

OUR FATHER . . .

> *some day.*

We've tried to pray and do our duty today

> *we shall overcome*

We've walked with Thee today

> *we shall overcome*

As we come to the close

> *we shall overcome*

Of this mass meeting

> *some day*

We pray that our hearts

> *oh-oh-oh deep in my heart*

Will still be turned—

> *I know that I do believe*

In one united thrust and effort

> *oh-oh-oh we shall overcome*

FOR FREEDOM.

> *some day . . .*

OUR FATHER . . .

> *we shall overcome*

We pray that tonight

we shall overcome
Thy *gre–ee—at* spirit
  we shall overcome
Will hover and express itself
  some day
IN CITY JAIL.
    oh-oh-oh deep in my heart
Let our freedom fighters . . .
    I know that I do believe
In prison there KNOW . . .
    oh-oh-oh we shall overcome
That we are praying for them.
    some day . . .
OUR FATHER . . .
    we shall overcome
Our heavenly father . . .
    we shall overcome
Go with us to our several homes.
    we shall overcome
Keep us in thy great love.
    some day
Grant us that peace which passeth
    oh-oh-oh deep in my heart
All human understanding—
    I know that I do believe
In Jesus' name—
    oh-oh-oh we shall overcome
AMEN.
    some day . . .
Then the words:
  WE SHALL OVERCOME
  WE SHALL OVERCOME
  WE SHALL OVERCOME
  SOME DAY
  OH OH OH DEEP IN MY HEART
  I KNOW THAT I DO BELIEVE

OH OH OH WE SHALL OVERCOME
SOME DAY . . .

With that in the background of my mind, with that to
return to at almost any hour during the day, every night in the
packed-in, ecstatic heat, I tried—I tried to know the surface
of what was happening in the mighty clashes of the movement
with the white officialdom of Albany, to keep abreast of the
story. On the surface of official actions, important events there
were after the release of Dr. King and Dr. Abernathy from jail:
the resumption of massive demonstrations which this time
demanded protection of the right to demonstrate and establishment of a biracial committee to set a timetable for desegregation of public facilities . . . other demonstrations at specific
facilities, like the library and swimming pool, laying a groundwork for a massive desegregation court suit . . . the restraining
order by Judge Elliott and its reversal by Judge Tuttle . . . the
attack by guards at the prison camp on Mrs. Slater King and
the clubbing of C. B. King by the sheriff after the beating of
Bill Hansen in the city jail . . . the third jailing of Dr. King and
Dr. Abernathy during early August for ten days . . . the cooling
of enthusiasm (perhaps plain weariness in the face of no gains
either in negotiations or through the courts) among Albany
Negroes . . . an announced shift in emphasis from demonstrations to voter registration and economic boycotts, a shift of
leadership from SCLC back to local people.

The dry telling of what happened belies what really happened. Demonstrations were mounted against the temporary
restraining order not at first by SCLC, though later Dr. King
made a remarkable call for and justification of civil disobedience of it. Reverend Wells led one of them, a night march.

Reverend Wells in the church: "I heard about an injunction.
I heard a few names, but I didn't hear mine. I've heard about
Emmett Till . . ."

Shouting: "Not tomorrow—not at high noon—but NOW!"
A great shout echoes: "NOW! NOW!" People begin clapping
in the same, complex, increasingly fast way they had that other

night, clapping and stamping their feet in the same rhythms, shouting again in unison: FREEDOM FREEDOM FREE-DOM FREEDOM FREEDOM FREEDOM FREEDOM FREEDOM FREEDOM FREEDOM FREEDOM

Reverend Wells, who resembles Louis Armstrong, beams his appreciation, rapport, and shouts out as the great chant begins to diminish:

"We will go down to the city hall and protest peacefully the evils that have been grinding us down for these ninety-nine years. We will obey the traffic lights. If we are stopped before we reach city hall, we will come back to the church after we have had a couple of prayers peacefully."

The march assembles. A teenage girl cries: "Yes, Lord, I'm ready to go."

"Ain't go' let nobody turn me 'round," the marchers sing, as they move out of the church, down a block, turn to the left, the familiar route to the bus station and Jefferson Street where, just as familiarly, the police wait. Reverend Wells and a thir-teen-year-old boy are in the lead. They ask Reverend Wells if he has a parade permit, and he replies, "I do not have a permit," and then he drops to his knees and closes his eyes and lifts his round, black face, earnestly, expressively wrinkled, to the sky, clasps his hands in prayer, and cries:

> Oh, Gracious King!
> This time is the time to pray.
> We have striven well,
> We have waited with patience,
> We are they who would serve the Heavenly Father.
> We have suffered all kinds of injuries,
> And yet we know
> Every man is created equal,
> Every man is created free,
> Regardless to the race
> And to the kind.
> We have done our part,
> Oh, Heavenly Father.

> Oh, King,
> We pray:
> Don't leave us alone in this struggle,
> In this fight . . .

The police, scornfully looking down at the kneeling demonstrators, listening, stir as a girl goes limp on the sidewalk; they bring a paddy wagon and take stretchers out. The prayer goes on:

> We are striving for your will.
> They think they going to kill all of us.
> How many are they going to kill?
> They can't kill us all . . .

The stretcher stratagem has ended the going limp, and now the demonstration heads back to the church, singing as the onlookers in front of stores and dives cheer. Later that same night with the crowd built again in the church, Reverend Wells is crying out again:

"No need to say amen if you're not ready to go down."

And a woman rejoins from the audience: "If we do it tonight, everything will be over with . . ."

And soon, once again, a brave little band is marching out of the church, an old lady with a bandage on her leg in the lead. Hurrying alongside them in the soft wild wind of the southern night, a reporter with me, tough, sardonic, case-hardened, murmurs, "These are great people, great people," tears running down his cheeks.

That was the reality.

One important counterpart to the movement was SNCC's continuing work through those fateful summer months on voter registration in the surrounding counties—Terrell, Baker, Lee. Terrible Terrell. Bad Baker. Evil Lee. They were black-belt, farming counties with Negro majorities, as crudely ruled by racist whites as any in the South, with brutal law-enforcement. With two other reporters I visited Terrell County one night to attend a voter registration meeting, a small gathering in a little wooden church (with a calendar on the wall showing all the American presidents). The county sheriff, Zeke Mathews, squat, burly older man, swaggering, accompanied by other whites, maybe a dozen, interrupted the meeting, and they threatened the Negroes attending, the sheriff telling them he was "a little fed up with this registering business."

Charles Sherrod prayed for forgiveness and understanding of the whites, as they stood listening in the rear of the church. A local leader from nearby Lee County gave a report on the voter effort there.

"The only way to be a good Christian and a good citizen is to be a registered voter. We are trying to teach over in Lee County how to read and write and be a good citizen. As teacher, I preach good citizenship. We are interested in this in the South, because it is one way we can make peace on earth and goodwill among men here in America."

The people, about forty beleaguered believers in democracy, among them little children, sang,

> We are climbing
> Jacob's ladder

and then, standing in a circle, hands joined, building their courage, sang "We Shall Overcome," verse after verse, before finally going out to face what might be waiting in the southern summer night from the whites . . .

To come out of such a meeting and find our rented car's tire flattened (and later to discover its motor had been ruined by sugar poured into the gas tank), to be trailed on the highway driving back to Albany, to feel all the fear of such a moment, was to look to Albany, as bad as it was, as a safe harbor, a sanctuary. Three of the churches which were used for the voter registration meetings in those surrounding counties, including the one where I saw the meeting disrupted, Mount Olive Baptist in Sasser, were burned to the ground a short while later —contributing to the climax of anger and disillusionment which came to Albany in the wake of the movement's original fresh hope and spirit.

Even so, Charles Sherrod, still working in southwest Georgia in 1970, was still occasionally getting beat up, yet not mentioning it in telling the things he thought important in his work. Certainly, part of the sanity of the movement at its best was the ability of many of the people who endured the most outrageous brutalities to somehow assimilate them, keep them in perspective—not to understate the meaning and effect but not, like the press and so many of the segregationist whites, to abstract violence and make of it the whole meaning of the movement's experience.

In our 1970 interview, Bill Hansen said: "For some, non-violence was just the only thing to do. Most people didn't really believe in non-violence, but they didn't believe in armed insurrection either. Most were pushed by the vanguard into non-violent confrontations." Such a bleak view—with the corollary that some in the vanguard, particularly in SNCC, might not have shared the abhorrence of insurrection, were indeed making the first step toward it with what the people *would* be pushed into—is heard often enough in hindsight. Maybe such was the strategy and outlook within movement circles in these hot summer days down in Albany in 1962, but I doubt it. The movement there and then was mostly southern-led, and it drew on the ability of Negro Southerners to transcend the dominant culture's reliance on violence, if out of nothing more exalted than scorn for all that culture, more than it pushed people into things. That—the pushing—came later. Goldie Jackson, like many other local residents (not of any vanguard) at scenes of great movement activity, told me of the many times she and other local leaders quelled the impetus to violence—as often as not among Northerners who came to help and who stayed in her home, which was something of a movement headquarters.

"Many were undesirables. But we were able to stop them from starting something. We'd go days and nights without sleep . . ."

One night, she said, a crowd of three hundred threatened

violence—"some from outside, some from here." The Albany leaders persuaded them to disperse. "Otherwise, it would have been a real mess."

The normal American reaction to the treatment the movement received in Albany (or for that matter to the treatment the average Negro received in everyday life) would be violence. The cultural conditioning to it was always there in Albany, in all the places of the movement in the South. The miracle was that the tension between cultural conditioning and the discipline of non-violence held for so long, and as often as it did. So much creative energy was released from the tension. Not all the impetus to violence was quelled in Albany, but as we shall see, a slight outbreak of violence only magnified the meaning, the magnificence, of non-violence.

A similar tension of love and hate for the whites existed, another indigenous strength upon which the movement fed. In various locales, when the name of some dread and evil symbol of white tyranny would be mentioned (Bull Connor in Birmingham, Jim Clark in Selma, Pritchett in Albany) a murmur would go up in the audience—in part disdain, loathing, but in part, too, a strange kind of laughter, almost fond, something in it of rich appreciation for adeptness at evil, perhaps a detached ability to stand off and chuckle wryly over life's embroilments, or perhaps simply an appreciation of having shared so much with such a person in enmity and struggle.

Ralph Abernathy, on one of those hot nights in one of the Albany mass meetings, at the Third Kiokee Baptist Church, took off on an inspired flight of humorous derision of the enemy, and I have not before or since heard such laughter as built there in the large crowd:

"The first thing we need to set the record straight on is that the city of Albany was not meant for the white folk. I've heard what Mr. Gray, the editor of your paper, and the owner of your television station, had to say: that during Christmastime in the past you all have always had a parade. *(laughter)* He doesn't have any better sense than not to know that the Negroes are not satisfied with a parade once a year. *(laughter, derisive cries, applause)* I want to ask a few questions about that parade. How many Negroes are on the planning committee for that parade? *(cries: "none." laughter. a soprano catcall)* How many Negroes are on the budget committee that decides the budget for that parade? *(again, laughing: "none")* We don't want a parade once a year. But they say I'm an outsider, so I ought to find out because you may want it. Do you want a parade once a year? *(great shout of "noooo . . .")* And then he said that, ah —I want to get him right *(laughter)* because I'm being sued now for three million dollars *(laughter)* for something that appeared in a newspaper that I didn't say—I just want to get it right. He said the symbol of Saint Nick would pass and throw out candy to the children of all races. *(several women's voices, bitterly: "To the white . . .")* Now don't you know *(yeah, Lord!)* that we want *more* than some candy. *(great laughter)* Now . . . now . . . *(laughter keeps on)* Now I understand that the first thing that is wrong with Mr. Gray is the fact that he is a Northerner. *(laughter)* He . . . the first thing that is wrong with him is that he is really from up North. *(general mirth)* I was born in Alabama. *(yes, yes)* Martin Luther King was born in Georgia. You talk about outsiders. Mr. Gray is an outsider. *(pandemonium)* You see . . . *(mirth continuing)* You see . . . *(continuing)* Listen to me tonight . . . Listen to me tonight. Do you know? Mr. Gray hasn't even picked up the southern way of talking. *(great laughter)* He doesn't even sound like a Southerner. *(laughter, applause)* He does not understand our way of life. *(laughter)* Our way of life is not a way of life where you pass out a little candy at Christmastime *(women's laughter)* by the symbol of Saint Nick. *(much laughter)* Do you know what? Do you know what our way of life is? Our way of life is that if you got to throw us out a little candy once a year *(cries of "yes, yes")* and you can't give us candy every day *(yes, yes)* and you can't give us money to buy our own candy, then we take the candy and throw it back to you and say there'll be no candy." *(great laughter, shouts of delight)*

He became serious for a few minutes, the crowd following his mood without pause, and then began anew the humor they had so responded to, this time like poetry:

> We don't want to *be*
> The white man's brother-in-law. *(shouts of assent, jocu-*
>> *larly)*
> Nowhere will you find it
> Where we have sought to be that.
> That's not our aim
> Whatsoever. *(seriously: "no, it's not")*
> All we want to be
> Is his brother. *(shouts of assent)*
> And it appears to us
> As we look around this audience
> Tonight
> That it is *he*
> Who has tried to be our brother-in-law.

(pandemonium, rich shouts, exclamations on the truth of the poetry . . .)

"I drove *(the mirth continuing)*, I went to my church *(continuing)*, I drove to my office *(continuing.)* I drove to the office of my church yesterday and just as I started to put the key in the door, a white insurance agent came down the street with a little sack in his hand. It was bulging out at both sides—records of his clients, people who owned insurance in his company, and they're just about all Negroes, I would predict. And he was real fat *(laughter)* and it was real hot. I was sweatin' *(laughter)* and he was sweatin' *(laughter)* and there sat a Negro woman on the porch, as she always does, right across from the rear of my church office. And he passed by and he says, ah, 'Good mornin', Auntie' *(derisive cries)* and she said, 'Good mawnin'' *(appreciative laughter for his imitation of a tone of utter impassiveness)* and I looked at him and said, 'When did she get to be your auntie?' *(pandemonium)*

> The Negro does not want to be
> His brother-in-law
> His cousin
> His aunt or uncle
> or
> BOY.
> All he wants to be
> Is his brother! *(applause, shouts in unison:*
> "AMEN, AMEN")

I listen to a tape of such extemporized poetry, the evocation in so many subtle ways of the truths that Southerners, black and white, know deep within them—such things as the shared human condition of the fat black preacher and the fat white insurance salesman, both of them sweating, such things as the rich intermingling of blood lines evident in any southern Negro community and (if one really looks) the white ones as well, such things as the shared contempt for the fancy-talking Northerner . . . I sit and lament anew that the movement did not reach southern whites, lament the southern cultural proscriptions that made it impossible for whites to enter such churches, hear such eloquence, feel the southernness of those meetings, and lament as much the forces, the compulsions of American culture that prevented any serious attempt by the media (television being surely the most appropriate) to present what was said and felt by the Negro people in those meetings. Back then, even then, I understood enough to say that if ever they would just put one mass meeting on television, for however long it might take, it would all be over. The white South and America would, then, understand. I used to say that. And I still believe most Southerners, most Americans, are capable of responding, capable of relating to such phenomena.

Some of the white Northerners who came down, sympathetic and idealistic in their way, found themselves being shaped and influenced by this spirit. Albany was where this first happened. I talked one night with Ralph Allen, one of those first white SNCCs that Mama Dolly took in, and he told me his rationale for coming down—a complicated, intellectual explanation compounded of Malraux, Sartre, Camus, of what he had learned in a class on religion at Trinity College. He had come down, he said, to act on his ideas; he could as well have gone to Algeria, but Albany was handier. He had been beaten, terrorized, time after time in Terrell County—probably more than any other white who worked in southwest Georgia.

And he said, after explaining so complicatedly why he was there, a simple thing: "I have never been so happy. It justifies everything that happens. I mean the by-products of being in the movement—the grin of a teenage girl when I tell her how to say something in French, a little kid who ran from me when I first came and now comes up and hugs me, the kids coming to bring you things when you're in jail . . ."

I tried to grasp what was happening all around me there in Albany, frenzied in the awareness that history was being made, that Albany was important beyond the localized issues and events, but seeing it mostly in terms of black against white, oppressed against oppressors, never fearing—even when rocks and bottles were thrown one night by a Negro mob—that the movement would falter, would lose its beautiful way.

In addition to demonstrations created spontaneously by the outrage or the victory of the hour, the demonstrations designed to provide evidence of discrimination in all public facilities continued day by day. One, low-key and dreary, was in the same cluttered, unsavory little lunch room in the Trailways Terminal where I had seen the arrests in December. Now it is hot inside; fans with dirty blades stir the hot, stale air. The proprietor is bent over his bookkeeping at the far end of the counter. A jukebox plays country music. The counter is about half filled. Three middle-aged waitresses move slowly, wearily, to serve the customers. A young man, equally weary in his movements, comes in, takes a stool. The coffee is weak, stale-tasting, and the water is served in scratched plastic glasses. The door opens, and in walk Charles Jones and a Negro boy of about twelve. They don't glance at us reporters sitting there, waiting them, with advance knowledge they would be there. They sit at the counter, the boy next to one of two white men, who are together. The waitresses all have their backs to the the two Negroes. Two old white ladies come in, carrying their suitcases, and seat themselves one over from the Negroes, not glancing at them. They are waited on immediately, order milk. Finally one of the waitresses, her face frozen, impassive, takes the order of the two Negroes. As she turns, Jones reaches, squeezes the boy's shoulder. The waitress returns, bringing them Cokes—in paper cups, not the plastic glasses. They drink them quickly. The jukebox has quit playing in the middle of a song. A big bus driver comes in, stands behind the two Negroes. Finally he goes out. A cop peers in, but does not enter. The two Negroes leave. The phone rings; a waitress answers it, calls the proprietor. More people come in, others leave. Outsized, synthetic rabbit's-foot charms, pink and blue, are among the offerings at the cash register. Someone starts playing the pinball machine. This much of those secular goals toward which the movement was more and more bending itself had been won by the great spiritual upheaval in December— but with paper cups. By 1970 a new terminal had been built; the restaurant is sleek and chrome-shiny and air-conditioned; Negroes, by virtue of the greatest of the movement's secular victories, the 1964 Civil Rights Act, are served alongside whites as a matter of course. The waitresses, black now, some of them, as well as white, still have that weighted, weary look to their movements; the minute hand on the clock, immaculate now and chrome-encircled, still sweeps in slow turns the dull, weary wasting of the precious time of the lives of these people within, working in such a place.

There are shouts and a feeling of glee at the city park when the test is made there—giggles and a contagious hilarity as the children move through the small zoo. The leaders have made reservations by telephone to use the picnic area. A white attendant wrangles with the leaders of the demonstration, finally with bad grace designates an area, isolated from the rest, where they can go. They unload from cars their picnic—grocery sacks full of it. A little black girl with a pigtail watches, fanning herself with a church fan showing two sweet-faced Negro children with their heads bent, eyes closed, hands together in prayer. A cop says of the picnic preparations: "Oh, sure they can stay. They can go take a look at the monkeys."

During the haggling, Negro children stare through the wire fence surrounding the swimming pool and the white children there, some getting out of the water to stand at the fence, stare back. Teenaged boys in the pool glare out angrily. A fat white lady sitting pool-side looks up through her sunglasses, her face perturbed, dismayed. In a passing car a nurse wearing an operating-room hat shakes her head angrily at the black faces, black bodies in the park. (After the 1964 Act the pool was sold to private interests. Negroes still could not swim there in 1970.)

When the picnic is in progress, a white woman and her two children, with their own picnic in a grocery sack on a park table, stare over at the black one. When the picnic is over, Charles Jones and two Negro boys go to the white rest room, ignoring one marked "Colored" in a cluster of trees. A man in a parks department uniform gets there ahead of them and locks the door. He says it is out of order, that he doesn't want it to get "messed up."

"I don't wantcha to take my picture," he says evenly to a cameraman.

He goes to an outbuilding, a little black dog, tail wagging, following him, and emerges with two apples, which he takes to the monkey cage and throws in. Police patrol the zoo, which, despite them, has the peaceful feeling, calm feeling, of an afternoon in the park. The elephant pacing his confinement makes soft blowing noises through his trunk. Hamsters and offspring dart about. A fox pushes his head out as far as his confinement will allow and snarls at the black children looking at him. Now the elephant dances for a white man and wife, overalls and yellow dress, and their little boy and girl. And the lion roars.

With that sense Southerners in those years always had for knowing that some untoward racial goings-on were underway, and with that instinct for staring at it (some with hatred, some with blank faces), which later they were to follow in their confrontation of hippies, a caravan of cars is now passing the scene of the Negro picnic in the park. Two cars almost collide as their occupants stare out. A Confederate flag flies with ragged edges from the aerial of a car containing four teenagers —the familiar, coarse-faced, somehow oversized new offspring of the yeoman South. Faces of hatred peering out of the car windows . . . and mothers and children, like Mrs. King and her children, unawares, on an outing.

Back where the picnic was held, a man wearing the uniform and emblem of Orkin Exterminating Company walks up to the empty tables and benches (all the litter has been scrupulously cleaned up) and begins spraying them. The Negroes are leaving, ignoring the insult. Charles Jones has outmaneuvered the attendants, has used the white rest room in the bathhouse. And the lion, pacing the confinement of his cage, roars once more.

All of these scenes and all the press conferences—Dr. King's, Chief Pritchett's—and all the rumor and inside information, all the American-conventional, culturally normal elements of a big, ongoing, fast-breaking news story . . . and I strained in the two directions of it—to go about my work with professional competence and to explore the new and unknown that the movement was holding forth. More and more, I found myself back in the church, back sitting and sweating, indulging myself, losing myself in the heat and the emotion, in the songs and the prayers.

The eloquence for which Dr. King was celebrated—his great addresses as at the Washington March in 1963, his writings, like the "Letter from the Birmingham Jail"—was more or less studied, polished. The eloquence he found in the little churches of the movement was something else—a weaving of appropriate themes from past speeches, sudden bursts of innovative, emotional talk out of the immediacy of events and the meeting, wonderous structuring of metaphor. He was never better, more effective than in Albany. Hear the familiar, slow cadence of his speech, building slowly in intensity and fervor, the audience, as always, reverently quiet for him at first, but soon carried by him to great response:

" . . . When you are close to a situation, you often fail to see the meaning and the greatness of the situation. Sometimes, to see the fullness of the forest and to see the trees from all of their outpouring dimensions, it is often necessary to see them from afar. The closer we are to a situation sometimes, it means we fail to see the greatness of it.

"The Albany Movement is a great movement. *(soft yeses)* And I think one of the things that makes it great is its universal quality. It equates all class lines—the lower, the middle and the upper classes all together. *(soft yeses)* It breaks all academic lines. The Ph.D's and the No-D's have joined together. *(laughter)* It breaks all denominational lines—the Baptists, the Methodists, the Presbyterians, the Holy Rollers, the Church of God in Christ, the Church of Christ in God and all of the denominations have come together. It breaks all age barriers. It is not a youth movement; it is not an adult movement; it is not a middle-age movement; it's not an old-age movement. It's a movement of the people of all ages from eight to eighty. *(applause)* So this is something remarkable and I think something very unusual in our struggle for racial justice all across the South and indeed all across this nation. And you are to be commended . . .

"Every now and then within the middle class those who have risen to certain educational heights and economic security live with a philosophy that goes something like this: 'I got mine, and it doesn't matter about anybody else.' *(applause)* But this isn't the philosophy of Dr. Anderson. For he knows something that every Negro must learn. And that is: as long as one Negro isn't free, no Negro will be free. *(great applause)*

"I understand that the city attorney has gone to Atlanta to get an injunction to get the undesirables out. Now I assume by the undesirables he's speaking of . . . Ralph Abernathy, James Bevel, Bernard Lee, Andrew Young, Wyatt Tee Walker, Charles Jones, Sherrod, and I could name many others. And of course I'm sure he considers me an undesirable. *(laughter)* But apparently the city attorney is laboring under an illusion. And it is an illusion that is not at all uncommon across the South. It is that strange illusion which says that the Negro doesn't really want to be free. It's that strange illusion that only the agitators are making a lot of noise and arousing the people, but at bottom they don't want to be free. They said this in Africa. They said it for years in Algeria. And so this goes through all our struggle—that it's just a few agitators. That is what they call us. But I think the city attorney will eventually learn that there is deep down within the soul of the Negro a new determination to be free . . . *(yes)*

" . . . We are making it lear that we are going on to the end in order to achieve justice. And so injunctions, various legal maneuvers, subtle delaying tactics, complexities of tokenism and all of these things will not stop us. For, as we've said all week long, we've gone too far now to turn back. *(great shout)*

"And it is clear that by trying to block Martin Luther King and Ralph Abernathy and others, you do not stop this movement, because the people of Albany are more determined than ever before. *(great shout)*

"Now the time for action has come. *(yes)* We've tried to communicate with our words. We've tried to talk with the city commission. They won't talk with us. They said under no condition will they talk with us. Well, there are two ways that you can communicate. One is with your words, and if they don't get over, you have to communicate with your action. *(yes, yes)* The students of the student sit-in movement were able to communicate something by keeping their mouths shut and their bodies active that I could have never communicated in words. In Albany, Georgia, we tried to tell the city commission that we are determined to be free and that we are not going to accept segregation in this community any longer.

They haven't listened to it. *(all right:* in a tone addressed to *them)* So we will have to demonstrate to them by our very lives and our willingness to suffer . . . *(Drowned out by shouts and applause.)* So, my friends, we call on you now to get ready. *(get ready, get ready)* Get ready for a significant witness.

"It has already been said here tonight, and I want to say it again: the salvation of the Negro in Albany, Georgia, is not in Washington, as much as we want to see significant and forthright stands on the part of the federal government. The salvation of the Negro in Albany, Georgia, is not forthcoming from the governor's chair in the state of Georgia." Slowly, solemnly: "The salvation of the Negro in Albany, Georgia, is within the hands and the soul of the Negro himself."

He tells the story of Gandhi and the salt march, ending: "He started with just a few people. He said to 'em, 'Now we're just gonna march. If you're hit, don't hit back. They may curse you. Don't curse back. They may beat you and push you around, but just keep goin'.'

" 'They may even try to kill you, but just develop the quiet courage to die if necessary without killing—and just keep on marchin.' *(yea—eeah)*

"Just a few men started out, but when they got down to that sea more than a million people had joined in that march . . . *and" (voice excited)* "Gandhi and those people reached down in the sea and got a little salt in their hands and broke that law, and the minute that happened *("all right")* it seemed I could hear the boys at Number Ten Downing Street in London, England, say: 'It's all over now.' *(pandemonium)*

"There is nothing in this world more powerful than the power of the human soul, and if we will mobilize this soul force right here in Albany, Georgia, we will be able to transform this community *(yes. well)* and we will see something *new* and powerful. And we'll be eatin' where we couldn't eat before. We will be marchin' where we couldn't march before. We will be doin' things that we couldn't do before.

"And so let's get our marchin' shoes ready . . . *(yeah, shouts, applause)* For we are goin' *(drowned out by applause)* . . . For we are goin' to Albany's March to the Sea. And we're goin' to see great things happen.

"And I do not need to remind you again that whatever we do we're goin' to be peaceful. *(yes)* We're goin' to be non-violent. *(yes)* And we're goin' on in the name and spirit of our savior, Jesus Christ, *(shouts: yes, yes)* believing and knowing that our efforts and the cause that we stand for is a righteous cause. When we stand up for our rights here in America, we are not standing up for something that we do not deserve . . .

"I can only say that freedom is our goal, and I know that we will win, because freedom is the goal of America. We are bound up with the destiny of America. For centuries we worked here without wages. We made cotton king. We built our homes and homes for our masters, enduring injustice and humiliation at every point. And yet, out of a bottomless vitality, we continued to live and grow. If the inexpressible cruelties of slavery could not stop us, certainly the opposition that we now face cannot stop us. *(pandemonium)* We go on with this faith knowing that we are right *(AMEN)*, that we will win. *(AMEN)*

"Now I know that it gets dark sometimes and we begin to wonder: How long will we have to face this? How long will we have to protest for our rights? When will they begin to listen to us? When will we be able to sit down with men of wisdom and good will and solve our problems without the inconveniences and without the suffering that we have to face? I know you raise these questions. But I submit to you this evening that if we will only keep faith in the future we will be able to go on, and we will be able to gain an inner consolation and an inner stability that will make us powerful and . . . give us strength to carry the struggle on . . . As I try to talk with you on the eve of a great action movement, don't despair. It may look dark now. *(yeah)* Maybe we don't know what tomorrow and the next day will bring. But if you will move on out of the taxi lane of your own despair, move out of the taxi lane of your

worries and your fears, and get out in the take-off lane and
move out on the wings of faith *(yeah)*, we will be able to move
up through the clouds of disappointment. *(yeah)* We will be
able to face the dangers that lie ahead. We will be able to move
through the clouds that may be gathered by the state patrol.
(yeah) Then we will get up to a point and we will see the
sunlight of freedom shining with all of its radiant beauty.

"This is what Longfellow meant I believe when he said, 'Be
still, sad heart, and cease repining *(yeah)* For behind the dark
cloud the sun is *still* shining *(yeah. amen)* Thy fate is the
common fate of all / Into *each* life some rain must fall.' *(yeah)*
Some days must be dark and dreary. Get on yo' walkin' shoes.
Walk together, children. Dontcha get weary."

And Dr. Ralph Abernathy, so often given, after the mantle
of SCLC leadership fell on him, to making bad speeches—too
long, stiff, self-conscious—was, in the little churches, like some
musician playing upon the audience with infinite skill, drawing
all the beauties from them, at one with them. He spoke that
same night after Dr. King had said, "Get on your walkin'
shoes" (a hard thing to follow):

" . . . And fellow soldiers in the army, I just had to come
back. I could not let anything stand in my way. Because I told
you the other night—that—I'm—not—goin'—to let—

> *Chief Pritchett (crowd joins)*
> *Turn me 'round*
> *Turn me 'round*
> *Turn me 'round*
> *Ain't goin' to let*
> *Chief Pritchett*
> *Turn me 'round.*
> *Keep on a-walkin'—Yeah!*
> *Keep on a-talkin'—Yeah!*
> *Marching down the*
> *Freedom highway.*

"I'm beginnin' to believe that you mean it . . .
"Now they'd be happy if we'd stay down here in the Third

Kiokee [Baptist Church], clapping our hands and pattin' our
feet and singin' and shoutin'. But we still have news for 'em.
We're here in Third Kiokee tonight because we are gettin'
ready for something great on tomorrow.

" . . . Three hundred and forty-three years . . . we have
known oppression, segregation and discrimination here in the
United States of America. Now this is our home. We are
citizens of this land. We fought to defend it in the time of war.
We sought to build it in the time of peace. We bought United
States war bonds. We've given of our energies and our resources. And still we are not free. Did you know that a *communist*, as long as his face is white, is treated better than you and
me here in America. *(big applause)*

"I looked and I saw this lovely hotel right across the street
in front of the jail. We had been spending the night in the city
jail, but we couldn't spend a night in that hotel. *(laughter)* As
I left the Mount Zion Baptist Church a few nights ago I went
by this fabulous, fine-looking motel that is near the church
there. And the lights were all bright—the Holiday Inn that has
prospered because of the American economy which we helped
to build *(yesss)*, and the driver kind of slowed up as though he
were goin' to stop, and somebody said, 'You better put speed
to the motor *(laughter)* because we cannot spend the night
here, regardless of how much money we have.' But do you
know . . . that Mr. Khrushchev could stay there? *(laughter,
fervent assent)*

"You better listen to me tonight. Because I know what I'm
talkin' about. Mr. Khrushchev is the world's greatest communist. And he has made it clear where he stands. He stands for
violence. He stands for the total destruction of the American
way of life. He stands not only for the destruction of Negroes,
but he stands for the destruction of white folk as well—Mayor
Kelley and everybody else that stands in the way of the communistic way of life. And yet they would open the doors and take
him in, but wouldn't take po' me and po' you in, because our
skins are black.

"Now if I'd had anything to do with my birth, I know I wouldn't have been born in Marengo County, Alabama. *(rich laughter)* If I'd had anything to do with my birth, I'd been born to . . . millionaires. This I had nothing to do with, and you had nothing to do with yours, either. But since we happen to be born black, since we happen to be born second-class citizens, we've been loyal to this nation all the way. And we're determined to enjoy the fruits of this nation . . .

"We must determine in our hearts that we want to be free. No army can free us. Chief Pritchett can't free us. President Kennedy cannot free us. If we are to be free, we must free ourselves.

"Now all the week long we've gone through that period of preparation, gettin' ourselves ready, askin' God to get us ready, askin' Him to purge us with His discipline and burn us with his fire and cleanse us and make us holy and ready to stand. *(fervent response)* For when you go down to downtown, you are goin' down there amidst mean and cruel people. *(yes)* You're goin' down there 'midst the police force and you've got to have God on your side. *(yes)*

"So you need to get ready. Ask Him to prepare you as He did Shadrach, Meshach and Abednego. You know when they went to the fiery furnace, they said to the King, 'We will not bow.' *(yes)* But God was on their side. They said, 'Heat the furnace hot. Heat it hotter than it has ever been heated before. We know how to deal with these people who will not bow before the King.' And they got it hot and they cast 'em in there and they stayed all night long. *(all night)* But when they got up the next mornin' they said to the attendant on duty, said, 'Check the ashes.' When he checked the ashes and opened up the top and began to stir aroun' in dere, he jumped back and said, 'Somethin' mysterious has happened. *(laughter)* Because, behold, we cast in three. *(yeah!)* But I see fo' now. *(oh yeah)* And there's somethin' funny about this fourth one. *(yeah)* His hair look like lamb wool. *(strange, dissonant: yeah)* It sparkles. His face and his countenance, we cannot stand to behold. It looks like the son of God.' *(shouts)*

"Just like God went in the fiery furnace with the three Hebrew boys, God will go with us on whatever operation we decide to go on. *(great shout, applause)* Now you can't win the battle at home. You got to go to the battlefield. Now when you go to the battlefield, ain't no need to go out there without expectin' to have some casualties. Somebody will get hurt. I don't know who it will be. *(AMEN.)* It may be me. *(AMEN.)* If it is me, I can only rejoice in the Lord that I had a little part to play. Somebody will have to suffer out there, when you go to the battlefield . . . If you go there with determination and *faith* in yourself and faith in the Commander . . . then you will win the battle.

"Now nobody can enjoin God. I don't care what kind of injunction the city attorney seeks to get, he cannot enjoin God. This is God's movement. *(yeah, Amen)* Nobody can enjoin God. There can be *no* injunction against God.

"Because Albany does not belong to the Democratic Party of the state of Georgia. *(yes. amen)* Albany does not belong to the Republicans of the state of Georgia. *(well)* Albany does not belong to Governor Vandiver. *(yes, yes)* Albany does not belong to the white people of the state of Georgia. *(well. talk it)* All-*benny* belongs to God.

For the prophet said:
>   The earth is the Lord's
>   And the fullness thereof
>   The world and they that dwell therein
>   And this is God's world
>   This is God's All-*benny!*
>   And God tells us that
>   Out of one blood
>   He created all nations
>   That dwell upon the face
>   Of this earth . . ."

Those were the great times, the joyous times—in the churches. The times of testing—on the marches, in the jails—

were serious, frightening, dangerous. The ecstatic mood of the
mass meetings carried through to the marches, contributed to
their grandeur and the courage within the people. But not all
was so exalted in Albany. It was the turning point, and part of
what was tested there was the exquisite tension between love
and hate, non-violence and violence, that was the greatest
achievement of the movement. So much of the meaning of the
movement became clear to me, seeing the tension begin in
Albany a little bit, a slight bit to slip. On that first night after
Dr. King and Dr. Abernathy returned for the jail term and set
the movement into motion again, a rock was thrown from the
dark beside Shiloh Baptist Church through a police car window. Movement people were distressed, said it was not of
them, that young toughs of the neighborhood did it. The next
night, the mass meeting was underway, the sweating, physical
heat of it, the vibrant emotion of it, Dr. Anderson speaking,
talking of justice dead in the jailing of Dr. King and Dr.
Abernathy. Wear a black arm band mourning the death of
justice, he urged. "Wear it till justice reigns. The Supreme
Court in this land ruled on the schools, but how many black
faces do you see at Albany High?" He talked of sacrifice, saying
the way ahead was dangerous: "Cotton-mouth mocassins and
diamond-back rattlesnakes are on one side, thorns and thistles
on the other . . ."

Suddenly, there is a stir in the church, people moving out
the doors. Outside a crowd stands, excited. Another brick has
been thrown at a police car. A paddy wagon pulls by, and young
people from the crowd laugh, jeer. It stops, and a small cluster
of police gather around it. More people pour out of the church.
From the group of police, Chief Pritchett, alone, crosses the
street and begins striding through the crowd.

A man says, "They've got guns on 'em."

A man near the church door cries, "Get 'em out of here."

Another man says calmly, "Let's get back. Let's not crowd
the door."

Incredibly, Chief Pritchett is entering the church. Police

have scrupulously refrained here in Albany from interference with the mass meetings, indeed even from interfering with marches within the Negro section, called Harlem, stopping them only at Oglethorpe Avenue, the dividing line between white and black sections of town. Now the chief was violating the taboo.

Inside, Slater King was calling for order, asking for fifteen volunteers to clear the doors, saying he was bringing the meeting to a close. "Let us try and give it the dignity befitting . . ."

He stops—and stares, and heads turn through the church to look back and see . . . Chief Pritchett standing, alone, arms crossed on his chest, just inside the vestibule.

Slater King says calmly, "I notice we have in our presence Chief Pritchett. No fear. Nothing here is secret. Would you like to say a few words?"

Someone cries: "Let's give him a big hand."

And they do.

Then Chief Pritchett, from that same place in the rear of the church, begins speaking—in that same flat-twanging, slightly sardonic voice I have heard at all too many press conferences, briefings, sidewalk-joking encounters: "I appreciate the opportunity to be here. I have often been told I would be welcome. I didn't know whether I would or not."

The church has been terribly, tensely silent. Now nervous noise, laughter, a hubbub breaks out. An old man cries out over it: "Let's hear . . . Let's hear de chief." There is laughter, and then that terrible silence again.

"I never have interrupted your peaceful assemblies before. All through this there has been no incident of violence. Many people misunderstand your philosophy of non-violence, but we respect your policy. I ask your cooperation in keeping Albany peaceful. This business of throwing rocks is not good . . ."

"Sho' ain't," a bass voice intones.

"Throwing bottles . . . is no good."

"No. Ain't."

"We want to continue to see that nothing happens. We ask your cooperation. I know that you as citizens will respect and abide by our wishes that there be no distrubance. Go about your business the way we've had it."

"Amen," choruses through the crowd, and they applaud Chief Pritchett.

People begin to crowd around him as he turns to leave, and a man, clearing the way for him, cries: "Let the chief out. Nobody questions the chief in the church."

This incredible thing has happened, and people try to take it in. "Go about your business the way we've had it." Soon, in the compulsive way of standard American cynicism, the knowledgeable, the press, would say privately that the chief had his eye on the Negro vote, aspiring to high office. Or we would say that it was another of his stunning tactical successes—that he had as much stake in non-violence as did the movement. Bill Hansen was to recall years later, with that bitterness that is inevitable in many of the former activists: "We were naïve enough to think we could fill up the jails. Pritchett was hep to the fact we couldn't. We ran out of people before he ran out of jails."

But in the actuality of it, the existentialist, alive moments of its happening, there was, for me anyhow, nothing so strong as that sense of love-hate so often experienced in the mass meetings, and this time, reciprocal. And more than once I had had the feeling that beyond all practical considerations of strategy and the doing of the bidding of the racist leaders of the town, this bluff, sometimes even beguiling, certainly competent cop got out of the experience of matching wits and wills with the movement the same kind of relief from the dull and depressing routine of his daily duty that I have suggested Negroes got from the ecstatic mood of the mass meetings and the great moments of confrontation.

Certainly, the night the chief went into the church was one of the strangest, most deeply significant happenings of all the southern movement. Once more it helps convince me, strengthens my will to believe that in Albany, and often in the movement, powerful forces capable of truly changing America, powerful forces out of the people, were at work. I still can feel the sense of reciprocal love-hate in that church—and that, after all, touched the highest meaning, the most ennobled goal of the movement.

After the chief walked out of the church, Slater King rose to the pulpit and began speaking—slowly, almost softly, as though to himself. I was so moved by what I had seen, and then further stirred by his introspective, searching words that—as more than once happened in Albany—I did not get down what he said, failed my first professional duty.

My notes say: "King analyzing his own reactions as resulting from the system." Then: "For eighteen years in Albany, we've been preaching the good things we are doing now." And: "Stop and check up to see where we stand." Later, I asked another reporter what of the remarkable monologue he had taken down. He gave me this in direct quotations:

"We want to give him respect, but not like he's some kind of God. Maybe I am guilty of this myself. It's the system we've been conditioned by—like we've been brainwashed."

There was more, much more of it than that. It was a man trying to explain to himself, talk his way through to understanding of, and freedom from, the deepest kind of barriers to real human feeling and intercourse with which the South's racism has cursed its people, black and white.

Back at the police station a short while later, Chief Pritchett mused in his own manner, not so profoundly or introspectively, but far more openly than usual. His ears were still scarlet from the emotion of what he had done. He said he had spoken with Slater King earlier, had told him the rock- and bottle-throwing would have to stop. "He told me they didn't sanction it. I told him to stop it or I would break the meeting up. He said they weren't associated with the assemblies and the Albany Movement."

Then, more musingly: "They respect you. I don't care how much they dislike you in principle. They respect you.

"When I went into that crowd I said to them to take me to Dr. Anderson. They cleared the way. They respect you."

And, awe in his voice: "That's as close as I want it to get. Something—a spark—could have set things off, and it would still be rolling down yonder. But they proved to me tonight they don't want it, don't want mob violence. I argue with them not about what they are trying to do, but the way they go about it. . . ."

Earlier that day he had presided over the arrest of the first demonstrators in the renewed campaign; they had started out to pray before city hall over the jailing of Dr. King and Dr. Abernathy, thirty-two of them in all, at least half teenagers and children. One of their preachers had led them out after praying:

> We feel much akin
> To those who went out
> Two by two
> In the days of old.
> We will march around
> Those jail house walls
> That symbolize segregation.
> We will walk around them
> Like unto Joshua
> Until the walls
> Come tumblin' down.
> Take care of us
> Take care of the policemen
> Take care of Chief Pritchett
> Take care of the mayor
> And the city council.
> We pray that as they see
> A prayerful and peaceful people
> Their hearts will be moved.
> Consecrate, dear God
> This whole community.

As he intoned the amen, the marchers were moving, and they sang before his words ended:

> We are marching to Zion
> Beautiful, beautiful Zion . . .

Dr. Anderson shouted the words at the head of the march. A boy not over thirteen was close behind him, and a woman in a straw hat singing a tremendous soprano. The familiar platoon of police met them, and Chief Pritchett, looking for all the world as though he were enjoying the moment, the first since December, confronted them:

"I am giving you the opportunity to disperse. It's not good for you or the city of Albany. If you proceed and disregard traffic signals and disrupt the flow of traffic, I will put you in jail . . ."

A voice from the rear of the march called: "Lead on!" and the little band was marched the familiar route down the center of Jackson Street to the little alley that led to the jail, singing "We Shall Overcome."

Pleasant, smiling, looking pleased with himself, Chief Pritchett greeted reporters soon after in his office, many of them the same who had covered the December demonstrations:

"Welcome, strangers. It gets hot down here in south Georgia, doesn't it?" An American flag stood in the corner. "It's a time of crisis for us here. Nothing here involves local people. A small segment of the population protests. The rest go about their normal jobs and actions." During the course of the long and rambling press conference, he said Dr. King and Dr. Abernathy, wearing green fatigues, had worked on a jail detail that morning, scrubbing floors. "They're good workers. We had no complaints from them."

He left Albany finally, went to head the police force in High Point, North Carolina. Some Negroes said he was driven out because he enforced the law too stringently on some of the business elements. One movement leader said with wry joy that when asked by his prospective new employers for an evaluation, they agreed to praise him to the skies—"to get rid of the S. O. B. once and for all."

The love-hate relationship, if it did indeed exist, as I have described it, was from the white side certainly too often over-balanced to hate, and that little Albany police department was deep into, as adept at police state methods (phonetappings, political surveillances) as any in America. And under the hot south Georgia sun, in the wild, the insane summer nights, the movement ability to hold love and hate in tension within itself and individuals broke several times. Most dramatically, it broke on the night following the day of the atrocity committed against Mrs. Slater King, after word of it had gotten around. The mass meeting that night, at Shiloh, in the packed heat had been, in a way, joyful, consumed with the telling of the good news of the overturning by Judge Tuttle of the temporary restraining order against demonstrations. There were praises for the lawyers, C. B. King and Clarence Jones, a courageous white lawyer from Albany, William Kunstler and Mrs. Constance Motley from New York, Donald Hollowell of Atlanta, and the retelling by one speaker of high moments of the procedure: "One of the most cogent questions Judge Tuttle asked Mayor Kelley when he talked about the threat of violence was, 'Whose violence?' "

Of the defeated city officials: "They feel as though we are a tiger that's been unleashed. They're waiting for us to spring on them . . . When we do, it will be to help them, will be in the best interests of the city."

No word was said about the treatment of Mrs. King. The prospect of a night march to celebrate the victory seemed to have dissolved. I left the mass meeting to start writing my column. The phone back at the motel rang. A. C. Searles, the Negro editor, said to come quick—"trouble at the bus station."

When I got there, Chief Pritchett and seven police were in

the middle of Oglethorpe Avenue, and big crowds of Negroes stood on the sides of the street.

"Git back," one of the cops was shouting. "Git back."

From the crowd, a jeer: "God is on our side. God is on our side."

I felt sick. The glare of a red light from one of the police vehicles caught the face of one big policeman there in the street, motionless for a moment, looking out at the crowd— angry, tired, fearful. The Negro crowd (on the Negro side of the street) surged into the street, then fell back. A much smaller white crowd stood across on another part of Ogle-thorpe. Now I recognized people of the movement, of the mass meetings, trying to persuade people to go back to the church. One pushed a frenzied, shouting teenager, yelling at him: "There you go, you hothead. Git on back."

From the crowd, someone threw a bottle. It crashed onto the pavement. A big rock went tumbling along the pavement, by my feet. The police backed off. Chief Pritchett told one of them to get the state police.

He said to reporters: "Judge Tuttle oughta see this."

A few more rocks were thrown. And then the file of police and state troopers came marching onto the scene as glass shat-tered again on the pavement. They moved toward the crowd, and it fell back.

A Negro man said, "They weren't marching like that when I was . . . on the front lines overseas."

Another bottle crashed, but the crowd was dispersing. Chief Pritchett was going from one to the other of the beer joints and dives, shouting: "Close this place."

Angrily now he yell~d at reporters: "You see them non-violent rocks." He said a trooper had been hit with one, had a bloody nose, probably a tooth knocked out.

Andy Young confronted three big Negro teenagers, his voice almost breaking: "You're too yellow to march. But you stand

over here and throw things and give us a bad name. Those folks
who marched could hold their heads high. Not y'all."

Later, the chief had his press conference under the bright
lights of television. He told of sending eighty men into the
Negro section—the first time he had ordered that.

"There was no violence on our part. Night sticks were not
removed. One of my men was hit with a bottle. A trooper was
hurt. With a love rock. This is a case where non-violence met
with violence."

It was a small enough "riot," compared with what was to
come in the North and eventually in the South. The provocation was, had always been, great. But it was a long distance
from the beauty of the beginning of the Albany Movement,
from the spirit of the mass meetings. The power that non-
violence spoke was dissolved by this reversion to standard cultural norms. Moving warily in the crowd during the height of
the excitement, watching, taking notes, I found myself confronted by a group of Negro teenagers. They demanded my
name, my paper. It was my first experience of a non-dis-
criminating and ugly hostility to my white skin that was to
become more frequent each year of the movement, and finally
common, stylish.

The rock- and bottle-throwing, the menacing character of
the Negro mob that night were as strong a departure to that
date from non-violence as the southern movement had seen.
The press duly recorded it, but it is doubtful if the public saw
it in true perspective—the relative rarity of Negro violence, the
relative tameness compared with the strong provocation and
savagery of white violence. Where Negroes had resorted to
violence in previous demonstrations, it was nearly always in
direct response to attacks by whites, the tension of non-violence breaking in the heat of anger—returning a punch, throwing rocks back. Albany never allowed such white attacks to
occur, in part by the kind of police work every southern community should have demanded and in part by tacit agreement

that the police with their illegal arrests would "handle the niggers."

Real perspective would have explained the provocation and frustration of such a situation, and the best reporters, among them Claude Sitton, Fred Powledge, Karl Fleming, conveyed it. But Dr. King's non-violent methods were on display and put to the test in Albany, and the minor ventures into violence by the people of the Negro slums surrounding the churches of the movement most ominously foreshadowed the effect to come on the movement, on black America of failure of non-violence to gain for all Negroes full benefit of the secular goals it seemed to be achieving, this in part a consequence of the resistance of the normal culture to the not normal, the essentially spiritual, methods by which the movement sought to win those secular goals. "I argue with them not about what they are trying to do, but the way they go about it," as Chief Pritchett put it.

What effect did that one instance of minor violence have on the people of the Albany Movement? Was it part of the process that caused them to lose their enthusiasm, their brave belief—seeing how they had not even been able to reach some of their own people with the message, the self-ennobling desirability of non-violence? Americans of our time probably more than any people of any age dread to feel themselves considered naïve, out of it. Some concern for this must always have been at work on the people of the movement, Albany and elsewhere.

The day after the night of near-violence, Dr. King and Dr. Abernathy set about to heal the wound, the hurt to the movement. It was a remarkable performance; they toured the dives and joints of the Harlem area, trying to tell the good news of non-violence, appealing against any resumption of violence.

The entourage included two white city detectives and a number of Negro youngsters, skylarking and excited by the television cameras inevitably in Dr. King's wake. Dr. King, wearing a short-sleeved shirt, open at the neck, waved to men standing around on the sidewalk and entered a pool hall. It had three tables; two were in use. Charles Jones, accompanying the two ministers, greeted the men at one of them; the one shooting kept on with his shot.

Jones said, "We want to talk to you about the situation out in front last night."

The man made his shot, the balls clicking. "Who wants to?" he said.

"Doctor King. This is Doctor King."

They looked at him with interest. He smiled at them, almost timidly. "How're you, gents?"

One of them said, "Hi."

"I hate to hold up your pool game. I used to be a pool shark myself."

A fat man at the next table pounded the floor with his cue, signaling the rack boy to come set up a new game. Dr. King began, his voice raised, as though addressing a crowd: "We are in the midst of a great movement, and we are soliciting the support of all the citizens of Albany. We have had our demonstrations saying we will no longer accept segregation. One thing about the movement is that it is non-violent. As you know, there was some violence last night. Nothing could hurt our movement more. It's exactly what our opposition likes to see. In order that we can continue on a Christian basis with love and non-violence, I wanted to talk to you all and urge you to be non-violent, not to throw bottles. I know if you do this, we are destined to win."

It was earnest talk; his brow was furrowed and he turned from side to side, speaking to one, then the other, of the men in the pool room: "We want thousands to join with us. But, above all, we want it to be non-violent. We don't need guns and ammunition—just the power of souls."

The men stood about; they had been attentive, but not overly receptive; they looked now as if they didn't know what to do next. Charles Jones spoke up: "Thank you for taking a few minutes with us, and for being in the movement. We're all together in this. Pritchett moved in last night where he's never been before. This was an attempt to get you to do what some people did last night."

Then Ralph Abernathy: "So often there is a different understanding of the meaning of non-violence. It's not an appeal to slack up or stop resisting the evil system of segregation. Non-violence is the way for the strong, not the weak. It takes a strong man to continue to press for his rights. We expect every Negro to demonstrate. Close the poolroom and come march with us."

His voice had risen; the men seemed a little more interested. "Those little guns," he went on, "that Negroes have for family protection are nothing to the arsenal the police have. But we have soul force. As they call for state troopers, we call God to send his heavenly angels . . ."

The words were, to me, incongruous in that setting. "Turn the other cheek," I thought, looking at the profile of a tough, sullen young face, a cigar in the center of its mouth. Before the entourage left, Dr. King bent over one of the pool tables, executed a couple of shots. At the South Grand Terrace beer joint, amid red-checkered tablecloths and a jukebox, Dr. King was served a glass of water in a thin cocktail glass. Later, down an alley in a dimly-lit smaller place, he shook hands with a woman customer wearing a man's felt hat. Five big men sat on a bench before the Beehive, a joint from which one of the bottles had been thrown. The group looked into a place called Dan's, which had cement walls, crude, homemade bar and booths. In here sat men in work clothes, one wearing a construction helmet, a man with a white cap and white tennis shoes, some with cowboy hats, a woman in a farm straw hat. Dr. Abernathy introduced Dr. King to this assemblage: "I have brought you the symbol of non-violence."

Dr. King stood in the doorway: "We want everyone to start with a sense of dignity within. Every person has dignity and worth. There is nothing worse than people who just sit down and adjust to evil. Such people make our white brothers think we love segregation. But we don't ask you to fight evil with violence. That is not our way. Our way is through non-violent protest without hate. What happened last night hurt our movement. They know how to deal with violence. But when they are up against non-violence, they don't know what to do."

The words seemed to me more nearly right; the crowd was more attentive than the others had been. Dr. King introduced Bernard Lee and Charles Jones. "These young men led students by the hundreds. Do you know what they have done? Do you know that all over this South there were segregated lunch counters, but that two years after the movement began lunch counters in more than a hundred and fifty cities are integrated —as a result of the work of young men like these. They didn't do it with violence. You have to be non-violent in spirit and militant in action. Then you can do what they have done in Atlanta."

He ended the talk: "Thank you so much and God bless you. And keep moving."

Charles Jones spoke to them, too, his voice ominous: "We know that money was circulated to get done what was done last night. And we know who did it. It is not for us to point the finger. But some among us were paid to do it . . ."

Outside, in the sun's glare, on the sidewalk, a little Negro girl of about four, wearing green pants and a white blouse, with her hair in pigtails and plastic rollers, and a bandage on her finger, stared up timidly as the group moved on, both the preachers of non-violence stopping where they could to greet people, passersby: "Hi, gentlemen. Shake hands." Two days later, they led the demonstration which sent them to jail for ten days—after which, on their release, the movement seemed somehow no longer what it had been.

I tried to understand such scenes, the many levels of meaning. The people in the dives knew, as much as the South has known, the harshest, hardest side of America, the side Malcolm X knew and told about so well. I felt that their lives had built a thick crust against such an influence as the movement's and that they had, inside them, similarly blocked the feelings that people gave to the movement.

But Mr. Page said in 1970: "We had help from two sources —the fair-minded whites from all over the country, even the South, with unsolicited funds coming from places like the University of Texas and the University of North Carolina— and the highest and lowest classes of Negroes. The middle class just stayed away . . . And the middle class people who did the least got the benefits."

SNCC, in its enmeshment in the culture of poverty, worked with some people of the kind who were in the dives with notable success. And after all, there was no more violence from the people in the dives after that one afternoon of effort among them by Dr. King and Dr. Abernathy.

Dr. King, even Dr. Abernathy whose common touch was surer, sounded to me hollow, almost ridiculous, intoning the magic words of the movement to those unresponsive people. I was aware of how abstract and in a sense intellectual their message was. But SCLC veterans maintain that it was not the words but the emotional tone Dr. King expressed that was important, that the Negro South commonly communicates on this level. Often in the mass meetings, they say, people who couldn't understand all the words responded to the tone. Here, then, was one more example of the movement's utilization of extra-cultural thrust and energy. And, spoken to the fervent, assenting, amen-ing, well, yes-saying people of the churches, the words were full of intense, deep, far-ranging meaning, great emotional content, had a life, a power. The preachers, the message itself, drew from the fervor of those who heard and responded. The meaning of the movement was out of the people, the morality, the strengths, the poetry inside them. And it seems clear that the people of the dives—who did violence no more—had the meaning inside them, too. What of the street people elsewhere—and even the middle class of America, for that matter?

The real menace was more mechanical. Had I but known how much Albany foreshadowed what was to come to the movement. On my last day of covering the Albany Movement, on my way out of town, I stopped by the Mount Zion Baptist Church (across the street from Shiloh) at sunset. The soft south Georgia wind was stirring; the big sky was purple at the horizon. I had stopped, thinking maybe to hear the singing once more. Instead, I heard from within the church the people of the movement staging a workshop in non-violence for the benefit of a television network crew. Their bright lights were shining within, making garish the deep hues of the stained-glass windows. I would not see Albany again until 1970.

Chapter
FIFTEEN

THE MOVEMENT STRUGGLED on there over the next months, years. Not until 1968, six years later, did it finally cease to hold weekly mass meetings, Dr. Anderson having moved in 1963 to Detroit, attendance down almost to nothing. In the months after I left that evening at sunset, the destructive forces worked more fiercely, ravagingly. More instances of white violence occurred, more police unconcern, more police brutality, more unconstitutional arrests (2,000 in all by July 1963). Reports to the FBI, Justice Department went unheeded. Justice did file a civil rights suit in the instance of the much-publicized disruption of the voter meeting in Terrell County, but eventually dropped it—in effect on the promise of the old sheriff, old Zeke Mathews, and others to behave better in the future. And finally, the Justice Department, with some thirty-five FBI agents involved in the investigation, was instrumental in the indictment of three of the Albany Movement leaders on a charge of obstructing justice—attempting to intimidate a federal grand juror, because his store was among those picketed in a boycott. Six others were charged with perjury. (The indictments were announced by the attorney general at a press conference in Washington.) The charges were not merely dubious;

in light of all the outrages, atrocities, rape of the Constitution
by the whites, they were grotesquely unjust—the last straw.

C. B. King, looking back on what was done to the Albany
Movement, said in 1970: "In the beginning, there was a moment of very high hope. It embraced a very warm and tremendous feeling of kindredness to the ideal that was America. We
felt that there would not be any reneging by the federal government. We had not before been in a position to rely on the
government. An aged black woman, after our disenchantment,
said to me, 'Son, I done found out that even the government
is a white man.' There is tremendous disenchantment, frus-
trated hopes."

". . . is a white man." The foes had been there always, but
in failure and bitterness and frustration, when what the friend
does or fails his responsibility to do brings so much defeat, the
friend becomes as the foe, and all white people became foes.
In late August, Dr. King issued a call for religious leaders to
come to Albany to "bear witness to the prophetic faith of our
Judeo-Christian tradition, to stand with the people of Albany
as they strive for freedom." Fifty-six religious leaders—three
fourths of them white—did come, were arrested in a demonstration, and went home. Others were to have followed, but by
then the steam had gone out. Nevertheless, the people of the
movement, the people in the churches welcomed those friends
from the alien North, told them they had made hope return
after hope had gone. As ever, the more sophisticated sneered
at those who came, questioned their motives.

Henry Schwarzschild, one of those white Northerners who
came at the first opportunity, the freedom rides, and later
became an effective worker in the movement, recalled in 1970
his impressions of Albany at the time the religious leaders came
down:

"I thought then (and in retrospect I think I was right) that
the movement, and especially Martin, were becoming habi-
tuated to a very harmful ploy that they wrongly thought was
good public relations. Whenever they sustained a defeat, they

made public noises that sounded like victory . . . To admit
defeat would have taught the country (and the liberals) a much
more important lesson, namely that this was a tougher struggle
than we all expected. And it would have consolidated the
movement forces and their supporters more than transparently
false pretenses of success . . . The mistake was infinitely repeated: for example, Danville, Birmingham (at least with respect to the local situation), Chicago, etcetera."

Movement leaders, especially those in SCLC, must have felt
much chagrin, embarrassment in the aftermath of the defeat
in Albany, after the victories of the sit-ins and freedom rides.
The defeat was to both the spiritual truth and the secular goals
of the Albany Movement. But newspapers, intellectuals,
friends of the movement analyzed it almost entirely in terms
of the secular goals. And the movement, from the beginning
containing tension between the spiritual and secular, was—
after such a defeat—more willing to think in terms of the
secular, more caught up in such analysis itself.

From the most astute of sources, "Albany, A Study In National Responsibility," by Howard Zinn (Atlanta: Southern
Regional Council, 1962), the treatment:

> There has been no consistent, clear-cut plan of action for the
> Albany Movement, despite a number of assertions in the press
> about how Albany was "selected" as a point of concentration.
> Like so many other developments in the deep South in recent
> years, certain specific streams of action were deliberate, but the
> confluence of those streams was a matter of chance . . . While
> there are advantages to such fluidity, there are also drawbacks.
> Sometimes there has been a tendency simply to repeat old ac-
> tions under new circumstances. The movement delayed legal
> action, for instance, . . . and continued to depend mainly on
> demonstrations, instead of linking the two. There has been a
> failure to create and handle skillfully a set of differentiated tactics
> for different situations.
>
> It is, of course, easy for observers to criticize the tactics of the
> Albany Movement. There was a rush of unanticipated events,

and if the response was not one of perfectly coordinated tactical efficiency, it was one of courage, passion and sacrifice, and it brought forth on American soil—too often hard and cold in recent years—some of the noblest qualities that human beings have shown anywhere.

Clearly, the attitude of this study and almost all else written then, including my own writings, was that it was all very well about those noblest qualities, but the important thing was tactics, strategy—winning next time.

I try now (and may not be able) to suggest differences in degrees of the movement spirit and degrees of the spirit of practicality. Another of the movement secrets of Albany had to do with Dr. King's being confronted during one of the times in jail by a person of the movement so caught in the religious feeling of the mass meetings and demonstrations that he believed that Jesus was, literally, in the jail, too. Dr. King was reported to be appalled, even frightened. The incident does not reflect adversely on either the man who believed what he did or Dr. King; it merely suggests differences in distances which people of our time and our culture may go in their own explorations outside cultural norms. In other times, other cultures, the man who believed Jesus was in the jail would have been exalted above all others—and his vision made a great inspiration to the people. In our own time and culture, Dr. King's reaction was, in the real sense, practical. The mass of people in and out of the movement were not ready to go as far beyond the borders of cultural normality as the man in jail.

But there were other degrees of practicality much further away from the man in jail than Dr. King was, and the movement after Albany, Dr. King himself, were to move further and further in their direction. Activists in the movement to whom, from the beginning, non-violence was merely a sophisticated weapon were to gain in influence over those who were imbued in their personal lives with it as a spiritual quality. The mass meetings were increasingly to be used by movement leaders to impose their wills, the necessities of strategy, on the people. "Realistic goals" were to become as important to SCLC as the magic moments in the meetings. SNCC was to become increasingly wary of demonstrations, forgetting the good they did inside people, remembering only the abuse they attracted to their bodies.

That final despair in Albany—the losing of steam—was it maybe most profoundly of all an expression of disappointment at having found and offered so much—and being understood so little?

"Why couldn't they have listened then?" Goldie Jackson lamented in 1970. "Why did it all have to happen? It takes a lot out of you to see people who fought us so hard—when you ask them out now for cocktails and they come, and I say, 'Have a drink' and think: Why couldn't you have been nice then?"

Was it a sense of loss from having stretched so far the limits of consciousness and being, and then having to fall back into the dreary reality of merely trying to win . . . and mostly losing, so long the lot of Negro Southerners?

When I talked in 1970 with C. B. King, a complex, sensitive man with an impressive pride, his remarks were nearly all tinged with bitterness—wry, almost self-mocking. At one point, though, I asked him if he thought I would be justified to characterize the mass meetings as ecstatic. In contrast to the weighted and ponderous answers he gave to my other questions, his reaction was immediate, enthusiastic:

"Yes, yes! I agree!"

But then, as suddenly, his voice became more profoundly gloomy than before, more bitter: "When I think back to what we did, what we felt, in reflection of what I see now, those meetings seem in retrospect almost a burlesque."

Chapter
SIXTEEN

FEAR HAD BEEN the foremost motivation for my coming to Albany in the first place. "What about violence?" I had asked Claude Sitton, and had gone out of fear of fear, not willing to admit to myself that my ingrained, conditioned fear of that beast we all knew about, beast of southern white racist terrorism, violence, had kept me from such scenes before. We live with so much fear in modern America, aware always on the edge of consciousness that the slums we ride by in installment-payment new cars are only one pay day, one serious sickness away, aware ultimately and over everything else and most deeply in our dreams of the horror beyond horror of nuclear warfare. More often than not we do not, cannot act against, despite fear, because it is so familiar, so constant that we don't question it, unaware of all the awareness of danger ever with us.

When I got to Albany in December and saw how the police so efficiently prevented white mobs from forming with as little concern for constitutional rights as in the arrests of demonstrators, and saw how scrupulously the police avoided public violence in their repression of the demonstrations, and as the routine and terrain and psychology of Albany became familiar, the sharp awareness of my fear soon left me—to be replaced in December and through the summer months of the movement with a queasy kind of ill-at-ease wariness of all the hostility of whites to the movement and our presence as a token of the movement's presence, and wariness of the police—my first experience of that dread knowledge to come to America that the police were not the benign agents of protection and lawfulness they had always seemed, were not necessarily any more unambiguously on the side of the law and justice (this true not only of the totalitarian-tending little Albany police force, but of the Federal Bureau of Investigation agents on the scene as well).

Whites on the staff of the motel where most of the reporters stayed were openly hostile, uncooperative, or they were overly friendly and full of questions. With the wariness we all felt and the paranoia that was part always of being so close to the explosiveness of racial hatred, there was the sense that the over-friendliness was purposeful, that, as in spy melodramas set in Latin American dictatorships, police spies were seeking information from us. It was possible to hear on our motel phones those sounds of abnormal functioning that indicate a wire tap, to hear sometimes even the breathing of someone listening—again for me the first of the eerie feeling of someone eavesdropping, someone watching you, that was to become familiar to more and more Americans in the ensuing years.

Did we just imagine it? No. When I was dictating over long-distance telephone the story of the sheriff and his gang breaking up the Terrell County voter registration meeting, sharing with the man taking my dictation outrage over the sheriff's remark that Negroes had been "happy" a hundred years there before all the registration business started, a south Georgia voice broke in on our connection: "You son of a bitch!"

The FBI men, ever lurking around the Albany Movement scene, made no secret of their unfriendliness to reporters, hostility to Negroes, and, to us, most ominous of all, friendliness to the local police. Report after report of violation of civil rights and of violence went to them from the movement, never to be heard about again—including even the attack on Mrs. Slater King and the beating of Bill Hansen. That feel of white hostility and violence and police condonement of it, the sense of police purposes that were more political than legalistic, and the sense that even the federal presence was sinister, all, created an atmosphere that was frightening in a way different from the stark fear we had of the rednecks or of the familiar fears of everyday. It was an alien fear, a feeling we more than once described as "like being in some other country—not the United States of America." Later, when following the movement took me into Alabama and Mississippi, the atmosphere was worse: We lived with the knowledge that there was often virtually no distinction between police and the worst terrorist elements, including the Klan. The people one had to deal with while traveling—motel clerks, car rental clerks, even sometimes the airplane ticket agents—insisted on knowing not just the routine information normally given, but things like whom you represented, how long you expected to be in town. And, in the paranoid part of it, no question seemed friendly or innocent. You could arrive in the Jackson, Mississippi, airport and rent a car and know for certain that before you got to your motel or wherever you were going, the police, local and state, were aware of your whereabouts. In Albany it was simpler; police could spot strangers and follow your car to see where you were staying. It was a strange feeling, an alien atmosphere. But now more and more Americans in more and more places and circumstances—anywhere the established order is questioned, from hippy neighborhoods to college campuses and in the northern ghettos most of all—know about it, have experienced it. We no longer say that it's not like being in America.

By summer I had more compelling reasons to keep returning to Albany then my original fear. Indeed, the love I had come to feel for the movement, the mystical, ecstatic experience I found in the mass meetings more than compensated for having to endure the unpleasantness, the low-key terror of the police-state atmosphere in Albany. But you never could be fully at ease, and always somewhere tiny inside me was the original fear of white racist violence. And so on one of the many hot days, when one of the movement workers kept urging reporters to go that night to Sasser to cover a voter registration meeting, because the local movement leaders were convinced that the sheriff of the county would try to break up the meeting, I didn't want to go. I already had plane reservations back to Atlanta. Hell, I was afraid. But not all the conventions, the compulsions of modern journalism which so buffeted us, buffeted the movement, were bad. The sense of duty, the integrity of the story, of getting all the story, was strong in us—is still in newspapermen I know. And I didn't want to admit my fear to myself or my colleagues who, I am sure, must have shared it.

Finally, we set out, three of us—Bill Shipp of the Atlanta *Constitution*, Claude Sitton and I. If all went well, I could cover the meeting and still make my plane. We drove out of Albany into the soft south Georgia night. The sky is very black, very big in the farmland, wilderness land of the black-belt South, the stars very bright. A soft, gentle wind, ocean wind from hundreds of miles away blew into the car, a sense of serenity, well-being in the smell of it. I could feel the presence of trees, woods, the cool, refreshing smell of them coming into the car. I leaned back, enjoying the ride. The music of the mass meetings sang, as always in Albany, in my mind. Suddenly I knew that I felt more alive, more complete, more happy than I ever had before in my life. In the heightened sense of danger, in the paranoia perhaps of such a situation, I knew that I faced possible death at the end of the ride. But I wasn't afraid of that. All my life I had been afraid—full of large fears, small fears, all the accumulation of fears that are in part normal, in part imposed by the kind of country America had been in the years of my growing up—fears forever and always, but never fully known, fully faced, understood. Now I knew exactly what and whom I was afraid of, and why. I did not know this kind of fear even in the Army, when I was being trained to kill "Japs" (before that war ended so suddenly and unexpectedly soon in the middle of my basic training by virtue of a device that would fill all the world with a new dimension of fear). The death I fatalistically felt I faced then was yet far-off, unreal, as death nearly always is in our minds. Now I knew that it might not be far-off, and it was entirely real, and yet I never felt more alive, never more full of an evergy to prevent it if possible, of a comfortable confidence that, come what may, I was ready for it. Never after that, still burdened with all my own peculiar and all a culture's accumulation of vague awareness of peril and danger, have I ever been as fraught as I once was with fear.

And I think that is a part of what the movement knew, too, the people of the movement who lived constantly and for years in the unwholesome, fearful atmosphere of places like Albany, with a lifetime awareness of the dread fact that the police are not on your side or the law's, who built within themselves a will to rise from a far greater depth above their fear of the South's ancient, mystical threat of white terrorist violence than I ever knew, could know . . . That one time I felt what the movement's people must have felt each time they got up out of the church seats, singing, with that mysterious joy in all their being, to march in the name of justice and freedom and the movement's meaning. No wonder they accomplished so much. They, too, despite disillusionment and defeat to come, would never be as afraid again, as vulnerable. In giving them that, the movement won.

I remember another night's driving in the black-belt dark by farmlands and woods—this time in Mississippi in 1964. Reese Cleghorn and I were returning to Jackson (like Albany, in a contrast of lesser evils, seeming a safe harbor) from an interviewing trip into the Delta. We had stayed later than we meant, were driving along with that alertness to danger that you felt through small talk and private thought, driving after dark in that state in those times. Suddenly behind, in the rear-view mirror, I saw the flash of a red light, the swinging flash of a red light coming rapidly up.

"Oh, shit! There are cops behind," I said.

"Then I think you had better pull over," Reese said.

I did. And we both watched, relief flooding through us, an ambulance, red light flashing, go rapidly on by.

The fear that time was of a different quality. So much had happened since Albany. The fear now was like that of a drowning man—the sense of the futility, absurdity, needlessness of such a death. So, too, I suspect, the people of the movement came to feel, maybe first in Albany when the steam went out, and later across the South when, despite the will not to believe it, despite the ability still to marshal the movement's great braveness to march, the knowledge kept coming, undeniable, that the movement's purpose, the great thing it gave in the mass meetings and promised to give in everyday life, was not going to be achieved, despite all the death-facing effort, despite all the victories that it seemed to be winning.

Part Four

THE FALL OF THE MOVEMENT

Chapter
SEVENTEEN

"THERE WASN'T any real strategy in Albany," Andy Young recalled in 1970. "I remember being around and not knowing what to do . . . We didn't know then how to mobilize people in masses. We learned in Albany. We put together the team of SCLC staff people there that later won the victories. They hadn't even known each other before . . . There's always tension between the analytical and the religious in these circumstances. But they came together in Birmingham."

SNCC was little involved in Birmingham. I remember one night seeing three of their staff people waiting to see Dr. King at the Gaston Motel; they seemed left out, almost abashed. SCLC, through such local leaders as Reverend Fred Shuttlesworth, had laid the groundwork, done the organizing, built in the people a spirit, a will to confront white southern racism in one of its worst strongholds. Many of the elements which had seemed to me to make Albany so special were alive in the Birmingham Movement, in the mass meetings and marches. The joy, so different from the grim, dry everyday of the whites, spoke in the meetings even in the midst of brutal police handling of demonstrators and mass jailings—Reverend Shuttlesworth again and again taking off on inspired flights of humor and improvised homily:

"I think white water is better than black water anyhow.

"This morning, there was a lot of people in misery at the

courthouse, and not necessarily just because there was a lot of
injustice being cast out under the guise of justice.

"I have always seen the Negro fountains dry. But this morning both the black and the white fountains was dry. And all the
toilets were locked up. [This was because Negroes of the movement had had the temerity to use the "white" facilities on the
previous day.]

"So if the judge was ill at ease, he wasn't no worse off than
anybody in the court. *(great applause)*

"Somebody says, 'There ain't no water.' I said, 'Aw yes it is.
This is city hall, man.' Well, soon as I went and turned the
Negro fountain and wasn't none in it, I said, 'Well surely there
must be some in this white fountain. Let's use the best that's
down here. I think white water is better than black water
anyhow.' *(laughter, applause)*

"Sho' 'nuff, I went over to the white water, and it was off.
And just as I was turnin', Mr. Connor [Bull Connor, the police
commissioner, acknowledged racist adversary of the move-
ment] was comin' out his door, and he looked at me, and it
looked like he shook his head there and said, 'Awww, I got you.'
(a pandemonium of laughter, glee)

" . . . So I left there and went on over to the bus station,
to the men's room at the bus station, and there we were, all
of us there together, but what bothered me was three or four
or five [white] city policemen come in, and I said, 'What y'all
doin' over here? Got y'all in this, too, huh?" *(again, pandemonium)*

"You know what one of them said? Said, 'Yeah, Reverend,
you got this damn town rocking.' "

Or:

"You know the story about the little boy who asked his
daddy, 'Daddy, what makes the lightnin' bug light?' *(rich
mirth, anticipatory laughter)* Naturally, the man didn't want to
admit to this boy that he didn't know what made the lightnin'
bug light, because the father ought to know everything in the
eyes of his son. Like these segregationists think they know *all*

about us. *(laughter)* They been tellin' it in Washington that we are happy *(murmur)* and satisfied. I'm just wonderin' why so many *satisfied* folk want to sit in jail. *(applause)* All right. But anyhow, the story goes, this little boy said, 'Daddy, what make a lightnin' bug light?' He said, 'Well, boy, now I'll tell you,' *(pause, anticipatory laughter)* he said, 'Well, now, give me a little time to think it over.' The daddy tried to talk about somethin' else, to git off the subject. You know, like the segregationists—they like to git on somethin' else, you know. *(cries)* But this boy kept on callin' him to the point, like these Negroes keep on callin' 'em to the point now: 'But, Daddy, I want to know—what makes a lightnin' bug light?' So he reached up in his head, where there was supposed to be a handful of hair— he was gettin' bald *(laughter)*—and he said, 'Well, I'll tell you the truth, boy.' *(murmur)* He said. 'The stuff is just in him, that's all.' *(pandemonium)*

"And for the spirit that these Negroes be free, well, the stuff is just in 'em. *(that's right. amen)* All right. We want to be free. *(amen)* We goin' to be free. *(yeah, yeah)* I just think of the large amount of time that we are spendin' in the freest country in the world—tryin' to be free . . ."

And the idealism was there, rising out of the beliefs, faiths, of the people, played upon by such a skilled, dedicated preacher as Reverend Shuttlesworth, the idealism and simple, poetic articulation of the injusticies of segregation and the will, yet, to forgive, to offer redemption.

Reverend Shuttlesworth: ". . . Now this meeting every night puts an additional burden on all of us. But certainly we are capable of the task . . . For me, it's just a great thing to see the Negro citizens of Birmingham, Alabama—this hard-core city, this rock-ribbed, segregation-structured area, this place that could be the best, but insists on being the worst *(yes, yes)*, this place that could go forward, but loves to stay in the background. *(yes. amen)* It's good to see the Negro citizens at least standing up to make their protest of dissatisfaction against segregation and discrimination. *(yes. amen)*

" . . . It has been in Alabama for a long time the unwritten rule that if the mobs don't stop you, the police can. *(amen)* And if the police can't, then the courts will. *(yes. amen)* And this is exactly where we are comin' to now—the power of the state courts to detour, derail and sidetrack *(well?)* legitimate efforts by Negoes, peaceful, non-violent demonstrations, all aimed at freedom. And it's amazin' to me how the white man can in pious platitudes in the South git up and say, 'God is our Father, and all of us are brothers' *(murmurs)* and then use the laws of the land that are supposed to protect everybody to condemn and even harass those who just simply get up and ask for the privilege of being free. *(yes, yes. amen)* We got no doubt that if the police and courts had stayed out of it, the merchants would have been finished with a long time ago. *(yes)*

"Southern segregationists have been gettin' *fat* off of us. *(yes, yes. amen)* They been ridin' us, like we ride a mule. *(yes)* Negroes are jist tired of bein' mules to be rid' by somebody else. *(long applause)* So we have decided to straighten up our backs *(applause, "sho has")* and get these people off our backs. *(applause)* We are goin' into court hopin' that the God of this universe will stand by His children who stood up for Him. *(yes, yes)* For when we stand up for Him *(amen)*, we are standin' up for each other. *(amen)* And when the Negro stands up for the Negro, he is in effect standin' up for the white man. *(applause, Dissonant shout: yeah, brother)* He is not free as long as we are not free. *(applause, shouts)*

"This isn't just a show that we are puttin' on. These demonstrations are too expensive, callin' on folks to go to jail. And some have lost jobs and have lost time off from work. *(yes)* Some have become ill—and other things. *(amen)* This isn't a show—this is business. *(amen)* We're in the business of tryin' to win freedom in the United States of America in nineteen hundred and sixty-three. *(amen. yes, sir, yes, sir)*

"What's wrong with Negroes marchin' down the street in an orderly fashion, tryin' to get justice? *(all right)* What's wrong with Negroes carryin' placards sayin', 'This store discriminates against Negroes'? *(nothin'—nothin but segregation)* What's wrong with Negroes . . . [sitting] on a stool? And yet in another place can spend five thousand dollars—the same store, and everybody will be so kind and courteous. And sit on a stool and ask for a cup of coffee—they put a closed sign on yo' face and call a police officer and have you arrested. *(murmurs)* THE NEGROES ARE JUST TIRED OF IT! *(applause)*

"Segregation is a silly thing. *(yes, it is)* It makes the folks who are supposed to have a lot of sense act as if they never known what sense was. *(applause)* I was listenin' at Judge Brown yesterday, down at the courthouse. And all of a sudden—I believe I mentioned this last night—somebody tried to get some water out of the fountain, and rather than for you to get some water out of the fountain marked 'White,' they will close the white and black fountains. *(murmur)* This is a tragic thing. *(murmur)* Nobody drinks—white nor Negro. *(murmur)* But befo' we got here, God had put the water down here. *(Cries of "yes! yes, He did")* HERE WE ARE—ARGUIN' OVER SOMETHIN' THAT'S FREE! *(cries, applause)* Maybe if the segregationists keep on, they might try to segregate the air after a while. *(laughter, applause)*

" . . . We don't throw rocks to win freedom. *(no. no)* We don't carry knives to win freedom. *(no. no)* We don't need guns to win freedom. *(that's right)* We need non-violence. We need to have that will and that mind in our own hearts to keep on goin' on *(yes)*, and after a while the walls'll fall down before us. *(amen)*

"We got Ph.D's and all other kind of 'D's,' and we don't have a Negro policeman or Negro sheriff's deputy, Negro secretary. In fact, we don't have nothin' but segregation—AND WE'RE TIRED OF THAT! *(laughter, applause)* We do have, however, our self-respect. *(yes sir)* As long as we maintain that, we think we can get ahead in this country of ours. *(yes)* God bless you tonight . . ."

Most importantly, the movement was still drawing on the

strengths of the people, had not yet become so enmeshed in strategy as to leave the people behind, make the greatness within them irrelevant. That greatness was manifest mainly in the willingness, the ability of the people to undertake the marches where police savagery waited, and at the meetings they told about it—with an eloquence, as ever, beyond that of the preachers:

Young man: " . . . We just had a good time for the Lord. We was not fed for . . . one day. That Sunday we didn't get any food. But still we went on, and the Lord carried us in the night . . . It was just like children when they eat this food— two little fishes and five loaves of bread *(yes. amen)*, and that's just the way we did. And we got along just fine. And I'm goin' back *again. (applause)* They better git ready to see me again. I thank you. Thank yuh."

Young lady: "I was arrested in the march Friday with Martin Luther King and Abernathy and Reverend Lindsey. And I'd like to say that I had a very nice time in jail. We didn't have anything to sleep on but the iron beds—but yet still I enjoyed every minute of it . . . If I wasn't in school I would have stayed longer. When May come, if the thing still be going on, I would get in the march again . . ."

Young lady: "I was arrested Friday along with Dr. Martin Luther King and Dr. Abernathy. And while we were in jail we have a very nice time singing and praying in the name of the Lord. And won't you tonight submit youself as a candidate for freedom?"

Middle-aged lady (formal, fervent): "I was arrested on Nineteenth Street, paradin' in front of [a] store. I would say that this was a very much experience for me. They asked me why was I there? I told them that we was there for our constitutional rights." *(applause. amen)* Her voice trembling: "Because God has created man equal. *(amen)* And in the name of God I will go back again, if I have to. May God bless every one of you who has gone. And don't be afraid. For God is with you. He *walks* with you, day by night. Go in His name. Don't be afraid. I'll go again. Yes, I will." *(great applause)*

Young woman, a college student: ". . . So what I would like to say is: Even though there are places we can't go, we will go soon. *(murmured amen)* And even though there are things we don't know, we are learning. Because we realize the fact that there's a God somewhere, and he's a *real* God." *(fervent yes. amen)*

But in retrospect (and one even sensed it at the time), raveled edges were visible—that had not been in Albany. The setting was, of course, different. Birmingham is an urban, industrial one, and surely one of the world's ugliest cities. Negro Southerners there had been subjected to something much closer to the demoralizing physical squalor of the northern ghettos, had little there of the beauty of nature that was abundantly available to even the most impoverished Albany Negroes.

The effect of urban culture, sophistication, was evident in the music of the mass meetings. Instead of the hymns and freedom songs, often the music was provided by a choir, with organ or piano accompaniment, singing the complex harmonies of gospel music. This, of course, was a legitimate indigenous expression, but it usually precluded audience participation, that great release and profound expression of the Albany churches. If the music was often, in effect, entertainment for a passive audience, the speaking took on this aspect somewhat also. The audience responses *("amen"* and *"well")* seemed stylized, lacking often that beautiful bond of communication between the speaker and the people where each spurred the other on. Perhaps because of such things, or perhaps merely because city people in such a setting as Birmingham are more cynical, far more bowed under cultural compulsions of behavior and values, SCLC increasingly relied on young people for the demonstrations, unable to propel as much of the whole community into them. College students participated, but a greater percentage of high schoolers and grammar school children took part than had in Albany. It was a heart-catching, stirring sight to see them, so young, marching bravely and brightly, and a sure stroke in influencing public opinion to show their innocent faces in contrast with the cruelty, the viciousness of the police. But though the young people were innocent and mainly non-violent, there was the feel in some of the demonstrations of skylarking, even rampage. Certainly, the absence of many adults meant that the demonstrations were a distance from Albany's spirit of strength and wisdom feeding from the people into the movement and back into the people. In Birmingham the preachers and people still spoke the language of redemptive love, but it was not, as much as in Albany, on display—if America might have had the grace to see it.

On the other hand, something ominous, something ugly beyond the cruel ugliness of southern racist violence and terrorism was present in Birmingham. In that campaign America's morbid fascination with violence which had followed the movement through all it did was well rewarded. But that wasn't the all of it. Police treatment of demonstrators was, really, not as ferocious as the mob attacks on the freedom riders which had involved police complicity. Something beyond that was present, hinting, foreshadowing terrible events to come. Reverend Shuttlesworth caught one aspect of it at one of the mass meetings:

"It's hard for me to see how the people in the seats of power think they can sit happily on a powder keg, contentedly. I don't care what ever else happens—we have already demonstrated to the world that we want to be free, in Birmingham, Alabama. And, ah—I'm not foolin' myself. I want to say this, because I think we ought to be frank about it. After we were tried this mornin', the commissioner of police came down and told me somethin'. He said, 'I'm tryin' to be patient with this thing. You tell your people if there's any hurtin' of my officers, this is a two-way street.'

"Now what *Bull* was sayin' *(laughter—derisive, almost fond)* was a brief reflex action on what has been happenin'. You see, for the last few weeks, they have been givin' the world the impression that the Birmingham police department is the sweetest police force in the world *(laughter. that's right. well),* that we're not brutal to our Negroes *(murmur),* that we protect them from *all* hurt and danger. *(derisive laughter)* When the facts are that this has been one of the worst police departments in overall terms, and that Negroes almost fear to walk the streets at night. *(that's right. that's right)*

"It goes without saying that a majority of the men on any police department, even here in Birmingham, are law-abiding and nice people *(murmur of assent),* and certainly we have met some of the nicest people on the police department. *(murmur of assent)* But you see, now, friends, this town has for a long time sown to the wind *(yeah),* and it's begun to reap the whirlwind. *(yeah. all right. all right)* I wish it was like Mr. Connor is tryin' to act like it is. I wish the Negro could walk the streets any time of night, not cringing when he meets a policeman *(all right),* not goin' to jail on some trumped-up charge. *(yeah)* I wish it was so. *(all right)* I wish Birmingham was the city that gives Negroes the same rights *(yeah)* and protection of the law that other folks has. *(yeah. yeah. tell it like it is)*

" 'Course I stand here now, and I say it everywhere—I don't know another spot in this world I've ever been that I love as much as I do Birmingham, Alabama. *(yeah. amen)*

"This brings me to something else that I think is most important at this time. I want everybody to listen at this. Now Sunday there was a little violence *(murmur)*—not from our people *(amen),* because the Negroes who really want to be free know that they can't gain freedom by rocks and knives. *(amen)* We have been preachin' against violence *(amen)* or even violent thoughts. *(amen)* And I'm not concerned that any member of the movement is going to engage in . . . violence. But, you see, there's plenty that would like for violence to occur *(murmur of assent)* in our non-violent demonstrations, so that they can say in effect it is not non-violent. *(murmur of assent)*

And so the point to which I'm comin' is this: Everyone of us has to be a disciple for freedom. If in any demonstration, present or future, you see anybody who's been drinkin', tell him to get out of there, and go back home *(murmur of agreement)*, because we don't need drunk folks tryin' to help us win the battle for freedom. *(cries of agreement)* We don't need anybody with a pocket knife. *(that's right)* What I'm sayin' is that we don't need any weapons whatsoever. The only way is you can sing the song, 'I got Jesus, and that's enough.' *(amen. all right)*

"One of those fellows was identified as one of those who don't think like we think, even though they are black like we are. *(murmur)* A hint to the wise is sufficient. *(murmur of yeah)* See, I don't want to exchange white supremacy for black supremacy. We just want human supremacy. *(that's right)*

"And we have to be very careful that people with ulterior motives don't come into our movement and get in our demonstrations and make us look like that which we ain't. *(that's right. amen.)* So we were goin' up Fifth Avenue, nearly about to the trucks where the officers finally stopped us and [one Negro man] was so angry, and his eyes were fired up as though he were almost insane. He was shouting 'Give 'em hell.' I said, 'We don't need that kind of language in this movement.' *(murmur of assent)* And later I identified him as a person whom I know to be not of our faith. *(murmur)*

"Now I don't want to get up here and be personal, but we just don't need anybody but members of the Christian movement and people who want to be free non-violently in the movement. *(that's right. that's right)* So anybody you see that wants to cuss or fuss or clown—he doesn't have any business in our demonstrations. *(murmurs of amen. amen. amen)* No rock-throwers and no knife-wielders. *(amen. amen)* Violence is just not the way. He that fights with the sword shall PERISH *(amen. yes, yes)* by the sword." *(that's right)*

But to try, looking back, seeing it in retrospect, to catch the other more salient part of the sinister feel, a new frightening thing attaching itself to the movement, I go back always to another demonstration that occurred in the spring of 1963, which played out its short, significant life at the same time that the Birmingham demonstrations reached a peak of movement fervor and police brutality. Whenever I try to understand what happened not only to the movement, but to the soul of America in those fateful years of the 1960s, I go back to the Freedom March.

It began May 1, 1963, a week after a white postman named William Moore started out alone on his own freedom march, planning to walk from Chattanooga, Tennessee, to Jackson, Mississippi, with a handcart placarded with integration slogans. He was shot to death on the roadside near Attalla, Alabama. Five field staffers of SNCC and five of CORE announced they would retrace his steps and continue the march to Jackson, there to deliver a message of brotherhood, as Moore had hoped to do, to Governor Ross Barnett.

On the eve of the march, the ten held a press conference in a Negro church in Chattanooga. One of their prepared statements said: "We hope to impress the people we meet not with our uniqueness, but with our humanity . . . We are fighting the frustrations we have felt before when good men were killed in this struggle, and no one remembered why . . . We want to inspire people all along the way."

They were five young white men, five black ones—among the pick of the sit-in, freedom-ride veterans, working, by 1963, in various parts of the South, including Mississippi, on voter registration. I talked with some of them later that night at another church where they were spending the night; they were quiet, gentle men, possessed of that aura of invulnerability and largeness of spirit which non-violence imparted to otherwise not extraordinary men and women during the height of the movement. They talked together and to reporters and the like in the church; some read (one of them Gandhi's *All Men Are Brothers*) and sang the freedom songs from the churches:

> *All along the highway*
> *I'm gonna let it shine . . .*

And:

> *Brother, how can you stand it?*
> *How can you stand?*
> *Will you be an Uncle Tom?*
> *Or will you be a man?*
> *Which side are you on, now*
> *Which side are you on?*
> *Which side are you on, now*
> *Which side are you on?*
> *My mother was a freedom fighter*
> *On this you can bet.*
> *Will you be a freedom fighter*
> *Or a Tom for Ross Barnett?*

When they left the next morning from the Chattanooga Greyhound station, where Moore had started out, a gray-haired white woman in a blue wool coat, white dress and little white hat prayed over them and shouted: "They're not a-carryin' the Bible; they're not a-carryin' God . . . I'm for 'em every way in the world. But they don't have God with 'em . . . We all gonna have to die anyway. What matters is whether we die for what's right. We're a-goin' under the Catholic. We're gonna be taking on the Mark of the Beast, friend. We ain't got many more days. You know they made fun of Jesus. He don't make any difference in the race, friend. Ast Him to be with you on the road. Will you, friend? Oh Glory Hallelujah. Don't say this old woman's crazy. I'll leave you-uns all in God's hands. . . ."

Her apocalyptic vision was to prove appropriate for the mood of the march, a mood which held within me (and, I think, most of America) long into the aftermath of the march. Only a few good things happened along the way, as they wound their way out of Chattanooga's downtown squalor and into the countryside in the shadow of Lookout Mountain, and walked for three days through a little strip of Tennessee and Georgia.

On the first day, soon after they had set out, a teenage white girl went up and down their lines of march asking their autographs. "I just like this," she said when asked why. "I'd like to know who they are. Because they're doing a great service for the South."

A mountain white man, burly, middle-aged, in a blue jacket, brown trousers and a leather cap, talked with them at their first rest stop, beside a stream on the mountainside. It seemed he had talked with Moore when he came by.

"I wouldn't say that guy was fitten to be killed. I'd say he was doing what he thought was right. Whether I agree with him or you agree. He meant deep down in his heart to be doing the right thing."

A few other such words of encouragement came to them. Incredibly, at one stop, Billy Sol Estes, awaiting trial in connection with his commodities storage activities in Texas and become at the time a speaker in Negro churches around the South, got out of a car and went among them, wishing them luck.

And they took encouragement from small things. On the second day, a group of white teenagers gathered about them at a rest stop. A discussion ensued, various of the teenagers speaking, various of the marchers, Negro and white, responding.

"What'll y'all do when you git to Alabama?"

"Just keep going."

"Them folks have different plans. Maybe you'll end up like that other fellow."

"The other man's spirit lives as long as people are willing to keep it alive. If your idea is better than the other man's, you ought not to try to beat him up. You ought to try to persuade him."

"What do you want anyhow?"

A Negro marcher, Winston Lockett: "What do I want? I think a society where people are united. Segregation separates people. You can't have anything where people are segregated. . . ."

"What race of people do you think founded this country anyway?"

"Red, black, yellow, white people."

"No. White."

"Do you mean who discovered the country? Christopher Columbus discovered it, and he was what I suppose you call white. But his navigator was black. Black people were on his ship."

"On the same ship? Aww."

"Do you think black and white should mix?"

"It's not whether you're black or white. I'm in favor of people mixing, of equal rights . . ."

"There's equal rights for all. Y'all have your schools. Better schools than whites."

"But by having them separate, people don't get to know each other. You don't know me. I don't know you . . ."

Scornful laughter. "That's right."

"We have to get to know each other better. You and I could have talked about this five years ago and . . ."

"I don't want to talk to you. Because you're black. And I'm white."

"You're a person. I'm concerned about that."

The scornful laughter. "How about that?"

"There are a lot of questions I'd like to ask you, and I assume there are a lot you'd like to ask me. Do you play baseball?"

"This boy here—he's a professional boxer." (Snickers.)

A boy who had been quiet until this point: "Why do Negras want to go to school with whites?"

"The reason I feel they should go to school together is so they could know each other better."

An undersized boy probably seventeen or eighteen, with his upper front teeth missing, who had kept up a running commentary of jeers and wisecracks in a nasal mountain accent throughout: "You mean to cause trouble?"

A white marcher, handing him an election card from an Illinois school with a Negro running for student-body president, a white for vice-president: "Is this trouble?"

Several: "We don't want it down here."

The gap-toothed boy: "That's in the North. Not down here."

"What's the difference?"

"The difference is the South works. The North don't work."

A reporter, a Southerner, to the grinning gap-toothed youth: "Boy, what grade you in?"

Laughter from the others. A jeer: "The fifth."

The boy: "What's it to you? I started in kindergarten. I went to the eighth. Is that good enough for you?"

It was time to resume the march. Lockett, a ways down the road, spoke softly of the encounter: "Such talk as that back there . . . has its effect. Not now, but maybe tonight. Or tomorrow night. Or three weeks from now . . ."

At the outset, one of their statements had said: "The way America responds to our march will indicate how America feels about what happened to William Moore." They learned how America felt, in a microcosm—America's answer to all the movement. It seemed in moments such as the talk with the teenagers that they could, would break some of the hard crust of acculturated resistance to the mode of their demonstration and its essential moral message. Always in the movement, tantalyzingly, that chance seemed there.

And movement—not so much by design, I believe, but because it so persistently pushed at the deepest meanings—had a genius for exposing America in existentialist flashes of new insight and understanding. Walking, slowly, step by step, plodding on, hour after hour, is not a way we normally see the things that are the commonplace of news and public event. Time is slowed; vision is focused; things passed that are a blur from an automobile stand out in detail with isolated psychological, philosophical impact. To see far ahead on the rural roadside a filling station, garish colors gleaming, to perceive gradually that men stand in front of it, a little knot of them, to see them slowly become more distinct, more lifelike, standing, menacing, finally to see individual, hostile expressions, still to keep walking toward them, that long, long time, from the first sight of them to the moment of passing silently by them, is to feel at the fullest the menace of southern racism, and some new sinister quality to the ever-close threat of sudden violence in America, threatening . . . what?

One of the Negro marchers musters a smile and says, "Howdy" to one of the men before the filling station. A weak "Howdy" comes back. A sudden crack, as of rifle fire, and the marchers jump, and the crowd laughs. It was the backfire of a passing car. "Did you see that?" a man cries gleefully, something in him satisfied by the incident.

To walk the sidewalks of a southern city, American city, as the marchers did on leaving Chattanooga, and to do so with senses taut, perception heightened as such a situation demands, is to see, as though never to have walked a city sidewalk before, just how ugly, how grotesque and yet banal, how degrading to life are the buildings and signs and dingy decrepitude and the uses to which all the clutter of them are put. Restaurant, garage, warehouse, small office building with dim stairway, "Liquor," small factory, rambling, blue smoke issuing from smokestack, "Antiques," shop window jammed with cheap shoes, filling station with attendants, white faces smeared with grease, jeering, drive-in refreshment stand with fifteen-foot plaster of Paris ice cream cone in front and plaster boy in short pants and oversized head, idiot's face, climbing a ladder up it to the triple-dip, succulent promise of garish-painted chocolate and vanilla and pinkish-red strawberry mounds . . . It was along such a street (we were informed by television retracing the steps) that Oswald walked after he had returned to his rooming house (those life-killing rows of them ever near such a street) and then had set out for the movie theater (blinking lights, double-feature, shabby, tinny splendor) where he was captured, spawn of such streets through a dreary, stunted lifetime, returned to one of them appropriately, having somehow spread, extended its death out beyond where America intended it to go.

In the same way, I sensed then, and know more fully now, a connection, relationship of cause and effect, forever feeding back, between the cruelty that came from the people of the countryside and the graceless houses we passed in the open country beneath the mountains where cows and horses grazed in rocky pastures—red driveways gashed out of the clay up to those ugly wooden or brick houses with the mud streaked red on the foundations. What had America given in that tiny stretch of its great length and breadth (or to the most of those across all the length and breadth) that fostered real human feeling, love of life, dignity, decency, respect of self and others? During a rest stop, I entered a roadside joint, place of recreation, concrete-block, unpainted, square building streaked with the red mud, and, inside, a big clock on the wall in the shape of a pocket watch advertising beer, heavy, inept paintings of such things as "Lover's Leap in Beautiful Rock City," the sign: "We reserve the right to refuse service to anyone" and a toy panda hung by a paw alongside the cash register. A boy, wearing blue jeans and a white T-shirt, his face lean, pale, tense, sitting in the gloom at the counter, drinking a "malt liquor" from a can, clenched and unclenched his left fist at his side.

Or simply to walk beside an American highway and to see —alongside the velvet green rise of a mountain to the blue of a southern spring sky with fleeces of white cloud moving swiftly, with irises blooming, underbrush thick, birdcalls sounding—the incredible filth and litter on the road shoulder and spreading into the surrounding countryside, tossed there, left there by the thousands of heedless cars traveling by—paper wrappers, bottles, aluminum cans, rusted metal, mud-stained trash. It was the first real sense I had of what was to become a national scandal by the 1970s—the terrible damage America, in its obsession with over-producing and over-consuming, has been doing to the earth.

Cars by the hundreds were to pass as heedlessly the ugly treatment of the freedom walkers as it was occurring, none ever bothering to stop even to see what was happening, no one offering to help, cars with the license tag talismans of all the states.

From the start and to the end most of the white people passed by the march were silently hostile, with a few hecklers, their numbers growing each day, to speak for them.

"Bunch of morons if I ever saw it," a man yelled from a car in Chattanooga in the first block of the march.

A waitress watching from a café doorway a little further down the sidewalk: "The sons of bitches ought to be in a mental institution."

A middle-aged man leaned out of a Jaguar to shout: "Those look like pretty good niggers. I don't see why they'll walk with the damn Jews."

By the end of the first day, a small group of cars, some with Confederate flags on the aerials driven by teenaged, vacant-faced boys from Chattanooga, some with the ominous high aerials that usually in such settings meant a Klan two-way radio, and some occupied by merely curious people were following the march, driving, like reporters were doing, ahead to keep it in view, driving on again when it caught up. Dick Haley, one of the Negro marchers, older than the rest, by the end of the day took genuine hope from the existence of the followers:

"They were totally hostile at first. But the thing has caught their imagination. They are staying with us. Now some of them just like to watch. They're not tense any more. In a way, they've become part of what we are doing."

The marchers spent the first night in a beautiful little Negro church in a clearing alongside woods, with a mountain stream running cold, clear through the churchyard. Local Negroes were supposed to have supplied a key to the church, but none was there when the marchers arrived. Soon, however, a group of teenagers arrived, handed over the key, and then, casually, set up a baseball game in the churchyard. They played until dark, with cries and shouts—a well-dressed group of boys and girls, some with high cheekbones, aquiline noses, suggesting Indian ancestry. A marcher played a guitar, the twang sounding against the game noises. A local Negro boy came racing down the hill on a bicycle, shouting, "No brakes! No brakes!" In the casual atmosphere, the youngsters of the ball game talked with the marchers—and, with their presence, sent by the elders of the community who never appeared, probably dared not to, were a lookout for trouble from whites. Once more, I was seeing the solidarity of the Negro South, a "movement" that had been there a long time, and would endure.

Later a crowd of whites gathered, talking threateningly, glaring, and cars bumper to bumper drove by, stirring red dust on the little dirt road leading to the church.

A man: "We won't get them tonight. We don't sneak around at night. We'll do it in broad daylight."

A sinister-voiced teenager: "I can't sleep myself if I hear even a dog hollering that's been run over. Y'all reporters ought to leave. I wouldn't want y'all to have to hear human beings hollering . . ."

Three of us, reporters, spent the night in sleeping bags in the woods on a hill overlooking the church. The spring night was cold, the mountain air piercingly fresh, wonderful. I felt some of that new, fear-of-the-known kind of fear I had discovered. But mostly I gave myself to the delicious sleep of the outdoors. During the night a few cars drove by. Nothing happened.

The marchers were refreshed and in good spirits at the next day's start. They kidded about whether the black marchers needed suntan lotion. They sang in the cool morning's air: "We Shall Overcome . . ."

> Moore died not in vain
> Moore died not in vain

Moore died not in vain
I know.
Deep in my heart I know
That I do believe
Moore died not in vain . . ."

"I wish a bomb would hit 'em and blow ever' one of 'em up," said one of six men standing in the first driveway of the first filling station they passed. An old Buick paused beside them, then shrieked its tires speeding away. The first sequence of signs for a roadside tourist attraction ahead appeared:

DOG FIVE LEGS SIX FEET

EIGHT-FOOTED COW

SIX-FOOTED HOG

SAMBO THE TALKING DOG

They marched on in single file, singing occasionally "God is on our side." One of their statements of purpose at the outset had said: "This will not, of itself, open a lunch counter, integrate a school, or add a single Negro voter to the list of the nation's registered voters. But it affords a magnificient occasion for the people of the towns and cities through which we pass to participate in this Moore Memorial Trek. They can do so simply by giving their quiet consent to our passage."

It was, I think, the last pure offering by the activists of SNCC and CORE of the idealism and hope of the sit-ins, of the full spirit of redemptive love to America, the America they were marching through, and seeing in walking's slow-motion perspective. Did they sense, did any of us, all that blocked people along the way and the tourists in their blind shuttling back and forth in America's high-powered cars on America's super-roads from any capacity for appropriately responding?

"Yellow-bellied sons-a-bitches," yelled a man from a Georgia car.

They passed through two Georgia towns that day, and in each crowds watched silently, with hostility, as they passed through—not large crowds and not really dangerous. The county sheriff and one state patrol car kept order in the dreary little downtown sections where the crowds gathered. One was Trenton, a county seat, the courthouse in a square dominating the four surrounding streets of stores, many of them closed, ancient courthouse with its dilapidated offices and halls reeking of disinfectant, symbol of the South's old courthouse-ring politics, country-town control, feeding off of, manipulating the people, racism the foundation stone.

The line of cars following and passing back and forth increased in number during the afternoon. The shout: "Wait till you git to Alabama" became frequent, as did Alabama tags on cars. The encounter with the teenagers occured. The afternoon sun grew hotter; the stirring of red dust was oppressive; the marchers were sweaty, dirt-streaked. They complained of their blisters. Finally, at about four o'clock, they stopped at an ugly roadside gully and sat on dusty, grassless ground, waiting a "canteen truck," a contribution by the NAACP to the march, driven by a dauntless black man from Chattanooga, to take them to nearby Rome, Georgia. Teenagers there had invited them to appear at a mass meeting of their sit-in movement. Of the caravan of cars, some sixty had been parked, and a crowd gathered around the road gully. One of the white marchers, Bob Zellner, climbed up on the clay bank above the gully and, wearing a green alpine hat, yodeled a short song. The crowd stirred. When he sat back down in the breezeless heat, the green hat on the ground beside him, a big man walked up and deliberately stepped on the hat and dared Zellner to do something about it. Zellner spoke softly a minute or two of nonviolence; state troopers moved in and dispatched the man. The crowd had drawn its ring closer, was more menacing. The freedom marchers decided quickly not to wait any longer for the truck, to leave in available cars.

They were to resume the march at the gully the next morning, but had not arrived by eleven o'clock. By then at least two hundred whites were milling around the site, with cars parked up and down the road, including Georgia patrol cars and two identified as FBI. A small plane flew low back and forth over the site. People chatted, joked, an old woman there in a black dress down to her ankles, thick-bodied, with a white scarf across her shoulders and a black knit cap on her gray head, smiling a broad-mouthed, lip-pursed smile at people, nodding as they passed, as though waiting in a country churchyard for services to start. Or waiting for an execution.

The marchers arrived just before noon. They said they had debated about whether to delay a day or seek another route, because Alabama state troopers were waiting to arrest them at the state line a few miles down the road. They had decided to face what would come—that incredible will of the sit-ins and freedom rides expressed once more, that belief that somehow their action would prevail against Alabama, would move America.

The crowd stood watching on the opposite side of the highway. A woman with a lean face, a mountain woman, held two blonde little girls by the hand. While the mother stared fascinated at the marchers, the smallest girl, about two, squatted and slowly, carefully, picked from the trash and muck of the roadside a tiny blue flower, and held it to her nose a moment, touched it to her lips, and then rubbed it slowly against her cheek.

The marchers set off in single file, the crowd following in cars and on foot. From the lonely little column the words of the song drifted back:

We shall overcome . . .

They were grim, remote this morning, the exuberance of the other days' starts gone. Throughout, they had been a lonely band, isolated, and now their loneliness was more pronounced. The animosity they had encountered had been as nothing to the amount of hands-off reaction to what they were doing. The passing tourists, the local Negroes, sparse in that area, the press, except as necessary to the job, anyone who might have been sympathetic and helpful, had just kept away from them.

Fear of the hostile followers had operated in this; it wasn't prudent to become identified with them. I admitted that to myself and felt regret at not having come any closer to them, not having tried to talk to each beyond the events of the march, had not sought that in each which had put him in this lonely little line bobbing along the road shoulder, singing now:

Ain't going to let
Old Wallace
Turn me 'round . . .

Each had emerged as a personality. The three Negroes of CORE: Richard Haley, forty-six, assistant national director, a former college professor in Florida, cautious, introspective, generous in his judgments of the white harassment; Robert B. Gore, thirty-one, from Hickory, North Carolina, wearing what would now be called an Afro, friendly, jaunty, self-contained; Winston Lockett, twenty-two, from New Haven, ever making his soft-voiced attempts to communicate with the hostile whites. The two whites from CORE: Eric Weinberger, frail man of thirty-one, with large, very sad eyes, who had been working in West Tennessee among people evicted from farms for attempting to register to vote, a loner, an air of tragedy about him, the target previously of much white violence; Zev Aeloney, twenty-two, from Minneapolis, awkward, good-natured, gently but earnestly idealistic, later to work doggedly on for three years at voter registration in southwest Georgia, despite a heart condition. The three whites from SNCC: John Robert Zellner, twenty-four, from Alabama, in jails and crimi-nal proceedings in four southern states since 1961 for civil rights activities, soft-looking, quick to decision; Sam Shirah, twenty, son of an Alabama preacher, angry, a guitar player who seemed grim even during the songs; Bill Hansen, twenty-three, with that prominent lower jaw broken in the jail in Albany. The two Negroes from SNCC: Carver Neblett, twenty, called "Chico," from southern Illinois, big and easygoing, giving spirit, confidence, in crises; Jesse Harris, twenty-one, from

Jackson, Mississippi, veteran of various civil rights jailings, quiet always, wearing overalls and denim jumper and cap, uniform of the Greenwood, Mississippi, voter registration campaign, remembered in the instant at the church that first night when a visiting teenager from Chattanooga asked where was the bathroom, putting his hand on the boy's head, laughing, saying: "Lord, protect this one. He is an innocent . . ."

Shirah led that last day's march, because he was a native white Alabamian. He had sent a telegram to Governor George Wallace, as a former Sunday School student of his, asking that they be allowed to pass peacefully through the state.

Teenagers, fifteen or twenty, including some of those who had engaged in the previous day's discussion, followed the march on foot, a state trooper keeping them at an interval behind.

"Black heifers," one called, and others made barnyard noises.

"Head it up, coon! Troopers ain't goin' to help you in Alabama."

A young man with an angry face in an Alabama car passed: "You won't make it through Fort Payne, Alabama!" his voice almost breaking.

The teenagers: "Hang the white 'uns from a white oak!"

"All of 'em's black."

"Kill 'em white men first."

They passed the little town of Rising Fawn, Georgia, and few local people noted.

The same young man who had called before passed, shouted: "You'll never make it through Fort Payne, Alabama."

At a filling station two of the teenagers who had been in the discussion stood on each side of the line of march and squirted soft drinks on the legs of each marcher as the line passed. At a lunch break in the countryside, a crew-cut young white hit Lockett a fast blow on the side of the head, knocking him down, and escaped into the crowd. When the march resumed, a different state trooper was with the teenagers and made no effort to stop them when they crowded up some five feet behind the marchers, or when they began throwing pebbles and then eggs at their bent backs. There was one more rest stop, and then the marchers rose to go the short distance on to the Alabama state line.

They moved under a flapping row of Confederate flags strung across the highway from a tourist souvenir shop and ahead they could see the line. On the Georgia side, cars were parked in long rows on both sides of the highway, and a crowd of some fifteen hundred people stood waiting. The Alabama side was cleared, with a line of state trooper cars on one side, and troopers wearing riot helmets standing beside them.

The marchers moved out into the highway, and the teen-agers and crowds of other whites moved in behind, a long line of cars behind them. Ahead the crowd at the state line shouted. Someone threw a large rock dangerously close to the marchers; it bounced, rolled across the highway, almost hit a young woman. The little line moved forward; the ten marchers were dusty; their shirts, trousers were smeared with dried egg yellow.

On they came, and the silence of the kill fell over the crowd. The pace of the marchers quickened. They crossed the state line. All the crowd, those following, those waiting, came together behind them. Twelve troopers formed a line behind the marchers, held the crowd back with billy clubs raised to their chests. People moved to the roadside and began running through a pasture to the right overlooking the roadside, over a barbed-wire fence, down a hill, across a creek, up another one to an embankment looking directly down on the scene ensuing on the sunglaring cement of the highway.

The marchers stood halted in their line in the left lane. Col. Al Lingo, fleshy-faced, heavy-set man in civilian clothes, director of the Alabama troopers, notoriously racist, brutal, was shouting at them through a bull-horn. He told them they were welcome as individuals, but not as a group, and ordered them to turn back and disperse. (Turn back into the mob behind.) They stood, silent.

"Place them under arrest."

A trooper walked up to Shirah and removed a sandwich board sign he wore, inscribed with Moore's civil rights mottoes. The crowd shouted a wordless roar. The troopers began taking the marchers, one at a time, to the patrol cars.

"Bunch of communists!" a man yelled.

A trooper held Haley by the arm; his shoulders were slumped. Then came Hansen.

"Low white man! A dog and fox got better sense than you. They stay with their kind."

"Throw them niggers in the river."

Weinberger fell to the pavement when a trooper reached him. He lay on the pavement with knees bent, hands protecting his head—the fetal position of non-violent resistance. Two troopers grabbed his legs. Another jabbed at his side with a pole. It was the first time I had seen an electric cattle prod used on a human being, this instrument ordinarily in everyday inhumanity used to guide animals in stockyards and into slaughterhouses. Weinberger writhed on the pavement, but would not get up. The trooper burned him again with the prod pole.

"That's white men dealing with you, brother!" from the crowd.

Finally, four troopers picked him up and carried him to a patrol car.

A woman screamed, "Don't carry him. Drag him!"

Zellner and Aeloney also fell, and the troopers bent to them, burning them with the prod poles, repeated jabs. Neither would rise, and were carried. As Zellner hung from the hands of four troopers, another walked alongside jabbing him with the pole.

"Stick him! Stick him in his big fat butt!"

"Kill him! Kill him!" came the final shriek—from a woman with her hair in fat curlers.

The patrol cars, quick and efficient, drove away. The high-way was opened. The crowd soon was gone.

Lingo had explained the rationale of the arrests earlier in the day, when the troopers were lined up waiting the marchers the moment they set out.

"We can't let anybody get killed in here. We're going to have law and order regardless of what it takes. The FBI is in agreement with us that they couldn't get through this section alive."

So much for the FBI and constitutional rights and protection from police brutality. Back in the little town of Trenton, the courthouse square in the afternoon sun was deserted. An old man sat on a cement wall, looked up at me as I waited to use the phone booth and said:

"I hear they arrested them niggers down there."

I nodded. He pointed to a small truck parking beside the courthouse. It was loaded with furniture.

"I reckon them folks is moving," he said.

It was all the same to him—and, sadly, he even more than Lingo spoke for America the answer to the march's question about how America felt about its martyred idealists. The march, like the movement, was facing what were clearly insuperable forces set against it. It might have prevailed against the raw and unconstitutional repression of the Alabama state troopers and even against the open hostility encountered along the way and might even eventually have broken through indifference—as Dr. King was to do, with brief, hyperbolic effect, at the March on Washington later in the year. But all the forces of resistance coming together proved too much.

And there was more—including that new lethal quality I sensed in the private hostility and public repression encountered by the march. We drove that night to Fort Payne ("You'll never get through . . ."), where the marchers had been jailed. Reports that a white mob had gathered around the jail were unfounded; the downtown was dark, deserted. We heard aftermath reports of the jailing of the marchers. Weinberger had been seen, his thin face pale, still refusing to walk as he was being booked. They carried him from office to office and then heaved him into an elevator, his head making a loud clunk as it hit the steel wall.

We checked into a motel. The clerk wanted to know whom we represented; angrily we told him it was none of his damn business. His eyes pleaded with us. The Klan, he finally said, wanted to know.

"They won't bother you all when they know who you are. But they will me if I don't find out."

Our car had been followed twice on the lonely highway driving there. An Associated Press photographer was in a room of the motel with a chair barricading the door. The phone had rung when he checked into the room; an anonymous voice had threatened his life.

Something beyond the ordinary of ordinary southern violence, ordinary American violence, was afoot. Fear of the known could, then, become fear of some unknown, worse peril, lurking behind the known. The Freedom March had revealed this. There would be more.

Chapter
EIGHTEEN

WE DROVE to Birmingham from Fort Payne and saw the police pitted against the masses of marching demonstrators— the fire hoses mercilessly pushing them down, back, the police dogs lunging at the end of leashes, inches away from the flesh of the marchers, or tearing at their clothes, American violence near to being unleashed, normal American violence in abnormal functioning . . . and the murderous mood, the strange, quiet feel of something beyond normal violence that had hung over the Freedom March.

I try to find words that can convey it. It was as though in such great efforts as Albany and the Freedom March and hundreds of other manifestations of a spirit that spoke for the highest aspiration of a nation, a people, indeed all people, the movement had somehow compelled action, decision—either for or against that highest aspiration. The action against it was increasing, becoming more murderous, showing more and more mercilessly, as on the Freedom March, what in twisted, sick and ugly pathology the everyday grayness of American life had done to so many of its people. And the action that seemed demanded so unequivocally, so unevadable in support of that highest aspiration somehow was compromised or entirely evaded. The best in America, its people and institutions, had perhaps by those same processes productive of so much pathology, been rendered, at best, impotent, at worst, complicit in the pathology. And the movement, having pushed to such a moment of truth, began to fall back—appalled, dismayed, fearful.

The idealism of the Freedom March had been answered by one other aspect of American normality, this time manifested within the movement. On the second day out, with national press attention focused on its remarkable expression of what the best of the movement meant, SCLC stepped up its campaign in Birmingham. After more than a month of minor sorties and skirmishes, mass demonstrations had begun. Whether by design or not, the Freedom March had been upstaged.

It is hard to imagine that SCLC was unaware that competition existed for attention of the press and the public, but movement veterans insist that leaders did not intend for the dramatic events in Birmingham to detract from the subtle message of the march. The timing wasn't intentional. But the consequences were all too evident of the splitting apart of SNCC and SCLC. A coordinated movement would easily have allowed both the Freedom March and Birmingham full public exposure.

Hullabaloo over Birmingham was part of the cause of the collapse of even another important campaign, one of the most crucial of all the movement. In Greenwood, Mississippi, after the shooting of Jimmy Travis, a SNCC voter registration worker, the four civil rights organizations active in the state, SNCC, CORE, SCLC and the NAACP, had launched a joint campaign to force a showdown on the issue of Mississippi's across-the-board denial of the vote to Negroes and the federal government's failure to do anything about this violation of the most basic of constitutional rights. Full resources of the Southern Regional Council's Voter Education Project were available for the drive; foundations and other sources of funds were interested. The movement spirit sang out in churches as sweetly, as strongly as in Albany. Mass marches got underway in February 1963, and the Justice Department was moved to seek an injunction not only against violation of voter registration rights, but also demanding protection of the right of Negroes to assemble peacefully and demonstrate for redress of grievances. It was one of the very few instances in all the years of the movement that the federal government ever used its extensive court powers to counter lawless southern resistance to the movement, and the only time the Justice Department sought protection of the right to demonstrate. Had issues been pushed to the ultimate in Greenwood, the basic rights involving voting and equal justice would have been established in the South, years before they finally were by yet falteringly enforced civil rights legislation.

But the issues were never pushed, and disintegration of movement cooperation, an inability to come together in concerted action even for those strategic goals that had become so important, was primarily the reason. Only SNCC, with all of its Mississippi staff there on emergency basis, gave real support to the drive. Greenwood police allowed a police dog to attack demonstrators; shots were fired into the voter registration office, and it was finally set afire. The violence, in the familiar process of press and public fascination with it, overshadowed the important, indeed historical, issues at stake; America never really knew that the course of southern history, the priorities for reform of southern racial practices, were being established there. Then the big demonstrations in Birmingham broke out —with more exciting violence.

In the diffused situation that developed, the Justice Department was able to back away from the request for an injunction, agreeing out of court with city officials to withdraw it on the promise that they would do better. They did not, and though the campaign continued into July, few Negroes ever were registered, and voter registration and equal justice had to wait for the more abrasive, wearing power plays that mass demonstrations were to become—with, year by year, a whittling away of the movement's original hope that changes in law and custom might be achieved in coordination with a rapprochement, rather than further deterioration in relations, between white and Negro Southerners.

Inherent in the inability of the organizations to work together cohesively in such an important campaign as Greenwood or in such a serious matter as the timing of the Freedom March and Birmingham was—beyond personal and ideological conflicts—the increasing rivalry among them for financial support. The money to support the movement for the very most part had to come from individual contributions—small ones in response to fund-raising campaigns, large ones from wealthy sympathizers. Both were influenced by publicity, and this did have its influence on the organizations—to their credit, less than normal for such dependent organizations, but influence nevertheless. Some of the fund-raising efforts—public appearances before northern audiences, attendance at cocktail parties where rich individuals might be courted for contributions— were demeaning. And the quest for funds could influence policy in devious ways. Robert Kennedy, for example, was one of those who persuaded well-off friends to make sizeable contributions to the movement, and he had definite ideas about what the movement should and should not be doing. The need because of this to consider his ideas, correct though they might have been, more than ordinarily was another part of the unhealthy tie of the movement to the government it was trying to prod and change. There were ample channels, like the Voter Education Project, for foundation funds even to the non-tax-exempt organizations and groups, but among the saddest failures was that of the very most of foundations ever to support the movement. The handful that did deserve credit not only for lessening a little the pressure for raising money, but also for not overly interfering in policies and planning. This would not have been true of some of those which failed their responsibility, which never gave any money to the movement—some of them, being notorious for such interference in the affairs of the beneficiaries.

Competition for funds, as much as anything else, increased

the tendency in the movement organizations to weigh organizational concerns against the broader ones of the movement and Negro Southerners. In one more way, in coming more and more to base decisions and actions as much on the requirements for survival of the organization as on movement ideals and goals, in the organizations' coming more and more to exist in the minds of the workers as ends in themselves, in increasing bureaucratic tendencies, the movement showed itself sliding, unawares and uncontrollably, into standard American patterns, becoming more nearly a standard "institution," like the labor unions.

But more damaging was the way the press and the public had continued to perceive the movement. If one police dog in Greenwood could divert the press and the public, what chance of attention had any of those important spiritual qualities which were still capable of effective expression in Birmingham —with an entire pack of savage dogs snarling at marching children? The presence of Dr. King more than anything else made Birmingham the big news in the spring of 1963, overshadowing, upstaging the Freedom March and Greenwood. For where Dr. King went, the press had to go, and in the normal functioning of the American press, reporting personnel was, in most instances, too scarce, too thinly stretched to allow full coverage of more than one movement event at a time. One of the nation's most responsible newspapers had standing orders to its southern correspondent always to be on the scene when Dr. King was involved in a public affair. "Go where the Mahatma goes—he might get killed."

But even had Dr. King not been in Birmingham, the violence there, the splendid material for dramatic photographs feeding the national obsession with violence, feeding the national fantasies and prejudices of a South of one-dimensional people, saintly Negroes, depraved and savage whites, would have been sufficient to draw most of the press coverage. And the final irony: for all their photogenic and melodramatic feeding of a national neurosis, the Birmingham police were, on balance, no worse than most the movement was up against in the South and tamer than the average constabulary encountered by the movement in Mississippi and across the rural black belt.

But by the time of Birmingham the movement was deeply involved in strategic gambits, win-lose psychology, and Bull Connor was as fine a foil as might have been found. On one other score of its timing, SCLC had been criticized, mainly by some of the Birmingham Negro leaders. The city administration, typified by Bull Connor, had been defeated in an election prior to the start of the massive Birmingham demonstrations; he was a lame duck police commissioner, and moderates were soon to take over. Why not see what they would do first? The supposition has to be that, at least in part, SCLC, in a shrewd, normal-American, cynical stratagem, knew a good enemy when they saw him—one who could be counted on in stupidity and natural viciousness to play into their hands, for full exploitation in the press as archfiend and villain.

Birmingham's violence and a subsequent spontaneous outburst of mass marches and renewed sit-ins across the South were credited with compelling the Kennedy Administration to propose civil rights legislation. Here, then, was one more sad model for the defeat of the spiritual quality of the movement. The Kennedy Administration had presided during the three great years of the movement's most inspired, most effective history, but beyond lip service to the idealism for which Negro Southerners in the movement risked their lives, and occasional forced action to uphold school desegregation decrees or, as in the freedom rides, to prevent a massacre, had done virtually nothing in a practical way to support and further the movement. In intent and espoused belief, the Kennedy Administration was impeccable, but it imagined its pragmatic, political, strategic position to be such as to preclude such forthright action. To do so was to risk loss of face, political defeat. As Mr. Page in Albany so bitterly came to know, it depended, or imagined itself to depend, on the racist southern wing of the Democratic Party, not only for votes but for getting laws passed in Congress. The movement, in its spiritual phase, placed in such a situation, would have known that the only solution was to root the racist southern wing out of the party or perish in the attempt. But the movement was to see—and inevitably to suffer losses in its own ability to make moral judgments independent of pragmatic concerns—that the Kennedy Administration would not push the imperatives of belief over its estimation of practical reality. And when the movement itself forced the administration to action commensurate with its belief, the administration introduced civil rights legislation which, in a Congress dominated by southern racists, was predictably incapable of perfection or even, as time was to tell, functional enforcement. All that the administration needed to do, had needed to do all along, was enforce legislation already on the books—most basically, the Bill of Rights. If the highest power in the land could not prevail any better against the ongoing destructive forces in the normal functioning of America, what chance had the movement?

What chance, indeed? The movement organizations succumbed or sickened, but such an embodiment of the movement spirit as Reverend Wells, after all that had happened by 1971, had not ceased to speak the meaning of that spirit, and, in doing so, eloquently denounced the political immorality of friends and foes of the movement.

He said he had gone the year before to Bainbridge, Georgia, where two Nixon representatives were asking the people what could be done to put down unrest among Negroes. "I said to put a piece of tape over Agnew's mouth. I said that we could see through Nixon, that he had sold his soul to the devil to become President of the United States through Thurmond and the South.

"I'm an old crazy black Baptist preacher with faith and patience to stick with Jesus. But a lot of these little Negroes —their patience has run out. I see a beautiful message in the riots. They throw devilish bricks at buildings, but not at men. There's been no race riot since Dr. King walked among us. I see love for mankind even in a riot—the patience of black people, respect for life. They let out steam by destroying buildings, taking televisions, liquor, clothes from devilish stores.

"I weigh that against a hypocritical Congress that made laws with ninety strings attached and put Eastland and Strom Thurmond in charge of the strings.

"People see through them. We told them to do something about the problems facing America—and look what they did. When Negroes threw bottles in Albany, I didn't feel it was my responsibility to try to stop it. I had other goals—non-violence and law. But I can't put out the fires that hypocritical America started. America made Rap Brown. I have no criticism for northern Negroes in their movement.

"I say: 'You didn't hear me when I knocked and pulled off my hat and bowed and begged, marched non-violently. Who are you to tell me what's necessary? I don't have time.'

"They could still do something. They could give hope to black America just by starting to show good faith, just *starting* to work on the problems . . .

"If it gets to the point where black people take up arms, they will lose. But who are the power structure people to say don't do it? To say use the legal process? It's falling apart. They tried to get those blind boys on the Supreme Court so Nixon could pacify the South.

"I still try to hold on and say there is a chance. I said America would live forever if it would deal with its problems. There are a lot of confused folks. I've had moments of discouragement—these last few years, quite a bit . . . Lawmakers engaged in a conspiracy against effective laws will destroy America.

"I preached a Thanksgiving sermon about people sailing here looking for freedom and justice. I said we should keep their dreams alive, preserve their works. The closest thing to my heart is the Bible, and the Constitution of America is next. That's what I have fought for, and I say I will fight till I die.

"They say I'm a communist. I'm a full-blooded American. I have eaten the Constitution and digested it—every word of it.

"They're the ones that call the Supreme Court a crook and

then tell me to respect the law. I preach a sermon about you reap what you sow.

"It's right to stand for right—whether you get results or not."

Violence dominated the perception of Birmingham, and if, at the height of demonstrations, it was not really of the caliber southern terrorism was capable of, violence came, all too soon, to proportions that even the South had not theretofore experienced. Late on the Saturday night of May 12, soon after the massive demonstrations had ended, bombs exploded a half-hour apart at the Gaston Motel, a headquarters for SCLC staffers, including Dr. King, and at the home of his brother, the Rev. A. D. King. If one might assume that someone was determined to kill Dr. King, it is possible to believe this was the second of a series of attempts before success was achieved. (The first was the bombing of his home in Montgomery during the bus boycott.) Birmingham Negroes, in that spirit Reverend Shuttlesworth had warned against, goaded as even police dogs and fire hoses had not been able to do, some twenty-five hundred of them, milled around, threw bricks and stones at police and firemen. A taxicab was set on fire. A policeman was stabbed. Police with dogs arrived, further infuriating the mob. Movement leaders, others of good will moved through the crowds, urging calm, order—and finally the crowds began to quiet. At this point, Al Lingo arrived with a large contingent of state troopers and, despite requests from Birmingham Police Chief Jamie Moore to leave, began to clear the streets. Armed with shotguns, rifles and clubs, his men shoved people, randomly clubbed people, hit people with the butts of their guns, as fires blazed up in two stores and cast their red light in the southern summer's night.

This, with Jacksonville, Florida, earlier, was as close to Negro rioting as a southern city had come, and—ignoring the enormous provocation, the quality in it of reflex action, like the demonstrators who sometimes threw rocks back when attacked with them—the nation seized on this new element of violence almost with glee. This, too—Negro violence—had been anticipated since the beginning of the movement. And now dire predictions, soon to find their fulfillment in the North, were intoned—that non-violence could not contain the wrath of great masses of ostracized and deprived Negroes in the great industrial cities.

But all the while, during the big Birmingham demonstrations and for ten ensuing weeks in the summer of 1963, the magnificent spirit of the movement produced non-violent demonstrations across the South—at least 758 demonstrations, as counted by the Justice Department in its ignoble role as observer, in 186 cities. Press reports at the time indicated that at least 14,733 persons were arrested in the eleven southern states for demonstrating—a formidable number, compared with 3,600 in all the great days of the 1960 sit-ins. Some change was affected in segregation of public facilities in at least 261 cities and towns.*

The movement was still capable of such effort, such energy, such results. How many acts, unnoticed, of the quiet kind of courage that so ennobled Albany occurred on the city sidewalks and town squares of the South? How many great bursts of spirit and expansion of self and soul occurred in the little churches across the South, singing:

> There must be
> A God
> Somewhere . . .

Dr. King and Reverend Shuttlesworth led a full-scale campaign in Danville, Virginia, where SNCC, as in Albany, had laid the groundwork. Police violated the sanctuary of a church there, kicked an office door in and arrested three civil rights leaders. National Guardsmen patrolled the streets for weeks in Cambridge, Maryland, where a SNCC-led campaign produced some of the first public evidences of the loss in individuals of the will to non-violence—brandishing of guns, talk of killing—against a particularly ugly white terrorism and repression.

*All figures from "Direct Action in the South" (*New South*, Vol. 18, no. 10–11, pp. 19–20.)

Demonstrations and arrests wound on in the deep-South strongholds of segregation and terrorism—places like Americus and Savannah, Georgia; Jackson, Mississippi; even Plaquemines Parish, Louisiana, feudal holding of the late Leander Perez.

But what of this did the nation take note? Violence was the medium through which it all was seen. President Kennedy, in calling for civil rights legislation in a televised speech on June 11, invoked the prevailing theme:

"Fires of frustration and discord are burning in every city, North and South . . . Redress is sought in the streets, in demonstrations, parades and protests, which create tensions and threaten violence and threaten lives."

Not only because it was right and just—the only hope America had to cure itself, redeem itself—but because violence was threatened. The non-violent demonstrations were not a magnificent achievement within a violence-prone society, but rather, in the eyes of the country and its lawmakers, a threat to be quieted, a creator of tensions to be avoided.

And the very most of the violence which did come was still not from Negroes, as predicted, even, it sometimes seemed, masochistically or, in the sense of primitive justice, yearned for, but from the traditional and expected source—racist southern whites. Where non-violence did not hold, it was again retaliatory violence—the most serious in all the years theretofore of the movement being the killing of a white in an exchange of gunfire between whites and Negroes in Lexington, North Carolina.

That feel of violence-beyond-violence experienced on the Freedom March found expression in June 1963 in Jackson, Mississippi, when an assassin from ambush killed Medgar Evers, effective, well-known, beloved leader of the Mississippi NAACP, in the driveway of his home. The murder of leaders, lesser-known ones, had been a part of the repertoire of racist resistance to the movement through its history and to the struggle for racial justice through southern history. But the murder of Medgar Evers stirred a resentment deeper than usual, a symbolic response in Negroes, great and small, across the South—bringing to the surface for the first time on a wide scale the fear that the movement's great goal of redemption could never be achieved. Certainly as heavy an influence on the destruction of the movement as any other was the effect inside people, consciously and unconsciously, of the subsequent murder of other leaders. But the effect of the murder of Medgar Evers, its shock value, its insane waste, what it said about the chances of a good man against evil in a society, was profound.

Then, as though the last act in a tragedy of Birmingham, came the most obscene of all the insane violence against the movement, the bombing of the Sixteenth Street Baptist Church on September 15, 1963, where four little girls were killed, and seventeen other persons were injured. The four girls had been to Sunday School, were in the rear of the church (where the dynamite had been planted) putting on choir robes, preparing to take part in a special youth service during the main worship hour.

I stood in the wreckage of the church a few hours after it had happened—stood, numbed, looking at the shattered stained-glass windows, the debris, fallen plaster, broken wood, through all the sanctuary, the scattered Sunday School lessons of the children on the littered floor, "Primary Bible Lessons," a drawing on the front of a group of Negro children around a picture of Christ. I stood in the sanctuary of that church, where the spirit of the movement had many times soared, like the other Negro churches of the South which had become in my mind truly churches—the only places where I had ever experienced real religious feeling, in a lifetime within the South's church-oriented society, growing up in the Methodist Episcopal Church South—stood there and stared aghast, unable to cry or even be angry, only numbly sorrowful—for the church, the people, the movement, what had been done to religion there, but most of all, in a sickened sense of defeat, sorrowful for the South.

Later, outside, standing in the street, still numbly staring at the wreckage, I heard a familiar voice behind me, steely and precise and slightly sardonic, and turned to see a leader of the Black Muslims whom I had recently interviewed in Atlanta, and with whom I had, in a friendly way, argued the merits of integration.

"Ah, Mr. Watters," he said. "You see, you see, what integration leads to."

Here the voice of everyday, cynical, hate-conditioned America. For the bombing lived up to all the expectations—years of them—of violence to the movement. The headlines in the Birmingham *Post-Herald* told like poetry the realization of that expectation, and a further expectation—of retaliatory Negro violence, a repeat, maybe bigger, more destructive, of the near-riot in May. From the *Post-Herald*, Monday, September 16, 1963, the treatment:

BOMB BLAST KILLS 4 CHILDREN,
INJURES 17 AT CHURCH HERE

Troopers Rushed In,
Guard Is Alerted

Top Federal
Officers Help

Boutwell Requests
Aid From Wallace

All Agencies in Bomber
Hunt, Governor Says

State Offers
$10,000 Reward

Dead and Injured
Taken To Hospital

Cries of Grief, Anger Heard in Wake of Bombing

"Anger heard . . ." Police and press alike, in the strange quiet of the afternoon, as grief-stricken people walked numbly about the Negro section, expected God knows what retributive horror that night. And as the hot afternoon wore on, violence, like a mad dog loose, continued—white violence. White youths shot to death a Negro boy on a bicycle. Police shot a Negro youth to death, claiming he ran when ordered to halt (that most common of southern capital crimes).

We talked among ourselves, reporters, and reluctantly agreed that the only safe place and informed place to be that night was with the notorious state police. (It was my last time to cover a movement event as a newspaperman; I left the paper soon after—in essence because its management no longer wanted to cover such stories, and as I had realized it would be, I was interested in little else.) To my shame, I rode that night in an Alabama state troopers' squad car, patroling the strangely quiet streets of the Negro sections, looking for, fully expecting (as always America had expected) retaliatory violence—violence that never came.

I saw firsthand the quality of hysteria that gripped southern cops in such circumstances. Early in the evening the police radio in the car in which I rode relayed a report, a rumor from the northern part of the state that a caravan of cars carrying northern Negroes was on the way to the city. The assumption was that, like a posse, they were coming to take vengeance. Troopers—the ones with whom I rode among them—sped to the outskirts of town and set up a roadblock to halt the menace. For more than an hour they stopped each car that came along, assured themselves each was on a legitimate errand. One of these was driven by a Negro man and it towed another car, which had a northern license plate—Michigan. He explained that he worked in Detroit, had been visiting his people in Birmingham, had set out for home, and his car had broken down. Now he was hauling it in for repairs. They waved him on. As it became apparent no caravan was coming, it occurred to me that the man towing the car was the caravan, and I am sure it occurred to the cops (though they would never have admitted it), for soon they abandoned the roadblock and went back to patroling lifeless streets, looking for—as America kept looking for—Negro riots, Negro violence.

The press had, in the spring of 1963, found a catchword to express the expectation—"the new militancy"—and attached it most often to the young activists of SNCC and CORE, by then dug in across the South in what amounted to a non-violent guerrilla warfare against the forces of voter discrimination, racist oppression. I remember attending a southwide SNCC conference in Atlanta that spring, hearing them sing, hearing in simple and abstruse development their still-strong philosophy of non-violence. I felt fellowship, warmth and that degree of hero-worship we all had for these brave and seemingly unshakeable young Negro Southerners. We asked Julian Bond, then information officer for SNCC, about the new militancy. Did it mean Negroes had become angry at last (standard-American at last)?

"We have been angry over injustice all along," he said in that soft, ironic voice of his. "It's just that nobody until now seems to have noticed it."

The feel of the Freedom March, that strange feel finding expression in the violence in Birmingham, the murder of Medgar Evers, haunting the movement, haunting the South, haunting America that decisive summer of 1963, was relieved dramatically, symbolically by the March on Washington on August 28, when the spiritual meaning of the movement more than ever before (or again) was communicated to the nation —and more nearly than ever before or again got through to Americans. It was as though the movement, as Ralph Abernathy had said about Albany, had been called on to witness to the nation before it was too late, and, despite the warnings of friends fearful of Negro violence (that never came that time, either) and threats of powerful enemies, it just had to do it— not knowing what would happen. Dr. King spoke:

"I have a dream . . ." And Americans understood for once, for a short time, what beyond violence and tactics the movement really meant, its strong reaffirmation of the ancient truths of mankind—justice, dignity, love, redemption—and sensed what beyond even that (the spirit of the mass meetings) the movement was really all about.

White southern moderates were reached—ones who had seen each phase of the movement unfolding all around them and had persistently, step by step, opposed it with that heavy-handed scorn and contempt for idealism which, over the South, is a legacy from the turn-of-the-century apostles of the New South. For this one time, for a brief time, they understood.

I do not doubt that the many Americans who did glimpse from the March on Washington the deepest meanings of the movement were genuine in their conversion to its real goals. But it was temporary conversion. It could not be sustained against the ongoing, ordinary workings of American society and the extraordinary events, the murder of President John F. Kennedy in that fateful year of 1963 being, of course, the most devastating. America is not yet done with the devastation wreaked on the consciousnesses, the hearts of people, by that one tragic and insane act spawned out of the life-killing ugliness and banality of existence at the lower levels of its graceless, hard, materialistic culture. As the assassination of Medgar Evers did among Negro Southerners, the assassination of John Kennedy raised in many, many Americans—I think the most of a full generation—the fatalistic fear, the terrible doubt, of whether decency can prevail in such a society as ours.

We saw more clearly than ever before the evils, the pathologies (as I had sensed them on the Freedom March), and we began to sense that these were only the most ugly part of a vast human and institutional bulwark resisting decency, the most of it everyday people and customs and event.

I am persuaded that John Kennedy's assassination had direct bearing on such phenomena as the quick failure of non-violent direct action to prevail among Negro Northerners. The movement methods and spirit had just begun to spread into the northern ghettos in 1962 and 1963. Some rioting occurred in the summer of 1963, much more in 1964, and then, with Watts, the archetype, that ominous holocaust of it in 1965 and

1966, the meaning of which Reverend Wells so eloquently explained. Many other factors were, of course, involved—including the self-fulfilling prophecy of, and morbid fascination with, Negro violence and including the brutalizing effect of the North's far uglier, more degrading, versions of life at the lower levels of American existence. But Negro Northerners are of the South—for the most part either of this generation from the South, or with roots deep in its culture and psychology from past generations. Out of this southern heritage, they have within them the cultural equipment from which Negro Southerners drew to build the great spirit of the movement. America, in its ongoing processes, may more effectively have stunted within them the will, the necessary hope, to have built the same spirit in their movement, but I think it is at least possible to question whether this would have been so if John Kennedy had not been murdered.

I have no doubt that his assassination was an important one of the many causes of the deterioration of hope, of will, of redemptive love, within the southern movement. In early 1964, I interviewed Dr. King, John Lewis and James Forman, SNCC executive secretary, and one legitimate question at that time was whether, indeed, the civil rights organizations would resume direct action campaigns in the spring and summer. (After the immediate shock and period of mourning of the Kennedy assassination, the movement had been quieter than the usual quiet during the winter.) But all three men assured me that non-violent direct action would be pushed even more vigorously than before—in behalf of the then-pending omnibus Civil Rights Bill until it might be passed, seeking strict compliance should it be passed. All of 1964 would be "hot," Jim Forman said.

Chapter
NINETEEN

VICTORY AS GREAT as the highest hopes of the sit-ins envisioned seemed in sight in the pending civil rights legislation. But the highest hopes, the joy of the movement, had dimmed. Not a collapse, but deterioration of spirit was evident in SCLC's next major campaign—in St. Augustine, Florida, in the summer of 1964. It was to be the last massive one against the South's systematized segregation before passage of the 1964 Civil Rights Act. SCLC's presence in St. Augustine was, at least in part, to keep pressure on Congress to pass the act.

The local issues in the east coast Florida tourist town were essentially the same as in Albany and Birmingham—integration and release of Negroes jailed in demonstrations. Though the Birmingham demonstrations had compelled President Kennedy to promise the legislation which his murder was now moving Congress to act upon, little had been achieved in terms of the local Birmingham issues. A truce had been reached in May 1963, with few concessions from the white powers, and SCLC left Birmingham in little better shape than it left Albany. But it had the kind of strategic national victory Albany had taught it to win. If there is the suggestion that SCLC exploited the local Birmingham situation (and SNCC was by then accusing SCLC of such), the suggestion was stronger in St. Augustine.

In Albany, often, the people in the churches clamored to go to jail, while SCLC and the local leaders held back, waiting for an expected break in negotiations or for the overruling of Judge Elliott's injunction against demonstrations. In Birmingham, young people were full of that eager willingness to try to fill the jails—if adults were not. In St. Augustine, on occasion, there was the sad spectacle of SCLC stalwarts standing before the mass meetings exhorting people, pleading with them to go to jail, even scorning them for reluctance to do so.

"Is anybody going to jail—to join Dr. King? All right, come on down front. Would anybody else like to join him? Young man, are you going? Give him a hand. Who would like to be a witness for our leader?"

People yet unwilling to go were urged into other activities —a picket line which had not attracted arrests, non-violent workshops, telephone committees.

"Come on out and learn some of the weapons of the non-violent army. For we shall overcome—if we keep the schedule," said one speaker.

Another: "What it means to have Martin Luther King in town is that the attention of the world is focused on the problems of the Negroes of Florida. Friends, I say to you that Martin Luther King's coming to St. Augustine will be the worst thing that ever happened to the Negro people in America—the *worst* thing that ever happened to the Negro in America—if you don't follow him to jail. If you don't see the significance of this man's suffering and share it, then it's empty and meaningless and worthless. If you don't support him by sharing with him in the St. Augustine jail, then you will contribute to crushing the greatest leader that the Negroes in America have ever known."

The audience stirs, murmurs, as though puzzled. There have been no cries of "Amen," "Yes," "Well."

Another SCLC speaker: "You can't reason with some people. The excuses they come up with! Some of you Negroes ain't ever going to be free . . ."

Such exhortations, though, were a minor episode in St. Augustine's general drama of the ongoing movement, the people's great strength and incredible courage. The movement in St. Augustine had followed in the larger course of the history of the southern movement after Birmingham. Sit-ins—which had failed against white violence and police repression in 1961 —were resumed in the summer of 1963. They succeeded in removing discriminatory signs in public facilities and desegregating lunch counters at two chain variety stores. Schools were tokenly desegregated in the face of a lawsuit. But the cost to the movement was dear.

Law enforcement was repressive: Negroes were arrested for distributing handbills; four youthful demonstrators were sentenced to indefinite terms in the state reformatory. (The state intervened six months later to free them.) Private white violence, in that mood of new murderousness that came in 1963, was more vicious, more sustained, than the movement had known before. Finally, in the fall of 1963, after whites had fired rifles into many homes and fire-bombed some, Negroes shot to death a white man who was riding through the Negro district armed with a shotgun. Four Negroes, including the movement's leader, Dr. R. B. Hayling, attempted to eavesdrop on a Klan meeting in an open field near town, were captured and severely beaten—as the Klan crowd screamed for their death, and women shouted, "Castrate them! Castrate them!"

After a brief surcease demurring to the Kennedy assassination, the violence resumed more fiercely in St. Augustine in early 1964. Children of two Negro families had been admitted to the all-white school. While one of the families was at a PTA meeting, their automobile was destroyed by fire. The home of the other family was burned. Their child said, "Does this mean I can't go back to my school?"

Whites fired rifles into the home of Dr. Hayling while he and his wife and two daughters slept. Their boxer dog was killed. One of Dr. Hayling's daughters said, "Daddy, they just didn't understand about our dog. He looked real mean, but he wouldn't hurt anybody. They shouldn't have killed him."

The only law-enforcement action was in connection with the beating of the four Negroes at the Klan rally. Four Klansmen were arrested on charges of assault; an all-white jury acquitted them. The four Negroes, incredibly, were charged with assault; they were found guilty.

Non-violent demonstrations were resumed in the face of all this—during Easter Week, 1964. The city was sponsoring a big Easter Parade, featuring Mother Goose and Alice in Wonderland characters; some 40,000 people were on hand. Negroes picketed; sit-ins were resumed. A group of New England white people participated, including the seventy-two-year-old mother of the then-governor of Massachusetts, Mrs. Malcolm Peabody. She and others were jailed.

SCLC began sending its headquarters stalwarts into the city in late May to support the continued demonstrations of its local affiliate, led by Dr. Hayling. A series of night marches from the churches were begun on May 26—big marches, with no exhortation needed to bring the people forth full of (even yet) their joy, their great hope. The first night, the demonstration went into the white downtown, paused at a city park containing a building said once to have been a slave market. The next night, they marched to this same symbolic site, and were glared at—but not attacked—by a crowd of young whites, visibly bearing such arms as bicycle chains and iron pipes. Local law-enforcement, mostly in the hands of the county sheriff, did nothing about the weapons. The next night, when the demonstration reached the slave market, the young whites used them —on the Negroes and on newsmen at the scene. Again, the sheriff and his men did nothing.

Later that night, someone fired a shotgun from a passing car at Harry Boyte, fifty-two, a white official of SCLC, and his college-age son, as they drove back to their motel. Mr. Boyte had been attacked during the demonstration. And still later that night, someone fired eleven rifle shots and a shotgun blast at a beach cottage where Dr. King and other SCLC officials had been staying. (That night they happened to be away from the cottage.)

J. B. Stoner, since the 1940s noted in southern police and Anti-Defamation League of B'nai B'rith files as a violent-spoken, professional anti-Semite, anti-Negro, right-wing activist, appeared in downtown St. Augustine, speaking at Klan rallies, leading white demonstrations into the Negro section. He had also been in Birmingham. He later emerged as attorney for James Earl Ray, convicted assassin of Dr. King.

On the night after the bicycle-chain beatings at the slave market, the people of the movement marched once more out of their church, bravely going, in non-violence, to the slave market again, but were halted before they got there by the sheriff's men and state patrolmen, armed with a local court injunction against night marches. The movement went into federal court in Jacksonville, seeking reversal of the injunction on the grounds that it violated First Amendment rights and Fourteenth Amendment protection of those rights. Hearings in the matter revealed in ugly detail an alliance between the sheriff's department and the violent gang, a Klan-type organization known as the Ancient City Gun Club, headed by a man named Holsted Manucy, called "Hoss."

In court one morning, the sheriff, L. O. Davis, a buffoonish, burly, thuggish man, read a list of more than a hundred "special deputies" on whom he might call in an emergency. When he reached the name Holsted Manucy, District Judge Bryan Simpson, presiding, exclaimed:

"Why, that man's a convicted felon in this court!"

No outspoken integrationist, but faithful to precedent and other standards of the federal law, and outraged by the injustices and brutality to Negroes, Judge Simpson eventually enjoined the banning of night marches and the imposition of higher-than-ordinary fines and cruel and unusual punishment on demonstrators. Most importantly, he demanded that the city and state provide protection of Negroes' constitutional right to demonstrate—a rare thing from the federal bench during all the movement days. In Judge Simpson's handling of the case, day by day in his court, there was more than a hint of one of Faulkner's Sartorises exasperatedly coping with the indecencies of a bunch of Snopeses.

The violence, the overt alliance of law-enforcement with the white racist lawlessness, did not end even with the court action. Night marches were resumed and were attacked for two nights before state patrolmen began providing adequate protection. The city again sought a ban on the marches, and was refused in federal court. A motel manager threw acid in the motel swimming pool when Negro demonstrators jumped into it. J. T. Johnson of SCLC was burned by the acid. Again and again, Negroes trying to swim in the Atlantic Ocean were attacked, beaten. Whites beat old women and teenage girls in one demonstration conflict. Reporters were attacked. A state trooper watched one white slug a Negro man—and then offered the white his billy club to continue the attack. On another night, police stood aside and watched whites attack demonstrators; nineteen Negroes required hospital treatment. On another night, just one time, Negroes fought back—and injured three whites.

In the midst of this, on July 2, 1964, the Civil Rights Act was passed, President Johnson having intoned that it would:

". . . eliminate the last vestiges of injustice in our beloved country," and that it would:

". . . bring justice and hope to all our people," and that it would:

". . . bring peace to our land."

St. Augustine officials promised to obey that new law; demonstrations and court actions were discontinued. And whites once more attacked Negroes seeking service that they thought was at last available to them in restaurants. The restaurant owners themselves were attacked. They resegregated their places. Dr. King returned to St. Augustine, warning that such resistance to the new law, unrestrained by police, could set a pattern across the South. Finally, Judge Simpson named individuals, including "Hoss" Manucy, in injunctions against further violence and discrimination—and only then did peace come to St. Augustine.

What had been revealed most frighteningly in all that spate of white southern lawlessness and white southern lack of law-enforcement, white southern police repression, was something beyond the southern context. Again, the movement showed truth about America. The crude antics of the sheriff's department and the mob reflected the more sophisticated rule of the city, whose elected officials and business and bank backers were rigidly right-wing, of the Goldwater stripe. Barry Goldwater was then making his bid for the presidency, and to see a little city like St. Augustine in the grips of the home-grown authoritarianism he represented was to fear beyond any reasonable assessment of the political situation that this same thing could happen to the nation. (Already, out of the mood and effect of new violence, America was abandoned to choose between the likes of Goldwater and Lyndon Johnson.)

Dr. King in his eloquent "Letter from the Birmingham Jail" had made the point that there could be no "moderate" position on the questions of racism, that the dishonesty of whites' asserting such a position would soon drive Negroes into real radicalism. In St. Augustine the white moderates were literally, physically afraid—afraid not only to speak out in favor of a sane solution to the city's dragging-on crisis (which had proved ruinous to the summer's tourist trade), but also afraid, as people were said to be in Nazi Germany, of not showing support for those very ruinous racist policies being pursued by the city. They feared social and business ostracism and they feared violence from the same sources doing violence to the Negroes.

I interviewed such people; it was painful, sickening. Theirs was fear beyond the norm of the southern fear that all along had abetted racism, a part of a pattern of excess, national in scope, that began somewhere there in 1963—and has not finished.

One man began our interview by saying he assumed I realized that if I used his name he would be ruined. An owner of some forest tracts said simply he had to be friendly to the terrorists and the downtown right-wingers because anybody with a book of matches could destroy what he had spent a lifetime acquiring.

One restaurant owner had urged the restaurant association to adopt a cynical kind of policy he had seen in operation in the North—to let those who would not be hurt by it serve Negroes, while others discouraged them in the ways it was done in the North. He thought he was making headway—and when Negroes came into his place, he served them.

"They were clean, well-dressed and orderly," he said. "I couldn't refuse them."

Police watched from outside. That night the windows of his car, his restaurant and his home were broken. He gave up his efforts with the restaurant association and served no more Negroes.

"People are scared," he said. "They are banded together. You need to survive. You don't argue."

He grew up in Europe during World War II, had seen some of the fighting, occupation. Never once back then, he said, had he been afraid.

"But now I have to come to this peaceful, pretty little place in the United States of America, and I find, walking down the street, for the first time in my life, that I am afraid."

A sense of the sinister, even demented, quality of leadership in the town emerges from my notes of an informal press conference with Sheriff L. O. Davis and the publisher of the city's newspaper, A. H. Tebault, Jr., one morning in the sheriff's office. (A bulletin board in the outer office had letters from all over the country congratulating the sheriff's department for arrests of demonstrators, and the like. In the office, decorations included a big photograph of the sheriff dressed as Santa Claus.)

The sheriff began with ominous talk of how much the city had to lose from harm coming to Dr. King. He said the FBI was in town in heavy numbers to protect him and then made the remarkable statement that "the FBI insists Dr. King is a communist and communist leader."

Mr. Tebault spoke up to complain about demonstrations diverting police from normal duties. "The rights of the people are being violated. I have no law protection of my property. Burglary and minor crimes are on the increase."

A reporter asked the sheriff about complaints of inhuman treatment of arrested demonstrators. (I had seen the demonstrators who were being kept all day out in the hot Florida sun in an unshaded pen with an open toilet shared by men and women. When several of us reporters tried to talk with them, they warned us to leave before we got them and us in trouble.)

The sheriff's answer was jocular: "If we keep 'em inside the jail all day like we did Monday, they sing and cheer until two o'clock in the morning. But if they're out taking exercise all day, they're ready to sleep at night. The other people in jail are entitled to their sleep. The other prisoners were complaining."

He added: "Every time you approach one of those demonstrators, they fall on their knees and pray for you. It's a big help."

Asked about court evidence of Klan alliances with the sheriff's department, he expressed surprise that there were any Klansmen in the county. He said there had been none until "the incident" of the four Negroes being beaten at the Klan rally.

He said he had never thought much about integration until the demonstrations the previous summer. "Then I became a segregationist. There are hundreds and hundreds like me. Talk about building up resistance. These people do it."

Mr. Tebault volunteered the obviously untrue intelligence that the current demonstrations had not hurt business. He said tourism was fine, and "the colored" weren't supporting the boycott of downtown merchants.

The sheriff said that Mrs. Peabody had not written to him since being released from his jail, "and I haven't written to her." He said it had been a "hell of a strain" having "a woman like her, seventy-two years old, with her importance, lying around in my jail."

Then he returned to the ominous theme that had begun the session: "You know when King's usefulness is over, he'll be made into a martyr."

And Mr. Tebault exclaimed: "Medgar Evers was nothing but a two-bit local philanthropist until they made a martyr out of him. We don't want that to happen here."

One night that week, Dr. King concluded his speech at the mass meeting with these words:

"You know they threaten us occasionally with more than beatings here and there. They threaten us with actual physical death. They think that this will stop the movement. I got word way out in California that a plan was under way to take my life in St. Augustine, Florida. Well, if physical death is the price that I must pay to free my white brother and all of my brothers and sisters from a permanent death of the spirit, then nothing can be more redemptive . . ."

The applause was overwhelming, reminiscent of Albany, and continued through his final words:

"We have long since learned to sing anew with our foreparents of old that

> Before I'll be a slave *(yes. all right. well?)*
> I'll be buried in my grave
>   (amen. amen.)
> And go home to my Father *(amen.)*
> And be saved . . ."

Once more, as I sat beneath the altar on the floor of the church, sweating, the television lights glaring, there were these same gentle men of SCLC I had watched with awe in Albany, Birmingham—Ralph Abernathy, Andy Young, C. T. Vivian, Dr. King himself—and the heat, the packed heat, and the singing, the fervor, and the special beauty again of simple people caught in something bigger than themselves and present time, giving of so much from within themselves . . .

C. T. Vivian speaking now, reporting about what had happened in court that day:

"L. O. Davis was on the hot seat."

They applauded and applauded when he described the reading of the deputy list, Judge Simpson's denouncing Manucy. They applauded again when he broke off to introduce William Kunstler, the New York attorney who was part of the movement's legal team in St. Augustine. He had just entered the church, and he came forward with arms outstretched, grinning, and Reverend Vivian moved down from the pulpit to meet him, and these two men, white and black, northern and southern, embraced each other there in front of a church full of people who had seldom seen this sort of thing before, and in the silence of seeing it, a sweet soprano voice rose, and others joined in, and they sang to it—this sight that said so much, still, of the meaning and truth and simple hope of the movement—sang "Amazing Grace / How sweet the sound . . ."

It was still so good to return to such moments from ugliness and harshness and immerse myself, sitting in the hot church, sweating, losing some of myself in the meeting. There is Mr. Oscar Turner standing at the pulpit, slim black man, wearing a slackly-fitting suit and white, pointed-toed shoes, saying that he has been a railroad man for forty years, saying that he told Reverend Taylor and Dr. Hayling that he would not go to jail with them and . . .

"Bless my soul if I didn't beat 'em both to jail. I was charged with conspiracy—whatever that is . . . Any Negro who doesn't back this movement is in a bad fix. I was born in Georgia, and know what it is to have to go in the back door. Anybody says we're not making progress is crazy. They're nearer whupped than you think."

And at the slave market, in the hot sun, Hosea Williams of SCLC addressing a crowd of Negro demonstrators in one group and hostile whites in another, sweat running down his face:

"We know we're children of God . . . and citizens of the United States of America . . . the greatest nation in the world. We will go to jail . . . die if necessary for our rights. Negroes and whites have shed blood together that what Thomas Jefferson said may come to be true, that Lincoln died not in vain. Negroes and whites have shed blood that Jack Kennedy died not in vain . . . or Medgar Evers . . . or the children in Birmingham.

"Yes! They died, and we may die, but we will die with this in our minds: GOD WILL TAKE CARE OF YOU!

"And I say to the Ku Klux Klan and any other group—you try to take our manhood, our wise womanhood . . . and we'll show you we can not only fight in Germany or Russia . . . we can fight here. We don't fight with sticks and bricks. We fight as Dr. King does . . . as Jesus Christ did—non-violently.

"And I don't care how much whites may beat you up—you must love them. Love, my friends, love that makes you willing to die.

"If the black man loses his freedom, no man will be free. We are willing to die so that America shall be free . . ."

And, as the Negroes hum "I Love Everybody," he begins to pray: "We pray, oh God, for our white brethren . . ."

The movement, too, in St. Augustine had an energy capable of showing in dramatic highlight some of the underlying truth about all the spewing forth of hate and violence from the lower levels of a society which, at all other levels, seemed in danger of being consumed by the same insanities. On two nights, the whites demonstrated, making a march of their own through the Negro neighborhoods. They were led by the Klan spokesmen, including Stoner, a mild-faced, portly little man with a clubfoot. They carried Confederate flags and signs ("Kill the Civil Rights Bill" "Put George Wallace on the Supreme Court" "Don't Tread On Me") and in their number were some women and some children and some of the men in the mob that had nightly attacked the Negroes. They marched, like the Negroes, at night, with full protection of state patrol-

men, some 170 of them walking alongside. When the pro-
cession on the first night, with flashlights darting and dogs
barking, reached the intersection where the Negro section
began, eerie silence greeted them, and their lights played on
a hand-lettered sign put up in the middle of the street: "Welcome. Peace and Brotherhood To You."

They marched through the mostly darkened neighborhood,
several long blocks of it, in the silence. From the darkness, from
behind shuttered windows, the eyes of the Negroes followed
them. Occasionally, in light, you could see those eyes, filled
with a peculiar mixture of anguish, repulsion, loathing, and yet
—perhaps I only imagined it—compassion.

On the second night, Negroes lined the roadways from that
first intersection and, with no hint of mockery in their tone,
sang to the shabby little band the favorite of the St. Augustine
movement songs:

> *I love everybody*
> *I love everybody*
> *I love everybody*
> *In my heart . . .*
>
> *You can't make me doubt Him*
> *You can't make me doubt Him*
> *You can't make me doubt Him*
> *In my heart . . .*
>
> *For I love everybody . . .*

Again, the marchers were watched, followed by the eyes of
those people, singing that song. The march proceeded along
streets darkened as they had been the night before. As it passed
Big Daddy's Blue Goose beer joint, a young Negro man said
softly, to himself: "They don't need no police guard to come
down here. But when we go in there . . . we're glad to have
'em. I wonder how would they feel inside if we was to throw
bricks and all at them." Near the end of the Negro section, a
short line of Negroes stood on a corner singing: "We shall
overcome," and on the next corner, another group was singing

the song. It echoed in silent, dark streets, against the cadence of the feet of the marchers:

> We are not afraid . . .

The marchers, tense, probably terrified through both nights' performances, began to relax as they approached, now, the white section of town. Jokes, wisecracks went along the ranks. The police lights kept flashing, and two of them caught a young Negro woman in slacks standing on her porch, holding her baby in her arms, looking out. As the two lights held in a cross on her face, she bent and kissed her baby.

Back at the slave market, one of the marchers cried out: "Let's give a hand to our law-enforcement officers for protecting us from those black savages."

They had been outnumbered enormously each night. No one made a move toward them. There was no thought of, no real fear of, sniper fire. This was the mood still of the movement, and of most of the South's Negro people, even as far along in deterioration of spirit as St. Augustine. But beyond that there was a communication, fragile, and not soon to be heard again, between the elements in the black community who did respond to, did find a place in, the new spirit of violence and something beyond violence abroad in America and the same elements in the white community. A teenage white tough, Klan-connected, with blond crew cut and tight T-shirt, stood before the teenage Negro tough, connected with the Negro "gang" which had spread out ahead of the white marchers to head off any potential Negro violence. Said the white one to the black one:

"Y'all did a damn good job of policin' last night."

It was a communication of sorts between those most blighted by the ongoing processes of America, most touched by such extraordinary events as those in St. Augustine, the oldest enemies and yet the most natural allies of all in the South. The white marchers prided themselves on maintaining their own non-violence during their demonstrations. The

Negroes were aware they had achieved some success in drawing such an imitative response.

There is a danger, indulged heedlessly by intellectuals, in romanticizing such as the Negro gang members, the Klan—all those from the underside of America whose anger and pain are real and acute, but who express them in violence and, as often as not, in racial antagonism. Intellectuals find the Klan particularly fascinating, imputing to it a kind of "noble savage" aura which just isn't there, finding in communication with the ignorant and thwarted men in it a flush of false masculinity, for themselves perhaps, and seeing the Klan violence as justified and merely misdirected. (The ministry of Will D. Campbell of Nashville to the Klan is another matter altogether—a part of his genuine ability to serve the humanity of such men.)

The pathology of such groups as the Klan is understandable and sad, but it is also extremely ugly. I interviewed Dr. Hayling during the St. Augustine campaign and tape-recorded his account of the night he was attacked by the Klan. His understated, almost pompous, telling of what happened caught the ugliness, the depravity, the berserkness of such violence-prone groups from the underside of America better than anything I have heard or seen, and serves as a preventative any time I am tempted to romanticize such people.

He said he got involved because he wanted to see a "real live Klansman," never having seen one in his twenty-some-odd years as a native Southerner.

He and three companions had driven out south of the city on U.S. Highway 1, where handbills had advertised a Klan rally would be held. They were shocked to see Klansmen in robes out on the highway, directing traffic into a side road for the rally. They could see a cross burning. They drove past the scene, turned around, went back to the site and parked on the side of the highway to hear what was being said over loudspeakers at the rally. A car came up behind them, forced them onto a side road, and hooded Klansmen armed with shotguns took them captive.

They were marched before the crowd at the rally, amid shouts of "Nigger! Nigger! Nigger!" Because he wore a coat and tie, Dr. Hayling was called a "Martin Luther Coon type nigger." Klansmen searched their wallets for civil rights organization cards and identification.

"It was a gruesome experience because, as fate would have it, as I was seated in the automobile along the highway I had heard the speaker say only minutes before, 'I'll tell you something else. You've got a nigger in St. Augustine that ought not to live—that burr-head bastard of a dentist. He's got no right to live at all, let alone walk up and down your streets and breathe the white man's free air. He ought to wake up tomorrow morning with a bullet between his eyes. If you were half the men you claim to be, you'd kill him before sunup.' Lo and behold, there I was before them.

"There was a bit of confusion. We were confused and a bit alarmed at the time, but I think the Klansmen were even more confused. For here, right before their very eyes, was the man that they had said only moments before . . . should be killed before sunup. They did not know what to do with us. We spent from ten to fifteen to twenty minutes while major decisions were being made.

"Lo and behold, a lady broke through the back of the crowd and charged, 'What are you waiting for? That's that blankety-blank dentist that's leading—that's causing all this trouble. Why don't you kill him, castrate him? Make it so that he will never bother us again . . .

"Within moments I felt severe blows on my head and other portions of my body, and this signaled the beginning of what ended up to be an awful night. For I had to spend . . . fourteen days in the hospital recovering from that beating. I can . . . remember them saying while they were beating me to 'Work on his right hand—he's a right-handed dentist . . .' I think they were well aware that at that time my practice was at least fifty per cent white. I was the city dentist; I was the local county jail dentist and the state prison farm dentist . . .

"From this point on, the Klan meeting and the beating was a nightmare to be forgotten, if this is ever possible. For I saw the tragedy of human misunderstanding. Persons in this audience had been former patients of mine. A gentleman only six feet to eight feet away from me had operated a business near my office for more than sixteen months. There had been . . . times when he had accepted my mail from the mailman, and I had done the same for him . . . And yet this man was willing to stand only six feet to eight feet by and see four of us as Negroes beaten to the ground literally.

"To cap all the brutality, as I think I was coming back to consciousness, as we were piled on top of each other as logs would be, I heard one Klansman [ask] the other if he had ever smelled a nigger burn. And the other Klansman said no. He said:

" 'Well, wait until Klan Brother So-and-So returns with five gallons of gasoline. You'll be able to smell a nigger burn . . . It's a mighty good smell.' "

At this point, the sheriff and deputies arrived and eventually got the four Negroes out of there. Dr. Hayling's car had, in the meantime, been destroyed.

He concluded the account with this statement: "It is my hope and fervent prayer that men of goodwill in the nation's oldest city shall be able to sit down in the not-too-distant future around some type of bargaining table. For this is one of the few cities in the nation where even the clergymen have not been able to attempt to reach some agreement on racial desegregation . . ."

There, once more, the incredible contrast between the movement spirit and that which opposed it. The Klan was only the most obscene of the opposition—and not the worst of it. I was aware then, as far along as I was in the processes of my own disillusionment and despair, that even in the nightmare of the attacks on the non-violent demonstrations, the depraved whites in the mob were not the most sinister element in St. Augustine. The most sinister, lethal element included the many more whites in the town and in all of America who were incapable of any response at all to the movement. I wrote back then:

> If there has been a failure of the non-violent movement, the failure has been that of the many Americans who have been incapable of responding to its appeals to conscience and justice.
>
> And if the dread, pale and deathly spirit which prevailed for a time over St. Augustine should ever overwhelm America, the blame would not be on the ignorant and shabby and essentially pitiable people who follow the limping step of a professional hate-monger through dark and narrow streets. We would have to examine instead the institutions and society which produced them, and produced also the more numerous others who for many years were unable to act against human need and injustice, and were eventually incapable of acting for law, democracy and human freedom itself.*

At this stage of things—as far along in the fall of the movement as the summer of 1964—what of the people of the movement, the people of the St. Augustine Movement beset by Klan violence and betrayed by America's indifference?

Hear an eighth-grade boy who had been in the night marches when the whites attacked, who liked math and science and spelling and English best and thought he might like to be a doctor or a scientist, whose parents were divorced and mother worked to support him and five brothers and three sisters:

"I was in the demonstrations last year. The judge told me not to demonstrate any more. But I have been marching. The last time was night before last. I want to help with the movement. I guess I panicked a little night before last. When you're down there, white people stand on the side, and say: 'Git the niggers.' A white boy hit a Negro boy in the stomach and ran.

*"The American Middle Ground in St. Augustine" (*New South*, September 1964, Vol. 19, no. 9), p. 20.

At the post office they started throwing bricks. I didn't get hit.

"Friends on the street asked my mama if I could go march. She said yes. One night Mama told me I couldn't go—but I still went. ,

"I want to be a part of it, so when I get big, my children can go in restaurants and eat like other folks."

And there was Charles, who was sixteen then: "I wasn't scared. You get a funny feeling . . . but you believe the Lord will take care of you . . . so you are not afraid."

Chapter
TWENTY

THE NEW-DIMENSIONED terrorism struck the movement's other major campaign of the summer of 1964, the Mississippi Freedom Summer, before it had even gotten under way. Northern college students, mostly white, learned while still in training of the disappearance of Michael Schwerner, Andrew Goodman and James Chaney—later in the summer discovered to have been tortured and murdered by Mississippi white racist thugs and law-enforcement officials, that same combination that had been seen in St. Augustine. Before the volunteers even got to Mississippi, the terror and danger of their undertaking, described endlessly during their training session at Oxford, Ohio, became real. That virtually all of them came on anyhow is testament to their courage and seriousness of purpose and to the ability of the movement to imbue ordinary people with extraordinary qualities.

In their orientation sessions, they learned, too, the cultural differences between their world and the one they were about to enter, and began to learn parenthetically, as they would all summer, what the world they were about to enter had done to the admired workers of SNCC who were their chief instructors at the orientations. At one session, in a film about the South, a shot of a mean-faced, obese southern voter registrar was flashed on the screen, and the volunteers, straight out of their

northern middle-class backgrounds, probably nervously, burst
out laughing at the sight of him. SNCC veterans of suffering
at the hands of such men walked out of the session in anger
and disgust that the volunteers didn't regard the man as they
did—with a loathing kind of respect.

The strain within the movement, and especially within its
bravest, toughest wing, SNCC and CORE, was much on display during the Freedom Summer. The erosive forces and their
effect influenced the very origins of the Freedom Summer.
SNCC was desperate in 1963 to find some substitute for mass
demonstrations as a means of organizing the people. Whites
in Greenwood, after the default of the Federal government and
the shift of attention to Birmingham, had thoroughly defeated
the demonstration campaign there, and white repression had
wiped out a demonstration campaign in Jackson. The idea of
the Freedom Democratic Party, with disfranchised Negroes'
demonstrating their desire to vote by participating in mock
elections, was born of this need. The first of the Freedom
Democratic Party campaigns was in 1963, and a few white law
students who had come to do legal research for the movement
that summer helped organize it. These were among the first
white volunteers to work in Mississippi since Bob Moses had
established, in 1961, the first SNCC outpost in that most
difficult and dangerous of all the southern states.

White volunteers had participated from the beginning in
southwest Georgia and other SNCC projects; their blatant
violations of segregationist taboos were considered an important psychological part of the effort to influence whites and
develop the movement spirit within Negroes. But in those early
years, it was considered too dangerous for local Negroes and
SNCC staffers alike to bring whites into Mississippi; indeed
the presence of Negro SNCC staffers was often the cause of
violence and suffering to the people with whom they tried to
work. A few whites began working in Jackson and Greenwood
in January 1963. The different course followed in Mississippi
during the first three years of SNCC's growth and expansion

there, those vital years of the movement's greatest strength, has not been studied for what influence it was to have later on the movement. But it seems clear that the tone within SNCC was different there—that the building of its esprit was among Negroes only and, for the most part, Mississippi Negroes. (There was, though, a significant cadre of northern Negroes, including ones from Howard University, who had come with the freedom rides.) The dangers they faced, the terrible effort they expended for small gains, formed bonds among them stronger even than in the extraordinarily close-knit other groups of SNCC. It is likely that they identified more with their own group than with SNCC, and the movement for them was not, as elsewhere, an experience in black and white cooperation against the forces of racism, but a grim banding together of blacks to fight the most repressive white forces in the South. All of this is bound to have had its effect on the thinking and later action of Mississippi SNCC workers. Moses, himself a Northerner, former math student at Harvard, mystical in his leadership years in devotion to the non-violent ideal and philosophy and a selfless leader in the movement, eventually ceased talking to white people and disappeared from the movement scene. And Stokely Carmichael, born in Jamaica, raised in the North, educated at Howard, came out of the Mississippi SNCC to overturn the traditional leadership and essential philosophy of SNCC in 1966.

Some of the difference in thinking was apparent as early as 1964 in a debate that occurred within the Mississippi SNCC over whether to invite white volunteers for 1964 Freedom Democratic Party work, the decision finally to invite them resulting in the Freedom Summer. Those against having whites feared they would take over. The argument in favor was that the whites would give the Mississippi movement exposure to the rest of the nation which it could not otherwise get, and offset the no-win frustration in the Mississippi SNCC staff. Behind the quest for more exposure was the grim knowledge that violence attracted to whites created more clamor in the press, more national outrage, than the kind of ongoing violence to Negroes which they had faced for those three years in Mississippi.

The debate over whether to invite white volunteers was the beginning of a continuous black-white debate in the Mississippi SNCC. Consequences of that debate had a fatal effect on the movement eventually and during the Mississippi Summer frequently showed in the friction between regular SNCC staffers and the summer volunteers. One of the volunteers, recounting his experiences a few months later, told me about the friction as he encountered it. At the beginning, during the training period, he had been overwhelmed by the caliber of people in SNCC, with the organization's mystique.

"They had achieved so much, worked so hard, suffered so much, were so warm, feeling, sensitive."

He described the feeling of strength coming from them when they linked arms and sang "We Shall Overcome." But when they got out in the field, it was different.

Against a constant shared awareness of tension, worry and danger, there were also constant reminders of differences in culture and disagreement over policy and the SNCC field workers' fear that the white volunteers were trying to take over. He said his courage and confidence increased during the summer, and relations with the SNCC people improved. But project leaders remained insecure; some people cracked under tension; one SNCC worker who had been at the project for two years had to leave. All this was within the staff, he said; relations with local Negro people were wonderful.

Among the cultural conflicts, one was exacerbated by SNCC's style. The young northern volunteers, conditioned and accustomed to efficiency and organization, would have been appalled at normal southern inefficiency and disorganization. But what they were up against was something beyond the southern norm: SNCC made a virtue, almost a fetish, of inefficiency and lack of organization—not returning phone calls, never being on time, not attending to details, rejecting bureaucracy by refusing to perform even the minimal necessities of paper work, record-keeping, rolling along ever spontaneously, flexibly, in a slightly controlled state of chaos. Some of the northern students fell into these ways as easily as they absorbed and acted out the genuine alienation eating at the vitals of the SNCC veterans. Others were exasperated at all the waste involved, seeing it as an unnecessary added burden to the local Negro people in the movement. This concern with efficiency by some northern whites increased the distrust and jealousy some of the Negro staffers, products of Mississippi's appalling schools, felt for the superiorly educated Northerners. And, out of this, some overcompensating volunteers developed a fallacious and demeaning attitude toward work and people, an attitude not yet run its course in New Left and Black Power circles—an insistence on thrusting people into supposedly prestigious roles for which they are untrained or unsuited by temperament, ignoring their real qualities and talents. More than one critical white volunteer saw in this miscasting of people and jobs a developing pattern among the battle-weary SNCC regulars of wanting to lose—a part of masochism, a cult of suffering and also a compulsion to prove to themselves and others that nothing could work within the American system, the growing rationale of revolution in their minds.

Despite such inner strains and all the overt opposition from white Mississippi—one thousand arrests; thirty-five shooting incidents, with three persons injured; thirty homes and other buildings bombed; thirty-five churches burned; eighty persons beaten; at least three other murders besides the three at the start—the Freedom Summer set into operation forty-seven Freedom Schools and nearly that many community centers, conducted extensive voter registration work across the state, and developed the Freedom Democratic Party into a statewide organization. The nearly one thousand student volunteers were augmented by cadres of lawyers, doctors and religious leaders serving the movement. Though all four civil rights organizations were involved, SNCC provided the bulk of staff people, and CORE most of the rest.

Mississippi was never to be the same after it was over, not the least of the impact being the demonstration to local whites that segregationist taboos could be violated. Few Negroes were actually registered to vote during the summer because of the fierce repression, retaliation, and because, even where fairly administered, the state's voter qualification test was so difficult as to baffle the best-educated, black or white. But more than 60,000 Mississippi Negroes asserted their desire for the ballot in the Freedom Democratic Party mock voter registration.

The Freedom Schools meanwhile gave a taste of real education and of equalitarian living to thousands of Negro youngsters, and the community organizations developed a permanent base of grassroots leaders and followers, still active six years later and probably the strongest in the South, where Negroes before had been most cowed, most repressed of all in the South.

One white northern volunteer, a young woman, told me:

"The people around us by the end of the summer had stopped saying nothing could be done about Mississippi conditions. They had begun to question the conservatism of the local Negro leaders. At the last mass meeting before I left, local people were in charge of everything. A young man conducted the meeting, and he challenged a local minister, confronted him about his opposition to starting a boycott. Some of the preachers were beginning to come around . . ."

The young volunteers spoke of the rigidity the Mississippi children were accustomed to in schools, as though this were an anomaly. But here, as in so much else, the movement revealed a national problem by showing its extreme in the South.

The Child Development Group of Mississippi, a headstart program run, from 1965 on, by grassroots Negro people, movement people, struggled against almost as great odds as the Freedom Schools and against the same forces of white repression and neglect to foster the precious potential in such children. And, as part of the Freedom Summer's legacy, local Negro people this time were the teachers, the admired, loved leaders of the schools. Illiterate some of them, they gave real learning for a time to their young.

Older people were in the Freedom Schools, too. Here, an essay by a woman sixty-five years old:

"After picking cotton I feel so tired I can hardly be able to sleep. To learn about picking cotton you first break the land. Plant the cotton. Cultivate and grow the cotton. Give it time to make and open. Then you begin to pick cotton in August and you have to stoop all day picking. And when nite come you are all beat out. Stiff. Back hurting."

The children would escape that, and the Freedom Summer meant that many would find the kind of escape that Mrs. Hazel T. Palmer of Jackson did. She was co-chairman of the Hinds County Freedom Democratic Party when I talked with her in late 1964.

"I'm trying to get across to people what it is to just be born," she said. "We want the world to know that we can do things for ourselves in Mississippi."

She told about her work—organizing on the precinct level —of the fear, even hostility people showed and, some of them, overcame. She spoke of "slavery all those years," when people who tried to vote would disappear, be dragged away, be hanged. "Scare and scatter . . . but now they've done all they can do, and we will not be scattered. They'll have to kill more than one at a time. I went to Atlantic City and I pledged myself to work harder and harder."

Her eight children, seven years old to twenty-two, were all members of the movement, too, she said. The young ones went to the Freedom School.

"They just loved it. They learned to be members. They learned to speak right up and not hold back . . .

"I had worked for white people for twelve years. They were friendly. But it was like I might as well have been a slave. I was just a maid to them. I was not pictured as being a woman."

And finally: "The white people are bad, and the mayor and police are bad, too. I told the FBI in Washington about this. Martin Luther King gets protection—but not a little citizen like me. The Constitution says, 'Life, liberty and the pursuit of happiness.' But they can't protect me. Yet they fight a war to protect people in Vietnam. Those folk must have more sense than we have . . .

"We are trying to keep going in the right direction. As long as we can hold to non-violence, we will. But I don't know how long we can when I see white people beat my own children for nothing . . ."

The many like her at this stage of the movement, knowing such ambivalence, might have been led, encouraged, in either direction. Certainly the human as well as cultural impulse was to meet white violence in kind. "Many are trying to decide whether the white man's soul is worth saving," Aaron Henry, leader of COFO and the Freedom Democratic Party, was saying by the end of 1964.

Mississippi whites had believed that hordes of communists were coming to rape and pillage when they heard announced plans for the Freedom Summer. (The barbarity of treatment of the three murdered volunteers expressed this hysteria grotesquely.) Soon the whites realized that what they had amid them was a motley collection of young people who flaunted custom in everything from racial practice to dress and hairstyles, and finally indignation centered (as it did nationally a few years later in the celebrated generation-gap enmity to hippies) on the beards that the young men grew and on the casual hairdos of the young women. Some middle-class Negroes shared the aversion. "I just can't get along with those long-beards," snorted one pompous, prestigious leader.

Here was a state full of white Americans who, for the very most part, could shrug off the summer's murders and the continued violence against the movement, but who expressed

in every way possible indignation about beards and beatniks
. . . and communists.

If white Mississippi thus revealed an appalling value system
(testimony to the movement's ability, even still, to bring forth
existential truth), then what of the ostensible friends of the
movement, the nation's white liberals? Through the Mississippi Summer and the months afterward, many liberals, black
as well as white, expressed genuine concern, worry over
whether, indeed, the taint of communism had attached itself
to the movement. The cold-war mentality expressed itself fully
in this concern, and so did that phobic kind of anti-communism based on experience in the 1930s with communism—
either as an agent of it or an enemy—in the labor movement
and other liberal causes. The very language of the concern
sounds quaint now, only six years later—a mark of how far the
nation has been able to move from the political straitjacket of
communist phobia, mostly thanks to the young, whose model
in dismissing the communist issue as irrelevant was SNCC.
We talked seriously in 1964 and 1965 about whether there had
been "infiltration," or even—dread thought!—"a takeover."
Through the movement years there had been, uneasily submerged among liberals, the fear of such taint—one more example of how the routines of national thought hindered
understanding of the deepest meanings of the movement. But
in the Mississippi Summer, along with the mainly middle-class,
conventional college youth came enough people, old as well as
young, possessed of a radical orientation—to bring the submerged fear fully to surface. Some of those who came were the
college-aged offspring of old wily communists who had somehow survived all the years of McCarthyism and cold-war hysteria; others were out of such little-known radical camps as the
International Independence Institute of Voluntown, Connecticut. Some were individualists, free-lance reformists. I remember one man who was old enough to have fought with the
Lincoln Brigade in the Spanish Civil War and was in the

Mississippi Summer as the latest episode in a continuous concern with reformist causes ever since.

Like other reporters on the scene of this confluence of
American radical thought and idiom in Mississippi, this imposition of all kinds of ideologies on the essentially simple, reli-
gion-based, civil libertarian idealism of the southern
movement, I moved about asking the questions that worried
us. Among those in the movement bothered by the same questions, the concensus was that no "takeover" or even real infiltration had occurred, but that SNCC was endangering the
reputation of the movement by refusing to deny it, or even to
discuss the question. This was the most exasperating thing of
all—their stubborn insistence that if a person believed in integration and was willing to work with them, even risk his life,
his past or even present political persuasion, made no difference. We had not ever encountered such an attitude; it took
me a long time, years, to realize that it was the essence of real
civil libertarianism and to understand how deep into doc-
trinaire acceptance of cold-war repression I was in 1964. Negro
Southerners, the people of the movement, were better able to
comprehend the SNCC position. I asked Jack Young during
those 1964 interviews whether he thought there was "infiltration," danger of a "takeover." A veteran civil rights attorney
who had worked in the days when there were only four Negro
attorneys in all of Mississippi—an eminently respectable and
idealistic man, he answered that he thought there might be a
few scattered individuals with the taint, but they weren't influential.

"There are a lot of people with radical ideas, though," he
went on—and thoughtfully: "Maybe it's time for that. Just
because somebody is radical, he isn't necessarily communist.
Maybe we ought to call them progressives." Most of our liberal
concern was the one about reputation; we had a realistic, I
think, fear of smear campaigns and right-wing ability to attack
and destroy anything suspect of communism. The most prominent southern victim of red-baiting during the movement years

was the Southern Conference Education Fund (SCEF), a continuation largely by Carl and Anne Braden of the Southern Conference For Human Welfare, itself a target of charges of communism in the 1940s. Mr. and Mrs. Braden, newspaper writers at the time, were involved in civil rights activity in Louisville, Kentucky, in the 1950s, including sit-ins as early as 1951 by a local group at the bus stations. When they attempted in 1954 to sell their home in a white neighborhood to a Negro family, the house was blown up, and Carl Braden was tried in a state court on charges of sedition and, as he recalls the wording, "conspiracy to destroy property to bring about a political end, to wit, communism." He was found guilty of the first charge and sentenced to fifteen years in the state penitentiary. With bond set at $40,000 he had to spend eight months in prison until the fantastic conviction could be appealed and overturned. Of his jail experience (which included two months in solitary), he said in 1971: "I spent that time going over my life, trying to decide whether it was worth it to do the kind of work I had been doing. I finally decided I was not going to live under a system where a man could be put in prison for selling his house to a Negro. I decided I would spend my life trying to change that system."

In 1958, he was called before the House Un-American Activities Committee, and to questions about whether he or various associates were communists he replied (as he recalled it in 1971): "Gentlemen, my beliefs and my associates are none of the business of this committee." Asked if he were pleading the Fifth Amendment (against self-incrimination), he replied: "No, sir. I am standing on the First Amendment to the United States Constitution which guarantees my right to associate with whom I please, to write what I want to, to say what I please." He was cited for contempt and sentenced to a year in Federal prison. And he lost an appeal to the Supreme Court.

He and Mrs. Braden began their work with SCEF in 1957 (after the sedition trial) and through the movement years, its solid contributions and its acceptance by Negro people with whom it worked were not only denounced as communistic by the segregationists, but were regarded as harmful by some of the older, "respectable" civil rights organizations and people. The facts of the matter, the rights of the Bradens were not considered—only the hysterical fear of the taint. SCEF was still alive in the 1970s. It had been trying and continued trying to reach poor whites, with real respect for their dignity. One of the greatest legacies of SNCC was that SCEF"s work was no longer as hampered by mistaken attitudes of its allies.

For what we came to understand, and this was perhaps the movement's, SNCC's, most important contribution to a continuing straightening out of the American mind, was that to acquiesce in red-baiting and witch-hunt hysteria was as bad as to participate in it. But in the first flush, the startling encounter with people genuinely unafraid of witch-hunters, we had difficulty even comprehending that this was the situation. SNCC took the stand it did on the communist question with awareness of the larger civil libertarian implications. I heard a tape of a speech Bob Moses made in late 1963, in which he said the organization "must come to the point of an absolute stand on the right to associate with whom we please."

This, he went on, would be "the next frontier." The question for SNCC was "whether or not we contribute to the hysteria dormant in people when confronted with so-called alien ideas, or whether we throw our weight on the side of free association."

The undergirding southern-movement wisdom of the stand was stated by Aaron Henry in an interview: "We should so conduct ourselves in the Freedom Movement that any lie told by anybody about us will not be believed, because our work will be so outstanding."

The major achievement of the young, beginning there in the Mississippi Summer, cannot be faulted; they freed themselves, and soon a significant portion of the nation from the fetters of cold-war thinking. The effort of will necessary to this is suggested in the startlement I felt when I saw my first anti-

Vietnam War poster. It was in the COFO headquarters in Jackson during the Freedom Summer. It had not occurred to me or to many people then, I think, to question the legitimacy of that war. In a few short years, I came, and many others with me, under the tutelage of the young from such unthinking acceptance of the essential aims of American foreign policy to awareness of just how ugly, how hurtful of the rights and interests of people, how often morally mistaken, that foreign policy has been—not merely in Vietnam but in many countries across the globe. And from that kind of ability to question the military part of the complex of national control, we came to see, too, how similarly hurtful and destructive the industrial aspect has been in this country—to the rights and interests of people and the environment we live in.

It all began with the young, and much of it began during the Mississippi Summer, began in what was called, then, the SNCC-izing of the volunteers. Actually, it began in SNCC with that first great thrust of the movement against the century-old system of segregation in the South. It took the same effort of will to resist southern conditioning and the same hope and courage to be able to believe that the seemingly immutable, ultra-powerful segregationist system could be destroyed as it did, finally, to challenge the seemingly immutable, ultra-powerful machinery and mentality in control of America.

In like manner, the southern movement had reasserted in America the validity of civil disobedience as a means of protesting laws one considered unjust. This was accomplished not only by reviving intellectual debate, but more importantly by injecting the basic questions of that debate into the public consciousness. The distinction was established in the popular mind between the movement's willingness to go to jail as a consequence of its refusal to obey laws it considered unjust and lack of that willingness among such as the southern politicians who had urged resistance to laws they didn't like. The tradition of civil disobedience had become, by the 1970s, an important one in all the areas where people were pushing against the established order, and if it was not accepted universally, it was at least better understood because of the movement.

Even as far along in the processes of mainstream erosion of the movement organizations as the Freedom Summer, the radicals among the volunteers and SNCC could be accurately described as simply standing—in their action, if not in all their thinking—for the copybook maxims of freedom and democracy. To older people, Mississippi whites and America's white liberals alike raising the communist question, they could reply with contempt that they were only trying to live what the questioners claimed to believe.

I wrote that summer of an "anti-anti-communism" as rigid and dogmatic as anti-communism. I was wrong about that—but not entirely wrong in sensing dogmatism. The dogmatism was a counterpoint to the truly creative thought also going on then. (How much of the creative thought came from SNCC, from the movement; how much of dogma was superimposed from the more erudite volunteers and their mentors?) Many who encountered the embryonic radicalism during the Mississippi Summer spoke of an arrogance and contemptuous smugness among some of the young there.

"Some are really distasteful," a white liberal told me in 1964. "You get the feeling they're not communist or even radical—but just have closed minds. You ask them a question and get a lecture. It's not spontaneous. And they are rude. They flaunt their contempt for whites down here—are always looking for trouble—in order to prove themselves to the Negroes."

This was a kind of insight the communist phobia of the times prevented. We should not have been concerned about the peril of some creaky, enfeebled communist apparatus, or about century-old, obsolete economic and political theory which, incredibly, some New Left youngsters did eventually come to spout. We should have been concerned about tendencies to totalitarianism in the new radicalism which had been imported to the South, imposed on the movement, the various ways its exponents showed themselves willing to disregard individuals, even dehumanize them, and to dismiss civil libertarian institutions designed to protect the individual because those institutions had been perverted. The movement, in its opposition to racism, stood for reform, restoration of perverted institutions, and stood most of all for individual rights.

There were other examples during the Freedom Summer of the volunteers, mostly unconsciously, exerting mainstream influence on the movement. Instead of worrying about whites as such taking over their movement, the Mississippi SNCC workers, those who were indigenous, might legitimately have been concerned about class and sectional differences. Middle-class Northerners, which most of the volunteers were, had been subjected to far more conditioning in the thought processes and methods of mainstream America than had the movement's people.

I listened to a young woman from the Middle West, well-educated and well-intentioned, leading a discussion group among Negro teenagers in a Freedom School. The teenagers told various terrible things wrong with their high school and about its inequality with the white school. They were led skillfully to the realization that their parents, though poor, paid a lot of taxes in a state with a 4 per cent sales tax, and so should be able to demand better schools. Then the young woman leader asked if it would be a good idea to fight for better things at the white schools as well.

"Yes," emphatically came the answer in unison.

"Why?"

A low, slowly spoken southern Negro voice: "We don't do people like they do us."

And several in the group chorused: "Do unto others as you would have them do unto you."

That was not the kind of thing the young woman sought. She suggested another reason. They might themselves go to the white schools. They agreed on the point that they ought to be able to, but clearly, here, two distinct, if not opposed, value systems were in operation, indeed the two—greed versus altruism—at the root of American schizophrenia through history.

I heard the story of the group of Negroes from McComb, Mississippi, who presented a play in New York that they had produced at their Freedom School. Black Muslims took over the discussion session afterwards, and the young people from McComb argued with them, saying, "What ails you folks? You've got no barriers to voting. Why don't you organize a big vote and make things better?"

A movement Southerner watching the scene said that the white volunteer with them was embarrassed by what they said, and one of the Muslims said of the volunteer: "Look at that white son of a bitch; he's been brainwashing them all summer."

Soon after the Summer I interviewed Dr. Robert Coles, the Harvard psychiatrist and writer, who had helped screen the volunteers. He spoke of dogmatism and other qualities in the movement which were inimical to the real beauty and truth in the people of the movement, their moments of becoming bigger than themselves, greater than they knew they could be, "moments of grace." There was, he said, "a common denominator among Negroes that could be led to great things for America—and was not being so led." Does the nature of American society preclude Gandhi-like leadership? he asked.

In a Freedom School that kept doggedly in existence in Ruleville through the fall and winter of 1964–65, I talked at length with the white northern volunteers. They described the difficulties that at first occurred between them and the SNCC project leader, a young Negro Mississippian. It was the standard thing of mistrust, fear of a takeover. He acknowledged such feeling in himself, but said he had come to think highly of the volunteers—a "sweet bunch," he said; those who had gone home were still sending letters, cards. But, he added, he hoped the next summer would bring older volunteers, people experienced in business, who could help alleviate the severe poverty of the people. I watched with interest the contrast of his handling of a mass meeting—easy, relaxed, effective—with that of the northern volunteers, who were, even after that long in the South, tense and, though not condescending, unable to speak the people's language. They had regarded the SNCC leader there as "withdrawn" and less than effective, basing this on standard values. His name was Charles McLaurin, and later I was to read in the files of the Southern Regional Councils' Voter Education Project the weekly reports that Charles McLaurin wrote from that project during the dangerous, long, patient effort in 1962 and 1963 to build a movement. His reports were among the most excellent in an awesomely moving collection of the accounts of the voter effort; he was ever hopeful, believing and eloquent in his admiration for, faith in, the people. He was still working in Mississippi in 1971, still true to the movement ideals.

The young whites there in 1964 shared the lives of the people—a dangerous departure from the racial norms of Mississippi. A Negro restaurant owner, James King, who served the white volunteers while they were there and suffered economic and terrorist reprisals, said, "I think it's right to feed people, regardless of who they are. People are human beings, no matter the color. I never saw any people nicer than these."

That fall, he had, he said, "put pictures of the President and Mr. Humphrey" in the window of his café.

"I thought that was right. They threw bricks through Mr. Johnson's picture. I believe in doing right, though, regardless to the consequences. When you learn better, you must do better. If a person learns better and then doesn't do better— something's wrong."

One of the women who shared her home, a small shack, with the volunteers, she a widow, said of the living arrangement: "There's nothing bad about it. We stay in they houses from sun to sun anyhow when we work for them. People tell you things to frighten you. But we needed help, and if we don't let these young people stay with us, they can't stay. If they blow us away for it, we'll just have to go."

I watched one night as the widow tried to calm the young woman who lived with her. The volunteer was tense about a bomb threat—conscientiously worried about the danger her presence meant for someone with problems enough of her own.

The Negro woman chuckled at her and said, teasingly, fondly, "Awww, you know, if I'd believed that when they said about bombing us, I'd of waked you right then and said, 'Let's go.'" She kept laughing, the laugh saying that you have to laugh, you can't be afraid—and finally the young woman smiled and then laughed, too.

There was, then, reciprocity of benefit in the meeting of the world of the northern volunteers with that of Negro Southerners. Among the volunteers was, perhaps, a tendency to over-idealize these people, to miss the full dimensions of them as people like all other people—as capable of smallness of spirit, meanness, evil, as they were more capable than most Americans of the great and beautiful expressions of their humanity.

But far worse was the inability of some ever to appreciate the beauty, the greatness, to understand that this was the essence of the movement. The mistake was to be repeated. The little struggling Freedom Schools and community organization projects were to be models for the federal poverty programs to come—the Head Start schools, VISTA outposts. And these, as some of the volunteers did, too often sought and encouraged skills and attainments among poor people that were at worst obsolete, and at best inferior to skills and wisdom such people already had. They only needed encouragement and confidence to employ their own wisdom for the general good—imparting, for example, to the neurotic middle class such things as spontaneity and depth of feeling.

Another strain that showed through the Mississippi Summer of what had by then happened to the movement was a tendency among the volunteers, but more pronounced in some of the SNCC veterans. Non-violence and saintly bearing had, in some, become no longer a flexible new way of creative life, nor even a viable tactical weapon, but—in classical psychological fashion—a cover, a disguise for murderous rage so great that one dare not show it, even (or most of all) to himself. More than one story was told of the rage breaking loose in SNCC workers who had been the epitome in the past of real non-violent gentleness and, more recently, a sick sort of saintliness. Too much integrity can be a neurotic paralysis. You can become so right, so uncompromising, that you no longer can function in this wicked world.

I remember one man who stood out as saintly even among the gentlest-spirited people of the movement. When he came down to help in the Albany demonstrations, he questioned seriously whether a boycott could be strictly justified as non-violent. When fashion changed, he emerged as one of the most rigid advocates of black separatism.

Charles Sherrod, one of those former SNCCs who somehow held onto perspective and kept on with his lonely, little-noted work in southwest Georgia, said to me wryly in 1970:

"Hell, we didn't even let ourselves cuss when we were so non-violent. All I ever got out of that was stomach trouble."

Dr. Coles described in clinical terms the symptoms of depression and battle fatigue among the young activists too long exposed to the danger and discouragement of work in the most resistant segregationist areas.

The symptoms, he wrote, "indicate exhaustion, weariness, despair, frustration, and rage. They mark a crisis in the lives of those youths who experience them, and also one in the cities which may experience the results, translated into action, of such symptoms."*

In my interview with him he emphasized that, considering the conditions, the circumstances in Mississippi, the vast majority of the volunteers had showed great strength and resiliency. He described a cycle in their careers—from early idealism to arrogance and cynicism to depression. But then, for most,

*"Social Struggle and Weariness" by Robert Coles (*Psychiatry*, Vol. 27, No. 4, November 1964), p. 308.

there came a "philosophical" adjustment; they were able to relate the very worst that they had seen and experienced in Mississippi to all of life, rather than abstract it as the meaning of life.

Some in SNCC, who later led it to its destruction, were, I fear, by the time of the Mississippi Summer, losing the ability to make the kind of distinction Dr. Coles described. They were like the front-line soldier who is disgusted, appalled, at the frivolity of life back home. But this does not mean that either of his apprehensions is faulty—the horror of the hell on the front lines or the essential quality of life back home. SNCC had great truth to say about the worst of racist repression in the South and about dangerous ailments in the rest of the country. It may be that the most profound thing of all it said about the South and America was that it couldn't continue to fight them both creatively. By early 1965, people spoke of a "black nationalist" faction among SNCC workers.

In a study of the Freedom Summer and its effects on the movement, I concluded:

> . . . The most hurtful and hurting danger to the movement . . . is that Mississippi may after all win—not by murder and intimidation, but by the spread of the contagion of racism . . .
>
> [This] is lamentable not so much in the light of the reality Negroes face, but in the light of what the southern Movement first promised and sought, which was a suggestion of a way out of all the trap of hostility and fear in the nation, and the world. The suggestion may never have been realistic or even right, but it was a mustering of will to try to find some new truth out of all the old good truths that are preached in the Negro churches, and the inability to muster such will for survival is one of the modern world's most frightening characteristics.*

That is the sum of all that I have since come to understand in more detail and depth about the southern movement, but I was mistaken on one count. It was less simple even than I thought then. The danger was not that Mississippi—southern

*"Encounter with the Future," by Pat Watters (New South, Vol. 20, no. 5, May 1965).

white racism—would win. The movement did not, even in its most strident black separatist quarters, become racist in the sense of white southern racism—which, in most white Southerners, was a product of acculturation, a part of childhood conditioning. Not Mississippi, but America won.

Chapter
TWENTY-ONE

STRAINS WERE EVIDENT in SNCC and CORE during the Freedom Summer, but there was at least as much strength as weakness; more of the young activists than not were still determined in the struggle for integration, were still able to function effectively. But then, as the climax to the Freedom Summer, came the traumatic attempt by the Freedom Democratic Party to challenge the seating of the regular Democrats of Mississippi at the 1964 Democratic National Convention in Atlantic City.

The Freedom Democratic Party demanded that its own delegation be seated. It was a truly democratic delegation, Negro and white (sixty-four Negroes, only four whites, though it was open to all whites), rich and poor, sharecroppers and field hands alongside farm owners and merchants, and it had been elected scrupulously according to law and procedure—except for one detail: The thousands of Negroes who elected it were not allowed to vote under Mississippi law and therefore could not really be members of the Democratic Party. It was an effective demonstration, the most forceful ever, I think, against disfranchisement. Somewhere in its development, many of the SNCC and CORE activists and summer volunteers and Negro people of the movement began to think of it as more than that, began to believe there was a real chance of the delegation's being seated. Its members were, after all, faithful to real democracy in Mississippi, while the regular delegation was a part of the power structure which denied the right to vote to Negroes and was thereby implicated in all the illegal trickery, all the intimidation, all the terror and violence (the murder of Chaney and Schwerner and Goodman) used to prevent Negroes from voting.

No more eloquent voice was raised during all the movement years than that at the convention of Mrs. Fannie Lou Hamer of Ruleville, Sunflower County, Mississippi, home county of reactionary Democratic U.S. Senator James O. Eastland. She had only two years before crossed that line which forever separates the oppressed person from the free individual when she responded to one of the little SNCC voter registration drives (Charles McLaurin's organization) and tried to register. She lost her job, was threatened and persecuted, but kept on trying to register—and finally succeeded. Now, in the bright light of television, before the most cynical American gathering possible, she told what that meant, what the voter effort and the Freedom Democratic Party meant, and brought tears to the eyes of some of the delegates.

But to stir stifled instincts of decency and democracy in people steeped in the scheming and intricate manipulations of American politics at the highest level was by no means to assure that even a vestige of decency and democracy might prevail. The movement was in a new arena. Here was no white racist lunchstand proprietor, for whom the threat of disruption was too serious to continue risking, against whom a dramatic demonstration of the injustice of his segregationist policy could be counted on to win the sympathy of liberals. Here was the mainstream in full operation in one of its most destructive, amoral forms. And here, many of those whose sympathies could be relied on against lunchstand injustice were as deeply implicated in the injustice of Mississippi's disfranchisement of Negroes as the regular party delegation from Mississippi itself. And here, the threat of disruption could be put down with a force and determination the hapless lunchstand operator never had.

Here was the ultimate in American pragmatism—a perversion of both qualities that finally had come to mean that winning was more important than anything else, including morality and justice. If nothing else, the Freedom Democratic Party revealed this to many who watched the convention on television and raised, even in the minds of some politicians, the question: When does a line have to be drawn in the exercise of the art of the possible, what issues are there that are impossible of compromise?

The Freedom Democratic Party ran up against the iron will of Lyndon Baines Johnson. The Republican Convention that year displayed grossly the kind of strong-arm tactics that have attached themselves to the staging of what is supposed to be the ultimate expression of government by the people. But the defeat of the Freedom Democratic Party showed enough of such tactics to prepare those watching it for the utter disgrace of totalitarian methods on display at the 1968 Democratic Convention.

Liberals under the manipulative sway of Johnson, old-line labor and Democratic Party liberals, tried out of honest conviction and otherwise to persuade the Freedom Democratic Party people that the compromise finally offered them was—under the practical circumstances—honorable and generous. Hubert Humphrey, in one version of what happened, told leaders of the Freedom Democratic Party that they had a Civil Rights Bill, a good civil rights plank in the platform, the ousting of Alabama's unpledged delegation and a liberal vice-presidential candidate—what more could they want?

As in so much else, they wanted a change in the practicalities of the situation, were radical, wanted to get at the roots of what was wrong in Mississippi, what was, as has finally become clear, wrong with the Democratic Party, its unholy alliance with the racist, reactionary rulers of the South. Ed King, a native white Mississippian who was chaplain at the all-Negro Tougaloo College and candidate for lieutenant governor in the Freedom Democratic Party mock election of 1963, told me in an interview that what they also wanted to challenge was the belief in the party's liberal wing that a few "experts," leaders, should make decisions for the good of the people—without consulting the people.

They were offered two "at large" seats in the Alaska delegation, leaving all Mississippi regular party delegates who would take a loyalty oath still segregated. They refused the compromise, saying it was a compromise with murder, insisting that the Mississippi delegation be forced to integrate or walk out. Some said a crucial point was the Freedom Democratic Party's not being allowed to name who would get the two seats—regarded as not only an affront to SNCC's devotion to letting the people make decisions, but as a deliberate effort to keep SNCC from seating its own as delegates, from gaining that much power. Probably both levels of motivation were operative in the refusal to accept the compromise.

Poetically (which was the movement's proper mode), the Freedom Democratic Party told truth not to be denied about the Democratic Party and American politics.

But Atlantic City lost for the southern movement its most devoted, competent workers. All the processes of alienation that had built through the years and showed themselves in the Freedom Summer were reinforced by the experience. Bitterness was expressed even against the other civil rights organizations—SCLC and the NAACP had "sold out." It was only a matter of time before disintegration of SNCC and CORE would be complete, the young who had for a brief time been inspired with the vision of saints and geniuses having lost their vision and faith there. Never again would many attempt to work within what they called "the system"—and working within the broader system of human morality was at the essence of the movement's original meaning. Its goal had always been reform of institutions and, ultimately, of people—real and radical reform, not a botch of compromised principle.

For a time, at least some in the liberal establishment had real fear that the Freedom Democratic Party concept would spread —not just across the South, but to all the many areas of discontent with the performance of the Democratic Party. There was fear in other Democratic quarters, too. Bob Moses cited the source in 1963 when he spoke of the possibility of the Negro vote's "changing the nature of the representatives in the U.S. House and Senate from the South . . . and thereby fundamentally changing the political structure of the country." (That possibility, that need, still exist.)

Jim Forman talked darkly during an interview in early 1965 of a deliberate campaign aimed at discrediting SNCC because of the Democratic Party's ties, through its southern wing especially, to big business, big oil. There was probably as much truth as paranoia to the notion—like SNCC's similar belief that powerful people in Atlanta were out to get it because it had exposed the sham of the city's liberal image.

Forman still talked then about new lines of power developing: the old idea of a few Negro leaders telling the mass of Negroes what to do reversed—the mass of people instead telling the leaders what to do. A Mrs. Hamer, up out of the people, speaking for them, was a force the old-line politicians didn't know how to cope with.

There was great potential in all this for highly effective action within the system—either to use the threat to the Democratic Party, the liberals and labor, to push for real reform, or, indeed, to begin a party of the people. But SNCC, which might once have developed the potential, was no longer interested. About the only thing that came of it was a national splinter of people similarly disenchanted, asserting in varying ways unwillingness to work within the system. And, mostly unbudged, liberals, labor, and the Democratic Party were to be the main beneficiaries of the movement's great political breakthrough—the winning of the Voting Rights Act in 1965 with the Selma campaign. SNCC had been working on voter registration there since 1963, and, as in the first of the massive campaigns in Albany, in this last of them, SNCC's ability to galvanize people was joined by SCLC's genius for propelling them into action. Now SCLC was skilled in translating the action into national legislative victories: eventually the 1965 Voting Rights Act. But the antagonism between the two organizations, kept below the surface in Albany, flared publicly in Selma. The main focus of dispute was over the basic SCLC method of protest—the mass marches. SNCC workers condemned them, not entirely unjustly, as exploitative, and discouraged people from participating. The old resentment and jealousy were at work. SNCC had labored unsung there for two years, but SCLC would get credit for what was achieved. (Actually, James Orange and John Love of SCLC had been working in and around Selma since 1963 also.) When I asked Selma young people who their hero was, they named Andrew Marrisett, who had come in recently for SCLC to organize them, not Bernard Lafayette, who brought his bride to Selma to start the SNCC work, seeking a quiet place where they could be together.)

SCLC came on January 2, 1965, and on March 9 the campaign precipitated one of those grotesque displays of brutish southern racist violence that could arouse the nation to indignation and Congress to action. (In Sheriff James Clark, SCLC had another apt symbolic villain.) This time it was the attack by state troopers and sheriff's deputies on horseback, wielding clubs and whips, against a band of five hundred and twenty-five marching Negroes attempting to cross the bridge out of Selma for a march to Montgomery. SNCC had opposed the march, but, ironically, it was a member of SNCC, John Lewis, who provided the most courageous leadership, staying firm with the people, staying with those bearing the brunt of the onslaught. Dr. King had gone out of town that weekend; Hosea Williams of SCLC was the other leader of the march. John Lewis had taken exception to SNCC's opposition to the march and had participated in it as an individual—not as SNCC chairman. But once the outrage occurred, those in SNCC who had been so opposed to demonstrations began urging continuation of the march in the face of an injunction which movement lawyers were fighting, eventually successfully. Failing to prevail in Selma, some of them, led by James Forman, set off for Montgomery and engaged in ugly, cop-baiting demonstrations. It was here that Forman affronted a gathering of movement supporters, including some nuns, with a quote to become admiringly repeated in those tattered days of the movement's decline—something to the effect that if he couldn't have his way at the conference table, he was ready to kick the fucking legs out from under the table.

Despite the movement's then-severe internal difficulties, the American public made its great response in Selma to the movement's spirit. The hundreds of people, ordinary people, who, when they saw television coverage of the atrocity on the bridge, dropped everything and came to protest, spontaneously and angrily, found once they got there an amazed joy in what they were doing.

During the Freedom March I had watched in wonderment all those out-of-state tags on the cars whizzing by, not even slowing to see what was happening. There went America, I thought, unheeding. And I knew then that America needed the movement, the movement experience, as much as the movement needed help. Now, in Selma, America had come, responding as it never had before, its people there, in contact with the reality of racism and with the movement's great spirit. It was as near as America came, ordinary Americans, to responding fully in simple faith to the simple offering by the movement of its grace and redemptive love. The subsequent public questioning of their motivation by the movement and its sympathizers was but one more sign of how, within itself, the movement's faith, its spirit, had dwindled. Suppose it had been strong enough still to sustain their support, feed it and keep it alive in all the places they went back to? . . .

An SCLC official was quoted in the *New York Times* of March 17, 1965: "As much as I dislike middle-class whites, we need their help." James Forman was quoted in the same story: "Remember one thing. They aren't going to beat up white people. What do you think will happen to the Negroes when the white folks leave?" They did, of course, beat up whites—eventually killing three in Selma and its aftermath.

I went back to Selma one evening in 1969 in company with John Lewis. (We spent a few hours there waiting to catch a plane in Montgomery.) It was the first time, almost four years later to the day, that he had been back. He walked slowly from one site to another around the big Brown's Chapel A.M.E. Church where the mass meetings were held, the great music still ringing out in 1965 ("We shall overcome"), where the marches started. He walked about, murmuring to himself:

"We were here . . . There is where the march formed . . . I can remember Martin standing up there on the steps, with that Greek archbishop with the beard beside him. Right up there . . ."

We talked with some of the people who had been in the movement, ordinary people, and some of their young, clamoring around John, remembering him. He asked them if they remembered Dr. King—remembered the things he had said there. He told me he always asked young people if they remembered Dr. King, that he believed one of the real hopes was the number of children all across the South whose lives had been touched by Dr. King, Dr. King's words.

In Selma, as in Birmingham, many young people, children, were influenced by Dr. King, by the spirit of the movement. I remember the boy, about twelve, at the end of the Selma-to-Montgomery March, who said to me, "Excuse me, do you mind if I put my flag here on the table? I don't want it to touch the ground."

In 1965 I interviewed dozens of the Selma youngsters—galvanized, as in Birmingham and St. Augustine, to bear the brunt of brutality and know the exhilaration of demonstrating. As many as a thousand at a time, six to eighteen years old, marched, demonstrated. Once, a group of them, around 250, were taken on a forced march three and a half miles on a country road to jail, sheriff's deputies using cattle prods to keep them moving. A girl fell by the side, was burned with prods until she staggered to her feet. Boys carried her along the rest of the way. "They were baptized that day to the way Sheriff [James] Clark treats folks," said Andrew Marrisett, describing what had happened.

He told of another time, when the sheriff had to be hospitalized for overwork during the campaign. At first, the young people were cheering about this, joyful. "I told them that, even though Clark was our enemy, and we hated his ways, we could not advocate violence or rejoice over his being sick.

"I said, 'I think we should pray for Brother Clark. Pray that he will get well today and that tomorrow he will let our parents register to vote. Pray that he will get well in mind and body.' They were real enthused about hating what he does but loving him as a human being."

The young people made prayer signs and marched, some 200 of them, in a hard rain to the courthouse and prayed for Sheriff Clark. "The philosophy of non-violence is in the kids," Andrew Marrisett said. "They talk a lot about violence but, in the act of demonstrating, they are very organized and disciplined. They are real, real good people to work with."

When they spoke for themselves, some of these Selma young people sounded the same idealistic, believing themes that those in Albany, in Birmingham, in St. Augustine had—the same essential spirit that the sit-ins had expressed five long years before.

John Henry Suttles, sixteen, a tenth-grader, said he had been in the movement three years, that he joined the SNCC work after the police picked him up one time when he was just walking down the street doing nothing: "I said next time it would be for something."

What did he hope the movement would accomplish? "Everybody would be together, be able to associate with each other, eat at the same places . . . They would pave the streets Negroes live on, and we would have a chance to vote and everything. Negroes would have a chance to be sheriff, mayor —governor, even."

Bernard Sims, sixteen, told about the time they tested the

theater for compliance with the 1964 Civil Rights Act: "Sheriff Clark came around the corner and told us we were not going in. We started walking in . . . slow. His deputies ran at us and hit us side the head and used cattle prods." (He pointed to a scar on his head where he was hit with a blackjack.)

What had he felt? "It was *fun!* Because we had made Sheriff Clark mad. The man who hit me said, 'Move on, nigger.' Sheriff Clark threw his billy at someone. One of us picked it up and said, 'Here it is, Sheriff' and handed it to him."

What would come of it all? "I believe integration will come. But it will be a little more time. Whites down here are very hard to understand . . ."

Some other expressions of what was then in the Selma young people:

"Sheriff Clark himself is not brutal. Its the power behind him—the Citizens' Council and all."

"Before we can go hand in hand, whites and Negroes must believe in God. Some now don't—of both races."

"Freedom means for your mother to get a better job. And better homes."

"If I was qualified for an office and could hold it, nobody would hold my color against me."

"We were marching and singing 'I Love Everybody,' and one of them stuck me with the cattle prod and said, 'You don't love everybody,' and I said, 'Yes, I do.' "

"It's hard to say why I am in the movement, but it is adding to my idea of man's humanity to man and feelings toward each other. I hope to see a right Selma—with all people united instead of separated."

Cliff Ray Moton, thirteen, a seventh-grader, said: "The movement means . . . I have to do it. People should have done it before now. So that if I want to live on a street I can live on it. Freedom is to be what you want. I want my parents to get better jobs. I want them to pay Mama same as they pay others, if she does the same amount of work. When I grow up I want to be a carpenter—and be able to vote. So my children won't have to be in this mess like we are now."

He said the first time he decided to march his parents told him not to. "But I told them it was right. 'The Lord had told me it was right.'

"My mama said no that night. But the next morning she said I could march. She was scared she would lose her job. But she said go on . . ."

Here was a spirit that could be led, guided, as Andrew Marrisett did, toward the same greatness the movement had expressed before. But there were indications of less than that spirit among others of the Selma young. It was the first place ever in covering the movement that I encountered several times—and each time from young people—blanket hostility to my whiteness, with no distinction made between whether I was friend or foe. No longer was there the feeling we reporters used to have in a place like St. Augustine—that once we were in the Negro section of town we were safe and welcome.

We were still safe, but not always welcome. SCLC still talked, taught, redemptive love. But there was the indication that SNCC was, if not encouraging anti-white feeling among the young, at least not discouraging it, giving the young their heads in a sorely provoked, entirely mainstream ugliness of spirit, standard American antagonism.

Finally I concluded in an article about Selma:

> The tone of what the Selma youngsters say—an entirely un-sparing, unfooled, yet somehow forebearing, attitude toward whites—is consistent with attitudes still miraculously found among Negroes across the South. Certainly no one has to indoctrinate Negro youngsters about the injustices and inequities of their lives. And the miracle of their generally non-violent, mainly constructive, responses can't be expected to last indefinitely.*

At one of the mass meetings at Brown's Chapel Church, Dr. King had warned: "Sheriffs and troopers over the South have brutalized and beat us. Slumbering giants of discontent and

---

*"Why the Negro Children March," by Pat Watters, *New York Times Magazine* (March 21, 1965), p. 21 ff.

even violence threaten to rise up in us . . . But there is another way."

The Selma to Montgomery March took on aspects of the circus, the Army—much ado about logistics, little to do with the movement spirit—a television spectacular. But, at its end, after the endless list of speakers all were finally done, Dr. King rose to speak—and at the moment of movement history when the most radical of the young activists in SNCC and CORE seemed more and more the creatures of the "slumbering giants within," more and more moving into the mainstream, he began to enunciate a radicalism new to him—and deeper than any the young militants had expressed. He spoke of what had happened in Selma:

"If the worst in American life lurked in the dark streets, the best of American instincts rose to confront it . . ."

And he spoke of normalcy—American normalcy: "Normalcy in Marion, Alabama," where Jimmy Lee Jackson, a young Negro man, was killed while participating in a demonstration; "normalcy in Birmingham," where the four young girls were murdered; "normalcy on Highway Eighty," where the mounted attack on the marchers had occurred.

"No," he declared. "We will not allow Alabama to return to normalcy.

"Normalcy," he said, "all over this country leaves the Negro on an island of poverty."

Then he sounded the note of southern populism, promising, along with continued marches against segregation, a march on poverty—white and Negro poverty. It was an important change in the focus of concern of the movement.

He was to lead SCLC a way into this deeper radicalism before he was killed, was to lead the movement into concerns beyond southern segregation, into confrontation with the essential evils of America at home and abroad, of which white southern racism's continued ability to survive against all the might of the movement was but a symptom. But normalcy, American normalcy, continued its erosive effect on the movement, and, as his speech suggested, violence continued a major instrument of normalcy. It had been real violence for so long now—no longer anticipatory fantasy, murder now, not a snowball battle or fist fight exaggerated out of all proportion. Two people were killed during the Selma campaign: Jackson in Marion, and James Reeb, a white churchman, one of the pilgrims, beaten to death by white terrorists in Selma. Two more were to die in the campaign's aftermath—Mrs. Viola Liuzzo, another of the white pilgrims, shot to death in her car in Lowndes County between Selma and Montgomery on the night of the great march's end, ferrying people home to Selma, and Jonathan M. Daniels, a white seminarian who had come to Lowndes County to work in the movement's cause.

Normalcy was gaining. The movement—in the special sense of organizations and leaders working together toward agreed goals, in the sense of big programs staffed by volunteers—somehow fell apart after Selma. In early 1965, before the Selma campaign reached its height, the organizations and leaders were describing grand plans for what would have amounted to a southwide Freedom Summer in 1965, with far more northern students involved, with efforts to correct whatever were seen as flaws in the 1964 summer. Certainly, in the aftermath of that summer, enthusiasm was high among students for civil rights work in the South, and expectations were high among movement people in the South—not merely the leaders. Everyone had a plan, a dream. I remember a white project leader in Mississippi who had stayed on after the summer, talking confidently about setting up a large-scale special school for blackbelt Negroes. It would provide training in manual skills for building community centers and in social skills for running them.

One version of the big summer that never came had SNCC taking on Alabama, southwest Georgia, part of Arkansas and maybe Cambridge, Maryland. CORE would be in Louisiana and Florida. SCLC would work in the upper South and Georgia, South Carolina and Florida. The Mississippi NAACP drew up, but never got implemented, a comprehensive plan for its own work in that state. (It had withdrawn in late 1964 from

331

COFO.) The plan called for ten summer volunteers at each of twenty-six local branches (preferably juniors, seniors and graduate students in political science and elementary school teaching). They would work with local people on political action, citizenship schools, testing of the Civil Rights Act, and a labor and industry program. In part, the plan reflected Aaron Henry's view that the state NAACP ought to do something on its own or quit complaining about COFO. (He was a strong leader in both.)

Grievances during the Freedom Summer expressed by the NAACP reflect the real and human strains that had been building out of SNCC's early decision to go it alone and out of its evolving radical perspective—a mixture of incisive social analysis and plain damn foolishness. Local NAACP leaders said they were never consulted about COFO actions (which amounted to SNCC actions), but were expected to provide money for legal fees, bonds and the like. They said volunteers were indoctrinated against them and that COFO had been impossible to work with—with no planning or follow-through. These were the concerns of older, ordered people, and in the South such people through the NAACP had accomplished prodigies before the young, innovative people of SNCC came along. One of the wise older Mississippi NAACP men mentioned another difference: The young people had no ties to powerful whites in local situations—and, with the beginnings of Negro power emerging, such ties were necessary. He did not mention, of course, that without the young people, Negro power would not have begun to emerge. If only they could have combined their strengths . . .

As it was, only SCLC actually launched a volunteer program that summer. It was called Summer Community Organization for Political Education (SCOPE), and it reflected effort on the part of many to keep the movement going as a coalition of labor, liberals and the civil rights organizations. What happened to SNCC? Why didn't it follow up on the really extraordinary beginning made in Mississippi in 1964?

Perhaps all of the answer was contained in Bill Hansen's

statement to me in 1970 that, while the fatal blow had been
struck in Atlantic City, it was not fully felt until 1965 while
SNCC was working in Alabama. "We were fomenting a statewide thing there and, while we were trying to do it, the realization came that it was all a joke. It came to different people at
different times, but it culminated in Stokely being elected
chairman of SNCC."

SNCC had been going through even more than its ordinary
turmoil over inner organization through the fall of 1964 and
winter of 1965. For a time, in perhaps a surreal last cry of its
southern soul, it operated with virtually total autonomy, not
just of local groups, but of individuals. One faction partook of
a phase called "freedom high," which forshadowed the hippie
culture, with emphasis on personal inner awareness, freedom
and interest in life style and the drug culture. In early 1965 a
SNCC insider told me that all of the wrestling with internal,
organizational problems—the need to get them settled—
might well mean that SNCC would have no summer program
that year. That seemed incredible at the time.

Those involved in the conscious effort to keep coalition alive
(among them, Allard Lowenstein, a young New Yorker who
had been instrumental in recruiting for the 1964 summer, later
a Congressman) seemed to take the attitude that SNCC was
welcome, but that it could not dominate. Jim Forman expressed SNCC's attitude when I interviewed him in early
1965. (At that time, he spoke with confidence of a SNCC
summer black-belt project in the eighty-five southern counties
where Negroes were a majority. The main idea would be to get
across to the nation an image of the black belt as a wider area
of poverty and segregation fully as bad as Mississippi.)

"The root of the question," he said about coalition, "is
whether you accept the proposition of change with consent of
the national administration, of real change without embarrassing Johnson, without cutting off your entrée, without breaking
up the coalition with liberals and labor, without embarrassing
your friends." SNCC, he said, just couldn't accept that—a

coming after five years to full awareness of the danger implicit at the beginning of SNCC from allowing friendly federal and other financial power to manipulate the movement. But by the time the full awareness had come, the will to resist creatively was gone.

"People say SNCC is not willing to work with labor and other groups," Jim Forman went on. "We are prepared to work with them, but not to the extent of selling out the people with whom we work."

The ability of the conventional forces of labor and liberalism to erode (rather than sell out), to cheapen, a great expression of a people was on display at the orientation session held in Atlanta in the spring of 1965 for the SCOPE volunteers. So was the resilience of the movement. The tone of the sessions veered crazily from one extreme to the other, from greatness to banality: wonderful singing of freedom songs, a guitar twanging the very breath of hot, heavy summer in the Delta, and a Negro representative of Coca-Cola leading the volunteers in a sad revision of one of the cries in the churches: "What do you want?" "Coke!" "When do you want it?" "Now."

A northern voice, full of urgency: "We've got a very full morning this morning. Let's get on with it."

And the soft southern one of James Bevel of SCLC, answering a question about what the movement would do once Negroes obtained freedom. "Non-violence will work against the enslavement of Negroes to things. There are two movements: the civil rights movement by Negroes who want to be white people and the non-violent movement by people who understand brotherhood."

Among the strongest carriers of the movement spirit there were the young volunteers themselves. One had the same turn-about feeling as when Mississippi Negroes took care of the white volunteers—that now the volunteers were bolstering those who sought to impart to them the movement spirit. I sat in on the discussions of one small group of volunteers about problems confronting them. First they elected a group leader by unanimous choice, with no ceremony. Then they discussed whether to allow one of their number who had quit the group to return. It seemed obvious that they would be better off, safer even, without him, but they decided unanimously to let him return, because "if he wants to be with us, we have to accept him—as a human being." Finally, they had been assigned to work in a city, and some felt that it would be a deeper experience to work with country people. They decided to accept their assignment, because "after all, we didn't come here to be entertained."

SCOPE originally was to have 2,000 volunteers working across the black belt. As it finally turned out, no more than 500 volunteers (and it was impossible to get an exact count) worked in some forty counties, mostly in Alabama. They were less ostentatious (the orientation included instructions on what both older Negroes and white Southerners considered proper dress), less dramatic, than their predecessors in Mississippi; they were far more intent on work than ideology, and none attracted to himself during the summer any serious violence. They left behind the same kind of bases of community organization and emerging local leadership that COFO had and they worked effectively to organize people to take advantage of the Voting Rights Act passed that summer.

Other civil rights groups, affiliated with the organizations and otherwise, did similar work. But the great surge in Negro voter registration that came in the months after passage of the Act (an increase of 430,000 in the eleven southern states by the following summer) was a manifestation of something more than organizational effort. It was, more than anything else that occurred during the movement years, an expression of the will to citizenship and responsibility of the mass of Negro Southerners—the underlying strength of the people that had given rise to the movement in the first place.

The move into citizenship by those people so long blocked from it, condemned as not aspiring to it, as incapable of it, so patient and brave in the long wait and quest for it, had an epic quality, symbolic of the long, slow, struggle toward freedom through history.

One of the federal examiners—an older man, a white Southerner—sent to accept registration applications under the new law in Demopolis, Alabama, had awe in his voice when he told me about the first day there.

"There were one hundred and fifty in line when we arrived to open the office at seven-thirty in the morning. There were two hundred and fifty when we opened the office at eight-thirty. There were three hundred after all that we had already processed by ten-thirty."

That scene was repreated across the South, and continued for months—the long lines of people, orderly lines, good-natured, indeed subduedly jubilant lines, of plain, decent people come at last to what the rest of America took for granted, to the duty that the rest of America was exhorted to perform, come at last to the right to vote. In the processing, the press missed not only the grandeur, but the irony of it.

Myself included. I was assigned by a magazine to write about the first week of it in Demopolis. My story was rejected. There had been no violence or dramatic confrontation; the editors found my account of the human qualities displayed by the Negroes, the examiners and the local whites too prosaic, and they were right. I missed, somehow, that far along in trying to understand what America had missed about the movement, the immense meaning in the silent, patient lines of people waiting to register to vote. They had come from the little houses in the Negro section of the town and from the surrounding little towns and the farms of the countryside, old and young. Some had responded to organizing efforts of a SCOPE group there, but the very most were people who had been untouched by the organized efforts of the movement through its years, who had heard about the new law on the radio or by word of mouth, but who, through the movement years and by their presence in the lines, were the embodiment of the real strengths, the undying ones that had sustained the movement to this great moment in its life.

A man eighty years old from a farm, wearing a short-sleeved, square-patterned tan shirt and a blue tie and brown suspenders, with light gray hair, a gray moustache, wearing a heavy wrist watch, answers one of the questions to the effect that he does not plan to overthrow the government. He is told to sign his name and, smiling, does so with big fingers high up on the pen. He is told to take the certificate to the polls, and that will allow him to vote.

"That's all?" he says.

"That's all."

"Thank ye," he says.

"Thank you,"

and he goes out, a thin, bent figure, and stops at the door and turns, and smiles upon the room where he has registered to vote.

A fat lady in a yellow dress says, "I am not too good at writin'," and the examiner says, "Can you make an X?" and she says, "Yessuh" and does, solemnly.

An old lady in a checkered, faded dress approaches the desk with shy eyes, looks back to a SCOPE representative to be sure she is at the right place, sits and begins answering the questions. She is fifty. She is very anxious that the white man gets her address right. He asks her what beat she lives in. She is confused. "I've lived in Alabama all my life." Yes, but what beat number? "Are you talking about church?" They finally determine what it is.

Then the white man, attempting levity, but gently, to relax her, asks her if she has ever belonged to the Army or Navy. Solemnly, she answers, "No suh."

"You're just a member of the church?"

Quietly, bravely, she says: "I am a United States citizen, too."

A man apologizes about his signature. The examiner says, "That's all right." The man smiles. "I ain't never been mixed up in no voting business before. I'll have to learn."

The old humorous-eyed lady, taking her certificate, gives a long "Ooooooh" sigh of relief: "I made it."

"Take that to the next election," the examiner says.

"Oh, yes."

"Don't lose it."

"I'm too proud of it to lose it."

Chapter
TWENTY-TWO

THE MOVEMENT had built to that great moment of south-wide Negro voter registration—and in other ways seemed in that crucial year, 1965, to be building on other of its strengths, so that, even though I was aware of malaise in SNCC, I had no inkling of the debacle soon to come. One of the most hopeful things afoot, and I think significant, in view of how much anti-white feeling had built in SNCC, was renewed emphasis on working with, reaching the movement out to, southern whites.

SCEF that year began sending organizers into white communities. Harry Boyte, the older white man working full-time for SCLC, was organizing a "new approach to dialogue" in early 1965. Annelle Ponder of SCLC described the plan to me. It would be an attempt to bring whites "with positive attitudes" into contact with ones without them. It would try to reach poor whites at any level. Then the attempt would be made to bring whites and Negroes together—not the "same old liberal whites," but newly informed ones.

Even during the racial tension of the Mississippi Freedom Summer, there had been tentative, hopeful signs of the movement's touching white people positively. Robert Swann, a middle-aged white man from Voluntown, Connecticut, served for a time in an effort to rebuild Negro churches burned by racists during the summer. He said there had been some success. "In

Mississippi some whites with a religious background really do deplore these things."

In Ruleville the workers said that several times curious, non-hostile whites came by the community center. The police would run them off. One Saturday night, a middle-aged local white man, a proclaimed segregationist, came, and a good discussion with Negro staff members ensued. The police came and told him to leave or go to jail. He stood his ground, and was hauled off to jail. College students, members of an Association for Tenth Amendment Conservatives, came several times for discussions; police did not harass them.

How much of this occurred across the state—and the South —and with what effect? And how much more might have occurred without police harassment, augmenting the conditioned fear held by most white Southerners of interracial encounters on an equal footing? SNCC made some efforts at reaching whites with white staff workers in Mississippi before establishing the punitive policy that whites could not work in black communities.

White college students formed the Southern Student Organizing Committee (SSOC) in 1964. Its original purpose was to show support in any way it could for the movement. Its members were few, but dedicated—and it might have grown. It came to be a rallying point for southern college radicals and for a time held to a non-doctrinaire, creative policy. Finally, in a sordid power play in 1969, it was destroyed by a faction from Students for a Democratic Society during that organization's dying days. Saddest of all, some of the young radicals who had been its mainstay were able to rationalize this act of destruction, somehow absorb it, as they had also rationalized Black Power's rejection of what had been at the outset their primary interest—integration. It was as though the effort to break with their families on segregation (which their families rationalized in the same ways) was all the noncomformity they were capable of.

But always there was the fragile, tantalyzing hope. By the time the movement had consolidated its legislative victories and might have made real overtures to whites, by the time whites of the South were in varying ways and degrees adjusting to desegregation, the movement organizations were too divided, too beset by internal difficulties really to find out whether southern whites might respond to its intrinsically southern spirit. In the best of the organizations, that spirit was, anyhow, about gone.

At the one more movement event before SNCC and CORE could be said no longer to be a part of the southern movement, the White House Conference "To Fulfill These Rights" in Washington in June 1966, disillusionment, despair, and cynicism made up the major mood of movement regulars. President Johnson, it was said, had pre-empted the movement; it was demoralized. Perhaps he had, having sensed with his instinct for such things just how much of the movement had slid into place in volatile, violent, contending America.

This was demonstrated in full on the Meredith March that same month when the cry "Black Power" was raised, and SNCC and CORE abandoned advocacy of non-violence. SNCC had come out against the Vietnam War early in the year, but one sensed it was as much in opposition to anything American as in humane concern for peace. This did, though, reflect the people; a wave of anti-war feeling had spread across the Negro South in 1965. A sizeable contingent in SNCC had opposed Julian Bond's campaign (eventually successful) to be elected to and seated in the Georgia House of Representatives. He was, they said, trying to become part of "the system"—this after all the SNCC struggle, all the suffering for the vote.

Negro Southerners, through the movement years, had been aware of the Black Muslim separatist movement, but few had been converted to it. They probably would not have, even if the alternative of the movement had not been so much more prominently before them. It was a northern phenomenon, appealing to the different kind of dissatisfaction felt by Negroes in the North—disappointment and disillusionment over promises unfulfilled, rather than the southern Negro's broiling dissatisfaction with the promise of America being withheld by the system of segregation. Movement leaders would, as the Reverend Shuttlesworth did in Birmingham, occasionally make brief references to the Muslims as the antithesis of the movement's meaning, and they would sometimes suggest to whites the difference between their willingness still to seek reconciliation and the Muslim's hostile alienation. And the Muslim movement was always there as the ultimate retreat for those embittered by personal circumstance, or, as more than once happened, by bitter experience of movement defeat. Some of the Albany leaders were said, after the great days ended there, to have found rapport for a time with some of its tenets. But it was a remote thing for the most part —like so much else—central to northern consciousness, but of little importance to the movement. (In a similar way, one thinks of figures friendly to the movement, like Bayard Rustin and Harry Belafonte, who were, in the North, deemed important to the movement, but seemed little-known, remote, in the South.)

When SNCC and CORE espoused separatism on the Meredith March, certainly some of the emotional response, the strong responsive chord it struck, was a reflection of impingement, consciously and unconsciously, of the Muslim message on southern Negro consciousness. But far more of this, I think, was intrinsically southern. In part, it was an expression of ancient anger, as old as slavery, anger I had seen in my years of following the movement—real and strong and certainly justified. In Mississippi and across the black belt, more than one Negro farmer took his hunting rifle off the wall and vowed to kill anyone who might attack his home. After the murder (never punished) of Herbert Lee, a local voter registration leader in Liberty, Mississippi, in late 1961, SNCC came to a sort of unofficial policy that while field workers might, according to their own judgment, continue to eschew weapons, they could no longer reasonably request local people to do that. The Deacons for Defense and Justice was a self-defense unit formed in 1965 in Bogalusa, Louisiana, after much white violence, including murder. (But never in all the movement years did people within the movement do any shooting.) Always in the mass meetings, the anger spoke along with the joy and hope, most often in scornful derision of segregationist enemies, those various symbolic villians the movement singled out.

But the anger had been directed at specific people and institutions, and had, in the movement's greatest achievement, been held, always, in balance with the spirit of redemptive love. Late in the night once in 1964, I gained new insight into the strength of this balance, sitting, talking—the South's droning talk—with one of the most resourceful, toughly militant local leaders I know, an older man, a wise one.

"When I move in relationship to my white brethren," he said at one point, "it is with steps of caution—not anger or righteous indignation. When it is a dispute, this tolerance makes it just a battle of two philosophies. I can't win the battle when I'm mad . . . The anger went out of me a long time ago. My battle was to learn to trust any white person."

He told how his father, who had "no use for white folks," had stopped him once, a young man, when he set out with a pistol to kill a "cracker" who had hit him in the head with a stick during an argument.

"The anger had to pass off. I had to learn to believe there was something sincere in whites somewhere. I don't move in anger now against any white man—even the worst. I feel sorry for them."

His daughter, when she was eleven, told him she didn't believe she liked white people. "I started to talk to her. I didn't want her to grow up with any feeling of hatred in her heart."

There was the movement's strength—no feeble or naïve thing. The people and such leaders, a tiny but greatly significant portion of the South's Negro minority, had willed that, for once in an American context, anger and violence would not hold sway. They sought a new, more effective, less hurting (for all concerned) way of striving in America for the ideals America had always without success striven for, violently clamored after. Often, as in the Albany rock-throwing, it took the strongest kind of leadership to hold violence and non-violence, hate and love, in balance.

Zev Aeloney described to me by long-distance phone in July 1964, his own efforts and those of Negro SNCC workers Sam Mahone and Bob Mants to prevent interracial violence in Americus. There had been years of provocation—and the immediate outrage of what had happened the night before:

Whites were roaming the streets angrily after Negro attempts to test public accommodations desegregation. Small groups of Negroes were talking together of defending themselves. The civil rights workers persuaded them to go home. Twenty or twenty-five whites then rampaged through the Negro sections in cars, firing into at least two homes, chasing down Negroes and beating them.

The next night, even as I spoke with Aeloney, Negroes were forming defense groups, arming themselves, and again the civil rights workers were frantically urging people just to keep off the streets. Finally, in 1965, Negroes (not of the movement) killed a white man in Americus during a flare-up over demonstrations. But while non-violence was still the guiding light of the movement there that night in 1964, the civil rights workers were able to prevail.

What SNCC and CORE did on the Meredith March was to cease to exercise the high responsibility of this kind of leadership, or, in another way of putting it, cease to respond any longer as leaders to the best in those they led. Instead, they actively encouraged all the entirely justified negative feelings in Negro Southerners, the old anger and a newer kind of despair (the northern kind), disappointment at promises held out in movement gains to Negro Southerners, but not fulfilled. The lack, in subsequent years, of any serious Negro violence in the South at least suggests that non-violence, reverence for life, is an intrinsic part of southern Negro culture.

A large part of the tragedy of SNCC's and CORE's default was that, in 1965, 1966 and the ensuing years, they were greatly needed in the struggle, still continuing, to force fulfillment of the promises. School integration, more than all the rest of the requirements of the civil rights law, would have provided them with a great issue around which to organize people in the ways they knew so well, and school integration remained the most basic of the secular goals by which the movement might yet accomplish in the South its spiritual one of changing the hearts of people. Of all the movement struggle that continued into the 1970s independently by local people, the seeking of school integration was the most fervently supported, most widespread.

But the stubborn persistence of southern racism and the failure of the federal government to enforce the laws the movement had won continued to frustrate real integration. An idea of what SNCC and CORE would have been up against is suggested in the experience of the American Friends Service Committee which, in 1965 and 1966, operated a little-publicized task force of volunteer workers (local Negroes as well as college students, lawyers and the like) to encourage Negro parents across the South to send their children to white schools. They accounted for much of the relatively small amount of school desegregation in those years. After seeing how much harassment such children and their parents went through, AFSC abandoned the program and began one of assistance to families so harassed, wisely acknowledging that, without exercise of federal responsibility, private agency action could not prevail. If the movement were still at its old strength, it could dramatize this point, demonstrate it in any number of areas—including hunger.

SNCC and CORE, in giving up on non-violence and integration, showed themselves pulled finally by the mainstream into its treacherous currents. They were no worse and no better off now than the majority of Americans caught there, too. The Meredith March itself had been one more opportunity for mainstream madness to express itself, the violence and hysteria over violence. James Meredith, whose admission in 1962 to the University of Mississippi as its first Negro student set off a murderous riot, had set out alone (like the postman, William Moore) to walk through Mississippi urging voter registration. On the first day out, he was shot from ambush by a white man. The civil rights organizations vowed to continue the march, and even as the mainstream cry of "Black Power" was being raised along its route, white terrorists attacked the marchers viciously in Philadelphia (where Chaney and Schwerner and Goodman had been killed), and police sprayed tear gas and brutally harassed the marchers at their encampment in Canton. As so often before, there was no Selma-like reaction against the violence, which had finally evoked at least verbal retaliation from the movement.

The wonder was not that as many Negro Southerners as did responded to the call for Black Power, but that as many then and in the ensuing years were able to resist its entirely normal, mainstream blandishments. One cannot condemn the former for doing what living in America had all along conditioned them to do; one can only be awed anew at what was required from the beginning to go against this conditioning—and try to change it. By their final capitulation, SNCC and CORE only emphasized what they once had been.

"It's no longer my movement," John Lewis said during the Meredith March, and left SNCC soon thereafter. "They had forced all the whites to leave," he told me later. "And most of the blacks just couldn't stay. I tried to stay, but I just couldn't. The things they espoused . . ."

He had been deposed as chairman of SNCC a month before the Meredith March, after three years in the job and six in the organization. I have heard several accounts of what happened from people who were there, including John Lewis, and they vary little in detail. Lewis told some of the background from his vantage point. He felt that his position in favor of the original Pettus Bridge march in Selma had been the start of his defeat. At a meeting in Atlanta, Courtney Cox, Stokely Carmichael, Jim Forman, others, opposed plans for the march. A few,

Bob Mants, Wilson Brown among them, joined him in supporting the march.

"We felt you had to stay where the people were—move with them."

It was finally decided that those who wanted to could march as individuals. He and Brown and Mants did so. Subsequently, he was criticized by those who didn't march for supporting Dr. King's position that the march should not be resumed until a court order for adequate protection could be obtained.

"I think those troopers under Wallace, Lingo and Clark would have treated all those ministers like they had treated us. I took the position it is okay to retreat—as Gandhi did—and that anyhow, SNCC, in refusing to support the first march, had lost the right to criticize."

He was also subsequently criticized for his role as a member of the planning committee for the White House Conference and for continuing to serve on the board of trustees of SCLC. James Forman was a leader of the opposition, finally, to him.

Forman remains an enigmatic figure. Personable, canny, erudite, often ironically humorous, he was a strong personality in the movement, a big bear-like man with a serious, sensitive face. In early 1965, one movement watcher, in trying to assess SNCC leaders in terms of right, left and center, placed Forman in the center. His re-emergence in 1969 as leader of the black separatist group demanding reparations from guilt-tormented church groups tends to reinforce that judgment; at least he was still practical.

One SNCC veteran spoke of him with awe. "He was the smartest. He was translating Fanon when Bob Moses was telling people to read Camus. He was two years ahead of his time, was a nationalist three or four years ahead of everybody else. Because the movement was there, he pushed it. He always knew where the people were—like knowing their ability to support the sit-ins.

"He also knew where the civil rights types were, where the vanguard was. He knew SNCC best, knew it was the most radical force in the country. He kept pushing it further and further out.

"He was always right. He was the only man I would obey and not ask why."

Another said: "Forman had a strong influence on SNCC. He was a very capable administrator; if he wanted something he persisted until he got it. He was persuasive, could win others to his point of view. I'm not sure he was always a good influence.

"He seemed cynical about non-violence. He talked about it, paid lip service, because he recognized that the majority believed in the philosophy. I don't think he really understood what made the student movement what it was—the feeling, the attitude, of so many young blacks."

Still another said:

"From the beginning, Martin Luther King had respect and love for SNCC. But there was a type of jealousy, rivalry, on the part of Forman and others toward Dr. King. I didn't understand it then. I don't understand it now. I don't know if it was that they didn't trust him, or what. But I felt that they saw Selma as an opportunity to wrest the symbolic leadership away from Dr. King. And I'm convinced John's relationship to Dr. King was a factor in opposition to him."

Such were the entirely mainstream concerns in the background of Lewis's deposal and presumably the emergence of Black Power. Some said Stokely Carmichael was used by Forman and discarded as soon as he was no longer useful. (He left the chairmanship a year after elected and was replaced by Rap Brown.) Certainly he was flamboyant, theatrical, an able enunciator of the new spirit symbolized by the phrase "Black Power." And certainly the new spirit—whether calculatedly so or not—was a serious threat to Dr. King's leadership. (Dr. King was badly used on the Meredith March; his presence was still a magic attraction to the press, providing a national platform and sounding board for the Black Power rhetoric. The brainless taking up of this new rhetoric by much of the media, especially television, never questioning it or seemingly even seeing a difference from the movement's old spirit, was but one more disservice. Similar failure of many intellectuals to subject Black Power rhetoric to the kind of analysis they apply to other subjects suggests a kind of reverse-racist fadishness.)

Lewis was invited to go abroad in late 1965 by the Norwegian Student Association and stayed there on a speaking tour until shortly before the SNCC election. He returned, he said, thinking that he might ask not to be re-elected chairman—with the thought of returning to college. But he decided he had better stay on; the coming meeting would likely determine the future of SNCC. ("By then, there was a serious schism in the organization.") The black-white issue was involved. In 1965 Lewis had, as chairman, established the policy that SNCC and the movement should be black-led, but the policy supported integration as a goal and continued participation of whites in SNCC.

I asked John Lewis to explain the policy in early 1965. He described, first, his feeling that Negro people in America were caught up in a force, a universal spirit whereby they were coming to identify with Africa. Bob Moses about the same time had said Negroes identify with Africa, not Europe, and that neither America nor the world had progressed enough to include Africa and Europe in one community. Lewis said identification with Africa rather than America was cultural rather than nationalistic, involving things like dress and hair styles. It was a change from identifying with the white middle class.

Then he said the movement needed white people, needed white support, that it wasn't a matter of black or white, but all those who were for the "liberation of black people." But, he said, the movement had to be controlled "by people who are the victims"—because they have insights that the non-victim can't have.

He added that, on his trip to Africa, he had been struck with the feeling that American education had deprived Negroes of their right to know their relationship to Africa. "There are very few problems in terms of race," he said. "People are just trying to find themselves."

Lewis said in 1970 that, just before the 1966 election, "some people, including Forman, were raising legitimate questions about where SNCC should go—how it should relate to the third world, to the black movement, whether non-violence was still relevant . . ."

Stokely Carmichael had announced his candidacy for chairman—a thing never done in SNCC before, the chairmanship having always been conferred, not sought. Lewis said he had gotten to know Carmichael well in Mississippi, had admired and respected him as one of the most effective, hard-working voter registration workers and community organizers, and a devotee of non-violence. He had worked particularly hard on the Freedom Democratic Party challenge, was more disappointed than most at the results.

I heard Carmichael speak at an SSOC meeting in early 1965 in Atlanta. What he said was essentially what most of SNCC was saying then, but the style was vigorous, slashing. The country wouldn't be radical, even if Martin Luther King were president, as long as decisions were made from the top down . . . SNCC would fall in line with nobody; other civil rights organizations got their strength from the white middle class . . . Red-baiting Moses just isn't pertinent to Mississippi . . . It's ridiculous to red-bait Mrs. Hamer; she doesn't know what it is . . . You can't have coalition with people who run things from the top down; when Walter Reuther takes orders from the bottom, then you can have coalition with him . . . The problem is they don't let the people talk, don't let the people make decisions . . . How can you have respect for human beings when you're dropping bombs on them every day? . . . All education does is make you more and more what the system wants . . . A low-down, dirty little person has as much intelligence as Johnson does to make decisions. And so on. Carmichael had not been a part of "Freedom High." He did not participate in Selma, but moved soon after into a concerted voter registration effort in Lowndes County, Alabama, where Mrs. Liuzzo was murdered. He worked with and had a fast friendship with Jonathan Daniels—and the murder of Daniels, by several accounts, was the final breaking point for him. He had meanwhile developed a Negro political organization in Lowndes called the Black Panther Party, a title later to be appropriated by people further along in the mainstream than he was by then. I participated in a panel discussion with him in February 1966, again at a SSOC meeting in Atlanta, and was stunned to hear him enunciate (for the first time publicly) the basic tenets of the Black Power rhetoric he was to make so important four months later on the Meredith March. At the time I wrote him off as one more victim of movement battle fatigue. To see him in action later was like watching a carica- ture of the most blatant of white southern racists. He appeared on the southern lecture circuit in 1971 after a sojourn in Africa, talking a more sophisticated, toned-down line.

Also working in Lowndes had been Bob Mants, a veteran of the southwest Georgia voter registration effort, having joined it while in high school. He was to support Lewis for re-election as chairman, and of pressure for more emphasis on blackness at the time was to say: "We don't need anybody to tell us we're black." Most of the push for black emphasis came from North- erners and relative newcomers to SNCC, John Lewis said.

The accounts of the election agree that blackness was an issue, if not *the* issue, and that after considerable discussion, Lewis was re-elected by a sizeable vote (sixty-six to eleven) and that his victory was considered one for moderation on the black issue. Discussion then continued, with Lewis presiding, the tone of it becoming more vituperative, more expressive of the bitterness, despair and alienation within SNCC. At least two hours passed (some say more), and people drifted out, others in. Two men—one who had left SNCC after noble service (Worth Long) and another who was later to join, but was not then a member (Julius Lester)—came in and challenged the results of the election, saying it had violated the SNCC consti- tution. ("We had no constitution," Lewis said later.) After much more discussion, another vote was taken, this time in a far smaller crowd, and Stokely Carmichael was victorious.

One of those who knew the bitterness of the times to its depths said the men who had set up the second vote had done "a bad thing." But, he added, "Ideologically, they were right. Everybody loved John. We voted for him out of loyalty. We had nothing against him. But his politics were zilch. John's allowing it to happen epitomized his weakness."

The inference was that, like those who ran the Democratic Convention, he should have used his power as presiding officer to suppress opposition. I believe the contrary—that his strength, his ability somehow still to believe amid all those who had lost the ability, caused him to lose an election that would have been meaningless if won by normal American strong-arm tactics.

"What happened that night," he said later, "was the beginning of the end of SNCC. Breaches were created, wounds were opened that never were healed. I didn't consider it a repudiation of me. It was just a very sad thing, a very tragic thing for SNCC."

In terms of effective work and voice in the South by SNCC and CORE, the end came almost immediately after the Meredith March. Both still existed in weakened form in 1970— SNCC calling itself the Student *National* Coordinating Committee (non-violent no longer) and CORE promulgating the scheme for separate but equal schools, sadly in league with the southern strategists of the Nixon Administration.

But the spirit of the movement, even during the Meredith March's dreary mockery of it, was not yet dead—in the people or in all of the activists.

On the last day of the march, in Jackson, in heat so high, so humid, that merely to walk the route was a misery, some would shout "Freedom!" as of old, and others would shout "Black Power!" this intoxicating new thing, and sometimes the one would be louder, and sometimes the other. Once, the march crossed a railroad track, and a white man at the controls of a diesel engine on a siding there made a move as though to run the engine at the marchers. At once, a dozen or more of the young people, full of the new spirit, broke from the ranks and ran to climb up on the engine, to get at the "whitey" there in the cab. But faster than they, James Lawson, one of those who had been part of the profoundly non-violent Nashville group at its start and still faithful to its meaning, jumped up there, too, and quietly, with the force only of his personality and will, stopped them, sent them back down to continue the march. And Bob Greene of SCLC made the man at the controls desist by threatening to lie down in front of the engine.

The movement was not yet dead. Even at the White House Conference, amid so much hopelessness, I felt its rise of hope as strongly as I had felt it anywhere. I sat through two days of discussions in small groups of the delegates—movement people, leaders of poor people, activists, concerned citizens from all over the country—and came away with the knowledge that the thing I had responded to, the hopeful thing in the South, had its like across all the nation. They were so far ahead of the national leadership that had called the conference (and elements then of dispirited movement leadership) in their grasp of what was wrong. And hearing all at once the different dimensions of poverty, discrimination, unresponsiveness of government and social agencies all over the country, realizing the magnitude of problems was frightening. They were ahead, too, in their knowledge of what to do about what was wrong. More than this, they showed themselves, so many of them, all kinds of people, possessed of so much of that spirit which inspired the movement, something beyond the reach of cynicism and manipulation, something escaped from stale motivations and maneuverings. I remember especially the young Negro woman from Cleveland who spoke with soft compassion for police, saying how they needed to become part of the community instead of dreaded bullies, a force for good, servants of the society. The first step, she said, would be to demilitarize them—cease the emphasis on guns and uniforms. "Integrate them," she said, "into the community," and the applause was fervent.

I tried then, amid all the despair and disillusionment at the conference over the betrayals of leadership so rawly apparent, and tried even more afterward, to hold onto that sense of the people, the people of all America who were so far ahead of leadership, so capable of responding to real leadership toward the new kinds of cultural development the movement had hinted.

In the South the movement struggled on through 1966 and 1967—without SNCC and CORE. The prodigies of voter registration continued under the act that Selma won, with some surface political results, and, more importantly, the building of organization and development of leadership that promised the possibility of real reform, the direction of politics away from racism and to the real needs of the people, white and black.

SCLC, battered by its Chicago experience, returned to the South in 1968 and began the campaign against poverty Dr. King had promised in Selma. Physicians and others had reported terrible findings of poverty across the South, more widespread and severe than nearly anyone had known—people, little children, babies, literally starving to death. SNCC and CORE had known about this as early as 1962, the depths of it, and had tried to tell about it, but were not heard. I have suggested that the failure of communication had to do with the universal American problem of the difference between headquarters and the field—that SNCC and CORE, devoted almost entirely to the field, could see what in reality was important, but had lost the ability or patience to communicate with the headquarters (i.e., the media, national and movement leadership). And the headquarters, typically, stressed the importance of preconceived goals and strategies, regardless of reality out in the field.

As plans were being made for SCLC's Poor People's Campaign, the movement rose up in February of 1968 as close to the old spirit as prevalent attitudes would permit. It rose in Memphis, a place where Negroes had somehow never built the real movement spirit before. The whole community now was caught up, middle class leaders and the poorest of the poor joining to support a garbage strike—an effort to get decent wages and conditions for these workers (part of an effort still continuing across the South). Ed Stanfield was inspired by this revival of the movement spirit and described what was afoot:

> An elderly woman carried her [picket] sign and faced straight ahead, lips pursed and eyes darting from side to side. She was dressed simply, but neatly, and wore a hat. Asked if she was a member of a striker's family, she answered, "No, I'm just a church member and a friend. It's easier for me to march because I am alone now, and don't have children to take care of. I could be home in bed. But I remember. I been there. I've been without work. And I've been too poor and hungry to go to work when I had it." . . .
>
> "The ministers are in this thing until it is proven beyond the shadow of a doubt that our way [non-violence] won't work," said the Rev. Malcolm Blackburn. "Then, as one minister said yesterday, we shall just have to go fishing." . . .
>
> The Monday night meeting was drawing to a close. It had been in progress for three hours, which is not unusual for civil rights mass meetings. The Rev. Mr. Blackburn . . . introduced a tall young black man wearing a light, olive-colored jacket with the word "INVADERS" across the back.
>
> "I'm a radical," the young man began . . .
>
> "When you talk about fighting a city with as many cops as this city's got, you better have some guns! You're gonna need 'em before it's over."
>
> . . . The minister who had been presiding throughout the evening . . . apologized for not recognizing the young radical. It is a free country, he said, and while he did not agree with the brother, he certainly granted him his right to say what he thought. Then he reminded the crowd, "We have chosen our weapons. These are the weapons of non-violence."*

*"In Memphis: More Than a Garbage Strike," by J. Edwin Stanfield (Southern Regional Council, March 22, 1968). Mr. Stanfield went on to write two supplements to the report, one issued on April 3, 1968, the day before Dr. King was killed, and the other commenting on the murder.

Dr. King gave as one reason for his coming to Memphis such reports of revival of the old spirit. But that other spirit which had manifested itself on the Meredith March was obviously at work in Memphis, too. Young toughs, like those who had been discouraged from violence in Albany and all the other places of great movement action, broke windows along the route of the march, created minor havoc during the first demonstration Dr. King led there.

Such dreary, entirely mundane, mainstream violence was, in a sense, a part of the death that came a few days later to him in Memphis at the hands of a white assassin (a year to the day after he had delivered his great Riverside Church speech). He had determined to stay in Memphis to prove that non-violence still could work, to find a reply to those urging him to cancel the plans for a Poor People's March on Washington later in the spring. As in the instances of the murder of other leaders, including that of Malcolm X, fanciful speculation has persisted over who or what might have been behind the killing of Dr. King. In the perspective I seek, going back, it mattered little, really, to name as the murderer some particular agency of all those in the mainstream which his existence, his movement, opposed—the South's white racists, the nation's lunatic right, the national government itself as some, viewing the most sinister elements of what we call the military-industrial complex, have dourly suspected, or even—like the rampaging youngsters in Memphis—murderous elements in black America. The mainstream—its ugliest spirit—killed him.

The attempt by the Federal Bureau of Investigation, through most of the movement years, to peddle to the press illegally obtained information about his private life was possibly the most obscene that the movement revealed of all the overt mainstream resistance to that which he stood for—and one of the most frightening indications of sinister forces operating in the federal government. Projection of the sickest sexual fantasy onto Negroes generally has been a standard part of white southern racism, and the practice continued against the movement.

The press, to its credit, refused during Dr. King's lifetime to publish the FBI's engagement in the practice. The most notable posthumous publicizing of it was at the hands of a black writer, John A. Williams.*

Dr. King was foremost a symbol of all that the movement meant. But he was also a formidable personal influence on the South and America, the extent of which we cannot yet know.

"I'll tell you the truth," a white Southerner, a good friend, told me recently. "I resented all that civil rights stuff when it started. My mind had been set a certain way. I didn't hate— but it just seemed they were stirring up needless trouble. Then I heard Dr. King speak a couple of times, heard him on television, and read some of what he wrote. And I thought about it. And I realized he was right. It changed my whole way of thinking. When I heard he had been killed, it really tore me up—like he was somebody I knew."

When the mainstream murderousness, soon after, killed Robert Kennedy, America was, as it had been after the murder of John Kennedy, haplessly thrown back on political leadership of the most banal, mainstream, manipulative kind—Nixon, exemplar of the worst excesses of the Joseph McCarthy period, Humphrey, symbol to SNCC and CORE of a liberalism so enfeebled by compromise of uncompromisable principle, so ensnared in pragmatism, as to be indistinguishable from those old, simple, white racist foes of the movement in the rural South.

The young people, some radicalized, some of the same stripe as went to Mississippi in 1964, middle-class and conventional, rallied behind the enigmatic Eugene McCarthy, and Chicago police, at the behest of ruined liberalism at the Democratic National Convention, bludgeoned them before our eyes on television—like so many Alabama state troopers in action.

What went wrong? What was the fatal flaw? Had the most insane side of the South suddenly moved into, captured the

*John A. Williams, *The King God Didn't Save* (New York: Coward-McCann, 1970).

nation? Or had that insane side been merely all through history a more honest, more open expression of the mainstream of America? Dr. King was dead; his voice would not longer be raised against the ever more strident, more mainstream rhetoric of black separatism. Was the movement, as even its friends had been proclaiming for several years, indeed dead? What of the people, all the good people of the churches, the people at the Washington Conference? What of

> *There must be*
> *A God*
> *Somewhere?*

Chapter
TWENTY-THREE

ALWAYS, ALWAYS . . . I return to my memory of Albany when despair is deepest. The peak of the people's fervor, response in Albany was reached on the day in December of that great march which Dr. King led—that I have suggested the people had willed him to lead. He and other SCLC and Albany Movement leaders were huddled in a conference until well after noon; they had sent a message to the city officials saying that, unless negotiations were begun, a massive demonstration would be held that day. By this chance, the people—more than I ever saw again—were in charge of the mass meeting. All through the morning they waited in the church (Shiloh Baptist) to learn the city's answer—sometimes several hundred, sometimes as few as thirty or forty. Through the day they gave their own expression—local people, local leaders—of the meaning of the movement. I could hear the singing when I approached the church that morning: "This little light of mine . . ." accompanied by handclaps and foot-stamping, mighty music already. "All in the jailhouse . . ." "On the roadside . . ." "Down to Newton, Georgia . . ." Dr. Anderson was leading the singing; he would in his deep bass sing a phrase, then stop, the audience booming on, then sing another and stop. "All . . . in Dawson, Georgia . . ."

A slightly built man with mahogany skin, gray hair, standing on the pulpit platform, stamped his feet, each in a different, complicated rhythm pattern, and at various points, with his eyes closed, his head down, would blend his reedy voice into a counterpoint phrasing of the song's words, his body swaying with the power of the music. His coat was split at the seam, his white shirt showing through at the elbow.

A beautiful matron wearing a black hat threw her head back and, with her eyes closed, let her voice ring out, high above all the other raised voices:

> *I'm gonna let it*
> *shi - ii - ne!*

A stout woman in a white hat and a raincoat stood and began leading the song, and, as the song died and hand-clapping continued, humming continued, in quiet tones she rapidly spoke:

"Religion is freedom. *(yes, it is)*

"Christ is freedom. *(amen)*

"If the right decision doesn't come down today, get ready to march. We'll have church in jail tomorrow. There's no harm in church in jail. It will be the greatest Christmas we will ever feel in Albany. We will walk free." *(amen . . . uh-huh . . . yes)*

And suddenly the church was singing:

> *Let Chief Pritchett say*
> *A - MEN*
> *Let Chief Pritchett say*
> *A - MEN*
> *Let Chief Pritchett say*
> *A - MEN*
> *A-MEN, A-MEN.*

And then:

> *We shall overcome*
> *We shall overcome . . .*

Someone crying, "Let us stand on that one," and the front row joined hands, arms crossed in front, the rest with arms at their

sides, swaying in unison, heads, bodies, from side to side.
Softly:

> God is on our side
> God is on our side
> God is on our side
> Today.
> Oh-oh-oh . . .

The frail man with the elbow out of his coat rose to begin
speaking. He announced his text: "Freedom will not bow its
head . . ." Dr. Anderson interrupted to announce that Dr. King
was downtown, seeking the negotiations. The audience began
singing:

> Won't it be grand?
> We're going home to Jesus . . .

and at the end of the hymn the slight preacher began to pray,
the crowd humming, clapping hands, this slowly dying as his
words mounted:

> We thank Thee
> For our getting through the night
> We are weak *(well. WELL)*
> But there's no harm to try *(well)*
> Oh, Lord—Lord *(his voice high-pitched, a high tenor hum*
> *rising from the audience)*
> Oh, LORD *(singing)*
> Oh, LORD
> Please, Jesus
> Please
> PLEASE!
> Jesus
> JESUS
> Down at the river
> Down at the river—oh, Father.
> Trying time
> Troubling time

JESUS! *(high-pitched, sudden shout)*
Some of our loved ones
Are behind bars *(well)*
PLEASE, JESUS
Oh, Jesus. Oh, Jesus
Oh, Jesus. Oooh, Jesus
Bring 'em home today! *(yes, sir)*
JESUS! *(well)*
Break in somebody's heart
Today
Shake in somebody's mind!
Wake 'em up!
You know who I'm talking about *(well)*
I pray now
For Jesus sake
It's storming! *(loudly)*
It's storming!
It's storming in downtown!
It's storming in the White House!

The preacher was standing to the side of the pulpit, his arm resting on it, his eyes tightly closed, the words pouring out for half an hour or more. And then, suddenly, he said:

I can't pray no more,

his voice fading, and, as if on cue, a woman's rich contralto rang out:

What a friend
We have in Jesus

the audience joining in:

All our sins and griefs
To bear
What a friend
We have in Jesus
Take it to the Lord
In prayer

And from that, the music ringing, they went back into "This
little light of mine . . ." and from that to:

> Ain't no harm
> To keep your mind
> Set . . . on FREEDOM!
> Hallelu'
> Hallelu'
> Hallelujah . . .

"Goin' to jail / With my mind / Set on Freedom . . . / Singin'
and prayin' / With my mind / Set on Freedom . . ." and from
that to:

> Everybody say
> Freedom
> Everybody say
> Freedom
> Everybody say
> Freedom
> Freedom. Freedom . . .

"Mayor Kelley say . . . / Chief Pritchett say . . . / Mister Gray
say . . . / Johnny Reb say . . ."

> Freedom. Freedom . . .

Someone got up and began instructing the people in a new
song. "You've heard the song, 'Satan's on my track / Tryin' to
turn me back . . .' We're going to change the words:

> Pritchett's on my track
> Tryin' to turn me back
> I'm goin' on to freedom land!"

On it went: "Kelley's on my track . . . Policeman's on my track
. . ." and it seemed to me a needless, even tasteless, interruption
of the fine thing that had been going on in the church—so
much expression of so much straight out of the people. (Fervently, at one point during the earlier singing, my notes said:
"The songs are sung out of the soul and go back into the soul

to further stir it . . .") But the people took the banal song and quickly transfigured it, made of it one with their other songs, clapping their hands, stamping their feet, giving life to it. A man behind me reached, in a hoarse shout, some new height of his own inspiration, and the leader—who had sought to instruct—found himself being instructed, shouting in extra "Oh-oh's," stamping his feet, fed by the response, the music from the people.

Two women got up next to tell of having just gotten out of jail in Newton. One was an older woman, with glasses, wearing a black hat and coat, looking like the many maids, cooks I had known (and not known) all my life.

She said, "The food they served—honest to goodness— my dog wouldn't eat it. We were comfortable, though. We weren't packed in. Some white men came in and gave us that mean look. We got all shook up. We believed they would take us out that night and fix us up. When lights were out, some would sleep, some would stay on guard. We were ready to use our shoe heels to defend ourselves . . ."

In the midst of it, the electric word came to the press that the city officials were calling a press conference. We hurried to it. Tableau: Mayor Kelley at his desk, the three city commissioners standing behind him, their arms behind them. Talk of: City commission worked until ten last night on points submitted . . . Dr. King urging violation of the law . . . Since local leaders did not act through the biracial committee . . . we feel we cannot answer your demands. Under no circumstances will we work under duress . . . Worked until 10:30 last night, arrived this morning and had telegram making demands . . . Took it to mean an ultimatum . . . Had the responsible leadership of the Negro community acted in good faith, an agreement could have been made—with no demonstrations or threat of demonstrations . . . And so on. Talk of Georgia statutes: Parade without permission, disturb peace and orderly conduct of the City Commission and Recorder's Court, contempt . . . *Assemblies designed to unlawfully incite violence and riots* . . .

Back in the church, testimonials were continuing from those who had just been released from jail. A young man and an old one stood side by side, the young one speaking: "We were treated like dogs. There were fifteen to thirty in a cage. I got a feeling of a great spirit within me. I didn't want to leave. I have come back now to do it again."

The crowd was the largest of the day. The singing was louder, even more fervent than before:

> *Oh - freedom*
> *Oh - freedom*
> *Oh - freedom*
> *Over me . . .*

A huge man with jowls, bull neck, sang with veins standing out on his forehead. An old man in gold-rimmed glasses sang with his hands clasped, his feet beating the rhythm forcefully. A stout woman in slacks sounded in soprano syllables above the rest:

> *Over my head*
> *I see freedom in the air*
> *There must be*
> *A God*
> *Somewhere.*

Dr. King and Dr. Anderson entered the church. The singing continued.

Dr. Anderson said: "Slap it. Go on—slap. Slap the hands. Slap the hands everybody." His voice quavered: "Jesus loves you. God loves His people at a time like this. I love you. (scattered response: "I love you")

"I will not *(yes?)*—I will not sell you down the river this day. *(applause)*

"We're not threatening anyone with anything—not forcing anything on anyone . . . I know you are eagerly awaiting a solution. But it has to be a solution where all can maintain dignity, justice, freedom. We are not asking that someone go down in defeat or someone emerge reigning supreme. We are asking only that common ground be found for discussions. We await now a call from the mayor to indicate to us whether he will meet with us. How reasonable can men be without sacrificing their principles? If a solution could come at this moment so both sides could hold up their heads, I would be satisfied.

"You have been magnificent—wonderful—courageous. Many have been here singing and praying since seven o'clock this morning. Remain on your knees; continue these songs.

"There comes a time when the burden of the Cross no longer weakens you down but strengthens you up.

"We cannot turn back." *(naw . . . suh)*

He prayed:

> Lord have mercy
> Lord have mercy
> Lord have mercy.
> Praise the Lord!
> Sing the song.
> Pray the prayer.

Then Dr. King spoke, and he was clearly moved, exalted by the feeling in that church, all that had gone on in there—all of the people's speaking out in their own idiom the message he returned now to them:

"Hundreds of our brothers and sisters, sons and daughters are in jail. We are not issuing threats or ultimatums. We will not rest until they are released. I can't afford to stand idly by while hundreds of Negroes are being falsely arrested simply because they want to be free. We have a right to demonstrate. It is deeply imbedded in the Constitution—the right of assembly, freedom of speech.

"You hear it said some of us are agitators. I am here because there are twenty million Negroes in the United States and I love every one of them. I am concerned about every one of

them. What happens to any one of them concerns all in-
directly.

"I am here because I love the white man. *(yes. yes. well)*
Until the Negro gets free, white men will not be free. We can't
hate them. *(well)* We must cry out, 'Father, forgive them, for
they know not what they do.' *(amen)*

". . . I am here because I love America. I'm going to live right
here in the United States and probably here in Georgia the rest
of my life. I am not an outsider. Anybody who lives in the
United States is not an outsider in the United States. Injustice
anywhere is a threat everywhere." *(great applause)*

Dr. Anderson got up and announced that still no common
grounds had been found for discussion. "Pray now," he said,
"while I go and meet with men of wisdom."

The leaders retired to the church office. The people sang:

> *All in the city jail*
> *I'm going to let it shine.*

A woman in a black hat raised her voice to an incredible
volume:

> *TELL CHIEF PRITCHETT*
> *I'M GOIN' TO LET IT SHINE . . .*
> *TELL THE CITY COMMISSIONERS . . .*

An older man bent over the pew and gently put his hand on
her shoulder, in encouragement, appreciation.

In a hall in the rear of the church, a quiet drama of the
middle class, of standards, values: A girl of about twelve is
crying. Her mother, face fierce, eyes flashing: "I put my foot
down. You're not going home."

Dr. Anderson got up to announce the march would start.

"Join hands with me and my good friend Martin Luther
King . . .

"God will move in our midst this day. He will direct us. God
will be holding our hands.

"I always had faith God would touch the hearts of the

commissioners, who have decided not to talk with us. All we want to do is to talk about it . . .

"Though they be slain, yet will they live!"

Quiet faces in the great crowd look up at him, tense faces. A man nods agreement. They wait the word to go. Dr. Anderson stands erect, his fingertips on the pulpit. Tears are in his eyes as he comes down to lead his people in the march.

Dr. King on the right, Dr. Anderson on the left, they move out of the church, hundreds of marchers.

A brief way on, a girl from the neighborhood greets Dr. King: "Doctor, can I go?"

"If you want to join us, come on. God bless you."

They follow the familiar route, past the funeral home across the street, to the first corner, turn left through the Negro business section—more people milling around in the blocks of it than are in the march. Two Negro men peer out of a tailor shop to get a look at Dr. King. Two little boys eating ice cream cones stare. Men stand before all the stores.

One of the preachers calls to them: "Join the march. Freedom!"

A teenage girl says, "You ain't doing nothing, standing around here." She beckons to them, a Bible in her hand.

They reach the bus station; the police in yellow raincoats wait. Chief Pritchett confronts the two leaders. The people, the long orderly line of the people of the church, kneel and pray. Two little boys stand out a minute, scared smiles on their faces . . .

The prayer ends; the people march off between cordons of police, march toward the jail. The faces of the Negroes watching them go are strained—sad some of them, mad some.

> *Black and white together*
> *Black and white together*
> *Black and white together*

Today.
Oh-oh-oh, deep in my heart
I know that I do believe
Oh-oh-oh, that we shall overcome
Some day.

They march down the middle of the street, white-part-of-town street, whites watching them from the sidewalk, some idly, some angrily. The police turn the column into the little alley that leads to the booking office of the jail. An old lady with her Bible stands squarely, looking up at the door to the jail.

They are packed into the alley, and they sing and clap—the surrounding buildings giving resonance, new strength to the music. All their favorites:

Keep your eyes on the prize . . .
This little light . . .

Cheers come from inside the jail. A cop at the head of the alley yells at whites peering down it: "I want this block cleared. Break it up. Move on."

Oh - freedom
Oh - freedom
Oh - freedom

echoing in the alley. Singing, clapping—all their favorites:

There must be
A God
Somewhere.

One of their preachers lifts his voice in prayer:

Blessed Son of God
Who was born this time of the year
Two thousand years ago
Bring peace to this world.
After two thousand years
Here we stand
Two thousand years later.

His voice becomes a groan, a chanting, rhythmic groan:

> Oh, Lord
> Oh, Lord—Oh, God!
> Oh, Oh, Oh, God!
> Atomic flower
> Hanging over our heads!

A young Negro woman, part of the line waiting to get into the alley has fainted on the sidewalk. A state trooper snarls: "What's that—a phony faint?" Negroes carry her down the hostile sidewalk of police and onlookers. In the alley:

> *We are climbing*
> *Jacob's ladder*
> *We are climbing*
> *Jacob's ladder*
> *We are climbing*
> *Jacob's ladder*
> *Soldiers of the Cross!*

They kneel in prayer:

> All men are created equal
> And are endowed with certain
> Inalienable rights.
> But here we are today.
> We want to walk in dignity.
> We want to walk in pride.

People are being taken through the door into the booking office, to the jail. The singing continues. All their favorites:

> *Keep your eyes*
> *On the prize*
> *Hold . . . on*
> *Hold . . . on*
> *Hold . . . on*
> *Hold . . . on*
> *Keep your eyes*

On the prize
Hold . . . on. Hold . . . on.

A woman, middle-aged, thin, leans with one shoulder against the brick wall of the jail building, her head thrown back, singing, singing, her voice soaring over all the others—more sweetly, with greater strength than any of that exalted singing of the morning. Her face is serene, beautiful, bespeaking genuine, profound religious experience, bespeaking faith and joy. When I remember back to the movement, to the promise of the movement as it was, still, in Albany, when I remember back and lament that the movement did not mean more for more people, did not really ever reach most people, I think of her, think what it must have been like to have been where she was, to have reached the state of grace which radiated from her, made her plain and work-lined face so beautiful, eyes closed, mouth stretched wide, singing, singing in the alley:

We are not afraid
We are not afraid
We are not afraid
Today
Oh - oh - oooh deep in my heart
I know that I do believe
oh - ohh-oh
WE SHALL OVERCOME

Some day.

Little groups of Negroes, not of the demonstration, wary, watching the police, moved along the sidewalks, seeing what was happening to the marchers. In one, I saw a man who had much impressed me through the morning's singing with his exuberance, his seriousness. I had interviewed him briefly, hearing of his deep commitment. He saw me . . . and evaded my eyes. He had not been able to, had not had the heart to march. Somehow, he made all of it—the morning of song and prayer, the march, the courage, the singing now in the alley, more real, all the people in proper perspective, entirely human, capable, like him, at the last minute of failure of will, of fear, cowardice.

The beautiful singing in the alley—all their favorites—and those faces I had seen all week, had come to know—decent black faces of men, women, children, people of the Albany Movement whom I had come to respect so much, admire so much. I heard their songs and saw their faces, and once again, in an encounter with the movement, I found myself crying—not this time just out of hope still inherent in such a thing as had happened in Albany, not now just out of the joy of knowing old evil was dying, but now simply and unabashedly out of love, love of a great people, good people, knowing at the same time that they are like all other people, that others, too, have their greatness inside them, and knowing that a nation, a movement, leaders, cannot, without certain perishing, fail that in people which the Albany Movement manifested there for a tiny, significant time in the history of the movement and of America.

Part Five

WILL IT EVER COME BACK?

Chapter
TWENTY-FOUR

"Oh, yes," he says. "I marched and came to all the meetings. I was a member of the movement."

He is a working man, broad of shoulder, big in the neck. His black face is creased in earnest, polite attention as I tell him that I have come to see him to ask about that, what he remembers of being a member of the movement in Albany, and what has become of the movement.

"Oh," he says, "those good old days are gone now. But it's not over yet. There's lots still needs to be done."

I sit in the little apartment living room in Selma with John Lewis on that return visit he made in 1969 and listen as he and the middle-aged, brown-skinned woman who lives there talk about what happened in Selma, reminisce. She was, John told me, not a prominent leader, but one of those little people who would emerge in the movement, enduring, and with endless energy, ready to do any work, take on any responsibility, make any sacrifice. Her little apartment, already crowded with her and her husband and their ten children, was always available for meals, for sleeping room, was always full of movement people during the campaign.

My white presence is accepted, but not warmly. She reminds John that Jonathan Daniels (she calls him "Jon," saying the name fondly) stayed in the apartment for a while before going to Lowndes County to meet his death. She gets a picture of him with his arms around two of her boys. She speaks bitterly of white justice, its failure to punish his death. She tells of the slowed pace of movement activity in Selma. Her children are out now, getting signatures on petitions SCLC has sent asking Congress to make Dr. King's birthday a national holiday. She speaks freely of her disillusionment, of distrust of whites, speaks scorn for whites who still say "Negro," don't know that the word now is "black." She tells of her work at a day care center for the poorest of poor black children, a volunteer thing with no funding, just a handful of women trying to do for the children. She and John talk once more of the movement days in Selma. She says she remembers seeing John lying on the ground after the troopers attacked and tells how she feared he was dead. They speak of other events, of people who had been involved, local and from afar. Her eyes glisten, the lines in her face soften.

"Do you think," she says suddenly, "do you think, John, it will ever come back?"

Chapter

TWENTY-FIVE

It was there—in the church and the alley that leads to jail in Albany that day, in all the little churches of the movement across the South—and then it was gone. Ten years after the sit-ins started, to evoke their mood is to invite ridicule, cynical scorn.

It was there, and then it was gone. It happened before my eyes, but not in any orderly progression of sudden change, cause and effect, but gradually, slowly, as most things happen. The worst of America was present in the movement when the best of the movement sang forth. And the best of the movement was present when the worst of America seemed to have seized hold of it.

Its beleaguered little outposts struggled on, as full in the declining years of its great spirit as the sit-ins were in the beginning—some of them never noted, never heard of. I read now a field report from the Butler County, Alabama, We Want Freedom Club, an SCLC affiliate, dated November 14, 1965. Here is what was happening there after the legislation had all been won, after SNCC and CORE had lost their faith, and America most of its interest:

> The march [on Thursday] was scheduled for 3.30, but didn't get underway until 4.15 . . . One hundred and fifty marched

down to the courthouse, without a permit, escorted by the police, who directed the marchers onto a side street to get to the
courthouse. Once there, we had a prayer by Rev. Gandy, local
minister, businessman and treasurer of the We Want Freedom
Club. Then Ben Clark spoke, we sang "We Shall Overcome"
and marched back the way we had come in twos. We dispersed
and went to a mass meeting, 170 attending, where J. T. Johnson
spoke . . .

Today [Sunday] we were served notice that the church (Harri-
son St. Church) would be locked and we could no longer meet
there. We . . . were told that the police had ordered the chairman
of the board of deacons not to let us meet there. Although after
the march we ordered the people to return to the church, it was
supposed to have been closed, but the doors were found open.
Later we were assured by one of the deacons that the church
would remain open.

The owner of the house where the Chinaberry Tree is located
has ordered its tenant, Robert Brown, a blind man, to vacate the
premises because of our use of the tree as a rallying point . . .

Is it true, as I have said in tracing what seemed to have
happened, that the nature of modern America from the beginning foredoomed such struggling, its idealism and spiritual
quality? Is the movement really gone?

It was there, and then all of those forces were at work on it.
In sum:

White southern violence and political, economic and other
modes of resistance; the failure of the white South to respond
to what was essentially an expression of the better part of
shared southern culture; the failure of many Negro Southerners
ever to become a part of the movement; the failure of most
Negro Northerners ever to become part of it or understand its
non-violence; the failure of most white Northerners and some
white Southerners sympathetic to the movement to understand what it was really all about; the incapability of a ruined
white liberalism to identify with its truly radical thrust; the
failure of a manipulative federal government to respond to its
radical imperative for reform, or even to enforce the surface

reforms it achieved; the influence on the most militant, activist organizations exerted by young Northerners, black and white, with their lack of conditioning to respond to the deepest spiritual meaning of the movement; the increasing tendencies of all the organizations to manipulate the people rather than be led by their strength and wisdom; the fatal turn of the organizations toward over-emphasis on appearing to win; the move away by the organizations from spiritual meanings significant to the whole life of the people of the movement to more narrow, secular, strategic goals; competitiveness among the organizations; manipulation of them by ostensible friends, the federal government, foundations; the terrible stress on individuals of sustained confrontation with white racism; the further destructive effect on individuals of seeing ostensible friends betray the meanings of the movement; the national obsession with violence, expectations of white violence before it ever occurred, overemphasis of it when it did, the same thing with black violence, which never really came in the South; the (perhaps resulting) build-up of a mood, over the nation, of violence beyond violence, beyond the wildest expectations of media and public; the murder of leaders; the influence throughout of the media as a filter through which mainstream forces impinged on the movement and the movement was misinterpreted to the nation; the conflict, ultimately, between dominant values of America and those asserted by the movement.

In simplest terms, the movement opposed aspects of American culture and tried to change them; the culture, in reflex, resisted, and in turn changed the movement. In terms of individuals, people capable in the early 1960s of offering nonviolent redemptive love to the most murderous white southern racists and asserting it against the more mundane, stale murderousness of America were, by the late 1960s, some of them, responding to black separatism's own mirror-image of mundane, stale American antagonism.

In broadest terms, I think what happened was that the

movement, which started out seeking to overthrow the southern segregationist order, eventually challenged all that at the core of American culture which could have allowed such an order, as one symptom of a system-wide sickness, to exist for a century under the American Constitution. To the extent that the movement not only broke down the southern segregationist order, but also brought to light faults at the core of American culture and aroused dissatisfaction about them, it succeeded far more than the numbers of its adherents or the physical power they possessed would warrant. I have attributed this impressive achievement to the spiritual qualities in people that the movement drew upon, the energy released by its allowing a few people to express something like the whole of their inner power (in such things as the tension between love and hate), in a land where many people have been rendered incapable of knowing there is anything in them to express, and others are able to express only a part of what is within them —usually the ugliest part: greed, hatred, anger. I do not mean that the movement was defeated in its secular purposes by the forces of America it opposed, but rather that those forces gradually neutralized (at least for the time) the threat to them of the method by which the movement worked—its spiritual quality. And I believe that the people of the movement, though they were intent on winning the secular goals, had in the spiritual experiences of the movement, the ecstatic experience, something more satisfying, more important, even, than the secular goals. They had, and still have, a way out of the gray and drab, dull, dehumanizing patterns of life that are imposed on most Americans by the very forces the movement opposed.

When I make my long list of acts of people and institutions of America which opposed the movement and eventually fragmented it, for a time at least slowing it down, I talk for the most part about evil done without evil intent, about people and forces behaving normally, who, to have acted otherwise, would have had to see more deeply than is possible for most into the workings of the culture—in short, in the movement's religious

idiom: Father, forgive them; *for they know not what they do.*
It was not the American people but American culture—which
shapes the people—that opposed the southern movement.

Or—do I merely imagine all this—perception and ability to
understand inflamed by the mighty emotion attached to all I
saw in the movement, and more important, all I felt out of my
own private time of existence in America.

Was it ever there at all—what I believed I saw and felt in
the little churches of the movement? Sometimes, sometimes,
I suspect myself of having all unconsciously shaped my thought
about the southern movement on that most southern, most
misleading model—harking back to a golden age and lament-
ing all the disruption and disintegration that has come upon
us: There was an agrarian aristocracy, touched of ancient
Greece and gallantry, a paradise of kind masters, happy slaves,
and this was all destroyed by a crude and jealous North, and
the southern survivors were beautiful men of stoical nobility,
who were further humiliated and finally overcome by a combination of grubby and greedy whites of both the South and
North, and gullible, manipulated blacks. This myth of the
South—which is the central myth of mankind, that of Paradise
destroyed, Eden defiled—feeds our unconscious with a peculiar, parochial poignancy, black Southerners and white, and
shapes our perception of today and yesterday.

I remember, I remember . . . And what I remember is so
different, so much better, more real than all those other pasts
that Southerners, with the same kind of wistfulness and long-
ing, the same undying faith, and even hope, have remembered
through history.

I realize now that, like the volunteers Dr. Coles described
during their brief summer in Mississippi, I have been seeking
since the Meredith March and Dr. King's death some kind of
philosophical adjustment to all that the years of the movement
meant to me, to find a way to relate all I have seen of its
greatness, as well as of the traumas it came to suffer, to what
I know about life, not to abstract either its best meanings or

its worst defeats as *the* meaning of life. My quest, really, has been to put what I know of the movement and my experience of it into a perspective that makes its impact on my own life more bearable and makes its meaning in contemporary event and history a little more hopeful.

The personal part of it slowly resolves itself. I described my mood of hopelessness (one I think shared with many in and out of the movement) after Dr. King's death:

> . . . When the time came to attend the sad finale to his efforts, the Poor People's Campaign, there was no longer even any of the rage I had intermittently felt; nor the idea of going there not as a journalist but as a participant—white, southern, middle-aged, middle-class, without ideology, really, not radical, only radically angry—to show them, by God, they just couldn't kill what Dr. King stood for. That was gone. For the knowledge was there, underscored by the assassination of Robert Kennedy, that they had indeed killed it, that it was gone in this nation, and that violence, obscene violence, nuclear violence controlled.
>
> So when I arrived . . . it was with much the same feeling that has hung over the liberal establishment for some time now, and has spread to those varieties of left-of-center people who had thought they were better than the liberals. Numbness, let us call it, weariness, the sense of going through the motions, because there is not even energy enough, will enough, to call a halt, to say no more of this, it is hopeless . . . Normally I had worked with the conviction that trying to tell the truth had importance, could make a difference. But this time I didn't know that I would act even as a reporter . . .*

I tracked through the muck and ugly spirit of Resurrection City that SCLC had flung up near the Lincoln Memorial and brought poor people in May to squat in inane plywood tents (not honest, I noted, like real tents, which can be struck the next morning, but permanently bending the spirit as, night after night, people bent their shoulders to enter them). Dr.

---

*"Keep on A-Walking, Children," by Pat Watters (*New American Review*, Number 5, January 1969), pp. 8–9.

King, it had been reported, had been gladdened, greatly encouraged, just before his death by the numbers of poor people of different races (Mexican-Americans, Indians, poor whites, as well as northern and southern Negroes) recruited for the campaign. It would be a beginning of that broadened movement he had promised in Selma. At the beginning, 2,650 such people resided in Resurrection City, but by the time of the Solidarity Day March on June 19, no more than 800 remained, nearly all of these black. Black Power bullying accounted for some of the non-black attrition; blacks and whites together had left because of the squalor of the encampment, drink and drugs and crime (some committed by poor people elevated to the position of security police and acting immediately like the worst of police who had ever victimized them). But even more than these things, idleness had driven people away. Flaws in organization, reflecting the demoralization of the SCLC staff, prevented all but a few of the planned series of marches and demonstrations ever being launched. People had come there, I noted, to get away from idleness back home, looking for something to do, to be caught up in—the kind of escape the movement had always meant. When they didn't find it, they went from the squalor of Resurrection City back to the squalor of their own homes.

Those who remained evidenced, by the time I got there, a malaise of spirit, hostility, something beyond hostility which I found frightening, a withdrawal that discouraged any contact, communication. All of this, the disorganization and spiritlessness, I can realize now, spoke the same numb despair I had felt —and how much more it must have debilitated SCLC's staff and followers, plunged as they were into what, under ordinary circumstances, would have been an enormously difficult operation. Their ability even to go through the motions of keeping the movement alive was one more example of the movement's strength, resiliency. I watched the march, bemused to see the same old crowd, larger than most had expected, mainly of innocent, middle-class, well-intentioned, but dangerously uninformed, unawares people, the same kind who had come to the

1963 Washington March and other big movement ceremonials, most recently to Dr. King's funeral. They harked back to the days of the movement-liberal-labor coalition, when only the Negroes delivered whatever was called for—votes, bodies—and the other two elements did the bargaining and the talking. Now the Negroes, symbolic "poor people," stayed aloof on their own turf in the wretched Resurrection City, and the others went through the motions of attending to the endless speeches of the program, singing at its end "We Shall Overcome," listlessly, stiffly, not really having heard some of the eloquent, true words from the platform, no more than they, really, had ever heard what Dr. King was saying.

Dr. Abernathy (echoing Albany) cried out that day: ". . . I read in my Bible that the Earth is the Lord's and the fullness thereof—and there is no need of God's children going hungry in 1968."

And: "We have been taught by two hundred and five years of bitter experience that we cannot trust the leadership of this nation. We cannot trust the elected representatives of Congress. We cannot trust the administration—whether Democratic or Republican—to fulfill the promise to the disinherited . . ."

And: "I will not sink so low as to imitate the very worst of white Western civilization violence. The United States government is the leader of the *violent* movement in the world. They believe in fire power . . ."

He had his own and the movement's experience, it seemed to me in a startling little surge of hope, in perspective that promised far more realistic resistance to the erosive forces of the mainstream than the movement had been able to achieve before. But then I realized anew how much havoc those forces had wreaked. I watched a little group of young Negro men listening to his words, not to the linear reasoning of them but merely the rhythm of them, and they intoned at the appropriate places the "Amen," "Yes," "Well" cries that had been the magic of ecstatic communication in the churches, but these young men did it mockingly, scornfully, denying a real heritage far more truly theirs than the one symbolized by their Afros and clothing affectations, repudiating, I thought, the one last sub-culture capable of resisting the America which they now so faithfully represented.

The next day I watched one of the few full-scale demonstrations of the Poor People's Campaign, a march on the U.S. Department of Agriculture, apt symbol of federal government complicity in all the worst practices of southern racism, an agent over the years, through one liberal administration after another, of systematic discrimination against Negro farmers and of niggardly refusal of the nation to feed the hungry. The marchers, some sixty of them, black and white, all ages, sought an audience with Secretary Orville Freeman (only recently, I noted, the symbol beyond Humphrey of ruined liberalism, standing accused on national television of allowing little new-born babies to starve to death in the interest of showing his boss, President Johnson, one of those two-million-dollar book-keeping gains so dear to the boss's heart).

They were refused, and set out to sit in the many doorways of the Agriculture Department buildings, to block access to them and, when quitting time came, to prevent workers from leaving. I watched the balding, bustling bureaucrat who gave the police (looking like southern police I had seen over the years in such situations, a little excited, hard, sure in the power of their clubs and pistols) the order to arrest them, and I felt more strongly than ever before a sense of mechanization, of impersonalness, in the ordering of such important public events. In the South you knew that nearly always behind the cruel and crude brutishness of the police were mean-mouthed little sons of bitches (George Wallaces rising every generation out of their ranks, thirsting for power) protecting mean little interests, probably getting mean little pleasures out of what was happening, perverted pleasure, but at least human. Here in Washington, it felt inhuman, something of machines and mathematics, efficiency—with no more nor less human meaning here than in the operation of it so savagely against people and all life in Vietnam or wherever else in the world a policy that had come to be more important than any human consideration dictated that it operate. The little bureaucrat who ordered the arrests had the look on his face of a man about to clear rats out of his basement. (And I thought of the man who ordered arrests at the lunch counter that first day in Albany; for him, the order to "take 'em out" was a moment of high drama—maybe the highest in his life.) When, later, violence erupted, police using their clubs "as necessary," some saying the police started it, some saying the demonstrators, my feeling was that the violence was the thing. It didn't matter who started it; neither side could control it.

I had studied one group of those who sat in the doorways —young middle-class girls and boys, black and white, and an older woman who looked like she might have come from the southern mountains. They had in common a look of beautiful calm, a sureness in their faces that I had never felt, a certainty that, come what may, what they were doing was worth the doing, what they stood for would eventually succeed. It was one of the very few hopeful moments of that trip to Washington. I had felt a menace from all the people of the movement gathered there, and most of all from the young—a feel that all the movement meant any more was an opportunity for them to force their ways into the seats of power which so ruinously ruled the nation, not to change the rule, merely to control it.

One of those Negro youths who had mocked Dr. Abernathy was introduced to me as a leader of the gang which had precipitated the violence on that march in Memphis that was to be Dr. King's last. I said then, "Offer him the opportunity either to blow up the Pentagon or take command of it, and his swagger stick and weapons analysis would become the envy of the military world." I have come to realize my fear of such young people was valid, but not in the ways I imagined. They have proved themselves since to be all too easily the dupes of those in control, allowing them fuller sway with savagery in everything from campus revolt to Black Panther shoot-outs.

But now, as at the time, I take heart from the calm-faced little group of demonstrators; such people had with the same sweet spirit offered their lives for what they believed in through history, and such belief has survived through history, if seldom to prevail. Age, I said then, noting the old mountain woman, had nothing to do with it—and took comfort from so obvious a fact. Later, I was to add—or race, and took comfort from that, too.

I left Washington that night and read a few days later of how they had arrested more demonstrators, including Dr. Abernathy, and how they had expeditiously routed what few "poor people" were left out of Resurrection City and quickly destroyed its plywood tents and planted grass over the mud there. And I read the story by Jack Nelson in the Los Angeles *Times*, the best one piece of newswriting about the movement ever done, I think, in which he described the speed and efficiency with which the federal government enforced the penny-ante laws that allowed it to remove Resurrection City from the landscape and consciousness of Washington, D.C., and contrasted this with the utter inefficiency of the government over many long years in enforcing vital, basic laws that would have made life livable for the poor—voter registration, equal education, protection of civil rights, farm programs, job programs, food programs.

Finally, out of all the experience, impressions, feeling of my small exposure to the Poor People's Campaign, I was to write:

> Despite all that hopelessness I carried up there to Washington, I must have had some small hope left that the movement, spread now to the poor of all races, still might just do it, might reactivate the conscience of society. This had been the ultimate delusion: that the least powerful, and then, even the least able, could do a job that may well not be accomplished even should it be tackled by the most powerful, most able. At last, the delusion was dead . . .

The movement is dead, I said to myself. And there is no hope

that lasts. They have known that for some time in other places
. . . Negroes in the South have known it, through slavery and
since then—existing, making do. How did the SNCC kids, with
all their reading of Camus, miss that? Keeping on, those of them
still at it, coining their rhetoric from the metal of hope, showing
in all their hate-talk now only the other side of the love-talk,
anything to avoid hopelessness. Dr. King knew about that. Making do, as southern Negroes always have done, with an irrelevant
and irrational religion, he forged a world-view of staggering insight. Making do with the worst of his followers by drawing the
best out of them, he built a movement that shook America,
almost converted some of it, at the very least put an end to
southern institutionalization of racism. And then he had seen his
philosophy and strategy of non-violent change lose influence, had
seen America steadily moving in the opposite direction from the
one he sought. You get down to hopelessness, finally, his kind of
hopelessness, and then you can see that it is still possible to keep
on, to find meaning in meaninglessness, like . . . Negroes with
no food and no purpose (who still organize their days around
meaningless, non-productive activity), like the demonstrators in
the driveway. "Keep on a-walking, children," Dr. King used to
say in the hot, fervent, sacred little churches of the movement's
great days. "Don't you get weary. We are headed toward the
Promised Land."*

I moved on with such a rationale, no longer numb, performing the chores of my work, not any more, as at Washington,
as a reflex, going through motions, but now seeking, as I had
said, meaning in meaninglessness. There was much to be found
in the South of 1968 and 1969, in the aftermath of the movement, with the new forms of struggle developing, SCLC in its
thrashings around about the only reminder of the old organizational forms—and this often, sadly, almost a caricature. I had
lamented that the middle-class people at the Poor People's
March, that congregation of decent and well-meaning people
had not really heard the words of realism Ralph Abernathy

*"Keep On A-Walking, Children," pp. 56, 58.

spoke. But now I realized that America had Ralph Abernathy firmly fixed in place, had dealt with him—not as it had to do with Dr. King and SNCC and CORE, with onslaughts of its erosive forces, but simply by ignoring him.

I came to understand that. I had remembered him in Albany, Birmingham, St. Augustine, Selma—remembered the sure common touch he had, and the thunder he could put into his mass meeting orations. It seemed to me more ought to come of what he and SCLC were doing. Some of the problem, I am sure, had to do with the men who surrounded him. I suspect he found himself listening to ones deepest in mainstream, strategic and image-making gimmickry, less to ones attuned to what he himself had best enunciated when he said that when you are called on to witness you don't analyze what the outcome might be because you can't know—you just witness. Young activists, formerly of SCLC, SNCC and CORE, had been attracted back to the Poor People's Campaign. Little of their great energies and talent was ever used, and they drifted away again.

I went in early 1969 to the little Georgia town of Sylvester, where SCLC had one of its minor campaigns under way, to see if I could understand better why so little came of what seemed to me, still, considerable promise, potential in SCLC. Demonstrations had begun in Sylvester over the outrage of a fourteen-year-old Negro girl's having been sentenced to an indefinite term in the reformatory for the alleged crime of having cursed a white boy in some race-oriented squabble on a school bus. She had been released through court action, and now the movement was pushing a list of demands, the usual ones—in effect, enforcement of the civil rights statutes. Sylvester was one of the many southern towns which had been bypassed during the great years of the movement. When it came, in 1969, whites there had responded as they had in the old days with the usual cruelties, violence (shots fired into the home of the girl, her brother arrested for firing back), and the familiar incredulity, the inability to give in.

But what of the Negroes, the movement, the people of the movement? It was raw and cold and intermittently raining when I got there in company with Neil Maxwell of the *Wall Street Journal,* one of the very best of the good reporters who had covered the movement, still perceptively and sympathetically reporting the South, and Winifred Green, from Mississippi, its white aristocracy, who travels the South for the American Friends Service Committee working for school desegregation and quality education for Negroes, still struggling, a tough-minded, unfooled young woman who, with her colleague, Connie Curry, remains among the few movement whites still accepted amost universally by movement black people.

We drove to the church, small, wooden, like all those others I had been in, and inside found gathered for what was to be a great "Freedom Day" march, with supporters coming from all over Georgia, a small crowd, no more than 150 people. I thought this might indicate ineffectiveness of SCLC, and in part it did, but I learned that the 8,000 Negroes of the county, about half its total population, almost unanimously supported the goals of the movement—but silently. They were inhibited by the old, crippling fear of white reprisals. Later, when I was trying to pick my way through the mud in the familiar neutral territory alongside the march, an old Negro woman in a flowered dress and black sweater standing on the sidewalk watching the marchers go by looked me in my white face with her old eyes and said very softly, "We wid you, buddy."

There, I felt in that good moment, was the old strength, the old canny anger and self-preservative wisdom. And then I realized there I was, as of old, floundering between her kind of strength and the courage of the marchers, not what she took me to be at all. The likes of me don't escape a share of the blame for what most of the rest of the day showed of just how much the movement had deteriorated.

In the church, when we first got there, people were announcing where they had come from to join in the march—surrounding southwest Georgia towns and hamlets, such places as Vidalia, Cordele, Waycross, Hopewell, Valdosta, Social Circle and . . . Albany.

"There's the Reverend Wells, God love him," Winifred had exclaimed as we walked in the door and she ran to him, and they hugged. And there, too, was a man I remembered— mahogany-colored, slight of frame, the preacher who had poured out that great poetry of prayer on the day of the first King march in Albany. I never had learned his name back then. Now the elbow was not out of his coat; he wore a well-fitting suit. I hoped to speak with him there in Sylvester, but again didn't get the chance; he was, to me, symbolic of so much of the greatness of the movement that never got to be known.

Those faces from Albany brought back so many memories. The people in the church began singing:

> Ain't go' let
> Nobody
> Turn me 'round . . .

and the good feeling of old flooded through me, the knowledge that the song, the music pouring forth, had always been more important than the terms of victory or loss back in Albany, through the years of the movement. They can still sing down here in south Georgia, I thought exultantly.

But then they began singing other of their Sylvester songs: "Time to wind it up . . ." "Corruption in the land / People take a stand . . ." "We go' march till we tear yo' kingdom down / Ain't no use in yo' hangin' 'round / You might as well put yo' shotgun down . . ." And:

> Oh, sock it to me
> Soul Power!
> Ooooooom—aaaaaaaaah.

Not pretty in thought or rendition, these songs were without
the dignity and beauty the movement had once been able to
impart to the most banal ditty. And then I felt foolish, out of
it, not attuned to harsh reality, sitting there concerned over so
frivolous a thing as the spiritual quality of the music when
children were starving and human dignity was still being destroyed in the black belt. The SCLC leaders, I thought, probably have to use such songs to attract the young people. These
were in a majority in the church, most of them resplendent
with Afros (though some of the girls wore their hair in pigtails).
The predominant style of the young (some of the girls wore
dashikhis) contrasted with the conventional garb of their elders, who wore everything from Sunday finery to overalls.

The SCLC leaders in evidence were young men I had not
seen before. Obviously, to them, the songs were an organizing
tool, no more, just as the demonstrations, I suddenly realized,
had almost from the beginning ceased to be solely spiritual,
sought less and less to persuade white Southerners, and became
more and more a tool of coercion to force white Northerners
to bring white Southerners into line, to make the federal government do that—non-violence used to compel the government to employ its formidable armed might to force reform in
the South. It had never occurred to me before that the lines
had been drawn, in that sense, black against white ally as well
as white foe, that long ago. Not before, either, had I realized
how drastic was the shift in purpose and essential meaning of
the movement when demonstrations ceased to be primarily a
means of shaming white Southerners, and became, instead, a
vehicle for coercing them.

The first way had roots deep in the sharing of southern
culture by Negroes and whites. From the beginning of childhood, whites had known the power of the Negro nursemaid's,
the cook's voice: "Shame! Shame on you!" As James McBride
Dabbs often pointed out, Negroes instinctively felt that the
appropriate and mutually more beneficent emotion white
Southerners should feel about treatment of blacks through

southern history was shame, not guilt. The second way of the demonstrations—coercion—was in line with the dominant tone of the national culture of the times, was American, not southern, far more in it of conformity than of pushing at the limits of the culture. *(What initial mistake, what fatal mistaken choice, whom or what injured . . . ?)* I cannot know whether the other way would have worked, would have accomplished even as much. If coercion had been damaging only to whites of the South, in justice no one could really say that they deserved better (for they had had the opportunity of grace, of redemptive love, before the movement institutionalized it, through the history of southern interracial entanglement). But the movement, the people of the movement were harmed, too, and what seemed a way out of America as it is today was blocked, diverted, turned inward.

They were waiting there in the church in Sylvester for two busloads of supporters from Atlanta, inexplicably late, true to movement form. A bearded young SCLC staffer in overalls gave a long discourse on the virtues and techniques of nonviolence, most of it strongly flavored with contempt for whites (talk of "buffoons," "sick minds," warnings to the girls to remove their earrings before marching, lest they get their ear lobes torn off).

"I never saw a white man stick his hand out to defecate," he said at one point. "He pulls his britches down just like a black one."

And: "Use your eyes as a weapon. We can't cut them or shoot them. But we can let them see that we see them for what they are. That will stop a coward."

The responsive cries from the audience through all the speaking, while they waited for the Atlanta buses, were a mixture of the old "Yes," "Well," "Amen" ("Call the roll," one old man cried as a speaker listed discriminatory defects of the local schools), and the new thing of shouts, cheers and the Black Power gesture of a raised arm, clenched fist. Leadership, as I had noted two years previously, watching Stokely Carmichael work a similar Atlanta audience up to the point of riot, could have taken this crowd either way—toward violence or to the old expression of sincere non-violent redemptive love. As it was, we were somewhere between the two.

Only once did the old spirit flame for a moment. Reverend Wells, having already donned a tan raincoat, got up after more than an hour of waiting and urged the scanty crowd to go ahead and start the march without the Atlanta supporters.

"It will demonstrate to the whites that we are going to fight if nobody comes from anywhere else."

That, I was gradually to realize, was also the essence of the best of a new movement spirit among Negroes working on across the South for the goals of the movement. Their work tended to make SCLC, in such a campaign as Sylvester, seem to be going through the old motions, mechanically, without the old spirit, indeed thrashing around. The rest of the day was mostly such a lackluster performance, and I concluded by the end of it that the reason America could ignore Ralph Abernathy as it could not Dr. King was that his organization was no longer fed by the people, no longer confident enough to lead them in the direction Dr. King had persistently set out, and yet not willing to give up entirely on that course, and so not able to galvanize the people or draw on their strength. Perhaps confidence would return; Reverend Wells, God love him and his counterparts in SCLC and across the South, was still there, and the youthful workers could gain wisdom from them.

Whites of Sylvester, their faces showing, as of old, bloated or bloodless hatred for the sight of marchers, jeered at them and made one or two half-hearted attempts at violence toward them. But it was low-grade unpleasantness; like the movement, they seemed to be going through motions. Maybe the whites of such towns who still turn out to hate demonstrators (most, as always in the movement years, stayed home) know themselves to be engaged in ritual, the reality of conditioned murderousness in them faded in acknowledgement of more effective, efficient murderousness loose now in public policy, approved form, in the police forces over the nation, for example. Maybe such whites of the South believe they have won, despite all the effrontery the niggers now dare to show and despite all the new laws and federal guidelines. Maybe they dimly sense that, somewhere back there, in 1963 or 1964, or 1962 in Albany, the real beliefs that the Negroes stood for had been abandoned, the movement defeated. It is unlikely that Negroes would concede this, any more than whites like those in Sylvester will ever realize that they, too, somewhere back there, were defeated, too.

The march ended with one of those endless SCLC ceremonials of many speakers, as whites on the opposite side of the street jeered and shouted obscenities—once during a prayer. Dorothy Young, the fourteen-year-old girl who had been jailed on the very charge of obscene speech, sat through it all silently, not making a speech herself. Her round black face was pretty beneath a short-cut Afro; her eyes had a depthless sadness in them. By chance I was to encounter her again in the summer of 1970, in another part of southwest Georgia. I was interviewing, at a farm home, one of the Negro "grassroots" leaders of the area, one of those determined and yet not grim middle-aged women who endlessly push at the multiple, monumental problems in such an area, somehow cheerful, hopeful in the face of the worst discouragements. She had been in an automobile accident coming home from some meeting of the movement in another town, and wore a cast on her leg. People had signed the cast, and in the midst of the interview, I noted one of the signatures, written large: "Odu Bu A Nkrumah—African name. Slave name—Dorothy Young." I was to see Dorothy a few days later, working in a voter registration project in Charles Sherrod's organization; a sheen of blank hostility shielded the sadness in her eyes. Cause and effect were not always so obvious.

The old movement activities have continued in the absence of SNCC and CORE, without Dr. King. Sometimes, as in southwest Georgia, some former field worker of SNCC or

CORE continues in leadership; sometimes the effort is entirely local. Some are conducted in the old spirit, some in a more harsh tone. ("I wonder," said a white of the movement after reading in 1970 some of my accounts of the old movement spirit, "what real difference there is today. The same will and determination are there. Only now, there would be a lot of anti-white talk, with your friends in the audience looking around at you apologetically.")

One important part of the work has centered on economic self-help. The Federation of Southern Cooperatives, formed in 1967 by a small group of Negro farmers, by 1970 touched the lives of some 100,000 Negro Southerners, serving as a clearinghouse for purchases, sales and fund-raising. School desegregation has continued a major effort across the South. The American Friends Service Committee served as an informal clearinghouse and trouble-shooter in this area. Voter registration and leadership training continued, with the Voter Education Project serving as a clearinghouse.

SCEF struggled on, its work including publication of a civil rights newspaper, *The Southern Patriot*. Some small groups, like the Southern Rural Action Project, headed by Randolph Blackwell and employing other equally effective movement people, including the Reverend Wells, seemed to exist mostly on faith, its labor support having ended. The better-heeled National Sharecroppers Fund continued its economics-oriented work, as it did through the movement years.

SCLC continued, and the Urban League and the NAACP still provided membership and organizational bases. The NAACP Educational and Legal Defense Fund, Inc., was pushing school and other civil rights cases of widening implications for the nation. The southern office of the American Civil Liberties Union, under Charles F. Morgan, Jr., continued its valuable movement work, including important cases on court reform.

The Southern Regional Council continued to serve as a clearinghouse, in effect as a broker (as it always has) between those who are doing things in the South and the resources which might serve them in the rest of the country. Will Campbell in Nashville, with his continuation of an old southern expression of the best of American religious tradition—the Committee of Southern Churchmen—acted, as he did through all the movement years, in his own individualistic ways to serve Southerners who are doing things, making no distinctions in his regard for all Southerners as children of God. The Delta Ministry, outgrowth of the National Council of Churches' participation in the 1964 Freedom Summer, struggled on with the problems of the Mississippi Delta, localized and increasingly aware that local people should have all control, New York none. And there were many more scattered elements of what might still be called the southern movement.

I traveled in 1969 with Baxton Bryant, then the director of the Tennessee Council on Human Relations, who provided another kind of movement leadership, distinctive but not unique. He is a bluff, hearty, life-loving white man in his early fifties, formerly minister to Methodist churches in Arkansas (where he was born) and Texas, still ordained; having also once come close to being elected to Congress from the Dallas area. He is possessed of enormous energy; since 1963 he had been in the middle of every Tennessee civil rights, human rights struggle, including the Memphis garbage strike, and more recently had involved himself in the cause of Nashville hippies. He has the respect of black leadership, including the most militant in Tennessee. A free spirit, as firm in understanding of, and living by, the Bill of Rights as any man I know, he was wearing his hair long and sweeping back from his William Jennings Bryan brow when I traveled with him. The last time I saw him, he had grown a long Santa Claus beard (To children's awed queries, "Are you . . . ?" he always replies, "No, I'm his brother.") and wore a robin's-egg-blue jump suit. His pet scheme in 1969 was a highly innovative, indeed eccentric, economic self-help program for west Tennessee, the five counties of that state which border on Mississippi and are more of

it than Tennessee. Baxton had spurred Negroes to form organizations in all five counties and to unite them in an umbrella
organization which was seeking funds from every available
federal and foundation source.

I went with him to the annual meetings of each county
organization, two a night for three nights, the last one a meeting of the big five-county umbrella organization. The people of
the meetings were the movement's old mix of a few who were
well-off and others who were not, including some who were
desperately poor. It soon became apparent to me that they
were not naïve, not easily fooled, would not likely be too surprised if the fine five-county dream never really materialized (as
it was not to). I think they were partly aware that Baxton's
utility to them centered on other values that will become
increasingly important if America ever does do the small things
necessary to assure adequate material living for all its people.
What Baxton trades in is essentially what the movement once
offered—the sense of being about something important, something that offers hope.

The people in that rural pocket of the black belt, the ones
at Baxton's meetings anyway, had not become adept at enmity
to whites. There were many touching, good moments. Baxton
spoke at each, long harangues appreciatively received. At one,
he spoke earnestly about the new spirit, the new mood in the
movement. Black separatism, he said, was a refusal of integration on the basis of merely being allowed to enter white society,
a demand that "beautiful and real values" of whites and blacks
come together.

"And those of us like are here tonight," he shouted, "are
what I am talking about. That's what we believe in—community. *(yes. amen)* We can look at each other and have respect
for each other's rights as human beings." "Tell the *trooth!*"
cried an old man in the corner and kept up a thumping response to the rest that Baxton said.

Toward the end, Baxton told of how his daughter had just

had a baby, was in danger for a while of losing it (and there were murmurs of concern), but did not (happy nods), the mother and son now doing well.

"And do you know," Baxton bellowed, "that I had five children and four grandchildren already and not a one of 'em was redheaded," fluffing his own pinkish, sandy hair. In the merriment over this, he walked down to stand before the fervent old responder and hollered, "But what color do you think that new baby's hair is?" and the old man laughed, and they both shouted, "RED!" and they embraced each other, and the people poured forth happy, appreciative laughter.

There are, of course, some who will call such antics at best irrelevant and at worst a downright impediment to the grim, desperate struggle for social and economic justice in America. I do not think so. I believe Baxton gives to the struggle qualities whose lack would make the struggle meaningless, and I believe Baxton elicits from such moments the very best of what Negroes gave to the movement; they share something few whites, North or South, know about, something which the Negro South might yet give to the nation to make whatever accomplishments eventually come toward social and economic justice worth having.

I speak from my own experience on that trip. At the first meeting, toward its end, I suddenly heard, aghast, Baxton hollering that he had with him "a great writer, a world-famous author," on and on, each hyperbole making me feel cheaper, smaller before these good people turning to glance curiously, politely, at me.

"Come on up here, Pat, and speak to these folks," he bellowed, and—sick, dismayed—I stumbled to the platform and stammered out a few words of greeting, which were politely, generously received.

When we got outside, I said, "God damn it, Baxton, don't ever do that to me again."

He laughed, with genuine enjoyment, and said, "Well now,

Pat me boy, I know you ain't much, and you know you ain't much, but those folks back there don't know that. It makes them feel important to think you're really somebody, come to talk to them. I did that for their sake, and I'm going to keep on doing it, and you'll speak to them."

And he did, and gradually I accepted his reasoning, so that by the last night, at the big five-county meeting, I was beginning to play my part a little, act like I really was something.

During that meeting, an old Negro man, a retired preacher, got up and spoke.

"This yere's a good projeck going on. If I can't pull, I'll push, and if I can't push, I'll get out of the way and not block traffic."

The crowd encouraged him with their response, and he went on with more in the same vein and ended with the consummate commentary on public speaking:

"When I'm sittin' down, my thoughts rise up. But when I stand up, my thoughts sit down. So I'll sit now."

When it came my turn to speak, I got up full of the spirit of such eloquence and for the first time on the trip—indeed for the first time in my life before an audience—spoke with real feeling, real fervor. I preached.

"I came here from the city," I said, "where people seem all discouraged, seem to have given up on America. Not poor people, but well-off ones with nice homes and big cars, all the things that ought to make 'em happy, but somehow don't—because something's wrong."

"Yes, tell the truth," came back at me, and I knew a moment of that exaltation I had seen so many times in the speakers at the mass meetings.

"And yet I come here," I bellowed, "and find among people who have every right to feel discouraged, to really give up on America, no such feeling at all. I find here hopefulness, constructiveness, the ability to keep trying, keep planning. I find all of your will and determination to make this the kind of country it ought to be. *(well?)*

"I was getting to be discouraged like the people back home, too. But I'm not any more," I said—and meant it. "You all have helped me, and I thank you for it."

They applauded and beamed on me. I had come more fully to understanding, beyond hope or hopelessness, what the movement had really been all about. It meant much more than merely losing fear.

Chapter
TWENTY-SIX

SNCC WAS IN A HURRY because SNCC knew that it had to move fast if it was not to be destroyed by America. This was a great insight. But SNCC was destroyed anyhow, while the organizations geared to the long haul at least survived, and would be available should the will of the people be galvanized again.

I think SNCC knew, unconsciously, as with most of its wisdom, the distinction between the movement as organizations and the movement as people, and that it was the organizations which were most immediately periled by America. Perhaps all of SNCC's looking inward, its constant preoccupation with organizational form, was nothing so much as a desperate effort to avoid the threat, the ability of America not to crush the organization with totalitarian force, but to reshape it, transform it into just another standard American organization, to process it. The greatest thing SNCC did in this effort was to try to keep the organization attuned to the people, to make it an embodiment of the will of the people.

Bob Moses said a remarkable thing in the 1963 speech. He spoke of the problem each SNCC worker faced of overcoming fear, of knowing one's own limits and staying within them. He spoke of the lone decisions on this elemental level SNCC workers had made in little towns for two and a half years, and he said that experience allowed them collectively to make decisions, independent of pressures for conformity, on their positions vis-à-vis the rest of the country and the other civil rights organizations.

That was a great place to be—out beyond ordinary limits, the limits of the culture, but within the known limits of one's own capacity. But it did not guarantee that the decisions made would be correct ones. The wonder is not that SNCC was finally done in by America, but that it was able for so long to stay out in that lonely place beyond cultural limits, to resist so long.

I have said that sometimes SNCC made a fetish of consulting the people, and this is natural, if consulting the people was the important survival mechanism I think it was. But perhaps the fetish was the fatal flaw, the final mistake. The most cynical remark I ever heard made about the movement was by a Negro member of the movement who said in 1964 that SNCC always did what the people wanted so long as the people wanted to do what SNCC wanted.

For a time, SNCC and the movement expressed the very best that was in the Negro people of the South. But if the movement taught anything, it was the complexity of individual people, that where there is good, there is corresponding evil. At the outset, with southern sureness, the movement approached whites on the basis of this knowledge, seeking the good that they knew must correspond to the evil of racism within individuals, the society. And it did this by holding in balance good and evil, love and hate within individuals, within masses marching, within the movement itself. But SNCC came finally to see whites and American society as totally evil and came to formalize in the early Black Power rhetoric expressions by Negro Southerners of justifiable anger, ancient anger, and to encourage this one part of what was in the people over the other parts, upsetting the balance of love and hate. Expressing the will of the people is one thing; expressing selected emotions like anger, hate, is another—demagoguery.

There were the many instances where Northerners in the movement showed their inability to respond to, comprehend,

the most important qualities of ordinary Negro Southerners—
their remarkable balance, their ability to transcend what southern society had done to whites. I don't want to say Northerners
in SNCC were the sole instruments of SNCC's destruction.
But I do think that northern influence was great in the deterioration of such an important thing as expressing the will of the
people.

One reason for this might be that Southerners in SNCC, in
all the organized movement, just did not have the confidence
that Southerners are beginning now to find. Maybe it all boils
down to such Southerners' having been, in the face of northern
education, sophistication, cynical understandings of the machinery of American culture, unable to hold forth in all its
culture-changing importance the simple rationale of the movement and the old, true faith of the people.

Here, a northern voice, speaking the bitterest of the disillusionment that came after the fall of the organizational movement:

"SNCC was the best time in my life, because I felt we were
changing things. But I got out when I realized we were not
changing things. I don't know what will do it. But it won't be
love.

"I did once think it would—when I was first in SNCC, into
the philosophy, the religious thing, and didn't know of any
violent alternative. I had been brought up in this country,
played with guns, battleships as a kid. And then I read this stuff
about non-violence, listened to people—all the emotion in that
idea: Conquer evil with love.

"I still in some ways believe in it. It's a nice thing.

"But it doesn't work. You can't love Hitler and his spiritual
sons. I spent years loving the shit out of people, and nothing
changed. The same people run things, and a black man who
loves a white man has got to be out of his mind."

I have suggested that one sad effect of the movement experience, its being pushed back and shaped by the forces of normal
America into more and more nearly normal American patterns
of thought, has been to move many Negro Southerners as

individuals similarly into a consciousness closer to American cultural norms. The most blatant (and easiest to over-simplify) example of this is the overtone of everyday, aimless hostility, low-grade nastiness in black separatist behavior.

Most indications have been that far fewer Negro Southerners than northern ones have embraced black separatism. It has seemed mainly a middle-class preoccupation in the South. The real enthusiasts have been such of the middle class who never were of the movement, but who were the first to gain from its advances—older people like Mr. Page talked about, those with training enough to take advantage of opportunities, younger ones entering college when the movement's great days were already ended. The middle class of all people in all times have not normally been visionary, nor much able to resist the sour joys of petty cruelty, of bullying anybody vulnerable. Black people who did once have the beautiful vision of the movement and abandoned it for the mainstream animosity of black separatism have been those like the young activists who could no longer stand up against the barrage of opposition to their vision, or those who, in both instances, show themselves avid followers of fashion.

Black power, as SNCC always did, put black bodies (and souls) where truth is—this time, truth about racism. From my own reactions and often preoccupation (normal, I think to any white who has been close to the movement) with Black Power, I have come finally to believe that, more than anything else, its scorn for those who had considered themselves the friends of the movement, whites like myself, liberal or radical, has been scorn for attitudes of such whites during the movement days. In our identifying with the racial struggle, we inclined to be more against the evil of racism than we were for the humanity of the Negro people most deeply involved in the struggle. We were against the evil and we tended to see those who fought it as all good. We thus failed to see the humanity of our black allies, refused to look into their hearts and understand there was as much complexity there, as much balance of good and evil there, as in any human heart. If Black Power has been saying anywhere near this wise and sane a thing, the only appropriate answer to it is to make the attempt more strongly in dealing with all people, black or white, to appreciate their complexity and individuality, to identify with whatever good is there and encourage it and to oppose whatever evil. And to demand the same consideration from others. I have realized finally that it is fruitless to dwell on what (from having grown up amid the sickness of white racism and from having seen the movement) seem to me profound fallacies in black separatism, and now I only mourn its shaping of part of the organizational movement into one of the least savory of all the features of the mainstream. The fact remains that the worst excesses of Black Power have been largely rhetorical, that, in its promulgation, the only violence suggested was self-defensive. Nowhere in the South has there been any widespread black violence, and what there has been, as largely true in the whole nation, was against property, as Reverend Wells pointed out, virtually never against human life. Compared with the violence of white racism, or, for that matter, with the routine violence of public policy, whether expressed by police at home or armed forces abroad, the performance of black Americans in their struggle for justice remains a cultural anomaly, a model for emulation. As I. F. Stone said, it has been unique in the annals of such struggle.

But what has mainstream America, white America, ever noted of this, and what has it availed? Frustration and anger grow, and the talk is of revolution in conventional terms, the stale terms of meeting mainstream murderousness, the unyielding destructiveness of normally functioning America, in kind. Is there really any hope of an alternative from the South, a reassertion of the movement spirit?

I seek now the proper perspective, the appropriate elevation of language and thought for pushing on to the end of my quest, to try to say what I feel to be the final meaning of the movement. There are really two perspectives. One is simply to see the movement as an episode, a most important one, in a more general drama—the continuing struggle, common to all people and all times, but come to some critical climax in our own time, that pits the best and worst in humanity against each other.

The other is to see the movement as the equally important chapter it is in the epic of America, to fix its place and meaning in what has been from the founding of the nation its central, unresolved problem—race, the problem that symbolizes all the paradox of the nation's best and worst qualities, its dream and the continuing struggle to realize that dream.

Violence has been a constant theme in this struggle with the problem, from the initial violence done human beings by making them slaves. The nation broke apart in rage and violence once, and that attempt to resolve the problem, all of that killing, came to naught. Once more, violence is posed by some as the only resort in the struggle to end the violence done by racism, by the evil at the core of American culture. Yet the problem of race all along has been how to end violence. The movement offered a solution to America, and America missed that meaning, indeed resisted it so effectively that the movement faltered, fell back, in its organizational form fragmented, dispersed. I seek now to hold forth that meaning again, and to tell how the spirit which offered it still lives, still might save America.

I have come to understand the importance of what Reverend Wells was saying that day in Sylvester about showing that local Negroes weren't depending on anybody for help. The regional clearinghouses are simply that. The real work is done on the local level by local people. They no longer need or depend on southwide organizations like SNCC or charismatic leadership like Dr. King provided. They accept help when it comes, but know that ultimately, as the leaders used to say in the meetings, they can depend on no one or no agency, the federal government included, for their deliverance. They know they must do for themselves. In this sense, the movement not only still lives, but is far more mature than in its greatest days. And its non-violence continues, the expression of the people, not leaders or organizations, more securely, naturally fixed.

So the movement continues. For the time, it is mostly to gain economic and political power for Negro Southerners. These are, of course, mainstream pursuits, though not yet conducted entirely in mainstream spirit. Negro Southerners no longer speak of redeeming the white South, but a practical effect of their gains so far of power has been effort to reform southern society.

And the mood of the movement lives on in many Southerners.

"The movement spirit still lingers with people," said Goldie Jackson of Albany in 1970. "Calls come on any emergency— like the flood two weeks ago. People wanted to organize and help out. We helped with evacuation of families . . ."

Many of those who were involved in its greatest days talked in the early 1970s of hope of a resurgence; Leon Hall, formerly of SCLC, later with the Southern Regional Council, was one of those who said that, just as there was a period after Montgomery of little action while it gathered resources and strength, so now the fragmented movement was building back toward some new expression, new form. If it should re-emerge, it would have not only the new strengths of local self-reliance, but that new kind of southern confidence that has become apparent in the 1970s.

Julian Bond said in 1970 that he could see the beginning of a southwide political machinery stretching from the eastern border of Texas all the way up to Washington, D.C., that would have a tremendous effect on not just who got to be governor in each of these states, but who got to be President of the country as well. It would be interracial. "I think it would be predominantly black certainly when it began, but it would follow the model of the National Democratic Party of Alabama and have a black base and white supporters or helpers or members as they saw fit. It's possible, I think, to extend that concept all across the region. Forget about state lines and county lines and just build a strong political machine."

Leon Hall spoke in 1971 of the many organization veterans

still working in local situations and the many more grassroots leaders and the thousands of people who relate to them:

"The structure is there. It's still there in Montgomery. You wouldn't need to organize there now; all you would need to do would be to mobilize it around an issue. The difference is now the new culture in the South. We could get whites now, too."

He spoke of his experience in organizing white and black college students across the South to go back to their home towns to develop biracial cooperation in the newly desegregated, troubled high schools. Everywhere he went, many young people in the colleges and the high schools were eager to be done with the adjustments of desegregation (which they regarded as largely an adult problem) and to get on to such problems as the sorry state of southern education. Other nonracial issues would provide opportunity for organization and action, with such groups as the hippies and poor whites ripe for involvement. He envisioned a coalition of young blacks and whites of all classes engaged in massive direct action on a wide range of political and economic issues.

James Lawson was well into the planning stages in early 1971 for forming a Soul-Force Institute which would begin development, among other things, of a non-violent army. This would mean "recruiting and training people to build up a corps able and ready to go into, and carry on, direct action at any level."

The intention would be "social warfare—non-violent warfare." As in violent warfare, the aim would be "devastation until a power shift occurs. We would bring institutions to a halt until drastic changes occurred in them." He gave as an example the possibility of making non-violent war on slums, on the landlords and political and financial institutions involved. Using such techniques as rent strikes, direct action, the non-violent army would seize the land, would institute work projects to rehabilitate the slums, and would establish cooperative operation of the property.

The immediate focus would, of necessity, he said, be on black problems, but the Institute would not be separatist. If a target area included poor whites, the effort would be made to involve them.

Many others with movement experience were trying to discover which way to proceed, he said. "A lot of searching is going on; there is a lot of awareness that something like what I am working on is necessary."

The impetus for re-collection of the movement might well come from the North—from an organization like Operation Breadbasket under Jesse Jackson in Chicago. Or it might yet come from SCLC.

We speak in the South of the hope of a rebuilding of the fragmented southern movement, and it is with some awareness of similarly fragmented, disparate struggling of many good people across America—the same thing I sensed at the White House Conference. They seek ways short of the vicious circle of revolution to end the many hurting things done by their country to the land and the people. If there is to be a new southern movement, it will be only a part of what amounts to a national movement, already under way. When I think, feel the rise in me of hope once more, about such a new movement, a national movement, I think I can discern, see in shadowy outline, the broadest, most abstract dimensions of what could come out of the thing that began with such southern specificity at lunch counters and marching in the streets. If the movement's best meaning is to live on, we will escape the notion of all-good against all-evil, and escape racial antagonism in the fight against racism. We will fight racism as the cancer that it is in the society and in individuals, opposing it in blacks, just as in whites, in the name of their humanity.

It will be an effort to break out of the economic, social and cultural traps that stunt and make gray the lives of so many people, an effort to understand and change the systems that peril the nation and the world, and most of all an effort better to know and understand and love, first ourselves, and then other people—in short, to find true integration with society, the environment and our fellow man. And what less, really, did the movement seek in the South?

For, beyond the context of southern history and politics, beyond even the resistance it showed to the American mainstream, or as part of that, the movement was most important as a part of a worldwide struggle to find human accommodation with the inhuman complexity and technology threatening to destroy the world either by fire or famine, the struggle whose foremost leader remains Gandhi. How similar the figures, the very postures of Indian demonstrators, glimpsed in newsreels of the past, and southern Negro non-violent marchers, a feel about both of mysticism and some new manifestation of humanity, new selfhood combined with a new form of collectivism, communion. All the thrust of this world struggle has been to know better the hearts of people, the evil there and the good, to bring back into human dimensions the evil; to find new effectiveness for the good. For a time, the movement was attuned to this broad worldwide struggle, and even now, when narrowing of vision has occurred, there remains alive in those who were there a feeling for what was hinted, what might be more fully achieved, and there remains an influence that has gone around the world and breathes in the diverse searchings everywhere for new values, ways of life, chances for survival.

But so far, even the disparate, non-revolutionary strugglings of the late 1960s and early 1970s across America in the name of humanity and decency are, all too often, conducted in a spirit of wrath. They do not join people together, but do something of the opposite: People increasingly are withdrawing into racial, national, class, even age, even sex groupings, all with mutual antagonisms as well as mutual problems and goals —and mutual enemies.

How desperately the nation seems to need the old healing, joining-together spirit of the southern movement—the strong, uncluttered humanism that, even in the destruction of SNCC, evoked from the losers sadness and understanding, concern, not standard resentment and vengeance-seeking.

James Lawson, in describing what "soul force" in the title of his planned non-violent army means, seemed to pose the same kind of alternative to the antagonisms engulfing America that the movement did. "We feel soul force is a capacity generally alive in black people, despite the hostilities and oppression of racism, to have feeling and compassion for life. It means with-it human beings in the face of the death-seeking traits of the society—the ability to stay authentically human in the midst of social struggle."

A movement guided by this spirit would be "far more radical than anything else going on now." It would impose a feel for life on institutions; it would make it possible to shape new life-oriented forms in such things as economic organization, community organization, education.

He saw soul force, as would most of us, as mainly a black manifestation, "critically our gift," not fully appreciated by all blacks. Similarly, I had felt that the spirit of the old movement, its extra-cultural thrust, is more securely in the keeping of Negro Southerners than any other Americans. But I know now that it is not exclusively theirs—neither exclusively southern nor Negro.

The kinds of things that happened in the mass meetings, ecstatic, beyond the norm of ordinary American experience, were not exclusively a Negro phenomenon, were not African, but were drawn from the repertoire of possible feeling and action in all people. Religious experience like the movement knew, like some Negro churches still know, is not unlike the best ecstatic experience in the fundamentalist churches of the white South—in the rural areas, in the city slums. The essence of what the mass meetings drew upon was the common heritage of all people—the best, highest wisdom of the Eastern and Western traditions. Negroes in the South have been, more than any other people at any other time, close to the roots of both traditions—the West in such things as their embracing of the Judeo-Christian religion and their allegiance to the ideals of democracy and individual freedom, and the East in the way they have always expressed their religious feeling and, through the movement, in the way they sought for themselves the rights of democracy and freedom—with mysticism, loss of self. They have been from the beginning, in this sense, integrated. And I think whites, and there have been many of us, who did respond to the deepest meanings of the movement have shown themselves capable of this same kind of approach to cultural integration—the discovery in oneself of chords of response to the best in the traditions of the East and the West.

Here, it is possible to say in the most generalized way that Negro Southerners are better off than northern blacks, and, more startling to conventional thinking, white Southerners are than northern whites. This is another psychological difference growing out of differing experiences of another extreme expression of the evil at the core of American culture. Southerners are not as alienated as Americans in other parts of the country.

Southerners are becoming aware of this and other advantages they have—like relatively clean air and water, less dense, more manageable cities. I have suggested that a new southern consciousness is evolving, a sense of confidence based on real advantages rather than the old jingoistic defensiveness, a will to hold onto these advantages historical accident bestowed upon us, to build on them, and avoid the mistakes the rest of the country has made, even as we become more like the rest of the country.

With their new consciousness, Southerners might try once more to move America to something beyond cold machinery in the resolution of conflict and the search for a better society, might find the confidence to rally all those Americans who (even as southern whites in an insane, apartheid society kept alive enough real hate in themselves to be able, however punily, to extend a crippled love across the color line in the days of what used to be) have kept themselves whole enough to resist mechanical animosity in the struggles to rid the country of all the results of all the animosity stemming from the evil at the core of the culture.

The movement's message is there, plain for all America.

Wise men through the ages have prescribed the same simple thing; any sane assessment of the total capacity now to kill all life compels that we listen to them. Yet the confines of culture require such an effort of will just to say the word "love," or to suggest that all the other repertoire of human emotion has got to be somehow involved in any process that truly reconciles conflicting interests, truly achieves human justice. Dr. King and redemptive love, SNCC and the beloved community . . . it was there for a time, flaring forth, and it lives yet, not merely in the movement of the Negro people of the South, but, strongly or flickering feebly, in all of alienated America, in all people everywhere.

At the small headquarters of the Southern Christian Leadership Conference on Auburn Avenue in Atlanta, during the years after Dr. King's death, the letters came and came, from all over America and from over the world, thousands of them, from people somehow still whole, not consumed by all that which battered the movement, expressing hope still, or wistfully seeking, or speaking faith in non-violence, faith in the movement, with understanding of what a momentous thing had occurred with the movement in the South and had sent its influences out. I go back once more in time, in memory, to the churches of the mass meetings and hear once more those exalted voices: "This little light of mine, I'm going to let it shine. This little light of mine, I'm going to let it shine. This little light of mine, I'm going to let it shine . . .

> *Let it shine*
> *Let it shine*
> *Let it shine.*

Index

423

Reuther, Walter, 349
Richmond, David, 74
Richmond (Va.), 91, 97, 100
Richmond *News Leader*, 97
Riverside Church, New York, 61, 355
Roberts, Gene, 78–81
Rock Hill (S.C.), 91
Rome (Ga.), 253
Rougeau, Weldon, 89
Rozier, Albert L., Jr., 73–5
Ruleville (Miss.), 312, 319, 339
Rustin, Bayard, 341

St. Augustine (Fla.), 7, 59, 64, 65, 125, 278–97 *passim*, 325, 326, 328, 389
Sanders, Carl, 174
Sasser (Ga.), 186, 227
Savannah (Ga.), 271
Schwarzchild, Henry, 220–1
Schwerner, Michael, 297, 319, 345
Seaman, Genie, 76
Searles, A. C., 157–8, 210
Seawell, Malcolm, 80
Seeds of Destruction (Merton), 84 and *n.*
Selma (Ala.), 47, 57, 60, 65, 108, 130, 188, 322–30, 345, 347, 349, 353, 372, 373, 383, 389
Selma to Montgomery march, 47, 60, 324, 325, 329, 330
Sherrod, Charles, 39, 152, 153, 154, 155, 165, 172, 186, 187, 197, 315, 395
Shiloh Baptist Church (Albany), 4–6, 11, 141–5, 159, 163, 169, 171, 175, 204, 210, 218, 358
Shipp, Bill, 227

Shirah, Sam, 255, 256, 258
Shuttlesworth, Fred, 103, 104, 233–42, 269, 270, 341
Siegenthaler, John, 105–7
Simpson, Bryan, 282–4, 288
Sims, Bernard, 326–7
Sitton, Claude, 53, 145, 146, 213, 224, 227
Sixteenth Street Baptist Church (Birmingham), 272–3
Smiley, Glenn, 51, 52
Smith, Lillian, 73
Smith (Johnson C.) College, 76
Social Circle (Ga.), 391
Society of Friends, 76
Solidarity Day March, 383
Soul-Force Institute, 409
Souls of Black Folk, The (DuBois), xv, 152
South Carolina, 52, 330
Southern Christian Leadership Conference (SCLC), 51, 169, 324, 338, 346, 352, 373, 388, 390, 392, 396, 408, 410, 414; in St. Augustine, 7, 278, 279, 281; role of, in Albany Movement, 15, 58, 147, 148, 149, 156, 157, 183, 221, 223, 233, 239, 278, 279, 287, 358; militancy of, 47; and Martin Luther King, Jr., 58, 135, 217, 281, 287, 358; and Chicago, 61, 65, 135, 353; in Montgomery, 86, 88; and Freedom Rides, 101, 126–37; and sit-ins, 126–37; and SNCC, 128–32, 136, 137, 149, 278, 323; program of non-violent direct action, 132, 157, 323, 393; and Ralph Abernathy, 200, 217; in Birmingham, 262, 266, 269, 278,